The Law of
WASTE
MANAGEMENT

David Pocklington

MA, PhD, CEng, FIM, MInstWM
Head, Environmental Engineering,
Society of Motor Manufacturers and Traders

Shaw & Sons

Published by
Shaw & Sons Limited
Shaway House
21 Bourne Park
Bourne Road
Crayford
Kent DA1 4BZ

© Shaw & Sons Limited 1997

Published October 1997

ISBN 0 7219 1520 5

A CIP catalogue record for this book is available from the
British Library

Printed in Great Britain by
Biddles Limited, Guildford

CONTENTS

Contents

PART II – PRACTICAL WASTE MANAGEMENT

LIST OF TABLES AND FIGURES

PREFACE

Over the past 20 years, the statutory controls associated with the management of waste have grown from relatively modest beginnings to become one of the most complex areas of environmental law. In addition to an increase in the scope of activities covered by such measures, there have been developments in the concepts employed, and in the details of operating procedures and technical assessments incorporated within the regulatory controls. Against this background is the essentially practical, everyday context of the legislation, and a result of the ubiquitous nature of waste generation is that there are few activities which do not involve its management. The importance of waste within corporate strategy will increase further as more organisations introduce environmental management systems, and as the principles of "sustainable development" and "producer responsibility" become incorporated within statutory measures.

As a consequence of these developments, it has been necessary for a wide range of professionals to become involved in waste-related issues, and *The Law of Waste Management* has been written to provide those with responsibilities in this area – environmental managers, regulators and consultants – with an appreciation of the legal issues involved in the practical application of this branch of environmental law. In addition, the book discusses the principles underlying these activities and as such will be of interest to lawyers, academics and students.

The solution to most waste-related problems demands an understanding of both the legal and the technical issues involved, and the first part of the book considers the legislative framework for the control of waste materials. Over 80% of current environmental law within the UK has its origins within the European Community, and consequently particular attention is paid to the framework of EU law and the Regulations and Directives upon which domestic measures are based. However, waste management law cannot be viewed in isolation, and consideration is also given to other relevant issues including water pollution, contaminated land and the role of the common law.

Whilst the early control of waste management was based almost entirely upon "black letter law", there has been an increasing trend towards the use of both statutory and non-statutory technical annexes and other guidance. In addition, developments in "producer responsibility" such as the packaging waste regulations are strongly reliant upon an interaction between industry and the regulators in the establishment of both mandatory and voluntary controls. Consequently, the formulation and interpretation of waste management law need to be approached from both the legal and technical points of view, and Part II attempts to provide such a perspective for a number of areas of practical interest.

There have been a number of important changes in the law relating to waste management during the time when this book was being prepared, and the willingness of my publisher to incorporate the many last-minute changes is acknowledged. I have attempted to state the law as at 1st September 1997, and recent developments which have been incorporated include *inter alia* the Treaty of Amsterdam, the Packaging Waste Regulations, the IPPC Directive, and the relevant case law, notably the *Tombesi* case on the meaning of waste. In addition, the proposals for new measures, such as the proposed Directives on the Incineration of Waste, Landfilling, and End-of-Life Vehicles, and the UK measures for the implementation of adopted primary legislation, such as the contaminated land provisions of the 1995 Environment Act, the IPPC Directive and the Hazardous Waste Incineration Directive, are also discussed.

The preparation of this book has involved the efforts of many people and organisations, from the opportunities for text preparation afforded by Great Western Trains between Didcot and Paddington, to the provision of some of the more obscure or unpublished material, and I would like to thank my colleagues and friends for their invaluable discussions and comments. In particular, I would like to thank Professor Neil Hawke of De Montfort University for encouraging me to write the book, and Professor David Hughes, also of De Montfort, for his continued guidance on matters legal and choral.

Finally, mention must be made of the continuing support of my family, my wife Geraldine, and the efforts of Duncan and Rachael in ensuring that legal issues north of the border were included.

David Pocklington

Wantage
September 1997

THE AUTHOR

David Pocklington is a chartered engineer with extensive experience in the practical implementation of waste management law. A metallurgy graduate of Sheffield University, he carried out post-doctorate work on steel refining and applied this modelling work to the operation of full-scale plant when working for British Steel. His association with environmental issues arose through developing processes for the recycling of metal industry by-products, and trouble shooting pollution problems in a number of plants throughout Europe.

His long-time interest in environmental law gained a formal basis through an MA at De Montfort University, the subject of his thesis being "Waste Management Legislation in the UK – The Waste Producer's Perspective".

Following a period with London Underground, during which he was concerned *inter alia* with advising management on the establishment of waste management practices and the disposal of a wide range of waste streams, he joined the motor industry where he leads a group looking at vehicle emissions, manufacturing processes and the treatment of end-of-life vehicles.

Dr Pocklington has published widely on both the engineering and legal issues associated with waste management, and is a frequent contributor to seminars and conferences. His children provide a ready source of advice and second opinions for his publications, Andrew on scientific matters, and Duncan and Rachael on the law. In his spare time, he sings in the choir of SS Peter and Paul Wantage, which gives regular concerts and has made a number of recordings.

ABBREVIATIONS USED IN REFERENCES TO JOURNALS

CLJ	Cambridge Law Journal
EELR	European Environmental Law Review
ELM	Environmental Law Monthly
JEL	Journal of Environmental Law
JPEL	Journal of Planning and Environmental Law
LMELR	Land Management Environmental Law Review
LQR	Law Quarterly Review
MLR	Modern Law Review

DEPARTMENT OF THE ENVIRONMENT, TRANSPORT AND THE REGIONS

In June 1997, the Department of the Environment (DoE) and the Department of Transport were merged to become the Department of the Environment, Transport and the Regions (DETR), reporting to a single Secretary of State. However, as the majority of the text of this book had been typeset by then, the old name is retained throughout and, where relevant, references to the DoE should be construed as referring to the DETR.

TABLE OF STATUTES

TABLE OF STATUTORY INSTRUMENTS

TABLE OF EUROPEAN MATERIAL

Directives and Decisions

Regulations

TABLE OF CASES

Part I

WASTE LEGISLATION

Chapter 1

THE CHANGING CONCEPT OF WASTE

"... they had indignation, saying, 'to what purpose is this waste?' "
Matthew 26, vv. 8-9

INTRODUCTION

Waste is a component of most industrial, commercial and domestic activities, and a wide range of individuals and organisations is involved in its generation, management, treatment and regulation. In view of the diversity of these situations with their different perceptions of what constitutes waste and how it should be treated, there is a requirement for a unifying framework of regulation based on the need to prevent harm or damage to man, his property interests and the "unowned" environment. There are, however, a number of problems associated with this simplistic approach, not least of which are the starting point of how broadly the term "waste" might be defined, and the end point of what is considered as "environmental harm".

Despite these difficulties, a corpus of law has developed which is concerned specifically with the regulation of materials which have been categorised as waste, according to one criterion or another. In addition to the statutory legislation which has been enacted specifically for the control of waste materials, there are a number of other provisions – typically those related to discharges to controlled waters and sewers, the contamination of land, and the creation of statutory nuisances – which have a direct bearing on those concerned with waste. Furthermore, although the concept of waste does not extend to English common law, the torts of nuisance, negligence and trespass must also be considered in relation to the liabilities imposed upon the holders of waste.

Prior to considering details of this legislation, a review of the development of these controls, and the extent to which the concept of "waste" is necessary to achieve their objectives, will be undertaken.

THE DEVELOPMENT OF WASTE MANAGEMENT LEGISLATION

In a recent publication,[1] Professor David Hughes of the Environmental Law Institute of De Montfort University stated:

---

[1]   "The Status of the 'Precautionary Principle' in Law", D Hughes, [1995] 7 *JEL* 224

"Of the development of environmental law over the past twenty-five years, a number of things can be said. In a kindly vein, it may be argued that it is a virgin system; more opaquely it can be stated that the law has developed incrementally; rather more brutally it can be riposted, 'no, we make it up as we go along' ",

suggesting that there was the emergence of a conceptual framework for environmental law comprising three strata – one of "everyday law", underpinned by a set of principles, themselves underlain by ethical and moral requirements.

The legislation associated with the management of waste provides a good example of the development of controls reflecting society's perception of the environmental impacts of man's activities. Unlike other areas of environmental law such as the prevention of pollution of rivers and emissions to the atmosphere, the controls on waste *per se* are a relatively recent development, and for a long time waste was considered merely as an unwanted substance with little or no commercial value, whose major environmental impact was aesthetic rather than one of direct harm.

Not surprisingly, it was the most harmful waste which first received the attention of the legislators and, although this was shortly to be extended to a wider range of materials, these early controls were restricted to the regulation of its disposal. These provisions had a number of shortcomings and, as part of their revision, the scope of control was increased to a much wider range of waste management operations.

These changes in society's perception of "waste" are set to continue as "sustainable development" progresses from a principal of environmental legislation into practical, and possibly mandatory, provisions relating to the re-use and recycling of materials, and the minimisation of waste.

A common feature throughout the development of waste-related controls has been the problem of formulating a rigorous but workable definition of "waste", since this has had to take into consideration the perception of the different groups involved of what constitutes waste, the physical nature of these materials which often limits precise description and the notions of their value and utility. Whilst many of these issues were the subject of the early case law on the definition of waste, the present situation is complicated by the international dimensions of waste movement and free trade, and the encouragement of processing options at the "upper", re-usage, end of the waste hierarchy which considers waste as a resource and emphasises its value.

A continuing practical difficulty in any consideration of waste is the heterogeneous nature of most waste streams, particularly towards the "lower", disposal end of the waste hierarchy, where the holder has little interest in the identity of the individual components and an element of mixing has been introduced to facilitate its processing. As a result, "waste" is often considered subjectively in terms of the actions of the holder, rather than in relation to its inherent properties and, unlike almost all other substances subject to environmental control, it is possible for it to change "status" and cease to be so classified, or for some substances to be regarded as waste under one set of circumstances, yet not under another.

In view of the range of environmental and health and safety measures which are available, the need to classify materials as "waste" at all is often debated, and there have been developments in three distinct areas – commercial transactions involving waste; recyclable materials; and the commonality between "hazardous waste" and hazardous chemicals" legislation – which have directly or implicitly questioned the range of substances which should be covered by waste-specific controls and consequently the manner in which waste is viewed in law.

Most discarded material is subject to further commercial transactions during its "life-cycle", and there has been an on-going debate on the importance of attaching the "waste" label to such substances. This was considered in the joined cases of *Vessoso* and *Zanetti*, where the European Court of Justice (ECJ) held in relation to the interpretation of the "waste" Directives in secondary (i.e. Member State) legislation, that "the concept of waste ... is not to be understood as excluding substances or objects which are capable of economic re-utilisation". Subsequently, in the *Wallonian Waste* case, the ECJ ruled that in relation to primary EU legislation – Article 30 of the EEC Treaty – all objects should be treated as goods, and the fact that waste had no economic value and was non-recyclable was of *economic*, but not of *legal*, importance. This thinking, acknowledging that waste may have a tradable, economic value was developed in the Molitor Report on the simplification of legislation and administration within the EU, which suggested that the EU definition of waste *should* be restricted to "only those substances which have fallen out of any production or manufacturing cycle". Nevertheless, it recommended that all wastes should be regarded as "goods" and thereby allowed to move freely throughout the Community.

An issue related to the economic value assigned to waste is whether recyclable material should be classified as waste, or not. There is a general feeling within the industry groups concerned that such a categorisation acts as a barrier to commercial activity, although environmentalists would see its removal as introducing a potential loophole into the control of wastes. The waste definition in the Framework Directive has not assisted matters and a number of requests for clarification of the position of recyclable materials have been made to the European Court of Justice. The Court recently affirmed the *Vessoso and Zanetti* ruling in relation to a number of related cases referred to it, concerning, *inter alia*, process residues from production or consumption cycles, scrap ferrous and non-ferrous metals, and other waste materials destined for re-use.

The recycling of waste has an international dimension and, in addition to the importance of a common terminology for these materials, there is a conflict between the restrictions placed upon their transboundary movement on environmental grounds and the existence of conventions and other agreements directed at free trade.

Finally, a common approach is now developing at EU level between "hazardous waste" and "hazardous substances" legislation, and the Hazardous Waste Directive, 91/689/EEC, as amended by 94/31/EC, uses the same 14 hazardous properties to categorise waste as those used in EU legislation relating to chemicals, such as the Directive on the Classification, Packaging and Labelling of Dangerous Preparations, 88/379/EEC, and the equivalent Directive relating to Substances, 92/32/EEC. Within the United Kingdom, this system of classification of hazardous properties forms the basis of, *inter alia*, the Carriage of Dangerous Goods (Classification, Packaging and Labelling) and Use of Transportable Pressure Receptacles Regulations 1996, SI 1996/2092, which relate to the carriage of both wastes and of hazardous materials, and the Special Waste Regulations 1996, SI 1996/972, as amended by SI 1996/2019.

Having briefly outlined the problems and issues associated with this branch of environmental law, its development will now be traced with reference to UK and EU legislation. In view of the controls which are or have been imposed in this area, it is instructive to consider the following factors:

— the objectives of the legislation involved;

— the range of activities covered by the measures;

— the manner in which waste is defined, if any; and

— the interaction of the legislation with other measures.

WASTE MANAGEMENT LEGISLATION WITHIN THE UK

Common Law Provisions

The designation of a substance as "waste" is unknown in English common law and, although concepts such as "ultra-hazardous activities" and "non-natural use of land" are employed to impose specific obligations, such usage is related to the *effect* of the substance rather than its classification. Consequently, waste materials are not specifically included or excluded from the application of common law, and in this context the term "waste" is immaterial.

As will be discussed in Chapter 4, the common law is primarily based upon the protection of property interests and, as a consequence, in the majority of cases it is inapplicable to the remediation of the effects of pollution on the "unowned" environment. Although some consideration is given to "environmental" harm, this is generally in relation to property or land owned by the plaintiff. The case of *Earl of Harrington v Derby Corporation*, for example, demonstrates the range of property-related environmental issues which a plaintiff might claim as damage under the law of tort. Here, the plaintiff suffered damage to his estate as a result of pollution of the River Derwent from a number of sources and sought an injunction restraining the defendant from polluting the river and causing a nuisance, and damages in relation to the silting up of a lake, the loss of a waterwheel and the expenses in its replacement by an engine, pollution to a well fed by seepage water, depreciation to a house on the river bank and to his castle, the expenses of obtaining a new water supply and injury to fishing.

As in *Earl of Harrington*, not all such claims will be allowable and much will be dependent upon the facts of the case. In relation to water pollution, for example, where the plaintiff has a right to fishing interests, damages may be awarded on the basis of him being unable to continue this activity, and for the re-stocking of the river with appropriately sized fish and any feed required. However, no claim will be allowable in respect of the loss or damage to other fauna and flora resulting from the pollution.

Statutory Legislation and the Deposit of Poisonous Waste Act 1972

The pollution of rivers and streams has long been a concern of communities, as a result of a need for uncontaminated water for both man and his livestock, and in *The Dirty Man of Europe*, Chris Rose points out that, as far back as 1492, there were local "village rules" whereby fines were imposed for polluting the village stream. Although comprehensive "environmental" statutes have only existed since the early 1970s, the statutory control of *water* pollution pre-dates this by about one hundred years, with the introduction of the Rivers Pollution Act in 1876.

There is evidence of an acknowledgement of the nuisance value of waste in some of the private Acts passed around this time. The Brompton and Piccadilly Circus Act 1897 relating to the construction of what is now part of the Piccadilly Line on the Underground states that:

> "... the Company shall not permit or suffer any cart or wagon or other vehicle employed in the removing from or bringing to the said works any soil materials or plant to be loaded or unloaded in any part of the public thoroughfare and the carts or wagons used for such purposes shall be so constructed and managed as to prevent any such soil dropping therefrom and if the Company their contractors or agents commit any breach of this section they shall be liable to a penalty not exceeding forty shillings for each offence and any such penalty may be recovered in a summary manner before any court of summary jurisdiction."

However, in general the disposal of waste was not seen as an important issue until public concern was expressed following the publicity surrounding the discovery of cyanide waste which had been dumped on open land in Nuneaton, presenting a significant threat to local children. This very quickly resulted in the passing of the Deposit of Poisonous Waste Act 1972, which was essentially an interim measure directed specifically at the problems raised by this particular incident – the uncontrolled *deposit* of *hazardous* materials. An interesting feature of the 1972 Act was that it was based upon an assessment of the *risks* associated with the deposit of waste, taking into account the measures taken by the person depositing the waste or by the owner or occupier of the land for minimising the risk. This concept, albeit in a more sophisticated form, now forms the basis of much environmental and health and safety legislation.

Waste was defined with reference to the Schedule within the Deposit of Poisonous Waste (Notification of Removal or Deposit) Regulations 1972, SI 1972/1017, and under Regulation 3, waste which:

— was of a description set out in the Schedule; *and*

— did not contain any hazardous quantity or hazardous concentration of a poisonous, noxious, or polluting substance,

was specified "as being not so poisonous, noxious, or polluting that it need be subject [to section 3 of the 1972 Act]". The Schedule listed five classes of substances which were *not* wastes including, *inter alia*, construction and demolition wastes, ferrous and non-ferrous metallurgical slags, waste produced in the preparation, processing or distribution of food, and animal carcasses or parts thereof.

In effect, there was a presumption that only those wastes *not* prescribed by the Schedule in the Regulations, *and* which met the hazardous, poisonous or polluting criterion, were subject to section 3 of the Act. Within this narrowly defined range of wastes, a number of controls were imposed including:

— civil liability imposed on any person who deposited the waste or caused or permitted it to be deposited in contravention of section 1(1), for damage resulting from the prescribed wastes (section 2);

— a duty to notify the responsible authorities before removing or depositing waste (section 3). This involved these authorities being informed of the nature and chemical composition of the waste, and the quantities involved, with details of any containers used. Details of the parties and sites involved were also required; and

— a requirement on the operators of commercial disposal sites to provide the local authorities with details of the materials deposited (section 4). Where the local authority itself operated the site, these relevant particulars were to be forwarded to the river authority or river purification board.

Under section 1(7), nothing which was done in accordance with the terms of any consent, licence, approval or authority granted under an enactment was taken to be a contravention of section 1(1), although planning permission was specifically excluded from such authority.

The Control of Pollution Act 1974

In addition to the shortcomings resulting from the definition of waste, the effectiveness of the 1972 Act was limited by the narrow range of activities coming within its control, a factor resulting from a desire to address the immediate problem – the deposit of hazardous materials – without taking a longer term view of the overall problem.

These provisions were replaced by the Control of Pollution Act (COPA) 1974, which was much more broadly based, both in terms of the materials included as waste and the range of offences relating to waste-depositing activities. The Act initially focused on the *deposit* of *all* types of waste which fell within a non-exclusive definition in section 30, which stated that waste *included*:

— any substance which constituted a scrap material or an effluent or other unwanted substance arising from the application of any process; and

— any substance or article which required to be disposed of as being broken, worn out, contaminated or otherwise spoiled.

In addition, there was a presumption that any thing discarded or otherwise dealt with as if it were waste was presumed to be waste unless the contrary was proved.

Whilst the provisions of the 1972 Act were based upon the preliminary elimination of listed categories of material not to be regarded as waste, followed by a secondary selection related to the hazardous characteristics of the remaining materials, the 1974 Act applied a non-exclusive definition which in effect considered the utility of the discarded item or substance. However, the concept of environmental risk was retained in section 4(5)(a) and additional Regulations were made in relation to the transport of waste and the control of hazardous ("special") wastes.

Within the overall definition, controls were imposed upon waste which fell within the term "controlled waste", a term still central to current UK legislation and which relates to household, domestic and commercial waste, "or any such waste". These controls were administered by the local authorities and required licences to be held by those involved in the disposal of waste. As in subsequent legislation, a number of wastes were excluded from the definition, e.g. explosive waste, mining and agricultural waste, and certain activities were exempted from the need to hold a licence.

A category of "special wastes" was designated to cover those materials which posed particular *risks* to human health or possessed certain physical characteristics, and these were treated as a sub-group of the general classification of "controlled wastes". This two-stage approach has been used in subsequent UK and EU legislation and, whilst at one level it follows a logical sequence – i.e. if something is not waste, it cannot be special waste – unless specific provisions are made, it may preclude from its classification certain hazardous wastes such as polychlorinated biphenyls (PCBs) from agricultural sources, which do not meet the preliminary definition of controlled waste.

The Environmental Protection Act 1990

The introduction of the Environmental Protection Act 1990 provided an opportunity to rectify some of the failings of COPA 1974, which in relation to waste included the lack of strategic national planning for waste disposal, a number of limitations within the licensing system and a conflict between the regulatory and the operational roles of the Waste Disposal Authorities.

Initially, the 1990 Act retained the definition of waste, the "presumptive" evidential provision and the Special Waste Regulations, but expanded substantially the ambit of control to include any activity involving the handling of waste – importing, producing, keeping, carrying, brokering, treating, and disposing – thus increasing the scope of general waste-related offences and regulatory control. A "Duty of Care" was imposed upon all those involved in waste management activities and the range of operations requiring a waste management licence was extended.

Changes to the waste management licensing regime and to the definition of waste were necessitated by the EU Framework Directive and these were implemented through the Waste Management Licensing Regulations 1994 and the Environment Act 1995. The latter additionally introduced the basis for a UK National Waste Strategy.

Waste Planning and Strategy within the UK

There is a link between the planning of waste-related activities and the regulation of waste management activities and, within the UK, these planning issues have followed two strands:

— the production of *development plans* under Part II of the Town and Country Planning Act 1990, concerned with policies and general proposals in the structure plan of a specific area. Drawn up by the relevant County Council, Metropolitan Council or London Borough, these relate to *all* planning issues but, under Schedule 4 to the Planning and Compensation Act 1991, there is a mandatory requirement for detailed policies and proposals relating to the deposit of refuse and waste material, other than mineral waste.

— the production of *waste disposal plans* by the Waste Regulation Authorities (now subsumed into the Environment Agency). These are based upon an assessment of the volumes and types of controlled waste within the WRA's area and include not only waste generated within it, but also that imported and exported. The plan is intended to establish the methods to be employed for the disposal of these controlled wastes. Under section 50(4) of the Environmental Protection Act 1990 there is a requirement for the WRA to consider the desirability of giving priority to waste recycling.

Guidance on the government's policies on the different aspects of planning and their relationship with pollution controls is set out in Planning Policy

Guidance Note 23 (PPG23). This only relates to England.

Early strategy issues were concerned with "waste" as a substance to be disposed of, rather than as an important component in the resource/conservation equation, although re-use and recycling issues are beginning to be given more consideration. As a result of the Environment Act 1995, modifications have been introduced into the Environmental Protection Act 1990 which lay down the *objectives* of the new National Waste Strategy (Schedule 2A) and require the Secretary of State to prepare a *statement* containing his policies in relation to the recovery and disposal of waste in England and Wales (section 44A). Since these planning provisions fall within Part II of the Act, they relate to waste as defined in section 75(2).

Initially, the Waste Strategy will be advisory and non-statutory, although those parts relating to the import and export of wastes are mandatory since they are governed by Article 7 of the Waste Framework Directive. However, it is the intention that a statutory National Strategy will be established and will give guidance on waste management policy, replacing the waste management plans of section 50 of the Environmental Protection Act 1990. In addition, the National Strategy will influence local authorities, who are required under the Town and Country Planning Act 1990 to "have regard to" national policies when drawing up their development plans, which themselves will provide a framework for individual planning decisions.

New guidance on waste planning is to be issued in a revised version of PPG 23, which is currently subject to consultation. This emphasises the role of the Agency, stating:

> "Such arrangements will need to recognise the role undertaken by the Environment Agency in respect of waste since the Agency has the responsibility for data collection and consideration of issues such as BPEO, and will be best placed to advise regional planning fora."

In addition, regional arrangements will need to provide adequately for consultation with industry and other interested organisations.

WASTE MANAGEMENT LEGISLATION WITHIN THE EU

Waste Management Policy

Community concern relating to the management of waste has been expressed through the Environmental Action Programmes and the associated provisions. The Second Environmental Action Programme of 1977 first outlined the principles behind the EU's policy in this area, and these were little changed when re-stated in the Fifth Programme, "Towards Sustainability" viz:

— *the prevention of the production of waste*, by clean technologies, the establishment of eco-labelling and product criteria, the re-use of materials, and by changes on the part of both producer and consumer;

— *the recovery of the waste produced*, through segregation and sorting, separate collections, material recycling and energy recovery; and

— *the safe disposal of waste*, through the reduction of disposal volume and by stricter standards.

While previous Action Programmes were almost exclusively based upon the use of legislative measures, the Fifth Action Programme suggested a broader mix of instruments "to bring about substantial changes in current trends and practices, and to involve all sectors in a full sharing of responsibility", i.e. legislative instruments, economic instruments, and horizontal and financial measures. The Action Programmes are discussed in more detail in Chapter 2.

Waste Management Strategy

Community perception of waste as a resource was first highlighted in the Second Environmental Action Programme, and in the Fourth Programme it was acknowledged that, of all the actions necessary in the field of waste management, the most important in the long term would be the achievement of a much higher rate of re-use and recycling. The importance of market forces in this area was also noted, although it was not until the Fifth Programme that the application of economic instruments was considered as a "horizontal measure" for environmental protection.

Article 3 of the amended Waste Framework Directive emphasises the priority to be given to re-use and recycling, and Annex IIB lists a number of operations "which may lead to recovery" and for which Member States are required to institute a permitting system. The issue of recycling and re-use is of central importance when considering the concept of waste, since this raises questions as to whether waste-related controls should be applied to such materials prior to their processing, and how commodities with a "market value" should be incorporated within the waste management regime.

A Commission Strategy Paper for waste management was issued in September 1989 and an updated version was adopted by the Commission in 1996. This was followed by a statement on the Community strategy for waste management in Council Resolution 97/C 76/01 (see *Official Journal* [1997] C76/1). The 1989 Strategy's primary concerns were the prevention of waste at source, the "proximity principle" for waste disposal at the nearest available facilities, the promotion of recycling and re-use, the optimisation of final disposal through uniform EU standards, and civil liability based upon the "polluter-pays-principle". In addition, it expressed concern at the lack of controls over waste movement which it was foreseen would result from the relaxation of frontier arrangements between Member States in 1992.

In order to encourage a wider acceptance and more rapid implementation of Community waste management measures, a "priority waste stream" programme was instituted in 1991, initiating a dialogue between the Commission and other interested parties – industrialists, "common interest groups", etc. – in advance of the drafting of legislation or codes of practice. A number of priority waste streams were identified, including used tyres, halogenated hydrocarbons, healthcare waste, construction and demolition waste, electronic waste and end-of-life vehicles.

A key element of the 1996 European Waste Management Strategy is the principle of producer responsibility and this will be integrated into future EU measures aimed at cutting the overall level of waste generated, increasing the amounts recovered and reducing the amount of waste disposed of. A number of actions are suggested, including:

— promoting the use of less raw materials in processes and products;

— placing a greater emphasis on environmental considerations in the setting of standards;

— imposing limits or banning the use of certain heavy metals in products and processes;

— increasing the use of economic instruments in the area of waste prevention, such as imposing charges on non-reusable/recyclable products;

— a further development of the eco-audit and eco-labelling schemes.

A number of defintional problems are acknowledged in the strategy; the Commission states that it will seek to clarify the confusion relating to incineration with and without energy recovery, and action is required in the area of environmental standards relating to recovery, in order ensure fair competition between Member States. There have been claims by Germany and the Netherlands that they are being undercut by Belgium on waste treatment costs, through the application of lower environmental standards.

The proximity principal is reiterated for waste disposal but not for recovery. It is also the intention of the Commission that, in the medium-term, only non-recoverable and "inert" waste should be accepted at landfill sites. Finally, the Strategy calls for an end to the "priority waste stream" approach in view of the considerable time expended to date, often with little achievement.

The Regulatory Framework

The regulatory framework within the EU is based upon the application of controls at two different levels. One group of measures is of *general* applicability and includes the "framework" Directives on waste and on hazardous waste, the Regulation on waste shipments, and proposed civil liability measures – a proposed Directive on civil liability for damage caused by waste and a Green Paper on Remedying Damage to the Environment. The other group is focused on more *specific* issues, such as particular types of waste or methods of waste disposal. Directives have been produced for several waste types – batteries, used oils, packaging, PCBs (polychlorinated biphenyls) and PCTs (polychlorinated terphenyls), and sewage sludge – and a number of priority waste streams have been highlighted for attention – halogenated solvents, used vehicles, demolition waste, clinical waste and municipal waste. These measures directed at a particular waste stream are subject to less ambiguity in the definition of waste than those which are non-specific.

The Definition of Waste

In the EU context, a common terminology for the identification and description of wastes is of particular importance since, in addition to the "environmental" issues associated with its treatment or disposal, are commercial factors and the need to ensure a "level playing field" between Member States.

Since the mid-1970s, the majority of Community measures involving waste have been made with reference to the standard EU definition of waste within the Waste Framework Directive. The first such definition was in the Directive 75/442/EEC which has now been amended by 91/156/EEC, 91/692/EEC and 96/350/EC.

In the English version of the amended Directive, "waste" means:

— any substance or object which falls into one of the sixteen categories in Appendix I of the Directive; which

— the *holder* must discard, intend to discard, or be required to discard.

Although as written the definition consists of two limbs, in an attempt to provide a "catch-all" for anything which might be considered as waste, Appendix I of the Directive is so broadly constructed that it provides little assistance in determining what categories of substance constitute waste. Consequently, the determining factor is the second limb of the definition which relates to the *actions* of the waste holder. Although the Directive requires that "a list of wastes belonging to the categories listed in Annex" is drawn up, the list, known as the European Waste Catalogue (EWC), is not part of the general waste definition and the inclusion of a material on the EWC does not mean that it is to be regarded as a waste in all circumstances and is only relevant when the definition of waste has been satisfied.

This definition has now been incorporated into UK law and supersedes the earlier version. As a consequence of the different emphasis of this definition, much of the existing case law is inapplicable, although to date no judicial consideration has been given in the UK courts. However, the UK is not alone in this interpretative problem and a recent summary in the *Journal of Environmental Law* ([1996], Vol. 8, No. 1, 197-198) indicated that, at the end of 1995, there were eight cases pending a decision of the European Court of Justice (ECJ) on the interpretation of the Framework Directive 91/156/EEC and a further eight concerning the compatibility of national laws of a number of Member States with this Directive. Furthermore, problems have also arisen as a result of linguistic differences between Member States' interpretation of "dispose", particularly in relation to those items destined for re-use or recycling.

Replacing earlier EU controls on hazardous wastes, the Hazardous Waste Directive, 91/689/EEC, is more specific than the general definition with regard to the criteria for determining whether a waste is hazardous or not *but*, prior to such an assessment, the material must clear the hurdle of the "general" waste definition in 91/156/EEC. The Hazardous Waste Directive is now incorporated into UK waste law and the definition of special waste has been changed accordingly. The criteria imposed by the Directive are based upon the *hazard* posed by a given waste, rather than the *risk*-based approach of the earlier UK Regulations.

Both "framework" Directives have associated lists of wastes, although the purposes of these are significantly different. The list of hazardous wastes, 94/904/EC, is a mandatory component in determining whether a "general" waste is also categorised as "hazardous". It also has a role in attaching a specific descriptive label on waste so classified. However, the European Waste Catalogue (EWC), 94/3/EC, from which this list was derived, is a non-exhaustive list of wastes associated with the Waste Framework

Directive. The EWC does not play any part in the "primary" process of determining whether a substance is waste or not, and its purpose is, *inter alia*, to enable the quantities of waste falling under each of its headings to be determined and recorded, and subsequently used in national and Community planning initiatives. The UK, however, has rejected the use of the ECW as a means of classifying waste, on the grounds that it lists mainly industrial wastes and does not deal adequately with other wastes or with the chemical composition of waste. Instead it has established a National Waste Classification Scheme, based upon "a taxonomy of pre-defined descriptors", although to date there have been strong reservations from industry and the scheme has only been introduced on a voluntary, non-statutory basis.

Certain EU instruments, such as the PCB Directive, use a "presumptive" clause in defining what constitutes a particular type of waste. This differs from UK usage in which the use of such a clause was evidential, with the objective of facilitating enforcement.

FREE TRADE AND THE INTERNAL MARKET

It is almost inevitable that the imposition of controls on waste management operations will have a commercial dimension, either in relation to the inherent value of the waste material, the choice of the lowest cost option, or the administrative burden of such controls. These influences extend beyond national boundaries and, since the First Environmental Action Programme, the Community has been aware of the potential for "repercussions on the functioning of the common market and on international trade". Within the Community, this issue has been developed in three areas:

— the selection of the correct legal base for environmental measures introduced by the Community;

— the effect of legislation, introduced by Member States, on trade *within* the Community; and

— the effect of Community and Member States' measures on trade *outside* the Community.

Although the first two were problematic during the early development of the Community, there is now within the EU Treaty an established basis from which trade and environmental issues may be resolved.

The Legal Basis of Community Environmental Measures

Community environmental legislation is introduced on the basis of the relevant Article(s) within the Treaty and in each of the major phases of the

Community's development – prior to the Single European Act (SEA); from the SEA to the Maastricht Treaty; and post-Maastricht – there have been essentially two routes for the introduction of environmental legislation. The choice of route was important in practical terms, for it affected both the voting procedures used to approve the proposed measures and the level of protection which they could provide.

However, there was an initial degree of uncertainty within the Community institutions on the selection of the appropriate legal basis for legislative measures which involved both "single market" and "environmental" components. The Titanium Dioxide Directive, 89/428/EEC, was annulled on the grounds that where environmental measures also contribute to the establishment of the internal market – the disposal of TiO_2 wastes in this case – they should be based upon the provision in the Treaty relating to the harmonisation of measures within the Community.

The legal bases of the amended Waste Framework Directive, 91/156/EEC, and the 1993 Council Regulation on Waste Shipments (replacing an earlier Directive, 84/68/EEC), have also been subject to challenge. Both of these measures were initially adopted under the "harmonisation" provisions of Article 100 or 100a, but in their revised form were adopted as "environmental" measures under Article 130s. With regard to the Framework Directive, the European Court of Justice held that, since its major objectives (its "centre of gravity") are to serve the interests of environmental protection at the expense of the free movement of goods, as in the *Wallonian Waste* case, *infra*, the Regulations could not be based upon Article 100a alone, since this would be incompatible with the purpose of that Article.

The 1993 Regulations were held to fall within the scope of environmental policy pursued by the Community and as such were rightly based upon Article 130s. This was notwithstanding the fact that, by harmonising the conditions under which movements of waste take place, the Regulations affected such movements and had a bearing on the functioning of the internal market.

The Effect of Member States' Domestic Legislation

For a number of reasons, individual Member States may introduce domestic legislation which is directly, or indirectly, discriminatory with respect to free trade with other Member States. This is contrary to one of the primary objectives of the EU, but the *Danish Bottles* and *Wallonian Waste* cases have shown that, within certain limits, environmental considerations may take precedence over those of free trade.

In both of these cases, although the measures introduced by the respective Member States were an infringement on the free movement of goods – a requirement for beer and soft drink containers to be returnable, and a ban on waste imports to a particular region, respectively – they were held *not* to be unlawfully discriminatory when the environmental issues were taken into account. In the former case, environmental protection was held to be one of the so-called "mandatory requirements" of the Community; and in the latter there was a Community objective that, wherever possible, (general) waste should be disposed of at source. Perversely, although the Court held that the *Wallonian* decree was *not* discriminatory in relation to the free movement of "general waste", it *was* found to be discriminatory in the case of hazardous wastes, since specific provisions were laid down for their transboundary movement by Directive 84/631/EEC.

The Effect of Community and Member States' Legislation on Trade Outside the Community

While the inter-relationship between free trade and the environment is now established for intra-Community trading, problems have arisen in two areas of trade with non-Member States: agreements made by the EU on behalf of Member States, and bilateral or multilateral agreements made by Member States and other countries.

INTERNATIONAL MOVEMENT OF WASTE AND FREE TRADE

This is perhaps the most problematic area of waste management control for, in addition to requiring a common terminology between all countries, the objectives of the legislation – the prevention of waste disposal in countries with little effective environmental control (and low disposal costs) – are in direct opposition to those of free trade. The Third Environmental Action Programme expressed concern at the possibility of dumping chemical wastes in non-Member States whose domestic environmental legislation imposed few controls or was ineffectively enforced. This resulted in the adoption of the Directive on the Trans-Frontier Movement of Hazardous Wastes, 84/631/EEC. However, this was restricted in its effectiveness by the absence of a precise definition of waste/hazardous waste and by disparities in the degree of implementation within Member States. Not all materials were covered by these controls and wastes designated as non-ferrous metals for re-use, recycling, or regeneration could by-pass the procedures.

Outside the EU, there has been growing concern on the trans-frontier shipment of waste, particularly with regard to the use of Third World countries as dumping sites, and this culminated in the Basel and Lomé

Conventions. These were incorporated into EU law through Regulation 259/93/EEC, which is directly applicable in Member States, and uses the EU Framework Directive's definition of waste. However, for wastes destined for *recovery*, in order to facilitate their movement within OECD (Organisation for Economic Co-operation and Development) countries, a supplementary agreement was introduced which employed a further form of classification.

The original form of this classification divided such materials into three lists – red, amber and green – according to their hazardous nature, but a working group on the Basel Convention is producing a revised grouping of hazardous wastes, in anticipation of the ban on export to non-OECD countries from January 1998.

The use of a number of different schemes for waste classification/categorisation is clearly incompatible with effective control and it is possible that such international definitions of waste might ultimately shape those used internally within individual countries both within the EU and outside the Common Market. In this respect it is interesting to note the extent to which the EU waste definitions or categories have been used or applied. In addition to the Basel Convention which used the EU Hazardous Waste Directive, 91/689/EEC, in both its original and in its final form, the Directive itself is in force throughout the European Economic Area (EEA).

As noted earlier, restrictions on trade have international repercussions and it is necessary to consider waste legislation within this broader framework. This is demonstrated by a recent GATT (General Agreement on Tariffs and Trade) ruling in which it was held that the US could not instigate a unilateral ban in order to protect the environment outside its borders. A consequence of this is the possible incompatibility of the ban on the export of hazardous waste from OECD to non-OECD countries under the Basel Convention.

The World Trade Organisation (WTO) was established on 1st January 1995 as a means of replacing the *ad hoc* arrangements for administering GATT. Issues relating to the environment are clearly of importance to both trade and international investment.

FUTURE DIRECTIONS

The Continuing Utility of the Concept of "Waste"

Over the past twenty years, the control of waste management in the UK has grown from relatively modest beginnings to become one of the most technically and legally complex areas of environmental legislation. A wide range of waste-related issues now comes within its ambit and an important factor in its development has been the change in the perception of waste, as society's awareness and concern for the environment has grown. The designation "waste" forms the basis of a wide range of statutory measures and, despite the overlap with health and safety legislation in the area of hazardous substances, the problems resulting from the imposition of environmental restrictions on free trade and the inherent value of many discarded products, there are nevertheless strong arguments for the continuing use of the term.

The concept of "waste" is an essential component of environmental legislation and provides a means of control for a class of substances and objects, the objectives of which could not be realised without such a categorisation. The absence of such provisions would inevitably lead to a number of lacunae in areas to which other control regimes could not be conveniently extended. However, this application is essentially *post facto* and relies upon the use of "command and control" enforcement practices to materials which have been produced (or are planned to be), and as such has a relatively limited *preventative* role in the protection of the environment.

Similarly, in the areas of planning and international trade, there are a number of benefits to be gained by utilising the concept of waste, where it provides a convenient basis for the establishment of a regulatory framework for a range of materials having no other basis of commonality. However, it is often difficult to obtain a reconciliation between the requirements for free trade and those for environmental protection due to basic differences in their objectives. An exception is perhaps within the "closed system" of the European Union where, by virtue of the EU Treaty and European case law, the basic "rules" governing the inter-relationship of environmental and intra-Community trade issues have been established.

The formulation of a workable definition of "waste" is critical to the success of any legislation in this area and has been a continuing problem, both in the UK and elsewhere. While for planning and policy issues there is a "core of settled meaning" in relation to the term, wherever there is a requirement for more specific controls, most attempts at a satisfactory definition have left a substantial "penumbra of doubt".

Having outlined the benefits to be gained from the classification of certain groups of material as "waste", the next consideration is to determine the requirements of the environmental or other controls, and how best these might be effected. In the past, waste legislation has been directed either towards offences relating to waste *per se*, or environmental protection measures based upon the development of strategies for the land-use planning process associated with the disposal of waste and for the regulation of waste management operations through licensing and similar regimes. Since then there have been a number of developments in the understanding of the factors contributing to environmental harm, the range of control measures which might be adopted to mitigate or eliminate such effects, and techniques for the measurement and monitoring of critical parameters.

Scientific and Technological Developments

Both common law and statutory legislation take into account advancements in knowledge, the level of knowledge expected of a competent practitioner and currently accepted social norms. In English common law, the torts of nuisance, negligence and, following *Cambridge Water Co v Eastern Counties Leather plc*, the rule in *Rylands v Fletcher*, are subject to "reasonable foreseeability" on the part of the defendant. While this precludes the *post facto* application of new developments in scientific knowledge, a company is expected to be aware of the "state of the art" in relation to its operations and the potential for harm or damage to persons or property, as demonstrated in *Margereson and Hancock v J W Roberts Ltd.*

The question of when a company is considered in law to be aware of such potential dangers is difficult to define and is complicated by the long incubation period of certain health-related complaints, the quantity of data required for epidemiological studies and a lack of unanimity among experts in the field. However, internal memoranda expressing concern at the potential deleterious consequences of some aspect of its operations may be taken as evidence of the awareness of this particular problem. Present-day issues falling into this area of uncertainty, of which the waste manager should be aware, include: the emissions of dioxins, discharges of polyaromatic hydrocarbons (PAH), the link between $PM_{10}/PM_{2.5}$ particulates (i.e. particles with an aerodynamic diameter of less than 10 and 2.5 microns, respectively) and respiratory illness, and the effects of electromagnetic radiation (emr).

The situation is different with regard to statutory legislation since, apart from the interpretation of the law by the courts, in general, the required standards of performance or conduct are laid down within the primary and secondary legislation and other statutory guidance. In anticipation of the need to update the law in line with EU initiatives and current knowledge, a number of measures, including the Environmental Protection Act 1990, are introduced as enabling Acts, leaving much of the working detail to be supplied by Statutory Instruments.

Science and technology play an integral part in these controls, in a number of ways, including:

— the provision of environmental standards directed at the source of the pollution, or towards the target which is being protected;

— the establishment of design standards relating to the construction and operation of plant and equipment;

— the development of quantitative parameters with which to assess processing operations and environmental harm;

— the development of methodologies of risk assessment and risk management.

The Influence of Sustainable Development

Article 2 of the Treaty on European Union makes sustainable development one of the objectives of the Community, and the Fifth Environmental Action Programme defines "sustainable" in terms of "a policy and strategy for continued economic and social development without detriment to the environment and the natural resources on the quality of which continued human activity and future development depend" (*sic*).

Community thinking on the perception of waste as a resource commenced in the Second Environmental Action Programme and the Fourth Programme acknowledged that, of all the actions necessary in the field of waste management, the most important in the long term was the need to achieve a significantly higher rate of re-use and recycling of waste.

This was included as a component of the EU Waste Framework Directive and is being incorporated in an increasing number of EU and UK initiatives, including the "priority waste stream" programme, the EU Directive on Packaging and Packaging Waste, the proposed Directive on End of Life Vehicles, and the UK landfill tax.

The landfill tax, introduced through the 1996 Finance Act, is an important landmark in the regulation of waste, for it emphasises the burden imposed by waste generation and the need to develop other solutions within the "waste hierarchy". When the tax became effective in October 1996, many businesses experienced an ~30% increase in their disposal costs merely to maintain the *status quo*, and it is likely that further increases will be experienced as a result of the restrictions being imposed on the landfilling of waste by UK legislation and in anticipation of those proposed by the Landfill Directive. Such measures will make it a commercial necessity to examine all waste products and by-products, and to re-assess potential disposal routes.

For example, within the steel industry, certain recycling options such as the plasma reduction of flue-dust have remained on the borderline of economic viability, mainly as a result of the low costs of the alternative landfill options. In addition, there may be further opportunities for the use of by-products as the result of environmental pressures on other industrial sectors. For example, the continued demand for aggregates and the pressures against future large scale quarrying will create an increased demand for secondary aggregates.

Economic Instruments

While the early EU Action Programmes relied upon legislative measures almost exclusively, the Fifth suggested a broader mix of measures including market-based instruments, with which to sensitise both producers and consumers towards the responsible use of resources and the avoidance of pollution. A review of the current use of economic instruments within the EU is given in the Commission communication *Environmental Taxes and Charges in the Single Market*, COM (97) 9 (final).

There is an equally strong commitment from the UK government for the wider use of economic instruments/market mechanisms, although reviews by the Royal Commission for Environmental Pollution (RCEP), the House of Lords and OECD conclude that a combination of both traditional controls and economic measures will be necessary in order to deliver most environmental quality objectives. As a consequence, it is possible that, overall, additional burdens will be placed on businesses by the information and other requirements of these schemes.

There are many different forms of economic instrument – tradable permits, pollution (emission) charges, product costs, subsidies and (indirectly) legal liabilities – and within the UK they are under consideration in four policy areas: the reduction of carbon and other emissions into the atmosphere, the management of rural land and water resources, waste disposal and recycling, and transport.

Tradable permits operate within a regulatory framework which establishes a maximum level of total emissions for a given compound within a selected geographical area, and creates a system of permits which, within a set of pre-determined regulations, may be treated as a commodity, i.e. bought, sold, banked, "netted" (for a group of sites), and off-set against other emission sources. Tradable emissions offer advantages where marginal abatement costs differ among polluters and maximum ceilings are imposed on total emissions. Most experience in the use of these controls has been gained in the United States and, although their potential for substantial resource savings and additional industrial growth has been demonstrated, they nevertheless have had limited national application and the amount of trading has been less than predicted.

Pollution (or emission) charges are most suitable where there is a restricted number of stationary point discharges which may be monitored and for which there is a potential for achieving a reduction. The 16th RCEP Report examined emission charges in relation to discharges to controlled waters and concluded that, backed by a complex trade-approvals structure, they might offer the necessary certainty for the achievement of water quality standards. However, for point discharges into freshwater, used by themselves they were not considered to offer an acceptable form of regulation.

The OECD Report stresses that the major evaluation criteria for economic instruments are "environmental effectiveness and economic efficiency" and, while one would not fault the logic that "given the right framework and the right market signals, they (market mechanisms) will do the job and do it efficiently", it is these two factors which have proved difficult to optimise in the past. As noted earlier, it is almost impossible to derive an unequivocal assessment of "environmental harm" and the more a measure is reliant upon market forces, the greater is the uncertainty in its operation in practice. In particular, many economic models are based upon a unilateral application of the measures at a single point in time, rather than a series of bilateral agreements over an extended period.

The Development of Techniques for Monitoring and Analysis

In view of the reliance within many systems of environmental regulation which is placed upon the composition of discharges and emission to the environmental media, monitoring and analysis techniques clearly have an important role in the controls imposed and there have been developments in three major areas:

— legislation relating to the acceptability of analyses and other measurements;

— "remote" techniques for monitoring, sampling and analysis; and

— new methods of detecting pollution.

In the past, difficulties arose as a result of the law's requirements for "tripartite" sampling procedures in relation to water pollution. However, significant changes in the admissibility as evidence of results from *any* sampling or monitoring procedure (i.e. not solely relating to water sampling) were introduced in section 111 of the Environment Act 1995 under which it is no longer necessary to employ tripartite sampling for the information to be admissible. Furthermore, the results from *any* equipment may be produced as evidence, including those from "automatic" or "remote" devices and these are presumed to be accurate.

Another important change is that omitting to record information relating to a licence condition may now be taken as evidence that the relevant licence condition has not been satisfied. This latter measure, in combination with an increase in the number and frequency of measurements and analyses required by a consent, provides the Environment Agency with a means of moving towards "self-regulation", while retaining a high degree of indirect control.

Developing technology will permit a greater use of both remote sensing or automatic techniques and the transmission/availability of information. Aircraft surveillance is an established method for the detection of marine pollution, as in *Micosta SA v Shetland Islands Council ("The Mihalis")*, and satellite remote sensing, with its capability for generating images with a resolution of a few metres, has significant potential for a wide range of environmental applications – detection of mineral, fish and water resources, and monitoring of desertification, deforestation, climate changes, air and water pollution, land use and industrial accidents. While much of the sensing and primary data retrieval is carried out by public agencies, an increasing amount of the data processing, analysis and sale is being undertaken by the private sector and this raises a number of important legal questions regarding the accessibility of these data to the public and non-governmental organisations.

In addition to remote sensing, there have been other important developments in the detection of pollution and assessment of environmental harm. The Environment Agency has proposed modifying the criteria for the controls of discharges of waste waters by the use of "toxicity-based" controls, whereby future discharge consents would place less emphasis on specific components of a discharge and more on the toxic characteristics of the discharge as a whole. The use of algae and invertebrates to gain a measure of the pollution present in the receptor has been adopted in the USA and elsewhere, and such methods are seen as a more direct means of controlling the impact of chemically-complex effluents, where traditional composition-related limits are ineffective. There has been unanimous opposition from the Chemical Industries Association (CIA), the Water Services Association (WSA) and the Confederation of British Industry (CBI) to the principle of toxicity limits in discharge consents, although the use of toxicity testing as a management tool has been supported.

Less controversial is the use of genetically-modified viruses as a means of tracing pollutants. These may be given a unique, identifying "tattoo" and a number of potential sources can be tested simultaneously. In addition to their regulatory application, they also have a potential use by contractors and site owners in tracing egress and locating drainage problems. "Fly tipping" has not escaped the application of technology and the Environment Agency is reported to be using special light-intensifying cameras and video recording equipment in order to prevent the illegal disposal of waste.

Most areas of environmental legislation are subject to the establishment and maintenance of public registers of information by the relevant enforcement authority, and many of the difficulties encountered to date have resulted from physical problems associated with placing the required information on the register and its subsequent accessibility by members of the public and others. However, this will change as greater use is made of information technology, both in the initial capture of the information and in its processing and dissemination.

In addition to sampling and monitoring, there is the potential for much of the formal communication between the regulatory bodies and their "customers" to be made electronically, and resultant information which is not subject to conditions of confidentiality to be transferred directly to the registers. As is demonstrated in Chapter 7, much environmental information is available through the Internet and, in addition to the primary information available from official organisations, other bodies may follow the lead of Friends of the Earth's initiative on the Chemical Release Inventory (CRI) and provide secondary sources of data through this medium. However, the application of information technology introduces a number of legal problems, when the concepts developed for "conventional" data storage, retrieval and transfer are applied to electronically-held information.

FURTHER READING

General Current Awareness

The ENDS Report, Environmental Data Services

Environment Business, Information for Industry

Environment Business Magazine, Information for Industry

Health, Safety and Environment Bulletin, Industrial Relations Service

Industrial Environmental Management, Faversham House Group

Local Authority Waste and Environment, Faversham House Group

The Waste Manager, Environmental Services Association

Legal Journals

Environmental Law, Journal of the UK Environmental Law Association

Environmental Law and Management, John Wiley & Sons

Environmental Law Monthly, Monitor Press

Environmental Liability, Sweet & Maxwell

European Dangerous Chemicals Law, Agra Europe (London) Ltd

European Environmental Law Review, Graham & Trotman

Journal of Environmental Law, OUP

Journal of Planning and Environmental Law, Sweet & Maxwell

Water Law, John Wiley & Sons

Reference

The Concise Lexicon of Environmental Terms, Ed. M Grant and R Hawkins, John Wiley & Sons, 1995

Digest of Environmental Statistics, Department of the Environment, HMSO, published annually

The Environment Acts 1990-1995, 3rd Edition, S Tromans, M Nash and M Poustie, Sweet & Maxwell, 1996

Environmental Law, 3rd Edition, S Ball and S Bell, Blackstone Press, 1995

Environmental Law, 3rd Edition, D Hughes, Butterworths, 1996

Environmental Law, J D Leeson, Pitman Publishing, 1995

UK Waste Management Law, J Bates, Sweet & Maxwell, 1997

General

"The Challenges of Environmentally Sound and Efficient Regulation of Waste – The Need for International Understanding", J T Smith, [1993] 5 *JEL* 91

The Dirty Man of Europe, Chris Rose, Simon and Schuster, 1990

Environmental Taxes in OECD Countries, OECD, 1995

"International Trade and the Environment – Recent Activities of the WTO", O Lomas and D Gibbons, [1996] 8 *ELM* 224

Making Markets Work for the Environment, HMSO, 1993

Planning and Pollution Control, Planning Policy Guidance Note 23, Department of the Environment, 1994 (currently under review)

"The Role of Environmental Action Programmes in the Development of EU Environmental Legislation", D N Pocklington, [1995] 7 *ELM* 221

"The Status of the 'Precautionary Principle' in Law", D Hughes, [1995] 7 *JEL* 224

Sustainable Development: The UK Strategy, HMSO, 1994

"The Term Waste in EU Law", J Fluck, [1994] *EELR* 79

"Transboundary Movements of Waste under EC Law: The Emerging Regulatory Framework", A Schmidt, [1992] 4 *JEL* 57

The UK Environment, Department of the Environment, HMSO, 1992

The reader is also directed towards the author's paper, "The Utility of the Concept of Waste", [1996] 4 (5) *Environmental Liability* 94, upon which part of this chapter was based.

Chapter 2

THE FRAMEWORK FOR CONTROL

"Nothing is more likely to bring disrepute on the system of control under the European Treaty than an over-rigid application of the criteria resulting in needless hardship."

Mr Justice Carnwath[1]

INTRODUCTION

Prior to discussing waste management law in detail, the framework within which this legislation operates will be examined. The objective of this book is to provide those for whom waste management is part of their responsibilities with an understanding of this now complex area of environmental law and the associated liabilities for them and their organisations. In this chapter, the sources of waste management law and the bodies responsible for its implementation will be outlined and, for a fuller account of specific issues, the reader is directed to the many authoritative texts available, some of which are included in the "Further Reading" section at the end of the chapter.

Environmental law is still in the early stages of its development and this is particularly true for the regulation of waste and waste-related activities. There have been significant changes in the statutory legislation and technical guidance in this area over the last three years and, in addition to keeping abreast of such developments, it is important to maintain an awareness of the associated case law, since this has a important influence on their interpretation and application.

Some branches of environmental legislation such as Integrated Pollution Control (IPC) have developed relatively little case law, whilst others with a longer history have received a significant amount of judicial consideration. However, despite the number of earlier judgments within a particular area, it is important to monitor current cases since these give an insight into the present context of the legislation or may explore areas which have not previously been considered.

A significant amount of case law had been established in relation to the meaning of "waste" under the Control of Pollution Act 1974 and the Environmental Protection Act 1990 prior to 1st May 1994. However,

---

[1]   *R v The Environment Agency ex parte Dockgrange & ors.*

changes to the definition of "waste" altered the applicability of many of these judgments and new case law is being developed as a result of actions within UK courts and the ECJ.

An example of the second point is found in *NRA v Egger UK Ltd*, where Mr Justice Bryant noted that, despite the long history of water pollution legislation, no court had ever been asked to say what the word "pollution" means and neither did any of the current legislation nor its immediate predecessors define the term.

There are two areas of particular importance which should be borne in mind with regard to the interpretation of environmental statutes: the "European" context of the measures and the technical/scientific component of many of the controls imposed. Most, although not all, EU environmental measures are introduced as Directives which are applicable throughout the Community and, whilst they are implemented by individual Member States, there will be a high degree of commonality between the controls imposed in each country. Consequently, the meaning of a particular term or definition is not solely dependent upon the interpretation given in the Member State's statutory legislation or by its courts. The Directive, including the preamble outlining its objectives, forms the "primary" source of the legislation and ultimately it is the European Court of Justice which has the power to determine its interpretation. This is well demonstrated in the Advocate General's opinion on the joined cases c-304/94, c-330/94, c-342/94 and c-224/94, *Criminal Proceedings against Euro Tombesi & ors*, where the diverse approaches of the Danish, French, Italian, Netherlands and UK governments on the meaning of "waste" were reviewed and contrasted, and the "European" opinion given (*vide* Chapter 8).

Waste legislation is one the more technically complex areas of law and much of the newer legislation, such as that on the classification of a substance as a "special waste" or the designation of "contaminated land", needs to be approached from both legal and the technical standpoints in order for a meaningful interpretation to be given.

THE LAW OF THE EUROPEAN COMMUNITY

The UK and the Establishment of the Community

An estimated 80% of the present "environmental law" has its origins in the European Community and it is therefore important to be aware of how these measures arise and are implemented by the Member States, and what mechanisms are in place for their subsequent monitoring and enforcement.

The European Community is based upon three separate Treaties – the

European Coal and Steel Community (ECSC) Treaty, signed in Paris on 18th April 1951; and the European Economic Community (EEC) Treaty and the European Atomic Energy Community (Euratom) Treaty, both signed in Rome on 25th March 1957. At their inception, these Treaties gave rise to separate Communities, each with its own institutions and, in view of the duplication in the administration and a commonality between many of their aims, a Merger Treaty, the Treaty Establishing a Single Council and a Single Commission of the European Communities, was signed on 1st July 1976. This instrument did not merge the three Communities but merely served to establish a single Council and Commission, each located in Brussels. The European Court of Justice was based in Luxembourg and some Commission and Council business is also carried out there. The European Parliament sits in Strasbourg but holds some sessions and its committee meetings in Brussels, whilst the secretariat is based in Luxembourg. Hartley[1] notes "the end result is highly inconvenient and inefficient, and shows that even in the simplest matters, the common interest has to give way to national interest".

The United Kingdom joined the Community in 1972 and the Treaties were incorporated into UK law through the European Communities Act 1972. As a result, all Community law became part of the UK's own internal law, imposing rights and obligations on individuals and organisations. Directly applicable EU law – Treaty provisions and Regulations – become automatically part of UK law and no domestic legislation is required for their enactment. As Lord Denning MR noted in *H P Bulmer Ltd v J Bollinger SA*, henceforth "any rights or obligations created by the Treaty are to be given legal effect in England without more ado".

Section 2(1) of the 1972 Act gives direct applicability of EU law to the UK and section 2(2) provides a general power for the implementation of EU obligations via secondary legislation. However, a number of restrictions are imposed through Schedule 2, relating to

— measures imposing or increasing taxation;

— retroactive measures;

— measures which create new criminal offences.

Although the primacy of EU legislation was acknowledged in section 2(4), as in other Member States this concept gave rise to a number of problems

[1]   *The Foundations of European Community Law, 3rd Edition*, T C Hartley, Clarendon Press, 1994, page 4.

in the national courts. Whilst one judicial view of section 2(4) was that it required the UK courts to give priority to EU law, as in *Simmenthal SpA v Commission*, case 92/78, another was that it laid down a rule of construction whereby domestic law must be construed, so far as possible, to conform with EU law.

Steiner[1] notes that there was "considerable [judicial] wavering in the early years on the question of the primacy [of European law]." In *H P Bulmer Ltd* Lord Denning stated that the Treaty "is equal in force to any statute" but, in a subsequent judgment, *Felixstowe Dock and Railway Co v British Transport Docks Board*, said that "once the Bill is passed by Parliament and becomes statute, that will dispose of all this discussion about the Treaty. These courts will have to abide by the statute without regard to the Treaty at all."

However, in the landmark case of *Macarthys Ltd v Smith*, two of the law lords took the "European" view giving community law priority, while Lord Denning adopted a broader constructional approach, stating "if ... our legislation is deficient – or is inconsistent with Community law ... then it is our bounden duty to give priority to Community law." Nevertheless, he also stated that "if the time ever comes when Parliament deliberately passes an Act with the intention of repudiating the Treaty or any provisions in it, or intentionally of acting inconsistently with it and says so in express terms, then I should have thought that it would be the duty of our courts to follow the statute of our Parliament. I do not however envisage any such situation ... Unless there is such an intentional and express repudiation of the Treaty, it is our duty to give priority to the Treaty."

The supremacy of Community law was considered in a number of subsequent cases in which there was a conflict between EU and domestic law, including *Garland v British Rail Engineering Ltd* (equal pay), *Pickstone v Freeman plc* (equal pay) and *Factortame Ltd v Secretary of State for Transport* (fishing rights). Such discussions were not unique to the United Kingdom and, although the principle is now established, Hartley notes that ultimate sovereignty still rests with Parliament, as expressed by Lord Denning, *supra*. Community law prevails only because Parliament wants it to prevail and the European Communities Act could always be repealed so that Community law would cease to have effect in the United Kingdom.

---

[1]   *Textbook of EEC Law, 5th Edition*, J Steiner and L Woods, Blackstone Press, 1996, page 72.

THE FOUNDATION TREATIES

The Treaties upon which the European Community is based – the so-called Foundation Treaties, made up of the EC Treaty, the ECSC Treaty and the Euratom Treaty – are fundamental both to its structure and its day-to-day activities. In addition to defining the membership of the Community and establishing its institutions – the Council Commission, Parliament, the European Court of Justice and the Court of Auditors – they also define the rights of natural and legal persons within the Member States.

Since the Treaties were first signed, they have been amended to accommodate the inclusion of new Members such as the UK in 1972, and changes to the decision-making and other procedures. Important developments in relation to the environment were made in the Single European Act 1986, which first established the formal legal base for EU measures in this area, and the Maastricht Treaty in 1992 which further extended the scope of these provisions.

At the Intergovernmental Conference (IGC) in June 1997, additional changes to the Treaties were agreed and included in the Treaty of Amsterdam, document CONF/4001/97. Before it becomes effective, the Treaty must be signed and ratified by Member States and, in Denmark, a referendum will have to be held. Although this new Treaty did not break as much new ground as the Maastricht and earlier Treaties, important changes were made in the area of the environment, and the modifications made to the voting procedures will further strengthen the role of the European Parliament.

Another important development in EU law resulted from negotiations with the EFTA states – Norway, Sweden, Finland, Iceland, Switzerland, Liechtenstein and Austria – which resulted in an agreement in 1991 establishing the European Economic Area (EEA). Under this agreement, existing and future Community laws from all sources – Treaty provisions, legislation and judgments of the European Court – become applicable within these countries. Although the ECJ initially held that the EEA agreement was incompatible with the EC Treaty, following subsequent amendment it was approved by the Court in 1992.

The establishment of the EEA has implications with regard to waste legislation, *inter alia*, since provisions such as those defining waste become applicable within both the EU and the EEA.

In addition to the EU Treaties, there are a number of other sources of law including Regulations, Directives and Decisions, as well as the rulings of the European Court of Justice. The manner in which EU law may be enforced is dependent upon its source and many of the early decisions of the ECJ were concerned with these issues.

THE INSTITUTIONS OF THE COMMUNITY

The basis for four of the principal institutions of the Community – the Council, the Commission, the European Parliament and the Court of Justice – is contained within Article 7 of the ECSC Treaty, Article 7 of the Euratom Treaty and Article 4 of the EC Treaty which also provides for the establishment of an Economic and Social Committee (ECOSOC). Article 4 of the Merger Treaty established a Committee for Permanent Representation of the Member States (COREPER) and, under the Single European Act, a Court of First Instance was set up in October 1988.

Following the Treaty on European Union (the "Maastricht Treaty"), the Court of Auditors was added to the other four "principal" institutions of the Community and provision was made for the establishment of a Committee of the Regions. Two new Articles, 4a and 4b, were introduced which set up the European System of Central Banks (ESCB) and a European Central Bank (ECB), and established the European Investment Bank, respectively.

The Council of the European Union

The role of the Council is to ensure that the objectives of the Treaty are attained by:

— ensuring co-ordination of the general and economic policies of the Member States;

— having the power to take decisions; and

— conferring on the Commission, in acts which the Council adopts, powers for the implementation of the rules which the Council lays down. In specific cases, it may also exercise directly implementing powers itself.

The functions and authority of the Council are laid down in Articles 145 to 154. The Council is made up of one representative from each Member State, who is required to be at ministerial level, and "authorised to commit the government of that Member State" (Article 145). The membership of the Council is not fixed and the nature of the business in hand determines which ministers are selected by their government to represent it. However, where major issues are to be determined, the Council generally consists of heads of state and, where such meetings are held to discuss matters on EU law or political co-operation, the body is termed the European Council.

The Council is convened by the President, who is elected according to the rules in Article 146 to serve for a period of six months. The voting procedures are contained in Article 148 and, except where specifically provided for within the Treaty, the Council acts by a majority vote of its members. The voting requirements are critical, since they effectively determine the influence of individual Member States in reaching the final decision. Initially, sensitive issues could only be passed by a unanimous vote and it was intended that in most cases agreement would be determined by qualified majority voting. However, at the insistence of the French in 1966, the "Luxembourg Accords" were agreed whereby a Member State could insist on unanimity where vital national interests were at stake. Although the Luxembourg Accords do not have legal status, they are generally followed in practice.

An increase in the number of Member States led to concern in certain existing countries, including the UK, that their voting strength would be diluted on issues where qualified majority voting was required. This resulted in the Ioannina Compromise under which modifications were made to the percentage of votes required to block a decision under qualified majority voting.

Unlike the Commission, the Council is not a permanent body and meets only a few days each month and as a consequence much of its work is undertaken by the Committee for Permanent Representation of the Member States (COREPER).

The European Commission

Described as "the Guardian of the Treaties", the function and powers of the European Commission are contained in Articles 155 to 163 of the Treaty. The Commission is currently made up of 20 nationals from Member States who are appointed by "common accord of the governments of the Member States", on the basis of their general competence and "independence ... beyond doubt". The five largest countries – Germany, France, Italy, Spain and the United Kingdom – each have two Commissioners, whilst the other countries have one. Commissioners are appointed for a period of five years, which is renewable.

The Commission is headed by a President who is appointed from the Commissioners for a renewable term of two years. Different aspects of Community policy are managed by the 23 directorates-general, those of relevance to environmental issues being: DG III, industrial affairs, information technologies and telecommunications; DG VII, transport (including trans-Europe networks); and DG XI, environment and nuclear security.

The Commission has three major functions:

— **to initiate Community action**, by making proposals in response to requests from the Council (Article 152), from Parliament (Article 136b) or on its own initiative using the Treaty as a basis.

— **for policing and enforcing EU legislation**. Under Article 5, Member States are obliged to "take all appropriate measures ... to ensure fulfilment of the obligations arising out of the Treaty", and the Commission must investigate potential infractions and take action through Article 169, where necessary.

In order to undertake this role, the Commission has extensive investigative powers, and may request both individuals and Member States to provide information pursuant to these powers.

— **to act as the executive of the Community**. The Commission is responsible for the implementation of the policy decisions of the Council, including the drawing up of a draft budget, although it is supervised by a number of advisory, management and regulatory committees, in a process often referred to as "comitology". Steiner[1] notes that, in conjunction with the overall power of the Council under Article 145, this tends to undermine the authority of the Commission.

The Commission has its own powers of decision under Article 155, which are used, *inter alia*, in relation to competition policy and Regulations concerning agriculture. In addition, it acts as the negotiator in matters of the Community's external policy, although it is the Council that concludes the final agreement.

The European Parliament

Since its creation as the "Assembly" in 1957 under the Treaty of Rome, the European Parliament has undergone a number of important changes in its membership requirements, its powers and, as a consequence, its influence on Community affairs. Direct elections were only introduced in 1979 and the electoral system is not yet uniform across the Community.

---

[1] *Textbook of EEC Law, 5th Edition*, J Steiner and L Woods, Blackstone Press, 1996, page 24.

The power and structure of the Parliament are contained in Articles 137 to 144 of the Treaty, and currently it is made up of 626 members of which France, Germany, Italy and the United Kingdom each have 87 MEPs, Spain and the Netherlands have 31, Belgium, Greece and Portugal 25, Sweden 21, Austria 20, Denmark and Finland 16, Ireland 15 and Luxembourg 6.

In addition to changing the name to the "Parliament", the Single European Act (SEA) of 1976 gave it important new powers, including:

— the right to be consulted through the new *co-operation procedure* (Article 149);

— the final assent for the admission of new Member States; and

— the conclusion of agreements with non-Member States.

These powers were further extended under the Treaty on European Union (the "Maastricht Treaty"), which repealed Article 149, replacing it with a similar procedure in Article 189(c), and introduced a new *co-decision procedure* (Article 189(b)). Under the Treaty of Amsterdam, the extension to the number of measures subject to the co-decision procedure, and the simplification of its conciliation procedure, will further strengthen the role of the Parliament.

Following *Roquette Frères SA v Council*, case 138/79, the Parliament has *locus standi* to challenge acts of the Council and Commission and under Article 175 may also bring an action against these institutions for failing to act. Although it does not have a general power of challenge, it may use Article 173 in order to enforce its right to be consulted and to ensure the correct Treaty base is employed for legislative measures. In addition, it has the power of initiative under Article 138b, whereby it may request the Commission to submit proposals on an issue on which it considers that legislation is required for the purpose of implementing the Treaty.

The European Court of Justice (ECJ)

The European Court, officially known as the "Court of Justice", comprises 15 judges who must be "persons whose independence is beyond doubt and who posses the qualifications for appointment to the highest judicial offices in their respective countries, or who are jurisconsults [academic lawyers] of recognised competence" (Article 167). This wording permits the appointment of academic lawyers who may not be eligible within their own country.

The judges are appointed for a renewable period of six years by the common accord of the Member States, and they themselves elect one of their number to be president for three years. They are assisted in their work by eight advocates general, who present "submissions" to the Court, consisting of a detailed analysis of the facts of a case and the pertinent law, together with a recommendation on the action to be taken. These recommendations have an important role, for although they are not always followed in the instant case, they may nevertheless be cited as persuasive authority in subsequent ones. Likewise, a judgment of the Court which is a single collegiate decision does not set a precedent which is binding in the accepted English sense and the ECJ is free to depart from earlier judgments in the light of new facts.

The role of the ECJ is determined by Articles 164 to 168 and is defined as "to ensure that in the implementation and application of the Treaty, the law is observed". It has the ultimate power to interpret the meaning of the Treaties and any legislation made by the other institutions. However, it has no jurisdiction over the action of the Council, and Article L in the Treaty of European Union defines the limits of its jurisprudence in relation to the provisions of the Treaty.

Article 177 provides a means whereby any court or tribunal of a Member State can request a ruling from the Court on:

— an interpretation of the Treaty;

— the validity and interpretation of acts of the EU institutions;

— determining the correctness of the implementation of EU law within Member States.

Such references may be made where "a decision on the question is necessary to enable the national court to give judgment". National courts of last resort may make such a reference, although the decision to approach the ECJ is at the *discretion* of the national court and is not determined by the parties to the case.

Steiner[1] notes that in view of the "framework" nature of the Treaty, the ECJ has fulfilled an important role in "filling in the gaps", and in so doing has been exceptionally activist and creative and has developed a number of innovative principles such as the doctrines of direct effect and the supremacy of EU law.

---

[1]   *Textbook of EEC Law, 5th Edition*, J Steiner and L Woods, Blackstone Press, 1996, page 26.

A Court of First Instance was set up in 1988 and its jurisdiction includes disputes between the Community and its servants, known as "staff cases", and applications for judicial review and for damages by "natural and legal persons", under Articles 173 and 175. Whilst there is a right of appeal to the ECJ against a decision of the Court of First Instance, appeals against decisions of the ECJ may only be made on the basis of new facts.

The Court of Auditors

Established in 1975, the role of the Court of Auditors is the control and supervision of the budget and as such has little relevance to waste management legislation.

The European Environment Agency

The European Environment Agency (EEA) does not constitute one of the major institutions of the Community and it currently has few powers and little influence even in respect of environmental matters. Established under Regulation 1210/90, its functions are restricted to the collection and dissemination of information relating to the quality of the environment, the pressures on the environment and the sensitivity to those pressures. Within this remit, certain issues including, *inter alia*, air quality and air emissions, water quality, water resources and pollution, land use and natural resources, and waste management, must be given priority. This role is complemented by the European Environmental Information and Observation Network (EIONET), a network established by the EEA for the co-ordination of work between the existing research and policy institutes within the Member States.

The EEA is required to prepare a report on the state of the environment every three years, and has a role in the dissemination of that information and the harmonisation of the methods of the measurement of data within the EU. Although provided for within Regulation 1210/90, the Agency currently has no regulatory or enforcement functions.

There is a requirement for the Council to reconsider the scope of its powers, although in 1995 it was decided to postpone the allocation of new tasks to the Agency for a further two years (COM (95) 325 (final)). The Commission has now made a proposal for a Council Regulation to amend Regulation 1210/90, although in its analysis of the Agency's performance and status, it notes that in general "it would not be appropriate to add major new tasks at this stage of its development" (COM (97) 2282 (final)).

Whilst some new tasks are highlighted, these fall within the Agency's current area of work and mandate, viz. support to the implementation of EU environmental legislation, criteria setting in relation to eco-labelling, environmentally friendly technology, and environmental impact assessment – and no radical new changes are proposed.

In the longer term, in view of variability in the enforcement of environmental legislation across the Community, there may be a role in visiting Member States to check their methods of collecting environmental data, or even monitoring the performance of national inspectorates – *quis custodet ipsos custodies*?

DECISION MAKING PROCEDURES

The procedures for the initiation, formulation and final adoption of the legislative acts of the Community – Regulations, Directives and Decisions – are determined by the provisions of the Treaty, and the route adopted is dependent upon the area of Community law and the appropriate legal base for the measure. The Article upon which the measure is based – 130s(1), 130s(2) or 100a, in the case of environmental issues – will specify the voting procedure and the extent to which the different institutions of the Community may have an influence on the decision. In addition, the legal base for the instrument will determine the scope or objectives of the measure, e.g. "a high level of protection" of the environment.

When the Community was first formed, many issues required unanimous decisions but following the Single European Act there was an increase in the areas in which qualified majority voting was required. These included the majority of the legislation for the completion of the internal market, and this was further extended in the Treaty on European Union. At present, the only areas in which a unanimous vote is required are fiscal measures, those relating to the free movement of persons and the rights and interests of employed persons (Article 100a(2)), and measures relating to professional training and standards (Article 57(2)).

Measures Requiring Unanimity (Article 189(a))

This is the only procedure in which the Parliament does not have a decision-making role. The procedure for such measures is relatively straightforward: a proposal from the Commission is sent to the Council, who might then involve COREPER. The Parliament is also sent a copy of the proposal, although this is on a consultative basis only. Following any necessary amendments, the measure may be adopted by Council on the basis of a unanimous vote.

The Co-operation Procedure (Article 189(c))

A proposal is made by the Commission and when this is received by the Council it is referred to the Parliament for the first time. Amendments may be made by the Commission or by the *unanimous* decision of the Council. The Council then, by a qualified majority, adopts a "common position" on the proposal (i.e. its view on the Commission's proposed legislation), which is sent to Parliament, who may then approve, amend or reject the proposal.

If the proposal is approved by an absolute majority *or* Parliament takes no action within the three-month period allowed, then the Council may adopt it by a qualified majority. However, if rejected, the Council may only adopt it by a unanimous vote.

Where Parliament amends the proposal, the amendments are sent to the Commission and if accepted will then be put forward to the Council, who may accept it by a qualified majority, or make further amendments on a unanimous decision. However, if the Commission rejects Parliament's amendments, they must send them to the Council who may adopt the Commission's proposal by a qualified majority, *or* adopt Parliament's amendments on a unanimous decision.

The Co-decision Procedure (Article 189(b))

This is the same as the Co-operation Procedure up to the point at which Parliament rejects the proposal, or indicates that it intends to amend it. At this stage, a conciliation committee may be convened by the Council and, if the Parliament subsequently rejects the proposal by an absolute majority, the measure fails. However, if Parliament amends only the "common position", the proposal is returned to the Council and Commission.

Where the Commission agrees with these amendments, the proposal may be adopted by a qualified majority but, if not, it is subject to the deliberations of a further conciliation committee.

If the Commission does not concur with Parliament's amendments, the measure may be adopted by a unanimous decision of the Council or, where not adopted within a fixed time period, it must go to a further conciliation committee.

For the two procedures under which the proposal is sent back to a conciliation committee, where it approves a joint text, this is returned to the Council and Parliament and, unless *both* approve by qualified majority, the measure fails. However, where a joint text is not approved by the committee *but* the Council confirms the "common position" by qualified majority voting *and* the Parliament does not reject the measure within a prescribed time, the measure will be adopted. However, if the Council does not confirm the "common position" within the time required, the measure will fail.

The conciliation procedure has been a source of delay in the introduction of Community legislation and a degree of simplification will be introduced as a result of the Treaty of Amsterdam. Under the modified Article 189(b), if within six weeks of being convened, the Conciliation Committee approves a joint text, the European Parliament acting by an absolute majority, and the Council acting by a qualified majority, will each have a period of six weeks within which to adopt the act in question, in accordance with the joint text. However, the act will be deemed not to have been adopted if, within the stated time periods:

— the Conciliation Committee fails to approve a joint text; or

— either the Parliament or the Council fails to approve the joint text agreed by the Conciliation Committee.

ENVIRONMENTAL ISSUES AND THE COMMUNITY

1957-1986: Prior to the Single European Act

The primary aims of the original EEC were economic and the Foundation Treaties made no reference to environmental matters, apart from health and safety provisions within the Euratom Treaty. In spite of the absence of a formal base upon which to introduce environmental measures, appreciable progress was made in this period using either Article 100 or Article 235 of the EC Treaty, and many of the measures currently shaping the control of the environment within the EU were initiated during this period. Article 100 was used for pollution control measures and the implementation of common standards, on the basis of avoiding distortions of competition due to different levels of environmental protection in different Member States. Such use of Article 100 was not unique and similar arguments were used to justify Community legislation on consumer protection, equal treatment and equal pay.

Article 235, relating to the Community's general and residual powers, was initially used for measures relating to the "unowned environment," where Community action was necessary for environmental protection and an improvement of the quality of life (Articles 2 and 3(1)), and to impose uniform standards of *protection* of the environment. However, its use was limited by the objectives of the Community and in a number of cases

Directives cited both Article 100 and Article 235 in case a challenge to their legal basis was made.

1987-1992: Prior to the Maastricht Treaty

In 1986, the Single European Act was passed and introduced, *inter alia*, specific measures relating to the environment. A new Title VII, relating solely to the environment and comprising Articles 130r to 130t, was inserted into the Treaty. Article 130r stated the objectives and principles of EC environmental policy and established that environmental protection requirements was a component of the Community's other policies. The action taken by the Community in this sphere was to be determined by the Council acting unanimously on a proposal from the Commission, after consultation with the European Parliament and the Economic and Social Committee (ECOSOC).

Articles 130r to 130t provided explicit law-making powers in relation to environmental matters and, although the new Article 100a was introduced to speed up the completion of the single market, it too provided the means of adopting environmental measures which were associated with harmonisation. Article 100a was primarily a provision to assist meeting the internal market objectives outlined in Article 8a and permitted the Council to adopt measures by a qualified majority, following the co-operation procedure. The absence of the unanimity requirement prevented the problem of one or two Member States blocking a particular measure and the co-operation procedure gave the European Parliament an enhanced role in the decision making process. A further criterion for measures based upon Article 100a was the requirement for a high level of protection, which was designed to prevent the lowering of standards on issues decided by a qualified majority. No guidance was given on the meaning of "a high level of protection" and this has been subject to subsequent debate.

The two possible routes for introducing environmental Directives, through Articles 100a and 130s, led to a number of challenges regarding which was the correct legal basis for the measure in question. Prior to the Maastricht Treaty, the choice of route was important since it affected both the voting procedure used to approve the Directive *and* the level of environmental protection which it could be expected to provide.

1992-Present: Post Maastricht

Signed in Maastricht on 7th February 1992, the new Treaty on European Union continued the process of integrating environmental issues into the activities of the EU. The objectives of the EU now include "sustainable and non-inflationary growth respecting the environment" as one of the tasks of the Community (Article 2), and "a policy in the sphere of the environment" as one of its principle activities (Article 3k). The principles of EU environmental policy are set out in Article 130r(2), viz:

— preventative action rather than remedial measures;

— rectification of environmental damage at source;

— the "polluter pays principle"; and

— environmental policies as a component of other EU policies.

In addition, Article 130r now includes:

— a new objective of promoting measures at international level;

— the introduction of a "high level of protection" (c.f. Article 100a) but *taking into account the diversity of situations in various regions of the Community*;

— the introduction of the "precautionary principle".

The Environmental Action Programmes, but not the legislation made in accordance with their objectives, became subject to the co-decision procedure set out in Article 189b, thus giving the European Parliament a greater influence, since if agreement is not reached by an absolute majority of all MEPs, not simply those in session, the text of the legislation must go before the conciliation committee.

All other environmental legislation based upon Article 130s became subject to the co-operation procedure introduced by the Single European Act and now Article 189c. The influence of Parliament has been increased by virtue of its two readings of proposed legislation, and the ability of one or two Member States to block legislation was reduced by the extension of qualified majority voting.

The exceptions from the qualified majority voting in Article 130s are specified to be "without prejudice to Article 100a", which provides for qualified majority voting on matters relating to the establishment and functioning of the internal market.

A significant development resulting from the Maastricht Treaty was the extension of the principle of subsidiarity, from a procedure which was applicable solely to environmental issues through Article 130(r) of the Single European Act 1987 to a more general principle applying to all areas of Community action.

The Amsterdam Treaty

The importance of environmental considerations within Community affairs was further strengthened as the result of a number of modifications introduced by the Treaty of Amsterdam, agreed in 1997. In addition to reinforcing the commitment to sustainable development through modifications to the Treaty on European Union (TEU) and the European Community Treaty (TEC), important changes were made to Article 100a, and the number of measures subject to a simplified co-decision procedure (Article 189(b)) was extended. These modifications increased further the influence of the European Parliament in relation to the environment and other areas, and in addition the Committee of the Regions was give the right to be consulted on environmental legislation.

Under the existing Article 100a, although a Member State may introduce new measures or retain existing ones which are more stringent to Community measures in the areas of health, safety, environmental protection and consumer protection, the burden of proof is with the Member State to demonstrate to the Commission that such provisions are necessary and will not disrupt the other goals of the EU, such as the free movement of goods and the single market.

Under the Treaty of Amsterdam, where a Member State introduces measures based upon new scientific evidence or "on the grounds of a problem specific to that Member State", *after* the adoption of the harmonising measure, the Commission is given six months from its notification by the Member State in which to approve or reject the measure. The onus is on the Commission to verify that the national measure is not "a means of arbitrary discrimination, or a disguised restriction on trade between Member States, and shall not constitute an obstacle to the functioning of the single market".

Although the burden of proof is shifted by these changes, they do give additional power to the Commission to make an initial ruling where national environmental measures conflict with Community commercial considerations, without reference to the European Court of Justice, as was required in the *Danish Bottles*, *Wallonian Waste*, and more recently the *Brandsma*, cases.

The Treaty makes a significant number of Community measures subject to the simplified co-decisions procedure (Article 189(b)), rather than the co-operation procedure (Article 189(c)), including *inter alia* environmental legislation under Article 130s(1) and action by the Community in order to achieve the objectives of Article 130r. Thus, with the exception of those provisions under Article 100a which still require unanimity, all environmental legislation will be subject to the co-decision procedure.

Among the other important changes introduced by the Treaty were a reinforcement of the principles of subsidiarity and proportionality, a new Article 191a relating to transparency and the right of access to European Parliament, Council and Commission documents, and the introduction of a new title – "Flexibility" – a mechanism whereby, within certain constrains, Member States could band together and develop new policies, providing these do not interfere with the single market or existing practices.

The Status of "Environmental Principles"

A number of "environmental principles" are now embodied in Article 130(2) of the EU Treaty, viz:

— a high level of protection;

— the polluter pays principle;

— the precautionary principle; and

— the proximity principle,

and these are generally included, where relevant, in the preamble to legislative acts of the Community. However, unless these instruments additionally impose *specific* obligations relating to the implementation of these principles, they have no legal standing other than in the interpretation of the measure concerned. In *R v Secretary of State for Trade and Industry ex parte Dudderidge & ors*, the High Court held that in exercising his powers under section 29 of the Electricity Act 1989, concerning the making of regulations on the supply and safety of electricity, the Secretary of State was not bound under the "precautionary principle" within Article 130r(2) of the EU Treaty, since this created no obligation on him to undertake national action.

The issue of EU principles was again considered in *R v Ministry of Agriculture, Fisheries and Food, and Another*, in relation to the Slaughtering Industry (Emergency Aid) Scheme 1996 administered by the Intervention Board for Agricultural Produce, when the court held that the fundamental principles of European Community law as formulated by the European Court of Justice, such as equal treatment and non-discrimin-ation, had no application to an action or a decision taken by a Member State under domestic law, unless and to the extent that the decision was taken in order to implement powers or duties conferred or imposed by Community law.

In *R v The Environment Agency ex parte Dockgrange Ltd, Mayer Parry Ltd, and The Robinson Group Ltd*, it was noted that in interpreting the Transboundary Shipment of Waste Regulations, 259/93/EEC, there was no justification in applying the precautionary principle when the facts were known.

Environmental Action Programmes

Since 1973 there has been a series of consecutive Environmental Action Programmes, which have reflected the current EU policy in this area and indicated the type and form of measures that might be introduced (see Table 2-1, pages 80-81).[1] It has been necessary to match the objectives and content of such programmes against the legislative measures available within the Treaty at the time, if any.

The First Action Programme was initiated at the request of the heads of state, on the basis that "economic expansion is not an end in itself" but, following the Single European Act, formal status was given to the Action Programmes. After Maastricht the Programmes, although not necessarily the legislation made in accordance with them, became subject to the co-decision procedure of Article 189(b), thus giving the European Parliament a much greater influence in their content.

The Fifth Environmental Programme, *Towards Sustainability*, was agreed at the end of 1992 and embodies the EU thinking on the environment as developed in the Maastricht Treaty. It acknowledges that the impact of the Fourth Action Programme will not be known for some time but states that, as the result of a number of factors, a more far-reaching and more effective strategy is required. These factors include:

— the continuing deterioration of the general state of the environment of the EU;

— the mismatch between the present approach/existing measures and the expected future burdens on natural resources due to growth in international competition and increased EU activity;

— global concerns about climate change/deforestation/energy, and the EU's responsibility in the international field.

The Programme highlights the enhanced position of the environment in the revised Treaty, and the importance of:

— sustainable growth respecting the environment;

---

[1]   These are discussed in the author's paper "The Role of Environmental Action Programmes in the Development of EU Legislation", [1995] 7 *ELM* 221.

— the high level of protection required;

— the principle of subsidiarity.

In the context of the programme, "sustainable" is defined in terms of "a policy and strategy for continued economic and social development, without detriment to the environment and the natural resources on the quality of which continued human activity and future development depend." However, some "dark green" environmentalists would argue that continued economic development is antithetical to sustainability.

The central concept of the Fifth Programme is that of shared responsibility between all the stakeholders in the environment, and the emphasis is switched from controls applied to the environmental media to a consideration of the horizontal effect of all the environmental implications of various sectors of the economy. While previous Action Programmes have relied upon legislative measures almost exclusively, the Fifth Action Programme suggested a broader mix of measures "to bring about substantial changes in current trends and practices, and to involve all sectors in a full sharing of responsibility", viz:

— legislative instruments, to set fundamental levels of protection, particularly in areas of high risk;

— market-based instruments, to sensitise both producers and consumers towards responsible use of resources and avoidance of pollution;

— horizontal, supporting instruments, such as improved base-line data, scientific R&D, improved sectoral and spatial planning;

— financial support measures, including the new cohesion fund, Envireg, and LIFE.

In common with the establishment of environmental agreements discussed later in this chapter, the introduction of any of this "broad range of measures" must be consistent with the entire corpus of EU law. This is particularly important in relation to economic instruments or other measures which might be regarded as barriers to the free movement of goods or restrictions on trade. In *Bic Benelux SA v Belgium State*, case c-13/96, the ECJ upheld a challenge to Belgian law on the marking of disposable goods, on the grounds that the Belgian government had not given advance notification to the European Commission of these requirements, as required by Directive 83/189/EEC as amended, in relation to technical regulations and specification.

The Directive defines a technical regulation as a technical specification or other requirement whose observance is compulsory, *de jure* or *de facto*, in relation to marketing or use within a Member State. This includes voluntary agreements between government and industry and, in *Bic Benelux*, the ECJ held that this was not restricted to national measures capable of harmonisation under Article 100a. The court stated that the fact that "a national measure was adopted in order to protect the environment, or that it does not implement a technical standard which may itself constitute a barrier to trade, does not mean that the measure in question cannot be a technical regulation within the meaning of the 1983 Directive."

However, in *Cali v Servizi Ecologici de Genova SpA*, case c-343/95, the ECJ distinguished between the exercise of the official authority of the state, and the state's conduct of economic activities of an industrial or commercial nature. It ruled that the anti-pollution surveillance services provided by a contractor of the public authority which managed the administrative and economic functions of the Port of Genova, were *not* covered by the anti-competition rules.

Five target sectors are identified for special attention under the programme – industry, energy, transport, agriculture and tourism – since in these areas "a Community approach is the most efficient level at which to tackle the problems these sectors cause or face". It could be argued that such a statement is contrary to the definition of subsidiarity in Article 3b and the European Court of Justice might have to decide whether the objectives of specific Directives "can by reasons of scale or effects of the proposed action, be better achieved by the Community".

Ultimately the success of the Action Programmes can only be measured in terms of their influence on the environment, and there are essentially three stages involved in the translation of the measures within the Programmes to effective mechanisms of environmental protection:

— the formulation of the required instruments at Community level;

— their incorporation into Member States' domestic legislation, where necessary; and

— their subsequent implementation within the Member States.

Although, in the past, the first stage presented significant problems, the Maastricht amendments to the Treaty have gone some way to alleviate these. In the majority of cases, Member States are now less able to block the introduction of new measures, although the co-decision procedure is complex and may result in substantial delays in negotiating an agreed text, as experienced with the Directive on packaging and packaging waste.

With regard to enactment and enforcement, this presents a number of problems associated with the detection of non-compliance by Member States and in the subsequent enforcement action. It was not until 1991 that measures were introduced for standardising and rationalising the reports on the implementation of Directives and as a consequence the Commission placed a great reliance upon the complaints procedure. Of all forms of non-compliance, failure to apply the measures in practice provides the Commission with greatest difficulty.

As discussed later, the position of enforcement action through Articles 169 and 170 was strengthened in the Maastricht Treaty, as a result of the modifications to Article 171.

TREATY PROVISIONS

The EU Treaties were incorporated into UK law through section 2(1) of the European Communities Act 1972 and, as a consequence, all Community law became "directly applicable" and formed part of UK domestic law. In addition to establishing the powers of the EU institutions and the procedures for decision making, some Treaty provisions such as Article 119 on equal pay also created rights of individuals which could be relied upon in national courts and tribunals. These provisions, creating rights which are capable of application by national courts at the suit of the individual, are referred to as being "directly effective" or "capable of having direct effect".

Direct effect in relation to Treaty articles was first considered in *Van Gend en Loos v Nederlandse Administratie der Belastinger*, case 26/62, where in a reference to the ECJ under Article 177, the court held that the principle of direct effect operated "vertically" between an individual and the state. A "horizontal" action of direct effect between individual and individual was implied in *Van Gend*, and this was confirmed in *Defrenne v Sabena (No.2)* (case 43/75).

The criteria for direct effect were laid down in *Alfons Lütticke GmbH v Hauptzollamt Saarlouis* (case 57/65), where the court held that for reliance to be placed on this doctrine:

— the provision must be sufficiently clear and precise;

— the provision must be unconditional; and

— the provision must leave no room for the exercise of discretion in its implementation by the Member State or Community institution.

There has been an on-going debate as to whether "environmental" provisions of the Treaty can give rise to direct effect. Since the EC Treaty itself allows Member States to introduce environmental requirements which are more stringent than Community measures, it has been argued that this is sufficient to render the majority of environmental Directives too imprecise and conditional to have direct effect. Some support for this view was given in *Luciano Accaro*, case c-168/95, in which the European Court of Justice held that the *Marleasing* doctrine could not be used to impose on an individual, a Directive obligation which has not been transposed into national law.

LEGISLATIVE ACTS OF THE COMMUNITY

Article 189 of the Treaty, as amended, empowers the European Parliament acting jointly with the Council to make Regulations and issue Directives, take Decisions, make Recommendations and deliver Opinions in order to carry out their tasks in accordance with the provisions of the Treaty. These legislative acts are defined within Article 189 as:

> A **Regulation** shall have general application. It shall be binding in its entirety and directly applicable in all Member States.

> A **Directive** shall be binding, as to the result to be achieved, upon each Member State to which it is addressed but shall leave to the national authorities the choice of form and methods.

> A **Decision** shall be binding in its entirety upon those to whom it is addressed.

> **Recommendations** and **Opinions** shall have no binding force.

Following the trend towards the broader range of instruments for environmental protection, there has been interest at national and EU level in the use of "environmental agreements". At present, such agreements have no status in EU law.

Regulations

Although the majority of environmental measures are in the form of Directives, Regulations have been employed where it is necessary to give effect to an international agreement, and in areas of agricultural policy and administrative matters. From their definition in Article 189, they are directly effective throughout the Community and legally they are not dependent upon further implementation. However, in most cases subsequent domestic legislation is enacted in which more specific details pertinent to the Member State concerned are included, such as the nomination of the "competent authorities" and the determination of offences and penalties.

The Regulation on the Supervision and Control of the Shipment of Waste within, into, and out of the European Community, 259/93/EEC, provides an example of their use. This Regulation implemented the provisions of the Basel and Lomé Conventions, *inter alia*, and was itself incorporated into UK legislation through the Transfrontier Shipment of Waste Regulations 1994, SI 1994/1137.

Although Regulations are defined as being "directly applicable" in all Member States, their ability to produce direct effects is dependent upon meeting the criteria stated above. In some cases, Regulations are conditional or require further implementation before they can take full legal effect. By virtue of their being of "general application", Regulations have both vertical and horizontal effect and can be enforced in national courts and tribunals against Member States or "emanations of the state", and between individuals.

In the "environmental" area, Regulations have been introduced to impose restrictions on the production and use of chlorofluorocarbons and halons, for the establishment of the European Environment Agency, the introduction of the eco-auditing and eco-labelling schemes, and the transfrontier movement of waste.

Directives

Directives and Direct Effect
Since Article 189 does not define Directives as being "directly applicable", for quite some time it was considered that they could not produce direct effects and the matter was not finally resolved until the case of *Van Duyn v Home Office*, case 41/74, where the court applying the principle of *effet utile* held that the effectiveness of Directives would be undermined if individuals could not rely upon them in national courts. However, in order to have direct effect, Directives must satisfy the relevant criteria: be sufficiently clear and precise, unconditional, with no opportunity for discretion in their implementation.

Provided these requirements are satisfied, an individual may rely upon a Directive in an action against the state or an "emanation of the state", in cases where the state does not implement the Directive within the time period or does not implement it fully or correctly (see *Becker v Finanzamt Münster-Innenstadt*, case 8/81). However, a Directive cannot have direct effect before the time limit for its implementation.

Whilst Directives may have *vertical* direct effects, the ECJ has on a number of occasions ruled that they cannot have *horizontal* direct effects (between individuals), as demonstrated in *Marshall v Southampton and South West Hampshire Area Health Authority (Teaching)*, case 152/84. However, the question of horizontal direct effect was again raised in *Faccini Dori v Recreb Srl*, case 91/92, in which the Advocate General urged the court to reconsider the *Marshall* decision, and extend the principle of direct effect to allow enforcement of Directives between all parties. The court was unwilling to accept this recommendation, although it did emphasise the remedies available through the principle of indirect effect.

The Principle of Indirect Effect
The principle of indirect effect arose, pre-*Marshall*, as the result of two cases relating to the equal treatment Directive – *Von Colson v Land Nordrhein-Westfalen*, case 14/83, and *Harz v Deutsche Tradex GmbH*, case 79/82. The court considered the issue of vertical and horizontal effects in the context of public and private bodies and stated that, under Article 5 of the Treaty, the state must "take all appropriate measures" to ensure the fulfilment of its Community obligations. It was held that this obligation applied to *all* of the authorities of the Member States, *including* the courts, who must interpret national law so as to achieve the objectives of the Directive. Thus, although Directives are not directly effective, they may be *applied* indirectly by means of interpretation.

However, one drawback of the *Von Colson* principle is its dependence upon the discretion used by the national courts in making such interpretations. Within the UK, whilst in some cases the courts have not followed *Von Colson*, as in *Duke v Reliance Ltd* [1988], in others the principle has been applied, see *Lister v Forth Dry Dock and Engineering Co Ltd*, and *Webb v EMO (Air Cargo) Ltd*.

This principle was emphasised in *Marleasing SA v La Comercial Internacional de Alimentación SA*, case 106/89, in which the ECJ held that national courts are "required" to interpret domestic legislation so that the objectives of the Directive are achieved.

The Principle of State Liability
An important development in the principles of direct and indirect effect was established in *Francovich v Italy*, cases c6 and 9/90, in relation to employee's rights, where the court laid down the principle of state liability under which a Member State could be liable to an *individual* for harm caused by a failure to implement a Directive. This required that certain conditions were met, viz:

— the Directive involves the conferring of rights on individuals;

— the content of such rights could be identified on the basis of the provisions of the Directive; and

— there is a causal link between the state's failure to implement the Directive and the harm suffered by the individual.

In effect, this ruling creates a new tort and, providing the above requirements are fulfilled, an individual may seek compensation from the state in relation to activities and practices which are inconsistent with the Directive.

Where the principle of state liability is applied, there is no need to rely upon the principles of direct or indirect effect, and the responsibility for such non-implementation is placed upon the state. The principle was extended as a result of the judgment in *Factortame v UK*, and *Brasserie du Pêcheur v Germany*, cases c46 and 48/93, in which the court held that the principle applied to *all* domestic acts and omissions – legislative, executive and judicial – which are in breach of Community law, regardless of whether they are directly effective or not.

In its ruling, the court echoed the judgment in *Francovich* and laid down three criteria to be met in order for the principle of state liability to apply, viz:

— the Community law which was breached must have the intention of conferring rights on individuals;

— there must be a "sufficiently serious" breach of that law; and

— a direct causal link must exist between the breach of the state's obligation and the harm to the injured party(s).

The "decisive test" of "sufficiently serious" is whether the national institution in question has "manifestly and gravely exceeded the limits of its discretion", taking into account "the clarity and precision of the rule breached, the measure of discretion left by that rule ..., whether the infringement and the damage caused was intentional or voluntary, whether any error of law was excusable or inexcusable, the fact that the position taken by a Community institution may have contributed towards the omission, and the adoption or retention of national measures or practices contrary to Community law." Further guidance on "sufficiently serious" is given in *Mulder & ors v Council and Commission*.

The *Francovich* principle was further extended in *Dillenkofer & ors v Federal Republic of Germany*, in which the European Court held that failure by a Member State to take any measure to transpose a Directive in order to achieve the prescribed end within the prescribed period constitutes *per se* a serious breach of EU law, with consequential rights for those affected, all other things being equal.

In such cases, it is not necessary for the infringement of Community law to have been established under Articles 169 or 177, nor necessary to prove fault, other than the "serious breach". Conditions for the "serious breach" criterion to be satisfied were considered in *R v Secretary of State for Transport ex parte Factorame Ltd & ors (No 5)*.

Decisions

These may be addressed to specific Member State(s) or individual(s) and, although not "directly applicable" by virtue of their definition in Article 189, following *Grad v Finanzamt Traustein*, case 9/70, Decisions are held to be capable of direct effect, providing that the requisite criteria are met.

Since they are binding in their entirety upon those to whom they are addressed, they can only be applied against such addressees. Unlike Directives, Decisions are only infrequently used in environmental legislation, although on occasion they have been addressed to some Member States. Their primary use is either in relation to information gathering or the entry by the Community into international agreements.

Recommendations, Opinions and Environmental Agreements

By their definition, Recommendations and Opinions have no binding force and as a result are not regarded as "enforceable Community rights" within section 2(1) of the European Communities Act 1972. Although in *Grimaldi v Fonds des Maladies Professionnelles*, case 322/88, the ECJ held that national courts should take Community recommendations into account, particularly in cases where they clarified the interpretation of national provisions in relation to their implementation or where they are designed to supplement binding Community measures, Steiner[1] notes that such a view is open to question and non-binding measures should only be taken into account to resolve ambiguities in domestic law.

The 5th Environmental Action Programme called for a broadening of the range of instruments for environmental control and, in view of recent interest in the so-called "environmental agreements" – formal agreements between an industrial sector and the relevant regulatory body within a Member State – the Commission has issued a Recommendation *Concerning*

---

[1]   *Textbook of EEC Law, 5th Edition*, J Steiner and L Woods, Blackstone Press, 1996, page 60.

Environmental Agreements Implementing Community Directives, 96/733/
EC. However, since the Treaty does not at present recognise such
agreements, these do not *per se* have formal status within EU law unless
they form part of a Regulation, Directive, or a Decision. In such cases, an
environmental agreement *may* constitute a legal instrument of
implementation but, as with other administrative agreements, Member
States may not in general rely upon such commitments. Furthermore, the
agreement must itself be compatible with EU law and World Trade
Organisation Regulations. For a fuller consideration of these issues, see the
paper by J C Bongaerts, under "Further Reading".

"EMANATIONS OF THE STATE"

The concept of an "emanation of the state" is important in relation to the
doctrine of vertical direct effect and has been considered by the UK courts
and the ECJ on a number of occasions. In *Foster v British Gas plc*, the
European Court referred to an emanation of the state thus:

> "A body, whatever its legal form, which has been made responsible,
> pursuant to a measure adopted by the state, for providing a public
> service under the control of the state and has for that purpose powers
> beyond those which resulted from the normal rules applicable in
> relations between individuals, *is included among the bodies* against
> which the provisions of a Directive capable of having direct effect may
> be relied upon",

which satisfied a test based upon a tripartite, cumulative set of criteria, viz:

— has the body been made responsible pursuant to a measure adopted by
the state for providing a public service; *and*

— is that service under the control of the state; *and*

— does the body for that purpose have special powers beyond those which
apply between individuals?

Prior to *Foster*, it was held that bodies responsible for public order and
safety came within the ambit of "emanations of the state" (*Johnston v Chief
Constable of the Royal Ulster Constabulary*) and subsequently the term
has been applied to local authorities (*R v Freight Transport Association ex
parte London Borough Transport Committee*) and a number of other bodies
over which the state authority or control is more tenuous. In *Doughty v
Rolls Royce plc*, although the company was nationalised at the time of the
action, the Court of Appeal held that services it provided in the defence of
the realm were for the *state* and not for the *public*, and consequently the

first limb of the *Foster* test failed. Nevertheless, the scope of bodies falling within the term "emanations of the state" has increased as a result of the judgments in *Griffin v South West Water Co Ltd* and *National Union of Teachers & ors v Governing Body of St Mary's Church of England (Aided) Junior School & ors*. In the *Griffin* case, the High Court held that, although it was a privatised company, South West Water was a "public body" and hence an emanation of the state, on the grounds that it provided a public service and was subject to the control of the Secretary of State.

In the latter case, the Court of Appeal reversed the decision of the Employment Appeal Tribunal (reported under *Fidge v Governing Body of St Mary's Church of England Aided Junior School*) and held that the governing body of a voluntary aided school could be regarded as an emanation of the state. Lord Justice Schiemann agreed that the powers held by the Secretary of State and the local authority "amounted to sufficient control for the present purposes to come within the concept of control". Although his Lordship was not persuaded that the powers of the governors were the sort that the European Court had in mind in *Foster*, he considered it inappropriate to apply its tripartite test as though it were a definition section, and for the doctrine of direct vertical effect the governors must be regarded as emanations of the state.

As noted in Chapter 7, it is uncertain whether, in the provisions of the Directive on environmental information, 90/313/EEC, the terms "public authority" and "bodies with public responsibility for the environment under the control of public authorities" are synonymous with "emanations of the state".

ENFORCEMENT ACTION

As discussed earlier, where a Member State does not implement a Directive, or implements it incorrectly or only partially, then individuals have recourse thorough the doctrines of indirect effect and state liability. However, in its role as "Guardian of the Treaties", the Commission has a duty to ensure that Community legislative acts are implemented and enforced, and has powers of investigation (Article 155) and of enforcement (Article 169).

There are many contraventions of Community law, particularly in relation to the environment, and many Directives are not implemented until after the time limit has expired. Furthermore, when implementation does take place, the Directive is not always fully or correctly incorporated into domestic law. There are a number of courses of action which may be taken, the most common of which is that instituted by the Commission under

Article 169. Although the majority of enforcement action is undertaken by the Commission under this provision, Member States may initiate action by means of Article 170 and the European Court also has powers in this area under Article 171.

Action under Article 169

Steiner[1] notes that Article 169 has three objectives:

— to ensure compliance by Member States with their Community obligations;

— to provide a non-contentious procedure for the resolution of disputes between the Commission and Member States on issues of Community law; and

— to clarify the law, as a result of references to the ECJ.

In view of the above, it is clear that the prime purpose of Article 169 is not to impose penalties and sanctions upon Member States although, following the changes made to Article 171 in the Maastricht Treaty, there is now the potential for such action. However, it should be noted that in practice only a small proportion of cases continue to the point where judgment is given.

There are two stages in enforcement action under Article 169: the administrative stage and the judicial stage.

Action Prior to the Administrative Stage

Expiry of the time limit for the implementation of a Directive does not automatically initiate action on the part of the Commission. No time limits are set for the commencement of such actions and in practice it may be up to five years or more before the administrative stage is started. Under Article 155, the Commission has wide powers to investigate both the formal and the practical implementation of Community measures within Member States but at present no such powers are held by the European Environmental Agency.

Individuals may also make complaints about the non-implementation of Community measures, either by letter or by using the standard form in the Official Journal. A further route for complaints is via MEPs, prompted by constituents, common interest groups or party political initiatives.

---

[1] *Textbook of EEC Law, 5th Edition*, J Steiner and L Woods, Blackstone Press, 1996, page 410.

The Administrative Stage

Under Article 169, the Commission *may* bring the non-implementation of a Directive before the European Court of Justice provided that two conditions are fulfilled:

— the Commission considers that a breach has taken place; and

— the Member State has been given the opportunity to submit its observations.

The state must be informed of *all* the charges which may be raised should the action proceed to the court, as in *Commission v Italy* (re: payment of export rebates), case 31/69, and the Commission should not reach its decision until after it has heard the Member State's observations. However, it is not unknown for Member States to fail to respond to any Commission communication during either part of the administrative stage, as in *EC Commission v Italy*, case 33/90.

There are two phases to the administrative stage and, in the first informal phase, the Commission investigates whether there is sufficient evidence to justify proceedings. Informal discussions are held with Member States in an attempt to ascertain the facts and reach a settlement. The Commission will only proceed to the formal stage when the factual and legal issues have been fully investigated.

There are no fixed time limits on the stages leading to the Reasoned Opinion and timings are set at the discretion of the Commission. However, the court may dismiss an Article 169 action on the grounds of inadequate time limits, as in the decision in *Gravier v City of Liege*. The Commission also has some discretion in whether to proceed with the formal phase of the proceedings and the informal stage may conclude with a decision by the Commission to take no further action.

The formal proceedings begin by letters of formal notice, inviting the Member State to submit its observations. In addition to specifying all the charges which may be raised in an action, a time limit will be given for the submission of observations. Further discussions may take place after the Member State's observations have been received and only if the Member State will not voluntarily accept the Commission's position will the Commission issue the reasoned opinion, formally recording the violation.

The Judicial Stage

With certain exceptions, such as Directive 76/464 which became immediately effective under Article 191 of the EEC Treaty, most environmental Directives contain an express provision under which Member States must take the necessary measures to comply with the Directive within a given time period. When a violation is recorded, the Commission is obliged to set a time limit within which the Member State must end its violation and, if it fails to comply with the reasoned opinion within this period, proceedings move to the Judicial Stage. The Commission has some discretion in whether, and when, it proceeds with the court action. The scope of the proceedings is limited to the infringements stated in the reasoned opinion and the Commission cannot bring any new allegations. Another Member State may join in Article 169 proceedings as a third party to argue for one side or the other, as demonstrated by the UK support for the Commission in the *Danish Bottles* case and the involvement of several Member States in the joined cases c-304/94, c-330/94, c-342/94 and c-224/94, *Criminal Proceedings against Euro Tombesi & ors* on the meaning of waste (see Chapter 8).

Although many defences to an action under Article 169 have been attempted, few have succeeded and it has been suggested that the best defence is to deny the obligation. The defence of *reciprocity*, claiming that another Member State has also failed to meet the time limit for the Directive, was attempted unsuccessfully in *Commission v France* (re: restriction on imports of lamb), case 232/78 and in *Steinike und Weinlig*, case 76/76. Similarly, constitutional, institutional, administrative or political difficulties within a Member State have all failed to satisfy the court as reasons for non-implementation and the ECJ has also ruled that financial difficulties in individual cases do not excuse non-compliance.

With regard to the time limits for implementation of Directives:

— extension of a time limit is not possible after the expiry of the date set by the Commission;

— implementation after the expiry date does not preclude an action being brought;

although an action may fail on the grounds of inadequate time limits set by the Commission.

If the court finds the allegation proved, it will issue a binding declamatory judgment to the effect that the Member State has failed to fulfil an obligation of the Treaty. The court has no power specifically to order a Member State to undertake any action other than interim measures, nor to declare invalid any national legislation which is found to be contrary to Community law.

In the past, the only action which could be taken for non-compliance with a ruling of the court was a second action under Article 169, on the basis of the Member State having failed to comply with its obligations under Article 171. However, following Maastricht, where the Commission considers that a Member State has not complied with a judgment, it may now issue a reasoned opinion and, if there is a continuing non-compliance, it can bring the case back to the court and specify an appropriate penalty. The first financial penalties under this procedure have been sought by the Commission against Germany and Italy, for failure to implement EU law. On 29th January 1997, the Commission applied to the ECJ for the following penalties to be applied:

Germany

26,400 ECU	Wild Birds Directive
264,000 ECU	Groundwater Directive
158,400 ECU	Surface Water Directive

Italy

123,900 ECU	Waste Framework Directive
159,300 ECU	Ionising Radiations Directive

These were based upon "a rate of 500 ECU per day, a figure ... multiplied by factors that are designed to take account of the gravity of the non-compliance and its duration, and the financial situation of the Member State involved".[1]

Action under Article 170

Under Article 170, another Member State may bring the matter of non-compliance before the Commission, which must deliver a reasoned opinion within three months. In the absence of a reasoned opinion, the Member State is entitled to approach the Court of Justice, as in *France v United Kingdom* (Re: fishing net mesh sizes), case 141/78. The procedure is very similar to that under Article 169.

UK DOMESTIC LEGISLATION

Crimes and Civil Wrongs

Whilst the greater number of "environmental proceedings" relate to criminal actions resulting from an infraction of some element of statutory legislation, the common law also provides remedies in this area in cases

---

[1]   From "This Week in Europe", 9th January 1997.

where a civil wrong has been committed. The essential distinction between a crime and a civil wrong lies not in what is done but in the legal consequences of the wrongful act. Where the act or omission is capable of being followed by criminal proceedings, the offence committed is regarded as a crime and, if capable of leading to civil proceedings, it is a civil wrong. In some cases, an action may give rise to both civil and criminal proceedings and certain offences such as a public nuisance may be tortious as well as criminal.

Civil wrongs relate to the harm or damage done to persons, their property or their rights and fall within the ambit of the "common law". Whilst the criminal law is statute-based, the "common law" results from decided cases without the aid of legislation, although the framework within which it acts may be subject to certain statutory constraints, such as the Limitation Act 1980, as amended by the Latent Damage Act 1986, which imposes time limits on actions brought in tort.

The procedure under which action is taken differs depending upon whether the action is civil or criminal and is discussed later in this chapter. The common law as it applies to England and Wales is considered in greater detail in Chapter 5 and, in relation to delictual liability, the reader is directed towards specific texts on Scottish law.

UK Statutory Legislation

The high percentage of environmental legislation initiated by the EU might suggest to a casual observer that in this area of law, the UK statutory process is merely one of "rubber stamping" decisions taken in Brussels. However, this is far from the case, for the majority of these measures are in the form of Directives and each Member State has a significant influence on the manner in which they are implemented.

As will be evident from the above discussion, the enforcement of EU legislation is an entirely different issue from that of its enactment and, whilst it may be argued that the latter will be determined on policy grounds within Member States, where EU legislation places an obligation on the state to ensure that a certain activity is undertaken, or not, then where this is shown not to be the case action may be taken under Articles 169 or 170.

The Legislative Process

Consultation
Legislation initiated within the UK is dependent upon the action of the government, in response to a perceived need identified within its own party

political organisation, through advice received from the relevant ministry or department, or as a result of lobbying by interested parties.

In some cases, the government will issue a consultative Green Paper to gauge the opinion of those likely to be involved and after considering the responses may issue a White Paper containing more definite proposals upon which the legislation will be based.

A similar process of consultation is followed in relation to EU legislation, although in this case the government is under an obligation to implement measures with specific objectives, within a given timescale and, as a consequence, less protracted consultation is involved. Under these circumstances, it is likely that the interested parties will already have had some input into the primary EU legislation and will be briefed on the scope of the measures to be enacted. The Department of the Environment is the source of many such discussion documents and consultation papers, which may cover not only the form and detail of the proposed legislation, as in the case of the guidance on the implementation of the contaminated land provisions, but also reviews of existing measures such as the Duty of Care and the Litter Codes of Practice, which were issued under statutory authority.

The regulatory bodies may undertake consultation exercises regarding the modification of existing guidance, such as those in relation to Integrated Pollution Control – the content of industry sector guides, or the introduction of new procedures such as Operator Pollution Risk Appraisal (OPRA). However, these consultations should be distinguished from those relating to the introduction of statutes or secondary legislation.

The Making of a Statute
The starting point for any statute is a Bill containing proposals for the new Act and this must be approved by both the Commons and the Lords before it receives Royal Assent and becomes law. The majority of these are public Bills, which are sponsored by the government in order to implement its political policy, although sometimes a private member's Bill is introduced by a single Member of Parliament, either on his own, or supported by other MPs or extra-parliamentary groups. In view of the demands on parliamentary time imposed by public Bills, there is little opportunity to debate private members' Bills and the likelihood of their success is not high. Nevertheless, some important pieces of legislation have resulted from this source, as in the case of the Road Traffic Reduction Act 1977, and it provides one route by which environmental pressure groups may influence legislation.

In addition, it is possible for non-parliamentary bodies to petition Parliament to be given specific powers by means of a private Bill, and in this case a parliamentary agent would be employed to guide the Bill in its passage through both Houses. An example of the application of such Bills is in relation to major transport projects, to give powers to construct and operate a proposed scheme and to protect the developer from claims of landowners. The construction of the London Underground was undertaken on the basis of some 97 private Acts of Parliament, the most recent being the London Transport Act 1992 in relation to Jubilee Line Extension. However, a public Act – the Transport and Works Act 1992 – now provides the basis for authorising such major projects, through the issue of appropriate Transport and Works Orders.

Before becoming law, any Bill must pass though both Houses of Parliament and, apart from measures involving public expenditure, may be introduced in either House. The Bill then passes sequentially through both Houses, and is subject to the same stages of discussion in each, viz:

First Reading. The title of the Bill and the MP introducing it is read out by an official and the Bill is ordered to be printed.

Second Reading. There is a debate on the major proposals of the Bill and, if it is approved, it goes to the Committee stage.

Committee Stage. Details of the Bill are considered by a committee of MPs, which may propose amendments.

Report Stage. The committee reports back to the House, indicating the amendments it has proposed.

Third Reading. This is the final debate on the major proposals, following which a vote is taken.

Once passed by both Houses, the Bill must then receive the Queen's approval – the Royal Assent – before becoming a statute. However, there are three further factors to be considered before a measure within the statute becomes law:

— the date upon which the *statute* is effective;

— the dates upon which the individual *sections* within the statute become effective; and

— whether *secondary legislation* is required before a section can come into force.

The Environmental Protection Act 1990 provides a good example of the implementation of a statute. The Act received Royal Assent on 1st November 1990 and under section 164(2) certain named sections became effective two months later. However, the remainder of the Act only came into force "on such day as the Secretary of State may by order appoint, and different days may be appointed for different provisions or different purposes" (section 164(3)). Consequently, many of its sections were dependent upon Commencement Orders and some of the more contentious sections (e.g. sections 61 and 143) were in fact never in force before their repeal in the Environment Act 1995. An indication of this piecemeal implementation may be gained from Tromans' annotated statutes[1] (pp 10 to 43), which lists section-by-section the date of commencement and the instruments bringing them into force.

Certain forms of control are reliant upon secondary legislation before they can be applied. For the introduction of Integrated Pollution Control, it was necessary to define which prescribed processes and substances came within the ambit of its controls and this was done through Statutory Instrument 1991/472, made under the enabling power of section 2 of the 1990 Act.

Delegated Legislation

Statutory Instruments are made by a Minister (or Ministers) and are one form of delegated legislation which also includes Orders in Council – orders of the Privy Council – and bye-laws made by local authorities and other bodies having statutory authority in certain areas, such as London Transport. The advantage of delegated legislation is that it relieves the pressure on parliamentary time, by allowing much of the detailed work relating to the "fine print" of an Act to be undertaken by others (in practice these are generally civil servants). Furthermore, it permits changes to be made relatively quickly and frequently, if necessary, including:

— the implementation of EU measures;

— the incorporation of advances in scientific knowledge, requiring tighter emission limits, etc.;

— response to a particular situation;

— the rectification of errors made in the drafting of earlier measures (e.g. the Special Waste Regulations 1996);

— delaying the implementation of controls (e.g. the bringing of scrap metal within the 1994 Waste Management Licensing Regulations).

---

[1] *The Environment Acts 1990-1995, 3rd Edition*, S Tromans, M Nash and M Poustie, Sweet & Maxwell, 1996.

The Environmental Protection (Prescribed Processes and Substances) Regulations 1991, SI 1991/472, again provide a useful example and Appendix I to Tromans' annotated statutes[1] lists the year-on-year modifications which have been made to this Statutory Instrument. However, the total number of changes which have been made is evidence of a significant drawback – that of maintaining a current awareness of all the measures relevant to a given area of activity. A good test of the "list of relevant legislation" required by environmental management systems is how up-to-date the secondary legislation is maintained. Current awareness will be facilitated as developments in information technology are extended to these areas, and mention should also be made of the regular updating of UK, EU and international environmental law provided by some journals, such as *Environmental Law and Management.*

Enabling Acts such as the Environmental Protection Act 1990 generally contain a requirement that delegated legislation is "laid before" Parliament and this may require *affirmative resolution* by which they do not become law until approved by Parliament. Alternatively, they may be subject to the *negative resolution* procedure, as with the statutory guidance on contaminated land, and in these cases they become law unless rejected by either House within a forty day period.

The Deregulation and Contracting Out Act 1994

This measure provides a "fast-track" mechanism for amending or repealing *any provisions made by an enactment* which imposes, authorises or requires the imposition of, a burden affecting any person in the carrying on of any trade, business or profession. Before a Minister may make an order, he must make a preliminary consultation of representative organisations and others and, if a variation seems to be appropriate, is required to undertake a further consultation concerning the proposed changes to be made.

The term "burden" is defined quite widely (section 1(5)(b)) and the Act may be used for the removal of outdated and unused legislation, as in the repeal of the 1906 Alkali Act in December 1996.

A draft order, together with the information specified in section 3(2), is laid before Parliament for a period of sixty days, after which it becomes law, provided neither House has raised any objections.

---

[1] *The Environment Acts 1990-1995, 3rd Edition*, S Tromans, M Nash and M Poustie, Sweet & Maxwell, 1996.

In addition, the Act empowers Ministers to make orders for the improvement of enforcement procedures, where the existing measures are perceived to impose a burden on business (section 5).

Statutory Legislation and the Courts

The courts play an important part in the development of legislation, through the interpretation of the words and phrases within statutes and other legislation. It is the courts that determine what the words in a particular enactment mean in relation to a given situation and, where such decisions are made by a higher court, they form a precedent to be followed in similar situations.

The courts are assisted in this task by the Interpretation Act 1978, which lays down certain basic rules for interpreting or construing Acts, such as the assumption that "male" includes "female", unless the contrary is indicated, and singular includes plural, and *vice versa*. Many statutory provisions include definitions of the meaning of some of the terms used although, as will become evident in later chapters, these are sometimes open to interpretation or the meaning of important words is not given.

In addition, the court may apply one of the general rules on interpretation which has been developed by precedent, viz:

— Words are to be given their literal or everyday meaning, unless this would lead to absurdity (the "Literal Rule"). However, Lord Denning noted that Acts tend to be construed by the courts according to their object and intent, rather than their literal meaning.

— Words are to be given the meaning which best expresses the intention of Parliament (the "Golden Rule"). This form of interpretation has been assisted by the ruling in *Pepper v Hart*, which held that, in certain circumstances, statements made in the House during the passage of a Bill can be construed as indicating the intention of Parliament.

— The court will determine the objectives of the legislation in question by asking "what mischief does the Act seek to remedy?" (the "Mischief Rule"). This is perhaps the most useful of these rules. In European legislation, the court is assisted by the preamble of a Directive which states the objectives of the measure, and its legal basis. In fact, the ECJ sometimes appears to give more weight to these factors than to the wording of the provision in question.

Statutory and Non-Statutory Guidance

One of the roles of the Department of the Environment is to provide guidance to those subject to the legislation, and this guidance may be in a number of forms:

— Guidance which has statutory authority, as a result of having been considered and approved by Parliament, albeit under the negative resolution procedure, for example the Regulations on the contaminated land provisions.

— Guidance *issued* under statutory authority which has not itself been approved by Parliament, such as Waste Management Paper No.4 on the licensing of waste management facilities, and the Codes of Practice on Litter and on the Duty of Care. Since these have not been laid before Parliament, they do not *per se* have statutory authority, although they may indirectly impose legal obligations.

With regard to Codes of Practice, the legal obligation is to comply with the legislation itself rather than with the Code of Practice. Nevertheless, Codes of Practice issued under statutory provisions may be admissible as *prima facie* evidence of compliance or non-compliance and in addition may be used in civil actions in negligence.

— Guidance which has no statutory basis. Documents such as Circulars issued by the Department of the Environment, and Integrated Pollution Control Guidance Notes are not issued under statutory authority and as such cannot be relied upon in court by either side, although they may have persuasive effect. However, as with recommendations within Waste Management Papers, when incorporated within a consent, permit or other form of authorisation, they will have the same authority as the remainder of the document.

There is a trend towards the production of "sector specific guidance" by trade associations and similar bodies, to assist sectors of industry with the interpretation of legislative instruments in relation to their activities. Such guidance may receive an endorsement from the Environment Agency or SEPA, as in the case of several sets of sectoral guidance on the Packaging Waste Regulations, but will nevertheless have no formal standing in law. However, in common with the Environment Agency's own "Interpretation/Policy" documents relating to special waste discussed in Chapter 9, it would be somewhat contrary for the Agency to initiate a prosecution in cases in which such guidance was followed.

THE DEPARTMENT OF THE ENVIRONMENT

The Department of the Environment (DoE) is the principal government department with responsibilities for the environment, the others including the Department of Transport, the Ministry of Agriculture, Fisheries and Food (MAFF) and the Department of Trade and Industry. In addition, the Scottish, Welsh and Northern Ireland Offices have specific responsibilities for the environment within their own geographical areas.

In June 1997, the Department of the Environment and the Department of Transport were merged to become the Department of the Environment, Transport and the Regions, reporting to a single Secretary of State.

The activities of the DoE are wide-ranging, and include four major areas:

— planning, national heritage including buildings and sites, development plans and control, minerals and land reclamation, and inner urban problems;

— environmental protection in relation to countryside and wildlife issues, the Environment Agency, radioactive substances, and policy in relation to toxic substances, air, noise and waste;

— most issues relating to water, from drinking water control through the Drinking Water Inspectorate (DWI), water quality and pollution, to sewage disposal policy; and

— environmental economics.

The Secretary of State is vested with very wide legislative and quasi-legislative powers in most of these areas, as a consequence of the "framework" structure of much of the UK environmental legislation and his role in the updating of relevant EU provisions. Although the DoE itself has few *direct* powers in relation to environmental protection, it has significant *indirect* powers in relation to the operation of the regulatory agencies, such as making directions, approving their actions, making appointments and responsibility for their budgets.

THE ENVIRONMENT AGENCY AND SEPA

The regulation of environmental matters within the UK was reorganised as a result of the Environment Act 1995 and involved the formation of two new regulatory agencies – the Environment Agency and the Scottish Environmental Protection Agency (SEPA). The Environment Agency is responsible for environmental issues within England and Wales and is the result of the merger of two central enforcement agencies – Her Majesty's Inspectorate of Pollution and the National Rivers Authority – and the 83 Waste Regulation Authorities (WRAs) formerly under local authority control (see Chapter I of the Act). In addition, the Secretary of State has delegated the day-to-day administration of the transfrontier shipment of waste under EU Regulation 259/93/EEC for the *whole* of the United Kingdom to the Environment Agency (*Hansard*, 19 June 1997, col 281).

The Scottish Agency was formed from Her Majesty's Industrial Pollution Inspectorate (HMIPI), the river purification authorities, the waste regulation authorities and the local air pollution control functions for "Part B" processes of the local authorities (see Chapter II of the 1995 Act). In addition to its composition, there are differences in SEPA's powers, such as those relating to bringing prosecutions.

In addition to undertaking the roles of their component bodies, the 1995 Act gave the new agencies new duties and areas of responsibility including:

— contaminated land (section 57);

— air quality (Part IV);

— waste strategy (section 92);

— producer responsibility (sections 93 and 94); and

— nuclear installations.

For a detailed consideration of the functions transferred to the Environment Agency and SEPA, and those *not* transferred, see Tromans' annotated statutes.[1]

The principle aim of the Environment Agency, given in section 4(1) of the 1995 Act, is to discharge its functions "so to protect or enhance the environment taken as a whole, as to make a contribution to the objective of attaining sustainable development", subject to relevant statutory provisions and *taking into account any likely costs*. No comparable statement is made in the Act in relation to SEPA.

The Secretary of State has a duty to provide guidance to the Environment Agency on the fulfilment of this aim (section 4(2) and (3)) and this must be subject to consultation and parliamentary approval through the negative resolution procedure. In addition, the Secretary of State is empowered to

---

[1] *The Environment Acts 1990-1995, 3rd Edition*, S Tromans, M Nash and M Poustie, Sweet & Maxwell, 1996, pages 438-453.

issue statutory Codes of Practice regarding the exercise of the general duties of the Agency.

The cost element within the objectives of the Environment Agency and SEPA is given a formal basis under section 39 of the Act, which states that *each* new agency must take into account the likely costs and benefits when considering whether or not to exercise its powers, or the manner in which to exercise these powers. This provision has aroused considerable controversy, although to date no challenge has been made by alleged polluters or common interest groups on the exercise of these powers.

Eleven draft functional strategies have been issued by the Environment Agency relating to the different aspects of its work: Integrated Pollution Control, waste management and regulation, radioactive substances, contaminated land, water quality, water resources, flood defence, conservation, recreation, navigation and fisheries.

With regard to waste, the Environment Agency and SEPA's duties include the regulatory supervision of its management and transport, enforcement action against illegal activities, strategic waste management planning and the provision of information and advice. An indication of the scope of this work is given by the following statistics:

— 465 million tonnes of waste are produced each year within the UK;

— 7,500 existing waste management licences must be monitored, and each year there are typically 400 applications for new licences and 300 for modification;

— 14,000 waste management facilities operate under the exemption provisions of the 1994 Regulations;

— 77,000 carriers of waste are registered with the Agencies;

— up to 11,000 registrations are anticipated under the packaging and packaging waste regulations;

— ~550,000 special waste consignment notes are produced each year;

— 9,000 international shipments of waste take place each year.

The powers and duties of the Agencies form the basis of much of the discussion on the statutory aspects of waste management throughout this book and Chapter 7 gives specific consideration to the powers of those acting on behalf of the regulators.

THE COURTS

Proceedings in Criminal Cases

Each year, a large number of alleged offences comes to the attention of the environmental enforcement agencies, both as a result of their own activities and from reports by third parties. Of these, there will be some which cannot be substantiated and others for which there is insufficient evidence upon which to base a prosecution. Whilst the Environment Agency and local authorities in England and Wales may institute criminal proceedings, the Scottish agency, SEPA, may not and must report the incident to the Procurator Fiscal who will then determine whether or not to take action. In addition to the insertion of one further level of discretion into the prosecution process in Scotland, there has until recently been a reluctance to bring "environmental" offences to court, as a result of the unfamiliarity with, and perception of, environmental law on the part of the Procurators Fiscal and in problems associated with the preparation of such cases by the enforcement agencies. The following discussion refers to procedures in the English courts.

Classification of Criminal Offences

Proceedings in criminal cases are regulated by the Magistrates' Court Act 1980 and the Criminal Justice and Public Order Act 1994, and criminal jurisdiction falls into three classes of offence listed in the Criminal Law Act 1977, viz:

— offences triable only on indictment before a jury;

— offences triable only summarily by magistrates; and

— offences triable either way.

Magistrates' Courts

A Magistrates' Court is the lowest of the criminal courts and is composed of at least two justices of the peace or magistrates, although three is more common since this enables a majority decision to be made in cases of disagreement. Lay magistrates are appointed by the Lord Chancellor and require no legal qualifications, although they are given some basic training and in court are advised by the Clerk to the Justices, who is either a barrister or a solicitor (section 6(1) of the Justices of the Peace Act 1979, as amended by section 65 of the Administration of Justice Act 1982). Stipendiary magistrates are full-time appointments and are barristers or solicitors with a seven years' general advocacy qualification, and generally sit in the busier courts where the volume and complexity of work is greater.

It is the task of justices to decide upon the guilt or innocence of the accused without the assistance of a jury, and to determine the penalty to be imposed.

Where it is felt that their powers of punishment are insufficient, the offender may be committed to the Crown Court for sentence. In addition to dealing with less serious crimes, justices also hear committal proceedings in which they determine whether there is a *prima facie* case to go to trial at the Crown Court.

It should be noted that whilst *in general* the maximum penalties awarded by magistrates are fines of up to £5,000 and custodial sentences of up to six months, these statutory maxima are significantly greater for environmental and health and safety offences.

Crown Courts

All serious criminal cases are tried in the Crown Court before a judge and jury. The seriousness of the offence determines where the charge is to be heard and by whom and, under the Courts Act 1971, criminal offences are classified into four groups:

— offences which may be tried only by a High Court judge, often referred to as a "red judge";

— offences which are usually tried before a High Court judge;

— offences which may be tried by a High Court judge, circuit judge or Recorder;

— hybrid offences which may be tried by any judge but which are usually tried by a circuit judge or Recorder.

High Court judges are drawn from the Queen's Bench Division. Circuit judges, who also sit in the County Court, are either former barristers or Recorders – practising barristers or solicitors who sit as a judge for a given number of days each year.

The High Court is divided into six circuits, each supervised by a presiding judge, sitting at various town and cities within the circuit. Within this structure, there are three tiers of court, the most serious charges being heard by the first-tier courts and relatively minor offences by third-tier courts.

Appeals in Criminal Cases

An appeal to the Crown Court may only be made by the accused and, in this case, the permission of the court not is required. Where the accused pleaded not guilty, the appeal may be against the conviction or the penalty imposed, on the basis of a point of law or fact. However, on a guilty plea only the sentence may be appealed against. An appeal against conviction consists of a complete rehearing of the case by the Crown Court.

An appeal to the Court of the Queen's Bench may be made by either the accused or the prosecution by means of the "case stated" and the court will determine the law to be applied on the basis of the facts before the justices. Where this is different from the initial decision, the appeal court will remit the case back to the original court with instructions to decide the case on the basis of their ruling. Such an appeal is available to a person who has pleaded guilty.

Appeals against conviction or sentence in the Crown Court are heard by a bench of three judges in the Criminal Division of the Court of Appeal which was established by the Criminal Appeal Act 1968. The Act distinguishes between appeals based upon points of law which may be brought as of right and those on fact which must receive leave of either the Court of Appeal or a High Court judge before they may be brought.

Either party may make a further appeal to the House of Lords, although a point of law of general importance must be involved and leave to appeal must be granted by either the Court of Appeal or the House of Lords itself.

As noted earlier, *any* court or tribunal has the discretion to approach the European Court of Justice for the clarification of a point of Community law.

Proceedings in Civil Cases

County Courts
The majority of civil cases are heard in the County Courts by a judge sitting without a jury and such hearings tend to be quicker and less formal than those in the High Court. In the past, County Courts were limited in their jurisdiction by the amount of the claim, which for contract and tort was restricted to a maximum of £5,000. However, as a result of the Court and Legal Services Act 1990, there is now no financial limit on the jurisdiction of a County Court, although there are regulations concerning where an action is commenced and where it is heard.

The County Courts are administered by district judges who determine where a case is to be heard. Where damages of not more than £50,000 for personal injuries are claimed, actions in contract and tort must be commenced in a County Court. Wherever an action starts, if the claim is less than £25,000, the district judge will direct it to a County Court for trial by a circuit judge. However, if the amount claimed is in excess of £50,000, it will be sent to a division of the High Court to be heard by a High Court judge.

The High Court
The High Court is made up of three divisions – Queen's Bench, Chancery and Family – and cases are heard by High Court judges, known as *puisne* judges. The Queen's Bench forms the largest division and is comprised 64 *puisne* judges and headed by the Lord Chief Justice. There are three functions of this Division:

— a court of first instance in relation to the larger claims in contract and tort, where the judge generally sits without a jury;

— an appellate function for matters from the Magistrates' and Crown Courts. For this purpose, two or three judges sit together and constitute a Divisional Court;

— a supervisory role in relation to the lower courts and tribunals.

The Chancery Division is headed by the Vice-Chancellor and considers companies, partnerships, bankruptcies, planning issues, mortgages and the administration of estates. This is the smallest of the three divisions and consists of 18 *puisne* judges. The court is based in London and a judge sits without a jury.

The Family Division has responsibility for matrimonial issues and comprises 15 *puisne* judges, headed by a President.

The Court of Appeal
Appeals from the Divisional Courts are generally heard by the Civil Division of the Court of Appeal, which is constituted by the Master of the Rolls and 32 Lords Justice of Appeal. Where necessary, judges from the High Court might also be asked to sit. The role of this division of the Court of Appeal is to hear appeals from the High Court, the County Courts and some tribunals, and to decide upon certain interlocutory matters.

An appeal consists of a rehearing of a case from the lower courts, on the basis of the judge's notes, the official transcript of the hearing and through arguments presented by counsel. In addition to upholding or reversing the decision of the lower court either in whole or in part, the Appeal Court may change the sum of damages awarded to the plaintiff or the allocation of costs.

The House of Lords
Appeals from the Court of Appeal may be heard by the House of Lords, provided that leave has been granted by the Appeal Court or the Appeals Committee of the House. Under certain circumstances, civil cases from the High Court may be heard *directly* by the House of Lords under the process

known as "leap-frogging", introduced by the Administration of Justice Act 1969. This applies in cases concerning the statutory interpretation of the legislation, or where the trial judge was bound by a previous decision of the Court of Appeal or the House of Lords. However, it requires the consent of the parties concerned and a certificate from the trial judge that the case is suitable for a direct appeal to be made to the Lords.

The so-called "Law Lords" comprise the Lord Chancellor, the Lords of Appeal in Ordinary and peers who have held high judicial office. The Lords of Appeal in Ordinary are life peers, appointed from the Lords Justices and other members of the Court of Appeal. There may be up to twelve Law Lords, with representatives of the Scottish and Northern Ireland judiciary, since the House is the highest civil court of appeal for Scotland and the highest criminal court of appeal in Northern Ireland.

Civil appeal cases are heard from the Court of Appeal (Civil Division), the Court of Session in Scotland, when one or two Scottish Law Lords sit, and the Supreme Court in Northern Ireland, when a Law Lord from Northern Ireland sits. Criminal appeal cases are heard from the Court of Appeal (Criminal Division) and the Divisional Court of the Queen's Bench.

A minimum of three Law Lords is required to hear appeals, although generally there are five. The judgments of each are given in the form of "speeches", and the decision is by majority.

The Hierarchy of Decisions of the Courts

When reading the reports of cases, it is important to bear in mind to what extent the judgment will be binding in the future. This is largely dependent upon the court in which the decision was made, as indicated below:

House of Lords — decisions are binding on all other courts.

Court of Appeal — bound by previous decisions of the House of Lords and in general by its own earlier decisions.

— decisions are binding on all lower courts but not on the House of Lords.

High Court — bound by decisions of the House of Lords and the Court of Appeal but not by other High Court decisions.

County Courts and — Bound by all decisions of higher courts but own
Magistrates' Courts   decisions are not binding.

In addition to the *binding precedents* as outlined above which the judge is bound to follow, cases from lower courts or other jurisdictions which are not binding may have *persuasive* value, such as *The Wagon Mound (No 2)* in relation to foreseeablilty in negligence.

The European Court of Justice does not itself have a doctrine of binding precedent and consequently, where references are made to the ECJ, its rulings are binding only on the national court in that particular case.

FURTHER READING

"Combating Non-Compliance within the European Community Environmental Directives", G Stuart, [1994] 6 *ELM* 160

"The Commission's Communication on Environmental Agreements", J C Bongaerts, [1997] *EELR*, March, 84

Customer Charter: Our statement of service standards, Environment Agency, May 1996

Delictual Liability, J M Thomson, Butterworths, 1994

EEC Treaty and Environmental Protection, L Krämer, Sweet & Maxwell, 1995

Enforcement Policy Statement, Environment Agency, May 1996

The Environment Acts 1990-1995, 3rd Edition, S Tromans, M Nash and M Poustie, Sweet & Maxwell, 1996

The Environmental Policy of the European Communities, 2nd Edition, S Johnson and G Corcelle, Kluwer Law International, 1995

The Foundations of European Community Law, 3rd Edition, T C Hartley, Clarendon Press, 1994

Learning the Law, 11th Edition, Glanville Williams, Stevens, 1982

"Maastricht and the Environment: The Implications for the EC's Environment Policy of the Treaty on European Union", D Wilkinson, [1992] 4 *JEL* 221

Paper 29, European Environment Agency, House of Lords Select Committee on the EC, Session 1994-1995, 5th Report, HMSO, 1995

The Penguin Companion to European Union, T Bainbridge and A Teasdale, Penguin Books, 1996

"The Principle of Subsidiarity: Its effect on Existing and Future EC Environmental Regulation", P Jewkes, [1994] 6 *ELM* 165

"Public Interest Litigation in Environmental Matters Before European Courts", L Krämer, [1996] 8 (1) *JEL* 1

"The Role of Environmental Action Programmes in the Development of EU Legislation", D N Pocklington, [1995] 7 *ELM* 221

Smith and Keene's English Law, 11th Edition, D Keene, Pitman Publishing, 1995

Textbook of EEC Law, 5th Edition, J Steiner and L Woods, Blackstone Press, 1996

Table 2-1: The EU Environmental Action Programmes*

OBJECTIVES	RESULTING MEASURES
Pre-1973	
	• Classification, packaging and labelling of dangerous substances, 67/548/EEC • Air pollution from motor vehicles, 70/220/EEC • Sound levels from motor vehicles, 70/157/EEC.
First 1973-75 *22 October 1972 (OJ 1973 C112/1-53)*	
• Establish objectives and principals of EC Policy • Introduce actions of essentially remedial nature: (a) to reduce pollution and nuisances, (b) to improve the environment • Promote international action.	• Objectives and principles laid down in OJ 1973 C112 and reiterated in subsequent Action Plans • Abstraction of Drinking Water, 75/440/EEC • Bathing Water Quality, 76/160/EEC • Dangerous Substances Framework Directive, 76/464/EE • Waste Framework Directive, 75/442/EEC • EC party to: (a) Paris Convention: Marine Pollution from land-based sources, 1974, (b) Barcelona Convention: Protection of the Mediterranean, 1976, (c) Convention on the Protection of the Rhine, 1976.
Second 1977-81 *17 May 1977 (OJ 1977 C139/1-46)*	
• Updated and extended policy of First Action Plan (a) emphasis on preventive action, (b) protection of land and natural resources • Reduction of pollution and nuisances with priority: (a) fresh and sea water, (b) atmospheric pollution, (c) noise • Action outside EC at international level.	• Decision on exchange of information on freshwater quality, 77/794/EEC • Decision, Advisory Committee on hydrocarbons discharge at sea, 80/686/EEC • Toxic and Dangerous Waste Directive, 78/319/EEC • Directive on protection of groundwater, 80/68/EEC • Quality of Drinking Water Directive, 80/778/EEC • Air quality limit/guide values for SO_2 and suspended particulates, 80/779/EEC • Determination of noise from construction plant and equipment, 79/113/EEC • EC party to: (a) Geneva Convention: Long range trans-boundary Air Pollution, 1979, (b) Berne Convention: Conservation of Wildlife & Natural Habitats, 1979.

* from *Environmental Law and Management*, 1995, 7 (6), 221

Table 2-1 (continued) 81

Third 1982-86
February 1983 (OJ 1983 C46/1-26)

- Development of an integrated strategy (a) action at appropriate level, (b) prevention where possible, (c) recognition of limited natural resources, (d) restoration where possible
- Prevention and reduction of pollution and nuisances.

- Supervision and control of trans-frontier shipment of hazardous waste, 84/631/EEC
- "Seveso" Directive on Major Accident Hazards, 85/337/EEC
- Establishment of Advisory Committee on Protection of the Environment in Areas under serious threat, 86/479/EEC
- Establishment of Limit values/Quality Objectives for Discharges of certain dangerous substances, 86/280/EEC
- Directives on Air Pollution from Industrial plant, Lead, Nitrogen Dioxide, and Lead in Petrol, 84/280/EEC, 82/884/EEC, 85/203/EEC, 85/210/EEC
- Bonn Agreement on North Sea Pollution from Hydrocarbons, 1986.

Fourth 1987-92
19 October 1987 (OJ 1987 C328/1-44)

- Environmental protection central to EC policies
- High standards of environmental protection
- Priority to implementation of existing legislation into national law
- Economic instruments for air and water
- Need for Freedom of Environmental Information
- Further emphasis – multi media controls.

- Maastricht Treaty (7 February 1992)
- Directive on Freedom of Access to Environmental Information, 93/313/EEC
- Establishment of European Environmental Agency, Regulation 1210/90
- Habitats Directive, 92/43/EEC
- Environmentally Sensitive Areas Regulation 2078/92
- Air Emissions from Large Combustion Plants, Directive 88/609/EEC
- Regulations on chlorofluorocarbons, 3322/88
- Convention on Trans-Boundary Movement of Hazardous Wastes, 1989.

Fifth 1993-2000
18 March 1992 (COM(92)23)

- Sustainable development
- Shared responsibility – EC/National/Local Government and industry, consumers
- Harmonisation of National Environmental Taxes
- Integration of environmental considerations into National Fiscal Policies
- Dialogue with industry/self-regulation.

- Regulation on eco-management and audit, 1836/93
- Decision on Waste Catalogue, 94/3/EC
- Green Paper on remedying Damage to the Environment, COM(93)47
- Proposal on Packaging & Packaging Waste, COM(92)278
- Draft Directive on Integrated Pollution Prevention and Control (IPPC)
- Draft Directive on Emission of Volatile Organic Compounds.

Chapter 3

STATUTORY LEGISLATION SPECIFIC
TO WASTE

*"The truth is that in many of these statutes, the legislature has left the
point open. So it has left the courts with a guess-work puzzle. The
dividing line between the pro-cases and the contra-cases is so blurred
and so ill-defined that you may as well toss a coin to decide it."*
Lord Denning in *Ex parte Island Records Ltd*, 1978

"That's the slovenly way in which these Acts are always drawn."
W S Gilbert, "The Mikado", Act II, 14th March 1885

INTRODUCTION

Waste is produced, handled and treated in a variety of different situations
and, as a result, many legislative instruments include some provision
relating to the control of its management. Waste managers need to be aware
of the waste-related legislation relevant to their operations, and that which
is concerned with contaminated land, water pollution and nuisance is
discussed in the following chapter. There is an equally important body of
legislation which concerns specific waste streams, and examples are
examined later in relation to practical waste management. However, the
focus of the present chapter is that statutory legislation whose *primary
objective* is the control of the management of waste.

Whereas such statutory measures relating to *water* pollution date from the
Rivers Pollution Act 1876 and earlier, the disposal of waste was not seen
as an important issue until the passage of the Deposit of Poisonous Waste
Act in 1972. The 1972 Act was of limited application, since it targeted
those wastes that gave rise to a risk of environmental harm (section 1(3)
and (4)) and imposed controls on the movement and deposits of such
wastes. The majority of "ordinary" wastes were excluded from its control
for, under the Deposit of Poisonous Waste (Notification of Removal or
Deposit) Regulations, SI 1972/1017, only wastes *not* prescribed within the
Schedule were subject to section 3 of the Act.

These provisions were soon replaced by those within Part I of the Control
of Pollution Act 1974, which initially focused on the *deposit* of *all* types
of waste falling within a non-exclusive definition (section 30) with a
presumption that any thing discarded or otherwise dealt with as if it were

waste was presumed to be waste unless the contrary was proved – a somewhat Gilbertian reversal of the approach taken in the 1972 Act. The concept of environmental risk was retained (section 4(5)(a)) and additional Regulations were made in relation to the transport of waste and the control of hazardous wastes, which were referred to as "special wastes".

The 1974 Act had a number of shortcomings, the most important of which were the "poacher and gamekeeper role" required of the local authorities in relation to regulatory and disposal issues, and the emphasis placed upon the *disposal* of waste. Part II of the Environmental Protection Act 1990 sought to overcome these shortcomings and introduced significant changes into this area of legislation, including:

— a reorganisation of the regulatory structure, with the separation of the operational and regulatory functions within the local authorities, and the creation of regional Waste Regulation Authorities (WRAs);

— the introduction of a "duty of care" on all those involved in the management of *controlled wastes*, as recommended by the 11th Report of the Royal Commission on Environmental Pollution;

— a substantial increase in the scope of the controls, to encompass any activity involving the handling of waste. This was achieved by a number of measures, including:

— extending the requirement for a licence, from waste disposal to the majority of waste management operations. Although certain processes were exempted from licensing, a degree of control was nevertheless achieved by requiring such exemptions to be registered with the regulators;

— exerting greater controls on the granting of licences, by introducing the concepts of the "fit and proper person" and "technically competent person";

— extending the controls imposed upon the planning, operation and closure of landfill sites. These include more stringent pre-licensing requirements, ending the ability of holders to surrender their licence at will, and placing additional duties on the regulator for operational and post-closure monitoring.

— more comprehensive information on public registers.

The 1990 Act and the Control of Pollution (Amendment) Act 1989 now form the basis of the controls on waste management within the UK and, since they received Royal Assent, a number of changes have been introduced through the Waste Management Licensing Regulations 1994 (themselves subject to a number of amendments) and the Environment Act 1995.

Some of these changes result from EU initiatives such as the Framework Directives on Waste and on Hazardous Waste, whist others are UK-promoted measures and deal with, *inter alia*, the establishment of the Environment Agency and SEPA, and contaminated land. The latter change involved a major structural change to the 1990 Act, with the insertion of a new Part IIA – Contaminated Land, and the removal of sections related to land contamination which had never been brought into force, viz:

— section 61 relating to problems caused by closed landfill sites; and

— section 143 requiring registers of land subject to contaminative uses to be drawn up.

Another important development was the requirement for the Secretary of State, in consultation with the Environment Agency, to prepare a statement on the strategy to be adopted for the recovery and disposal of waste in England and Wales (section 44A – the "National Waste Strategy"). A similar requirement was placed on SEPA in relation to Scotland (section 45A). Whilst these sections do not give the Secretary of State any further powers, other than those associated with drawing up the strategy documents ("as soon as possible"), they do incorporate within the legislation measures which are directly linked to sustainable development, thus strengthening the existing Act's provisions for waste recycling plans and payments for recycling of waste (sections 49-56).

Apart from those parts which relate to the import and export of waste, the Waste Strategy will initially be advisory and non-statutory. However, it is the intention that a statutory strategy will be established and will give guidance on waste management policy and replace the waste management plans of section 50 of the Environmental Protection Act 1990. In addition, the National Strategy will influence local authorities, who are required under the Town and Country Planning Act 1990 to "have regard to" national policies when drawing up their development plans, which themselves will provide a framework for individual planning decisions.

An important change resulting from the Waste Framework Directive was the introduction of a new definition of "waste", a consequence of which was that the "presumptive" clause of section 75(3) became otiose and was removed.

As it now stands, Part II of the Environmental Protection Act 1990, as amended, addresses five major areas of waste management:

— the national waste strategy (sections 44A and 44B);

— the framework for regulation and the statutorily-designated bodies involved in the treatment of waste (sections 30 and 32);

— waste-related offences (sections 33 and 34) and provisions for special waste and non-controlled waste (sections 62 and 63);

— waste management licensing (sections 35-44); and

— the collection, disposal or treatment of controlled wastes (sections 45-60).

THE NATIONAL WASTE STRATEGY

Prior to the modifications resulting from the 1995 Environment Act, the planning of waste under Part II EPA 1990 was undertaken at local or regional level. This formed one of two strands associated with waste-related planning within the UK, viz:

— the production of *development plans* under Part II of the Town and Country Planning Act 1990, which concerned the policies and general proposals in the structure plan of a specific area. These were drawn up by the relevant County Council, Metropolitan Council or London Borough and related to *all* planning issues. However, under Schedule 4 to the Planning and Compensation Act 1991 there is a mandatory requirement for detailed policies and proposals relating to the deposit of refuse and waste material, other than mineral waste.

— the production of *waste disposal plans* by the Waste Regulation Authorities. These were based upon an assessment of the volumes and types of controlled waste within the WRA's area and included not only waste generated within it but also that imported and exported. The plan was intended to establish the methods to be employed for the disposal of these controlled wastes. Under section 50(4) of the Environmental Protection Act 1990 there was also a requirement for the WRA to consider the desirability of giving priority to waste recycling.

Each of these strands was essentially concerned with "waste" as a substance to be disposed of, rather than as an important component in the resource/ conservation equation. However, a number of developments has taken place within the EU and elsewhere which require a more wide-ranging approach to the planning of waste-related activities. This is best achieved at national level and the framework for such a regime was established in sections 44A and 44B of the amended 1990 Act, with regard to England and Wales, and Scotland, respectively.

The European Community has been a major influence in this area as a result of the EU Waste Policy, the Environmental Action Programmes and the Waste Framework Directive. The latter has perhaps made the greatest impact and, under Article 7, in order to achieve its objectives, the competent authority or authorities within each Member State are required to draw up "as soon as possible" one or more waste management plans, with particular reference to:

— the type, quantity and origin of waste to be recovered or disposed of;

— general technical requirements;

— any special arrangements for particular wastes; and

— suitable disposal sites or installations,

which include:

— the natural or legal persons empowered to carry out the management of waste;

— the estimated costs of the recovery and disposal operations; and

— appropriate measures to encourage rationalisation of the collection, sorting and treatment of wastes.

In addition to Community measures, the Basel Convention has had a direct impact on the import and export of wastes and, nationally, the government issued its UK Strategy on Sustainable Development in 1994, which aimed to increase the proportion of waste treated by operations in the upper part of the waste hierarchy, here defined as:

— waste reduction;

— re-use;

— recovery, including composting and energy recovery; and

— disposal.

In UK terms, the importance of the insertion of sections 44A and B into the 1990 Act is that this represents the first occasion upon which a statutory measure approaches the problem holistically, viewing waste from the point of view of resource management. Before discussing this in more detail, it is useful to review the position prior to the amendments, since some of these measures will remain effective until the statutory policy provisions are enacted.

Prior to the 1995 Act

One of the conclusions of the House of Commons Environment Committee for the Session 1988/89 ("the Rossi report") was that strategic control of waste minimisation and recycling was lacking. This resulted *inter alia* in the inclusion in the Environmental Protection Act 1990 of statutory duties for the preparation of waste disposal plans, including the recycling of waste, and until 1995 these remained the only *statutory* measures in this area.

Another outcome of the Rossi report was the publication of the White paper *This Common Inheritance*, Cm 1200, in which the government committed itself to strategies of waste minimisation and recycling measures which imposed a target of 50% recycling of *recyclable* household waste by the millennium. The following years saw a number of related initiatives, including: the Government's Sustainable Development Strategy, Cm 2624, January 1994; the 17th Report of the Royal Commission on Environmental Pollution (RCEP), *Incineration of Waste*, Cm 2181; and the White Paper, *Recycling*, Cm 2696, November 1994.

The government's response to the RCEP Report was the decision to publish a waste strategy and in January 1995 a consultative draft of *A Waste Strategy for England and Wales* was issued. This was followed by the White Paper *Making Waste Work*, Cm 3040, presented to Parliament in December 1995, bringing together much of the earlier work and setting out the strategy for sustainable waste management in England and Wales.

Although this is a non-statutory document, until the statutory strategy produced resulting from sections 44A and 44B is enacted, it will form the basis of the government's policy.

"*Making Waste Work*"

The objective of this document is to identify the ways in which waste can be managed in a more sustainable way and to set targets for achieving this aim. It also provides the policy framework within which the landfill tax will operate and within which industry, local government and the Environment Agency will be able to plan ahead with a common understanding of the longer term objectives for waste management.

The scope of the strategy is restricted to non-radioactive, *solid* wastes and sludges, and includes not only "controlled wastes", currently arising at 245 million tonnes per year, but also the 190 million tonnes of waste falling outside this legal definition. The three key objectives are:

— to reduce the amount of waste that society produces;

— to make best use of this waste; and

— to select waste processing options that minimise both immediate and future risks to man and the environment.

These are supplemented by the "waste hierarchy" as discussed earlier, and the overall policy aim is to increase the proportion of waste managed by the options towards the top of this hierarchy.

The strategy sets a number of "indicative targets", a term used to denote targets which are not legally binding but are considered by government to be appropriate where the goals are longer term, where action cannot be taken by government alone, and a co-operative exercise with others is required. The "primary targets" are:

— to reduce the proportion of controlled waste disposed to landfill to 60% by 2005;

— to recover 40% of municipal solid waste (MSW) by 2005;

— to set a target for the overall reduction of waste by the end of 1998,

and, within government:

— for the DoE to set targets for minimising the solid waste it produces by March 1996; and

— for two-thirds of government departments to have office waste minimisation targets in place by the end of 1996.

In order to assist in the achievement of these targets, a number of secondary targets has been set. These relate to specific waste streams, and include:

— 40% of domestic properties with a garden to carry out composting by the year 2000;

— the cost and potential for establishing central composting schemes to be considered by *all* waste disposal authorities by the end of 1997;

— easily accessible recycling facilities to be available to 80% of households by the year 2000; and

— for 1 million tonnes of organic household waste to be composted by the year 2001.

As a result of the Minerals Planning Guidance Note 6, a further target has been added of:

— increasing the use of secondary and recycled material as aggregates in England from 30 million tonnes p.a. at present, to 55 million tonnes p.a. by 2006.

In addition to these targets with which to monitor progress towards meeting the objectives, a set of indicators based upon the objectives set in the Sustainable Development Strategy is to be published. In order to achieve the aims of the strategy, the government decided upon a five-point plan, comprising:

— a regulatory strategy;

— a market-based strategy;

— a planning strategy;

— a promotion strategy; and

— a data strategy.

The Regulatory Strategy
It is envisaged that regulation will continue to play a vital part in the management of waste and this will be effected through Part II EPA 1990 and the Waste Management Licensing Act 1994. Whilst no significant changes to the regulatory regime are planned nationally, there may be modifications as a result of EU or international legislation. However, in view of the lack of progress on measures directed towards civil liability for environmental harm, the major potential sources of changes are the Integrated Pollution Prevention and Control (IPPC) Directive, the modifications to the Basel Directive and the proposed Directives on landfill (in its revised version), hazardous household waste, and the "small installations" proposal for extending the IPPC regime.

The Market-Based Strategy
The EU 5th Environmental Action Programme, "Towards Sustainability", proposed a number of economic and fiscal measures to complement the regulatory controls for waste management and, within the UK, this theme was continued with the Sustainable Development Strategy and publications such as *Making Markets Work for the Environment*.

The market strategy is based upon four overlapping themes:

— waste management should be carried out on a commercial and competitive basis, separate from the regulatory function;

— the prices of the various waste management options should as far as practicable reflect the costs of any environmental damage;

— pricing signals should operate so that costs of the various waste management options fall as far as possible on those responsible for the creation of waste; and

— appropriate pricing signals should be in place between public sector bodies, and between them and the voluntary bodies.

The introduction of the landfill tax represents an important step in the use of economic instruments in this area. Other initiatives include the producer responsibility initiative which seeks to promote re-use and recovery, and is designed to ensure that industry assumes an increasing share of the responsibility for the waste arising from its production. To date, producer responsibility has been directed at specific business sectors – packaging, newspapers, consumer batteries, electrical and electronic goods, tyres and motor vehicles.

A further market-based strategy is the application of the concept of an efficient pricing system to the waste management services provided by the public and voluntary sectors. The major initiative in this area to date has been the recycling credits scheme introduced through sections 55 and 56 EPA 1990.

The Planning Strategy
Planning authorities play an important enabling role in the management of waste and have the responsibility, not only for restricting the development of waste facilities in order to prevent harm to the local community or unacceptable land use, but also for ensuring that there is adequate scope for the provision of appropriate facilities in locations where they are required. There is clearly a possibility of a "not in my back yard" approach if such decisions are taken at local level. However, the planning authorities are required "to have regard to" the National Waste Strategy and also to any waste disposal plans for their area. The advice on pollution planning and control issued by the DoE in 1994 in the document PPG 23 is now acknowledged to be insufficient and it is intended that a new Planning Policy Guidance Document will be issued.

It is a requirement of Article 7 of the Waste Framework Directive that a (national) integrated and adequate network of disposal installations is established, and this must take into consideration the proximity principle and the best environmental option for the disposal of waste. However, as with other areas of waste planning, the accuracy of the information concerning the quantities and types of waste arising will affect the effectiveness of any planning decisions and this is acknowledged in the data strategy, below.

The Promotion Strategy
It is envisaged that a co-ordinated promotion programme will be instituted to ensure that the content of the strategy is disseminated widely to all target groups – industry, local authorities, voluntary groups and householders. The Environmental Technology Best Practice Programme (ETBPP) is one channel by which the message of waste reduction can be conveyed to industry, and a number of initiatives are in progress.

The Data Strategy
The success of any planning initiative is dependent upon the data on which it is based and, both in the UK and in Europe, much of the information required for such purposes is either not currently available or is insufficiently precise to enable reliable estimates to be made. Prior to the 1995 Act, waste planning data were derived regionally and consequently there were problems in applying such information on a national basis in view of the different definitions, technology and methods employed. As a first step towards obtaining a degree of uniformity, the DoE published the document *Waste Management Planning – Principles and Practice*, which gives guidance to waste regulators on the principles and practice of co-ordinated gathering to obtain reliable information on waste. In addition, the DoE has published details of its waste management information requirements in the document *Environmental Information Strategy Review of Waste Management Information*.

A major impetus to the generation of waste-related information will be the *statutory* requirements of section 44A(6)(b)(I) EPA 1990, under which the Secretary of State may give directions to the Environment Agency requiring it to carry out a survey or investigation of the kinds and quantities of waste arising in England and Wales, and the processes employed for recovery or disposal.

It is acknowledged that prerequisites of any such data-based strategy are:

— the use of common terms and definitions;

— the establishment of *baseline data* for all controlled waste, against which future changes may be measured; and

— an encouragement to share data for common purposes.

The strategy discusses a number of current and future initiatives, the most important of which is the development of a national waste classification scheme which can be used in licensing, reporting and surveys, and the landfill tax, and which can be linked to the European Waste Catalogue.

Provisions for a Statutory Strategy

As a result of section 92 of the Environment Act 1995, new sections establishing the basis for a statutory waste management strategy were inserted into the 1990 Environmental Protection Act.

Requirements of Sections 44A and 44B

Section 44A(1) requires the Secretary of State to prepare a statement containing his policies in relation to the recovery and disposal of waste in England and Wales. In Scotland, this will be undertaken by SEPA (section 44B(1)) for, unlike the Department of the Environment, the Scottish Office does not have the appropriate staff available and SEPA are in a better position to undertake its preparation.

The Framework Directive does not limit Member States to the production of a single, national waste management plan and, within Great Britain, the 1990 Act provides for separate strategies for England and Wales (section 44A(2)) but a single strategy for Scotland. These strategies are to be reviewed "from time to time" (sections 44A(3) and 44B(2)) but annual reviews are considered to be inappropriate in view of the time scale of the targets established.

Scope of the Strategy

The strategies are directed at the disposal and recovery of waste. The meaning of "disposal" within Part II of the Act is given in section 29(c) and, although there is no corresponding definition of "recovery", a list of recovery operations, as well as those relating to disposal, is contained in Annex II to the Framework Directive, which is reproduced in the 1994 Waste Management Licensing Regulations. The content of the strategies is specified in sections 44A(4) and 44B(3), and this must include:

— a statement of the Secretary of State/SEPA's policies for attaining the objectives specified in Schedule 2A to the 1990 Act; and

— specific provisions relating to:

— the type, quantity and origin of waste to be recovered or disposed of;

— general technical requirements; and

— any special requirements for particular wastes.

Objectives of the National Waste Strategy

The objectives of the National Waste Strategy are defined in Schedule 2A of the amended 1990 Act and follow those defined in Article 7 of the Waste Framework Directive, as above, and also take in other relevant Articles. They include:

(a) ensuring that waste is recovered or disposed of without endangering human health or using processes or methods which could harm the environment. Particular emphasis is placed upon the risk to the three environmental media, fauna and flora, nuisance through noise or odours, and adverse affects on the countryside or places of special interest (Article 4);

(b) establishing an adequate, integrated network of waste disposal installations, taking account of best available *technology* (not *techniques* as in IPC), on the basis of self-sufficiency and the proximity principle (Article 5);

(c) encouraging the prevention or reduction of waste production, and its harmfulness, through technological solutions (Article 3(1)(a));

(d) encouraging the recovery of waste by recycling, re-use or reclamation, or any other process with a view to extracting *secondary raw materials*, and also the use of waste as a source of energy (Article 3(1)(b)).

Whilst (a) and (c) are typical "soft" objectives found in many environmental measures, (d) is more focused in its requirements and relates directly to resource management and conservation. Tromans[1] notes that (a) also forms the "relevant objectives" of the Environment Agency and SEPA, and those of the planning authorities in relation to the planning of waste recovery and disposal.

Although (b) provides a firmer commitment to action than the other items, it is dependent for its success upon a knowledge of the quantities and types of wastes arising within the UK, and this is one of the objectives of the National System of Waste Classification, discussed below.

Drawing up the Strategy

The requirements placed upon the Agencies when drawing up the strategies are given in sections 44A(5)-(8) and 44B(3)-(7). In drawing up the strategy

---

[1] *The Environment Acts 1990-1995, 3rd Edition*, S Tromans, M Nash and M Poustie, Sweet & Maxwell, 1996, page 147.

for England and Wales, the Secretary of State must consult the Environment Agency and other bodies or persons in industry and in *local* government who appear to him to be representative of these interests (section 44A(5)(a), (b)). Additional consultees may also be included as appropriate. In Scotland, this consultation process is undertaken by SEPA (section 44B(4)).

As noted in relation to the "information strategy", the Secretary of State may direct the Environment Agency and SEPA to undertake waste surveys or investigations in order to provide data for use in connection with the strategies (sections 44A(6)(b) and 44B(5)(b)). As well as specifying the technical and regional scope of such surveys, the Secretary of State may direct the manner in which they are undertaken, reported and made available to other persons.

Prior to undertaking such a survey, the representatives of the planning authorities, industries and other appropriate parties must be consulted. Tromans[1] points out that whilst the provisions relating to *consultation* on the strategy concern *local* government or authorities, prior to undertaking an investigation or survey this is to be with *planning authorities*. This is necessary in view of the planning authorities' requirements for waste-related data for drawing up development plan policies for waste.

THE REGULATION AND THE DISPOSAL OF WASTE

Definitions

The basis for the regulation of the above five major areas of waste management is established in sections 29-30 and 32 of the 1990 Act, which specify the relevant authorities involved and define some of the more important terms used. In this context, "the environment" is considered as consisting of all or any of the three environmental media (section 29(2)) and, by comparison with the equivalent definition for Part I of the Act (section 1(2)), implies that the controls in Part II are restricted to the natural environment.

"Pollution of the environment" is given a broad definition and relates to pollution due to the *release or escape* into any environmental medium, *from* land on which controlled waste is treated, or kept, or in or on which controlled waste is deposited, *of substances or articles* constituting or resulting from waste and *capable*, by reason of the quantity or concentrations involved, *of causing harm* to man or any other living organism supported by the environment (section 29(3)(a)-(c)).

---

[1] *The Environment Acts 1990-1995, 3rd Edition*, S Tromans, M Nash and M Poustie, Sweet & Maxwell, 1996, page 148.

The definition of pollution of the environment includes pollution from fixed plant used for the treatment, keeping or disposal of controlled waste (section 29(3)(d)) and section 29(4) extends the application of the whole of section 29(3) to mobile plant. A distinction is made between the controls applied to "fixed" and "mobile" plant, and section 29(10) gives the Secretary of State power to prescribe by Regulations descriptions of plant to be treated as "mobile" or not, in this context. Under section 29(9) "mobile plant" is defined as plant which is designed to move or be moved on roads or on other land, and a more extended definition is given in Regulation 12 of the Waste Management Licensing Regulations 1994, SI 1994/1056 as amended by SI 1995/288. These Regulations relate to exemptions from licensing and any forms of mobile plant not included will require a site licence for each location at which they operate.

The meaning of "deposit" is considered later in this chapter. "Harm" is defined in relation to the health of living organisms and includes the interference with ecological systems of which they form a part. In the case of man, this includes offences to *any* of his senses and harm to his property (section 29(5)).

It is important to note that the term "substance" means any natural or artificial substance, whether in solid or liquid form, or in the form of a gas or vapour. This meaning differs significantly from that used in the legislation associated with hazardous substances, e.g. the CHIP 96 Regulations, q.v., and particular care must be taken in the use of this term in the treatment of special waste, which is subject to regulations based upon *both* definitions.

Relevant Authorities

There are three authorities relevant to the management of waste:

— waste regulation authorities;

— waste disposal authorities; and

— waste collection authorities,

and these are defined in section 30, which additionally specifies the meaning of waste disposal contractors. Before discussing their respective functions in detail, it is pertinent to outline the inter-relationship of these bodies.

The regulation of waste is the duty of the Environment Agency and SEPA, and the functions of the former WRAs are now within their control.

Together with the Secretary of State, they give directions to be followed by the other bodies, as defined within the 1990 Act.

The waste disposal authorities are responsible for the disposal of the controlled waste generated within their area and collected by the Waste Collection Authorities (WCAs). However, the operational component of their activities must be undertaken by Waste Disposal Contractors (WDCs), which may be either an "arms length" company established by the WDA, or a private sector company.

Whilst the WDAs have the task of planning the *local* arrangements for the disposal of waste and the WCAs have a duty to formulate waste recycling plans for their area, the *overall* planning of waste-related activities is now undertaken at a *national* level by the Agencies, rather than *regionally* by the former WRAs.

Waste Regulation Authorities (WRAs)

Waste Regulation Authorities were first established under the 1990 Act to administer the regional regulatory, planning and administrative functions associated with Part II of the Act. The WRAs were subsumed into the Environment Agency and SEPA, whose general functions with respect to pollution control are defined in sections 5 and 33 respectively of the Environment Act 1995. In relation to waste management, relevant powers are included, *inter alia*, within the Control of Pollution Act 1974, Control of Pollution (Amendment) Act 1989 and Part II of the Environmental Protection Act.

Although the Environment Agency and SEPA assumed the role of the former Waste Regulation Authorities on 1st April 1996, Part II of the amended 1990 Act contains numerous references to "waste regulation authorities". Rather than changing each such reference, the Environment Act 1995 amended this part of the 1990 Act by repealing section 31, which dealt with the power to create regional Waste Regulation Authorities, and inserted a new section 30(1). This states that any reference to a WRA is a reference to the Environment Agency (in England and Wales) and SEPA (in Scotland), and that references to the *area* of a WRA are taken as references to the area over which these new bodies exercise all their functions.

The principal regulatory duties of the Agencies are the administration of the waste management licensing system: the granting of licences (section 35), their supervision and the acceptance of their surrender (sections 42 and 39) and the associated offences in section 33(1)(a) and (b). Although section 59 empowers them to remove unlawfully-deposited waste, their duties regarding the "general" pollution offence of section 33(1)(c) and the duty of care in section 34 are not explicitly stated.

In addition to these functions, the Environment Agency and SEPA have an important national role in the planning of waste-related activities and also have duties in relation to certain administrative functions such as the maintenance of public registers and the publication of annual reports (sections 64 and 67).

Waste Disposal Authorities (WDAs)
The Waste Disposal Authorities are specified in section 30(2) and include:

— the County Councils in the non-metropolitan English counties;

— the District Councils in other metropolitan counties in England and in Wales;

— the councils in Scotland, constituted under section 2, Local Government etc. (Scotland) Act 1994.

Specific arrangements apply to London, Greater Manchester, and Merseyside. A major feature of the 1990 Act was the separation of the regulatory and the operational functions of the local authorities and section 30(7) and (8) made specific provision to achieve this. However, since the Environment Agency and SEPA have subsumed these regulatory functions, such a provision has become otiose and this section has been repealed.

As their name suggests, WDAs are responsible for managing the *disposal* of waste within their area and the duties imposed on them under section 51 may be considered under two basic headings:

— the arrangements for the disposal of controlled wastes generated within their areas; and

— the provision of places at which householders may dispose of their waste, free of charge.

With regard to the former, whilst the Waste Collection Authorities have the duty to *collect* waste within their area, the WDAs have powers to direct them as to the places to which the collected waste must be delivered (section 51(4)(a)), which need not be within their own area (section 51(4)(b)).

The WDAs may not undertake the disposal themselves and such operational functions may only be discharged through waste disposal contractors (WDCs), as defined in section 30(5). In practice these are either Local

Authority Waste Disposal Companies (LAWDCs), established by the WDA itself under section 32, or private sector contractors.

The WDA may hold land and own equipment and make this available to the waste disposal contractors (section 51(4)(d)). In addition, the WDAs have discretion to contribute towards the costs incurred by the producers of commercial or industrial waste for the provision and maintenance of plant, equipment or "associated works" used "to deal with" waste prior to its collection (section 51(e)). This extends to the provision and maintenance of pipes or associated works provided by a WCA, within its area (section 51(f)).

In relation to arranging provisions for household waste under section 51(1)(b), the WDA may make arrangements through waste disposal contractors, either within or outside its area, for the provision of places for the treatment or storage of these wastes prior to their final disposal or other treatment (section 51(5)). This may involve the WDA making plant, equipment and land available to the waste disposal contractors for this purpose.

Both WDAs and WCAs have duties in relation to the recycling of waste and, under section 55, the WDA has powers to make arrangements with waste disposal contractors for the use, sale or other form of disposal of waste collected in their area. This includes both the recycling of waste and its use for the production of heat or electricity. Similar powers exist in section 56 in relation to Scotland.

Waste Collection Authorities (WCAs)
Section 30(3) identifies the waste collection authorities, in connection with Part II of the Act, as:

— District Councils within England and Wales, but not for Greater London;

— in Scotland, councils constituted under section 2 of the Local Government etc. (Scotland) Act 1994; and

— London Boroughs, the Common Council of the City or the Temple Authorities in Greater London,

and their responsibilities are outlined in sections 45 to 48. The WCAs have a *duty* to collect all *household* waste within their area, unless in the opinion of the authority the household is situated at a location so isolated or inaccessible as to make the cost of its collection unreasonably high *and* it is satisfied that adequate disposal arrangements have been made. No charge may be made for the collection of household waste, unless prescribed in Regulations by the Secretary of State (section 45(3)), such as in Regulation 4 and Schedule 2 of the Controlled Waste Regulations 1992, SI 1992/588. Whilst the emptying of privies serving one or more private dwellings is required to be undertaken *gratis*, a reasonable charge may be made for the emptying of cesspools. The scope of these terms is defined in section 45(12).

The WCAs have a further *duty* to collect any *commercial* waste on request of the occupier of the premises. With regard to *industrial* waste, the WCA may collect this on request of the occupier, provided that consent has been given by the WDA of the area. In both of these cases, the person requesting the removal of the waste is liable to pay a "reasonable" charge for its collection and disposal to the authority which arranged for its collection and it is the *duty* of the authority to recover this charge, unless in the case of commercial waste it is considered inappropriate to do so.

Under section 45(7), the Waste Collection Authorities have powers to construct and maintain pipes, both within and outside their area, for the collection of waste and may contribute towards the costs of the pre-treatment of waste prior to its collection.

Any waste collected by the WCA belongs to that body, not its employees or agents, and "may be dealt with accordingly" (section 45(9)). The authorities also have powers to specify the arrangements for the collection of household waste, including the receptacles used (section 46). However, unless the approval of the highway or roads authority is obtained in relation to the placing of such receptacles on the road or highway, an unlawful obstruction might be caused, as in *Wandsworth Corporation v Baines*. For industrial and commercial waste, the WCA may supply, on request, any person with receptacles for its collection. However, under section 46(2) and (3), if it appears to the authority that the inappropriate storage of such waste is likely to cause a nuisance or to be detrimental to the amenities of the locality, it may serve a notice on the occupier which requires him to supply specific numbers and types of receptacle, provided that this is reasonable.

Failure to comply with these requirements without reasonable excuse is an offence, which on conviction carries a fine.

Waste Disposal Contractors (WDCs)

A waste disposal contractor is defined in section 30(5) as a person who in the course of business collects, keeps, treats or disposes of waste, being either:

— a company formed for all or any of the these purposes by a WDA, whether in pursuance of section 32 ... or otherwise; or

— *either* a company formed for all or any of those purposes by other persons, *or* a partnership or an individual.

Waste disposal contractors play an integral role in the *disposal* of waste and, since the WDAs cannot undertake operational activities, they must make arrangements with such WDCs in order to fulfil their obligations under section 51. In practice, this is achieved either by the use of private-sector companies or the formation of a WDC by the WDA and, under section 32 and Schedule 2, Part I, existing WDAs or their constituent authorities are given powers to form waste disposal companies, either alone or with others. The Secretary of State is empowered to give directions to the WDAs in relation to the formation of WDCs and the associated transfer of undertakings (section 32(2) to (4)).

The Formation of WDCs
The Act lays down a number of restrictions on the function and operation of local authority WDCs in England and Wales, in order to ensure the separation of their regulatory and operational roles. (In Scotland, section 32 and Schedule 2 do not apply and the authorities continued to exercise *both* roles until the transfer of their waste regulatory function to SEPA.) Under section 32(7), the objectives of a WDC so formed may include activities which are beyond the powers of the local authority but, whilst it is within the control of the authority, its activities must be restricted to the collection, keeping, treating and disposal of waste. Within this remit, however, there are no restrictions on the *source* of its business.

The scope and meaning of the term "company" in this context is defined in the Companies Act 1985 and section 32(9) states that, where a WDA forms a company, it must be an "arms length" company for the purposes of Part V of the Local Government and Housing Act 1989. The 1989 Act considers local authority companies in terms of being local authority controlled, local authority influenced, or companies where the local authority has only a minority interest (sections 68 and 69). Companies may qualify as local authority controlled companies, where one of the following sets of conditions applies:

— the company is a subsidiary of the local authority by virtue of section 736 of the Companies Act 1985; or

— the local authority has power to control a majority of votes at a general meeting of the company; or

— the local authority has at that time the power to appoint or remove a majority of the board of directors; or

— the company is under the control of another company which is itself under the control of the local authority.

Where these criteria are not satisfied, but would be so if taken together with another authority or authorities, then the company is treated as being local authority controlled. Nevertheless, a local authority controlled company may be regarded as an "arms length" company for a particular financial year if before the beginning of that year the local authority so resolve and the conditions within section 68(6) are satisfied throughout the year.

The relationships between the local authority and the companies controlled by them or under their influence are specified in section 70, which gives the Secretary of State powers to make provisions for their regulation. Failure to comply, as far as is practicable, with such requirements will, for the purpose of Part II of the Local Government Finance Act 1972, result in the payments made to the company and any expenditure in contravention being regarded as unlawful expenditure and as such be subjected to sanctions of surcharge and disqualification.

Letting Contracts to WDCs
Under Part II of Schedule 2 to the 1990 Act, contracts for the disposal of waste must be put out to public competitive tender, a key component of which is the need to avoid undue discrimination between the local authority WDCs and the private sector companies (paragraph 18). The procedure is similar to that for Compulsory Competitive Tendering (CCT) and failure to observe the tendering procedure specified in the Schedule will render the resulting contract void (paragraph 20).

In preparing the terms and conditions for the contracts, paragraph 19 states that the WDA must have regard to the desirability of including terms designed to:

— minimise pollution, or harm to human health due to the operations to be undertaken; and

— maximise the recycling of waste under the contract.

Although a LAWDC may have been established by a WDA as a requirement of section 32, this does not guarantee that it will be given the contract. Detailed guidance on, *inter alia*, the letting of contracts is given in Schedule 2 to Part II of the Act and in Department of the Environment Circular 8/91.

In *R v Avon County Council ex parte Adams*, a waste disposal company, Terry Adams Ltd (TAL), brought judicial review proceedings against Avon County Council in respect of its decision to award five contracts to its own LAWDC, Avon Waste Management Ltd (AWM), on the grounds that the tendering process had been unlawful and distorted. The Court of Appeal considered all six contracts that had been let by Avon CC and, whilst the case relating to the TAL contract was dismissed, it did find that other aspects of the tendering process had been discriminatory in favour of Avon Waste Management and the ruling has provided important guidance in this area.

It was held that the contract for the transfer of waste by rail to Buckinghamshire *was* unduly discriminatory, since the terms of the contract were such that they precluded all but AWM in satisfying them. Furthermore, the local authority WDC submission for all six contracts was made on the basis of all its bids being inter-dependent, in order to secure the level of work required for the new company, but the court held that it was not open to Avon CC to accept bids on this basis.

The WDA was entitled to determine which bid to accept according to the honest judgment of those making the decisions, providing this was reasonable in the *Wednesbury* sense (i.e. *Associated Provincial Picture Houses Ltd v Wednesbury Corporation*) and met the statutory requirements. Thus, whilst the policy favouring incineration in itself was not discriminatory, the requirement in the contract for the tenderer to provide not only a new incinerator but also a site for it, was considered to be so; the existing incinerator and site were to be transferred to the LAWDC, thus giving it a distinctive advantage.

Hobhouse LJ considered the three duties upon WDAs imposed by the 1990 Act:

— to have regard to environmental considerations in the disposal of waste;

— to dispose of their own waste undertakings; and

— to subject the waste disposal operations under their control to competitive tendering,

but noted that Schedule 2 did not provide unequivocal guidance as to the ranking of these differing objectives, and suggested that this could be a source of difficulty to local authorities.

WASTE OFFENCES

The Scope of the Offences

The "general" waste offences within sections 33 and 34 of the Environmental Protection Act 1990 are directed towards *controlled* wastes. As a consequence, all "sub-groups" of controlled waste, such as special waste, fall within the ambit of these controls in addition to any specific measures relating to the "sub-group". As well as special wastes, those transboundary wastes which are subject to the EU Waste Framework Directive, rather than Regulation 259/93/EEC, fall within these controls (within Great Britain).

Section 33 – Deposition, Treatment and Disposal of Waste

Offences
This section concerns the unauthorised or harmful deposition, treatment or disposal of waste and requires that a person shall not:

— deposit controlled waste, or knowingly cause or knowingly permit controlled waste to be deposited in or on any land, unless a waste management licence authorising the deposit is in force, and the deposit is in accordance with the licence (section 33(1)(a));

— treat, keep, or dispose of controlled waste, or knowingly cause or knowingly permit controlled waste to be treated, kept, or disposed of:

  — in or on any land;

  — by means of any mobile plant, except under and in accordance with a waste management licence (section 33(1)(b));

— treat, keep or dispose of controlled waste in a manner likely to cause pollution of the environment, or harm to human health (section 33(1)(c)).

The wide scope of these measures and the importance placed upon the licensing of waste management operations is readily evident and contrasts with the former, more restricted controls imposed by section 3 of the Control of Pollution Act 1974.

Although some of the terms used in this section are defined within the Act, others are not and, in either case, it is useful to review the relevant case law.

"Waste": The definition of waste is of pivotal importance to the interpretation of the whole of Part II and the meaning of "waste", household, commercial and industrial waste, and special waste is addressed in section 75 of the

amended 1990 Act. A full examination of "waste" and "special waste" is given in Chapters 8 and 9 respectively.

"Knowingly causing and knowingly permitting": A significant volume of case law has been generated on the meaning of "causing" and "knowingly permitting" in the context of water-related offences and these applications are dealt with more fully in the next chapter. However, these words have been subject to less judicial scrutiny when applied to waste offences where, unlike section 3(1) of the Control of Pollution Act 1974 and section 85 of the Water Resources Act 1991, section 33(1) of the 1990 Act inserts "knowingly" before "cause", thus signifying the element of *mens rea* associated with the offence.

In *Attorney-General's Reference (No 1 of 1994)*, Lord Justice Taylor reviewed the meaning of "causing" in relation to water pollution and, applying this to waste offences, stated that:

— it is a question of *fact* in each case whether the defendant has caused the offence to be committed;

— the word "causes" is to be given its plain, common sense meaning;

— the word "causes" involves some active participation in the operation or chain of operations resulting from the pollution;

— "mere tacit standing by and looking on" per Lord Widgery in *Price v Cromack* is insufficient to amount to causing.

Although some authors have suggested that the use of "knowingly" in conjunction with "permitting" is otiose, since *means rea* is implicit in the act of "permitting", its use in conjunction with "causing" is significant.

With regard to the *extent* of knowledge required, in *Ashcroft v Cambro Waste Management* it was held that "knowingly" referred to knowledge of a deposit or other act involving the waste, and *not* to knowledge that the deposit was outwith or not in accordance with the terms of a licence. Furthermore, in *NRA v Schulmans Incorporated Ltd*, it was held than only constructive knowledge was required. Thus, even though the offence is not one of strict liability, these factors combine to assist the regulator in obtaining a prosecution. In addition, where waste is deposited from a motor vehicle, under section 33(5) the person in control of the vehicle is deemed to be responsible for the deposit and liable for the attendant offences, *supra*.

"Knowingly permitting" was also considered in the *Ashcroft* case, where the court stated that the prosecution need only prove that the waste has been knowingly permitted to be deposited on land, and it is for the defence to establish that the deposit was within the terms of the licence. This judgment was reiterated in *Shanks and McEwan (Teesside) Ltd v The Environment Agency*, in which Lord Justice Kennedy held that the offence in section 33(1)(a) is comprised of two parts:

— the *action* resulting in the offence of:

— depositing controlled waste;

— knowingly causing controlled waste to be deposited;

— knowingly permitting controlled waste to be deposited; and

— the *saving condition* "unless a waste management licence authorising the deposit is in force and the deposit is in accordance with the licence".

It was held that "knowingly" only qualifies two of the *action* limbs and does not qualify the saving condition. However, having been found guilty on the *action* limb, the waste holder becomes in contravention of the waste management licence.

The concept of "knowingly permitting" was widened in *Kent CC v Beaney*, where it was has held that a *provisional* inference could be drawn from the facts that the accused knowingly permitted the deposit and that, as in *Ashcroft*, such inference was capable of displacement by evidence called on behalf of the accused. It has been suggested that *Beaney* considerably widens the concept of "knowingly permitting" to include acquiescence.

"Discard", "dispose of" and "deposit": All three words appear within Part II of the Act, yet within the English language there are some situations in which they are regarded as synonyms and such usage (and some of the associated judicial consideration) tends to confuse their meanings within specific parts of the Act. This causes particular problems in the context of the definition of "waste" and these are discussed in detail in Chapter 8.

Although some sections of the 1990 Act, such as section 28(1), refer to "the *final* disposal [of controlled waste] by deposit in or on land", the definition in section 29(6) states that "the 'disposal' of waste *includes* its disposal by way of deposit in or on land". Thus, in the context of waste-related operations, "disposal" has a wider meaning than "deposit", although not every deposit in or on land will constitute a disposal.

Consternation amongst the waste regulatory bodies was caused by a decision in *Leigh Land Reclamation Ltd & ors v Walsall Metropolitan Borough Council* that the term "deposit" should be confined to the *final* deposit on disposal, thus excluding any intermediate stages such as at waste transfer stations, or allegedly "temporary" storage, from section 3 of COPA 1974. However, in *R v Metropolitan Stipendiary Magistrates & ors ex parte London Waste Regulation Authority*, the court held that *Leigh* had been incorrectly decided and that "it would unnecessarily erode the efficacy of the Act if offences under section 3 could only be charged once the waste had reached its final place of deposit".

With regard to the meaning of "dispose" in this context (i.e. not that of defining waste), Lord Justice Watkins continued by stating:

> "An article may be regarded as disposed of if it is destroyed, or if it is passed on from one person to another; the ordinary sense of the term, certainly in the context of the Act, rests upon the notion of getting rid of something. It has ... no more to do with finding a "final resting place" than has the word 'deposit'."

Attention should also be drawn to paragraph 9(3) of Schedule 4 to the Waste Management Licensing Regulations, which states that any reference to the deposit of waste on land includes a reference to any of the operations listed in Parts III or IV of the Schedule (Annexes IIA and IIB of the Waste Framework Directive) which involves such a deposit.

Penalties
Contravention of section 33(1) or any condition of a waste management licence is an offence (section 33(6)) which on summary conviction carries a penalty of imprisonment of up to six months, a fine up to £20,000, or both. On conviction on indictment, a person is liable to an unlimited fine, a period of imprisonment of up to two years for controlled wastes and up to five years for special waste, or both (section 33(8) and (9)).

Whilst section 33 makes no specific provision for civil proceedings to be taken and an injunction sought, there is nothing to prevent such action. Section 42(6A) provides for the waste regulation authority to take action in the High Court to secure compliance with licence conditions and, following the *Leigh* decision, some local authorities used their powers under section 222 of the Local Government Act 1972 to take action against illegal waste management activities and persistent infractions of COPA 1974. Although the National Rivers Authority sought to include an explicit provision on behalf of its successor, the Environment Agency, to institute and appear in any legal proceedings in England and Wales, section 37(1) of the Environment Act 1995 refers only to *criminal* proceedings.

It is, however, possible that a broad interpretation of section 37(1)(a) would include the power to institute civil proceedings. Such action has a number of advantages, such as the speed with which the courts are prepared to act, the submission of evidence as sworn affidavits and, on non-compliance of an injunction, the offender being guilty of contempt of court.

Defences

The defences available for these offences are contained within section 33(7) and include:

— that the person took all reasonable precautions and exercised all due diligence to avoid the commission of the offence (section 33(7)(a));

— that the person acted under instructions from his employer and neither knew nor had reason to suppose that the acts done by him constituted a contravention of section 33(1) and section 33(7)(b); and

— that the alleged acts were done in an emergency in order to avoid danger to human health, provided that:

— all reasonably practicable steps were taken to minimise pollution of the environment and harm to human health; and

— the waste regulators were informed as soon as reasonably practicable after the event (section 33(7)(c)).

The terms "all reasonable precautions" and "all due diligence" are widely used in environmental legislation and, elsewhere, the meaning of these phrases has been given consideration by the courts.

"Reasonable precautions" and *"reasonably practicable in the circumstances"*: The term "reasonable" was considered in *Austin Rover Group v H M Inspector of Factories*, in relation to section 4(2) of the Health and Safety at Work Act 1974, where Lord Goff stated that "the question was not whether there are measures which are reasonable, which could be taken ... but whether it is reasonable for a person in the position of the accused to take measures with these aims."

"Due diligence": In *Riverstone Meat Co Pty Ltd v Lancashire Shipping Co Ltd*, Wilmer LJ stated that "the obligation now imposed [by the Australian Sea Carriage of Goods Act 1924] is to exercise due diligence, not to see that due diligence has been exercised – still less is there any warranty that due diligence has been exercised. An obligation to exercise due diligence is indistinguishable from an obligation to exercise reasonable care ... and ... to be sharply distinguished from the obligation to which certain relationships give rise, to see that care is taken."

"Emergency": Clarification on what constituted an emergency in relation to a breach of the conditions for waste disposal (under section 3, COPA 1974) was given in *Waste Incineration Services Ltd v Dudley MBC*. The court held that the onus of proof in establishing whether or not an emergency existed rested upon the defendant, upon the balance of probabilities, and the court was entitled to have regard to *all* the relevant circumstances, i.e. the situation giving rise to the emergency was not to be solely from the defendant's point of view.

Application of Section 33
Whilst the offences of "knowingly causing" and "knowingly permitting" do not impose strict liability, the other offences of section 33(1) and section 33(5) involving the contravention of *any* condition of a waste management licence are clearly strict liability offences.

In addition, the section 33(5) offence overcomes the problem encountered in *Leigh Land Reclamation v Walsall MBC* where, in a prosecution brought under COPA, the court held that as long as the *deposit* was in accordance with the conditions of the licence, then other infractions of the site licence were immaterial. However, with regard to the infringement of a licence condition, in *Shanks and McEwan (Midlands) Ltd v Wrexham Borough Council* it was held that the words "a person" refer to the person who actually infringed the licence condition, which may not necessarily be the licence holder. In this case, a prosecution was taken out against the parent company, Shanks and McEwan (Midlands) Ltd, which held the licence and not the local operating company, Shanks and McEwan (Northern) Ltd. Consequently, the prosecution failed. A corollary to this judgment is that, if different parts of an organisation can under certain circumstances be regarded as separate legal persons from the point of view of *offences*, then under the same circumstances such offences can only be attributed to the persons guilty of these offences. This is of significant importance with regard to the assessment of "relevant offences" for a large organisation which comprises a number of smaller companies each having a separate legal identity (see Chapter 12).

The offence created by section 33(1)(c) relating to the treating, keeping or disposing of controlled waste "in a manner likely to cause pollution of the environment or harm to human health" provides the regulator with a particularly powerful tool on account of its broad scope and broad application. In relation to Part II of the Act, section 29 defines "pollution of the environment" in terms of harm to *any* living organism, and "harm" as harm to the health of living organisms or interference with the ecological systems of which they form a part. Furthermore, this subsection can be applied in cases where a waste management licence is in force and where all of its conditions are being satisfied.

The problem of "fly tipping" is addressed in section 33(6), which states that where controlled waste is carried in and deposited from a motor vehicle, the person who controls or is in a position to control the use of the vehicle is deemed to have knowingly caused the waste to be deposited, whether or not he gave any instructions for this to be done. This provision is further strengthened by section 6 of the Control of Pollution (Amendment) Act 1989, which allows seizure and disposal of vehicles used for illegal waste disposal, and by section 69 of the Transport Act 1968, by which a goods vehicle operator may forfeit his operators' licence if his vehicle is involved in fly tipping or other waste offences.

Household waste from a domestic property which is treated, kept or disposed of within the curtilage of that property, by or with the permission of the occupier, is not subject these requirements (section 33(2)). In addition, the Secretary of State may exclude by Regulations other areas, such as small or temporary deposits, "innocuous" means of treatment or disposal, or cases subject to other controls within Part II of the Act (section 33(3) and (4)). Such Regulations may make different exceptions for different areas.

Section 34 – The Duty of Care

Offences under Section 34
The introduction of a criminal duty of care in the 1990 Act extended the scope of individual responsibility to include the waste producer and each subsequent waste holder, and went some way towards providing a "cradle to grave" approach to the management and disposal of wastes. Section 34 states that "it is the duty of any person who imports, produces, carries, keeps, treats or disposes of controlled waste, or as a broker has control of such waste, to take all such reasonable measures applicable to him in that capacity as are reasonable in the circumstances:

— to prevent any contravention by any other person of section 33 (section 34(1)(a));

— to prevent the escape of the waste from his control, or that of any other person (section 34(1)(b)); and

— on the transfer of the waste, to secure:

  — that the transfer is only to an authorised person, or to a person for authorised transport purposes; and

— that there is transferred such a written description of the waste as will enable other persons to avoid a contravention of that section and to comply with the duty under this subsection as respects the escape of waste." (Section 34(1)(c).)

The term "authorised person" is defined in section 34(3) and includes waste collection authorities, holders of waste management licences, waste carriers registered under the Control of Pollution (Amendment Act) 1989 and organisations such as registered charities exempted under the 1989 Act. Section 34(4) defines those authorised transport purposes for which the carrier need not be itself authorised, and these include the transport of controlled waste within the same premises and certain transport operations to and from (but not within) Great Britain.

The Environment Act 1995 inserted a new section 34(4A) in order to clarify the application of the Regulations to the more complex movements of waste. This section states that a transfer of waste in stages is to treated as taking place when the first stage of the transfer takes place, and a series of transfers between the same parties, of waste of the same description, is to be considered as a single transfer taking place when the first of the transfers in the series takes place.

As with section 33, the occupier of a domestic property is not subject to the duty of care for household waste produced on the property (section 34(2)). However, the duty *does* apply to all other persons who handle such wastes subsequent to it leaving the control of the domestic occupier. This is of particular importance to specific/segregated collections of hazardous domestic wastes which under other circumstances would be classified as "special".

Penalties
Failure to comply with the duty imposed by section 34(1), or with any requirements imposed by the Secretary of State by means of section 34(5) (in relation to the making and retention of documents and the furnishing of documents or copies of documents), is an offence which carries a fine up to the statutory maximum on summary conviction and an unlimited fine on conviction on indictment.

Defences
There are no statutory defences to section 34, although implicit in the duty of care provisions is a requirement on the waste holder, *inter alia*, to take action to inform himself of the legality of waste management activities over which he has a degree of control. This has parallels in the defence, available within section 34(4)(c) COPA 1974, of taking care to inform

oneself that a deposit is lawful and which was considered in *Durham CC v Peter Connors Industrial Services Ltd*. Charged with depositing waste in breach of licensing conditions, the defendants raised the section 34(4)(c) defence, claiming that their drivers were instructed to check, as far as possible, that toxic materials were not included within the wastes collected. However, the court held that to have the benefit of this defence the defendant must take care to inform himself *on each occasion, in relation to each deposit* as to the nature of the deposit.

Lord Justice Beldam also stated that, if a method of working specifically requires that the person who provides the load must on each occasion give information to the person making the deposit, this may amount to the giving of the information required by section 34(4)(c) of the 1974 Act. This *could* be taken to imply that an adequately completed Transfer Note or Consignment Note might satisfy all the *information* requirements on waste transfer under section 34 EPA 1990, but the question needs to be asked as to what additional actions are required to satisfy the duty of care?

Application of the Duty of Care

General
The operation of the duty of care is for a large part dependant upon the documents generated on the transfer of waste, *infra*, and on a significant degree of self-regulation by those subject to the duty. The onus is on such persons to protect their own interests, by insisting on strict compliance by others, refusing to be associated with illegal activities or practices and reporting infractions to the regulator.

Codes of Practice
The duty is supplemented by the Environmental Protection (Duty of Care) Regulations 1991, SI 1991/2839, made under section 34(5), and a Code of Practice, under section 34(7). The Regulations provide a practical framework by means of a Transfer Note system of documentation, which is intended to provide an auditable trail, from the production of the waste to its final disposal or processing. Further details on the practical issues associated with the operation of the Transfer Note system and Code of Practice are given in Chapter 11.

Section 34(11) permits different Codes of Practice to be produced for different "areas", although it does not specify whether "areas" refers to geographical regions or to industrial sectors (c.f. the unambiguous wording of section 93(1)(e) Water Resources Act 1991). To date, only a general Code of Practice has been produced and the guidance given in the Department of the Environment's Waste Management Papers (WMP) has been issued under powers specific to the area for which guidance is given, e.g. WMP No. 4 on the Licensing of Waste Management Facilities is under sections 35(8) and 74(5) and WMP No. 26A on Landfill Completion is under section 35(8).

A Code of Practice issued under the powers within section 34(7) is admissible in evidence *by either side* and, if any provision of such a code appears to the court to be relevant to any question arising in the proceedings, then it is to be taken into account in determining that question.

Application of the Code in Practice
To date, a number of prosecutions have been made under section 34, including:

— the inadequate description of waste on a Transfer Note;

— the transfer of waste to a person not authorised to receive it; and

— failing to prevent the escape of waste,

although the majority have been made under the section 33 provisions. Nevertheless, there is a high awareness of the requirements of the duty of care within the waste industry and this alone has had a beneficial influence on the management of waste.

The wording of section 34, being specific to named waste management operations, is in most cases restricted in its application to the prosecution of a single defendant for each infraction and, unlike offences in relation to causation, cannot use the arguments in *Attorney-General's Reference (No 1 of 1994)* to include all those involved in a chain of events. In addition, following *Seaboard Offshore Ltd v Secretary of State for Transport* it may be argued that section 34 requires a lack of care to be shown on the part of the defendant itself and hence a company cannot be held vicariously liable for the failure of a subordinate employee who cannot be equated with the company itself.

One possible means of improving the management of waste through the use of the duty of care provisions would be to issue industry-specific Codes of Practice under section 34(7) and (11), based upon best-practice principles. Such a move would benefit both industry and the regulators, and could be introduced progressively to those industrial sectors or specific waste activities presenting the highest risks. The duty of care would also assume greater importance if measures imposing a civil liability for waste were introduced, *infra*.

OTHER WASTE OFFENCES

In addition to the above offences, sections 62 and 63 of the Act make provision for "certain dangerous or intractable waste"(i.e. special waste) and waste that falls outwith the definition of "controlled waste", respectively.

Special Waste

Section 62 empowers the Secretary of State to make provision by regulations for the treatment, keeping or disposal of *controlled wastes* of *any* kind that he considers so *dangerous* or *difficult* to treat, keep or dispose of, that special provision is required. The Special Waste Regulations 1996, SI 1996/972, as amended by SI 1996/2019 and SI 1997/251, currently provide such provisions and these are discussed in detail in Chapter 9. It should be noted that this section is subject to section 114 of the Environment Act 1995, whereby the Secretary of State may delegate his appellate functions to any appointed person who then has the same powers as the Secretary of State in such situations. However, under section 40(5) of the 1995 Act, he is bound by any direction given to the Environment Agency or SEPA when determining an appeal from a decision of that body.

Wastes Other Than Controlled Waste

Controlled wastes currently account for only ~56 % of the waste arisings within the UK and, under section 63(1), the Secretary of State may, after consultation with such bodies as he considers appropriate, extend prescribed provisions of Part II of the Act to mining and agricultural wastes, subject to prescribed modifications where necessary.

In addition, section 63(2) makes it an offence, in the absence of a waste management licence, to deposit, or to knowingly cause or knowingly permit the deposit of, *any* waste which is not controlled waste but would otherwise meet the criteria for its classification as a special waste. In addition, this applies to industrial and commercial wastes within sections 45(2) and 47(1). A defence in provided in section 63(3) whereby no offence is committed if the act charged was done under and in accordance with an appropriate licence.

CIVIL LIABILITY FOR WASTE

Statutory civil liability for hazardous operations is not a new concept and in the broad "environmental" field has been adopted in measures such as the Nuclear Installations Act 1965 and the Merchant Shipping (Salvage and Pollution) Act 1994. The former has recently formed the basis of a successful claim for £6 million damages (plus £0.5 million costs) by the

Blue Circle Group for the contamination of their land with high levels of plutonium from the adjacent site owned by the Atomic Weapons Establishment – *Blue Circle Industries plc v Ministry of Defence*.

Provisions relating to waste are included in section 73 of the Environmental Protection Act 1990 and the EU has for some time been considering the possibility of statutory civil liability, both in relation to waste and a more generally applicable liability relating to environmental damage.

A useful insight into the problems which may arise in the area of civil liability for environmental damage may be gained from an examination of the mandatory and voluntary schemes for maritime oil pollution – the Convention on Civil Liability Convention for Oil Pollution Damage, 1969 (the Civil Liability Convention or CLC); the International Fund for Compensation for Oil Pollution Damage, 1971 (the Fund Convention); the Tanker Owners Voluntary Agreement Concerning Liability for Oil Pollution, 1969 (TOVALOP); and Contract Regarding an Interim Supplement to Tanker Liability for Oil Pollution, 1971 (CRISTAL). The general issues which arise in this area of liability include:

— the definition of a pollution incident;

— the definition of pollution damage and the inclusion, or not, of pure economic loss;

— the extent to which liability includes preventative measures;

— the (geographical) area within which compensative damage may be claimed;

— the extent to which remediation of the environment is required, i.e. *restitutio in integrum*, or other criteria; and

— the persons empowered to undertake preventative or remedial action, *parens patriae*;

Liability under the Environmental Protection Act 1990

A restricted civil liability for damage caused by waste is provided by section 73(6) to (9), whereby any person who has deposited waste, or knowingly caused or knowingly permitted waste to be deposited, in or on land so as to commit an offence under section 33(1) or 62(2) of the Act *and* to cause any damage, is liable for that damage. This does not apply where the damage was due wholly to the fault of the person who suffered it or was suffered by a person who voluntarily accepted the risk of the damage being caused.

"Damage" is defined quite broadly in section 73(8) and includes the death of or injury to any person (including disease and any impairment of physical or mental conditions). The defences included in section 33(6) apply to section 73(6).

These provisions do not preclude other action being taken in relation to damage, either in common law or through other statutorily-based action, e.g. a breach of the Code of Practice issued under section 34(7) may be used in criminal proceedings under section 33 of the Act, or in a civil claim for negligence arising out of the handling of waste. With regard to the latter, the breach is only one of the factors upon which the plaintiff is entitled to rely. However, in *Powell v Phillips* it was held that a breach of a code "creates no presumption of negligence calling for an explanation, still less a presumption of negligence making a real contribution to causing an accident or injury".

EU Proposals for Civil Liability for Waste

In 1989, the Commission proposed a Directive on Civil Liability for Damage Caused By Waste (COM(89) 282 (final) – SYN 217), which encompassed all wastes other than nuclear waste and those covered by maritime conventions relating to oil pollution. This made the *producer* of the waste liable in civil law for damage to persons and property and for "injury to the environment" as a result of waste in his possession until its transfer to another lawful holder. The term "producer" was of critical importance and, in addition to persons whose activities resulted in the generation of the waste or were involved in its pre-processing, mixing or other operations resulting in a change in its nature or composition, a number of others were deemed to be the producer. These included importers of the waste into the Community, persons with actual control of the waste at the time the damage occurred, or those responsible for the licensed disposal operation to which it was lawfully transferred.

This liability was absolute – irrespective of fault with no statutory defences resulting from the possession of a valid licence or permit – although these conditions were modified in a subsequent draft. In addition, where more than one producer was involved, the liability was joint and several. (Joint liability is where each party is liable for its own contribution to the single acts, or damage to the plaintiff, but several liability is when each is also liable to the plaintiff for the damage caused by the other, although a contribution to these damages may be recovered from the other defendant(s).)

A range of remedies was available to the plaintiff, including injunctive relief:

— to prohibit or secure the cessation of the polluting activity;

— to reimburse expenditure on preventative measures;

— to reimburse expenditure arising from the damage caused;

— to restore the environment to its condition prior to impairment and to obtain recovery of the associated costs;

— to secure indemnification for the damage.

A further contentious issue was the *locus standi* given to "common interest groups" with respect to *some* of the above remedies. The initial proposals for the Directive were approved by the EU Parliament in 1990, subject to certain amendments. However, these measures have not been adopted and the issue of civil liability is now subject to the much wider consideration of all environmentally related damage.

The Lugano Convention

Under the auspices of the Council of Europe – a European political institution founded in 1949, comprising 32 member countries – a number of its members including Cyprus, Finland, Greece, Italy, Liechtenstein, Luxembourg and the Netherlands signed the Convention on Civil Liability for Damage Resulting from Activities Dangerous to the Environment in March 1993. However, at the time of writing, none of the EU Member State signatories has ratified the Convention.

Known as the Lugano Convention, this agreement was modelled on earlier conventions relating to civil liability for nuclear damage (Paris, 1960) and oil spills (Brussels, 1969) and imposed strict liability on those who have control of "dangerous activities". These are defined as activities which:

— produce or use dangerous substances;

— use genetically-modified organisms or micro-organisms;

— involve the treatment or the landfilling of waste.

Liability is joint and several and, although certain prescribed defences are available, operators are required to maintain financial guarantees up to specified limits, as determined by domestic legislation.

This strict liability is tempered by a number of statutory defences, including a provision under which an operator can claim that the risks posed by a substance could not have been foreseen in the light of scientific and technological knowledge at the time of the incident which gave rise to the damage. In addition, there is no liability where the damage was caused by emissions "at tolerable levels under local relevant circumstances".

The Lugano Convention has recently assumed a new significance with the possibility of the EU acceding to the Convention on behalf of Member States. However, there is uncertainty as to whether the EU has the legal "competence" to accede to the Convention, since this is limited to areas expressly allowed for in the EU Treaty or where there is existing community legislation. The position regarding environmental liability is uncertain in this respect and it has been suggested that accession to the Lugano Convention would be governed by a mixture of EU and individual Member States' competence. Only areas in which the EU has competence would be binding on Member States.

EU Green Paper on Civil Liability for Remedying Environmental Damage

In contrast to the initiatives on waste, the EU adopted a more tentative approach towards civil liability for environmental damage and a Green Paper (COM(93) 47) was issued as part of the consultative process, prior to the submission of formal proposals for a Directive. The Green Paper was produced shortly after the Lugano Convention and as such may have been influenced by its scope and conditions. In view of its consultative nature, the Green Paper is not as detailed as the proposed Directive for waste and, whilst it outlines a preferred framework, it tends to emphasise the numerous potential difficulties which are to be resolved rather than the possible solutions for discussion. A detailed analysis of these issues has been made by Jones.[1]

The basis of the envisaged system is that those whose activities result in environmental harm should be liable for the remedial costs for that damage (i.e. the "polluter pays principle"). A "dual system" is proposed whereby civil liability is used to allocate these costs and this is supplemented by a joint compensation system to fund remediation where liability cannot be effectively and efficiently imposed upon specific polluters.

Civil Liability
Following the pattern established in the Genetically Modified Organisms (GMO) Directives, 90/219/EEC and 90/220/EEC, the proposed Directives

---

[1] "Remedying Environmental Damage: The European Commission's Green Paper", B Jones, [1994] *Tijdschrift voor Milieu Aansprakelijkheid (Environmental Liability Law Review)*, 8, 1.

on landfill and on waste and in the environmental legislation of a number of Member States, the Green Paper favours strict liability over fault-based liability. In the present context, this also places the emphasis on making funds available for remediation, rather than the allocation of blame.

However, the Paper proposes that the strict liability regime should be defined with reference to the activity or process in which the defendant was engaged in causing the harm, and that a relatively restricted range of processes should be liable. The criteria by which such processes could be determined might include:

— the hazards posed, the probability of damage occurring (i.e. the risk) and the possible extent of such damage;

— the effectiveness of a regime of strict liability as an incentive for better risk management and damage prevention;

— the feasibility and cost of remediation;

— the potential financial burden on the economic sector concerned; and

— the need for and availability of insurance.

The Green Paper considers that the usefulness of civil liability is limited to measurable and immediate damage resulting from finite accidents where the liable parties are identifiable and insured. In addition, there must be a party with a legal interest to bring the action and the question of the *locus standi* of "common interest groups" must also be considered.

Joint Compensation Fund
A joint compensation system is envisaged which would provide the finance for remediation in cases where:

— the pollution cannot be identified or the environmental damage is attributable to a large number of sources; or

— the pollution results from "historical" activity or has built up incrementally over a long period.

As in the voluntary schemes for maritime oil pollution – TOVALOP and CRISTAL – industry sectors would set up joint funds and, in the event of environmental damage, clean-up costs would be recovered from the sector most closely associated with that particular type of pollution.

Following on from the Green Paper, the Commission sponsored two studies, one examining Member States' current liability regimes and the other analysing the economic effects of civil liability and the joint compensation schemes. The findings of these were due early in 1997 but a planned Directive on civil liability was dropped from the Commission's work programme for 1997. Nevertheless, the Commissioner is anxious to promote this measure and three possible alternatives have been mooted:

— acceding to the Lugano Convention;

— a further round of consultation, via a White Paper;

— drafting an EU Directive.

WASTE MANAGEMENT LICENSING

The offences of section 33(1)(a) and section 33(1)(b) of the Environmental Protection Act 1990 are both concerned with the activities of treating, keeping or disposing of controlled waste in relation to conditions included in the relevant waste management licence. The term "waste management licence" is defined in section 35 and many of the controls imposed by Part II of the Act are dependent upon the system of waste management licensing prescribed in the 1994 Regulations. However, this is only one of a number of statutory regimes imposing controls upon wastes and these will discussed in detail in Chapters 12 and 13.

It is likely that some processes which currently fall within Part II of the Act will become subject to a different regime of control under what is now the Integrated Pollution Control system, once the Integrated Pollution Prevention and Control Directive (IPPC) is implemented. In particular, this will require processes involved in the recovery of hazardous wastes and landfill sites of 25,000 tonnes capacity or receiving more than 10 tonnes of waste per day to come within IPPC.

FURTHER READING

Competition for Local Authority Waste Disposal Contracts and New Arrangements for Disposal Operations, Department of the Environment Circular 18/91

"Defining Waste", M Purdue, [1990] 2 (2) *JEL* 250

"The Definition of Pollution Damage in the 1984 Protocols to the 1969 Civil Liability Convention and the 1972 Fund Convention", M Jacobsson and N Trotz, [1986] *J Maritime Law and Commerce*, 17, 447

The Environment Acts 1990-1995, 3rd Edition, S Tromans, M Nash and M Poustie, Sweet & Maxwell, 1996

Environmental Information Strategy Review of Waste Management Information, HMSO, 1995

"High Court Injunctions: an alternative for WRAs", S Burns, [1993], *Waste Management*, February

Law and the Waste Industry, Institute of Waste Management/UKELA, 1994

Making Markets Work for the Environment, HMSO, 1993

"Moving the Boundaries of Compensable Environmental Damage caused by Marine Oil Spills: The Effect of Two New International Protocols", D Wilkinson, [1993] 5 *JEL* 71

"Remedying Environmental Damage: The European Commission's Green Paper", B Jones, [1994] *Tijdschrift voor Milieu Aansprakelijkheid (Environmental Liability Law Review)*, 8, 1

UK Waste Law, J H Bates, Sweet & Maxwell, 1997

Waste Management Paper No 1 – A Review of Options, Department of the Environment, HMSO, 1992

Waste Management Planning: Principles and Practice – A Guide on Best Practice for Waste Regulators, HMSO, 1995

Chapter 4

OTHER STATUTORY LEGISLATION RELEVANT TO WASTE MANAGEMENT

INTRODUCTION

In addition to the legislation directed specifically towards the regulation of waste, many statutory provisions contain parts, chapters or sections which impose equally important controls on these materials and an understanding of these provisions is essential to all those involved in its management. In addition, those organisations introducing one of the formally-recognised environmental management systems will need to undertake a review of the legislation relevant to their business and Table 4-1 (page 181) lists that which might be applicable to a typical company.

With regard to the regulatory bodies, the formation of the Environment Agency and SEPA will impose a greater requirement on their inspectors and officers to adopt a more holistic approach to the activities within their control. Local authorities have traditionally covered a broader range of environmental controls than the former "specialised" regulatory agencies and this will be increased further by the addition of the duties imposed by the contaminated land provisions.

This chapter considers the major items of statutory legislation relating to the operational aspects of waste management – discharge of trade effluent, pollution of controlled waters, remediation of contaminated land and statutory nuisance – and, although some of the associated planning issues are discussed, the specialist texts should be consulted for a more detailed examination.

WATER LEGISLATION

Ingress and Egress

A knowledge of the sources and composition of all ingress water to a given piece of land or premises is an important prerequisite to the allocation of liability, since it is essential to know whether a particular contaminant has arisen as a result of the operations of the organisation itself or those of a third party. This applies both to unwanted sources such as spillages, bursts and leaks, and to the "formal" arrangements for receiving water – under an abstraction licence or supply by the water utility companies. Many ingress problems affect the proprietary interests of the owner or occupier and as

121

such find remedies in common law. However, egress may additionally affect waters of the "unowned environment" or the sewerage infrastructure, and a number of statutory provisions have been imposed for their protection. A useful practical guide to control of egress has been produced by the National Rivers Authority in the form of a video, *Pollution Prevention Pays*, which is available, *gratis*, from the Environment Agency. A subsequent video, *Building a Cleaner Future*, and information pack directed specifically at the construction industry may be purchased from the Environment Agency.

Consideration of *all* discharges made to a foul sewer and to controlled waters is an integral part of any waste management system, since these may represent a significant part of an organisation's waste arisings and as such attract a disposal cost paid to the sewerage undertaker or to the Environment Agency. They are also important from the viewpoint of sustainable development, since effluent discharges will be subject to subsequent treatment at the sewage works and will generate waste for disposal as a result of these operations. However, in the context of the Waste Framework Directive, 91/156/EEC, "waste waters" such as these do not come within its ambit, whereas "waste in liquid form" does. The categories of "waste waters" which might arise at an industrial site include:

— waters resulting from the drainage of land;

— "foul waters" discharged to the sewage system;

— cesspools, septic tanks and settlement tanks;

— rainwater drainage;

— "trade effluent" resulting from processing operations; and

— "diffuse pollution" where there is no well-defined source of discharge, such as the spraying of herbicides, fertilisers, nutrients, etc.

In general, those sources of egress discharging to the foul sewer come within the ambit of the Water Industries Act 1991 (WIA) and are regulated by the privatised sewerage undertakers, and those discharged to "controlled waters" come under the Water Resources Act 1991 (WRA) which is now administered by the Environment Agency (formerly by the NRA). There is, however, an area of overlap in responsibilities for processes subject to Integrated Pollution Control (IPC) and other processes discharging "Red List" substances.

It is important to translate these "legal" liabilities into practical terms, and many organisations are unaware of the location and inter-connections of the drains and outlets on their property, and whether these connect with the foul sewer or discharge to rivers and streams. A number of areas within the UK have combined surface water and foul water systems and all such water is treated by the sewage works.

A further aspect for consideration is the priority of the relevant regulatory body. The sewerage undertakers are, post-privatisation, commercial organisations which have a major interest in the collection of trade effluent charges and ensuring that the discharges do not damage their infrastructure or sewage works. On the other hand, the National Rivers Authority and now the Environment Agency have duties as "guardians of the water environment" and as such their interests extend to the "unowned environment". An indication of the Environment Agency's priorities can be seen from the classification of water pollution incidents, in Table 4-2 on page 182, and the attendant prosecution policy.

Controlled Waters

Most naturally-occurring waters fall within the term "controlled waters" which is defined in section 104(1) of the Water Resources Act 1991 and includes relevant territorial water, coastal water, inland fresh waters – lakes, ponds, rivers, watercourses – and ground waters (i.e. water within underground strata). The term "watercourse" is widely used and, under section 221 of the WRA 1991 and subject to sections 72(2) and 113(1), includes "*all* rivers, streams, ditches, drains, cuts, culverts, sluices, sewers and passages through which water flows, *except* mains and other pipes which belong to the Agency or a water undertaker, or those used solely for the supply of water to premises."

Clarification of the *usage* of the term "controlled waters" was given in *R v Dovermoss*, in which it was noted that section 104(1)(c) WRA 1991 referred to "waters *of* any ... watercourse" and not "waters *in* any watercourse". Consequently the court held that the offence in section 85 of the Act could be applied to the contamination of a dry watercourse which caused pollution when waters again ran in it. Subsequently, in *NRA v Biffa Waste Services*, it was held that the river bed was part of the controlled waters and hence, when mud and silt were churned up into the water by the passage of vehicles, no offence under section 85 of the Act was committed. However, Mr Justice Rougier added that this decision did not give contractors *carte blanche* to disturb as much of the river bed as they wished, as in certain circumstances the stratum of the bed "would be very narrow indeed".

DISCHARGES TO SEWERS

There are two major areas of legislation relating to the discharges made to sewers: that which is concerned with the adequacy of the drainage and discharge "hardware" on the landowner's property, and that controlling the nature of the discharge itself. The former comes within the Building Act 1984 and subsequent Regulations and is beyond the scope of the present discussions. The majority of the controls relating to the latter are imposed by the Water Industry Act 1991, although there are other important provisions within the Environmental Protection Act 1990, as amended, and the Water Resources Act 1991.

There is a significant quantity of case law relating to the definition, ownership and responsibilities associated with drains and sewers but, in general, drains are regarded as serving a single property and are effectively considered as part of it, whereas sewers collect effluent from several properties and are the responsibility of a number of persons or the relevant sewerage authority. Statutory definition for the terms "drain" and "sewer" are given in section 219 WIA 1991 and section 221 WRA 1991 which also defines a "public sewer" as one vested in, for the time being, a sewerage undertaker.

Since these definitions of drain and sewer are specific to "buildings or yards appurtenant to buildings", they do not apply to the drainage of land for agricultural or other purposes. Where there are man-made modifications to natural rivers, streams and watercourses, such as the introduction of pipes, culverts, etc., the modified channel is not generally regarded as a sewer unless this is inherently part of its function – see *British Railways Board v Tonbridge and Malling DC* and *Hutton v Esher UDC*.

Whereas the sewerage undertaker has a duty to provide for the disposal of domestic effluent without cost, it has substantially greater discretion in relation to "trade effluent" for which it has the power to impose restrictions relating, *inter alia*, to its volume, composition and temperature, and may make a charge for its treatment.

Terminology

There are a number of definitions associated with the discharge of effluent to sewers and it is important to determine the scope and meaning of these terms. The expression "foul water" is in general use in relation to any discharge to a sewer but has the specific meaning under the Building Regulations 1991, SI 1991/2768, of waste from sanitary conveniences, other soil appliances and water used for cooking and washing. "Effluent" means any liquid, including particles of matter and other substances in suspension in the liquid, and "sewage effluent" includes any effluent from the sewage disposal or sewerage treatment works of a sewerage undertaker, but this excludes surface water. The term "surface water" includes water from roofs.

"Trade effluent" is defined under section 141(1) WIA 1991 as:

— any liquid either with or without particles in suspension, which is wholly or partially produced in the course of any trade or industry carried on at trade premises;

— in relation to trade premises, [trade effluent] means any such liquid which is so produced in the course of any trade or industry carried on at those premises, but does not include domestic sewage.

For the purposes of this definition, "trade premises" means "any premises used or intended to be used for carrying on of trade or industry". Under section 141(2) this is extended to include any land or premises with an actual or intended use for agricultural or horticultural purposes, fish farming, or for scientific research or experiment. This is applicable whether the undertaking is run for profit or not, and also when it forms only part of a larger undertaking.

Following *Thames Water Authority v Blue and White Launderettes*, it is the *purpose* of the undertaking, rather than the *type of effluent* that determines its classification as "trade effluent" or not.

DOMESTIC EFFLUENT DISCHARGES

As noted earlier, the owner or occupier of any premises, or of any private sewer draining premises, has the right to have his drains connected to the public sewers of the statutory undertaker for the discharge of foul and surface water. For the purposes of Chapter II WIA 1991, "domestic sewerage purposes" means:

— the removal from buildings and such land, of water which has been used for cooking or washing; and

— the removal from buildings and such land, of surface water, but excludes water used for the business of a laundry, or for the preparation of food or drink for consumption otherwise than on the premises.

However, section 111 of the Act places a number of restrictions on domestic discharges, which are not permitted to contain:

— any *matter* likely to injure the sewer or drain, to interfere with the free flow of its contents, or to affect prejudicially the treatment and disposal of its contents; or

— chemical refuse or waste streams, or liquids of temperatures greater than 110° F (43.3° C), which are a *prohibited substance*; or

— any petroleum spirit.

Following *Liverpool Corporation v Coghill & Son Ltd*, the balance of scientific evidence will determine whether a discharge prejudicially affects the treatment and disposal of the sewage. The term "prohibited substance" refers to substances in section 111(1)(b) which, either alone or in combination with the contents of the sewer or drain, are:

— dangerous;

— the cause of a nuisance; or

— injurious, or likely to cause injury to health.

This definition extends to liquids having these properties when heated.

Contravention of section 111 is an offence which attracts a fine on summary conviction up to the statutory maximum *and* to a further fine of £50 per day for each day the offence continues after conviction. On indictment, a custodial sentence of up to two years, a fine or both may be imposed.

TRADE EFFLUENT

Trade effluent, as described above, is subject to controls according to the nature of the process from which it is generated *and* the nature of the effluent. Three basic situations may exist:

— processes subject to Integrated Pollution Control (IPC);

— trade premises, not subject to IPC, which discharge "special category effluent"; and

— trade premises, not subject to IPC, and which do not discharge "special category effluent".

The *general* conditions relating to trade effluent apply to *all* three groups and require a formal consent to be obtained from the relevant undertaker.

Trade Effluent Consents

Offences

The occupier of *any* trade premises in the area of a sewerage undertaker may discharge *any* trade effluent into public sewers providing the appropriate discharge consent is in place (section 118 WIA 1991). Discharge without such a consent is an offence for which the *occupier* of the premises is liable on summary conviction to a fine not exceeding the statutory maximum, or on indictment to a fine. Unlike the provisions for domestic effluent, these measures do not include an additional daily fine for continued non compliance. More importantly from the point of view of corporate liability, is the fact that the offence is committed by the *occupier* and not the owner, unless this is the same person. This is clearly of benefit to an owner whose property is occupied by tenants and lessees, and the position is less uncertain than in relation to contaminated land and the pollution of controlled waters, below.

Application for Consent

Under section 111 of the 1991 Act, either the owner or the occupier of the trade premises may make an application for the consent, which must state:

— the nature or composition of the trade effluent;

— the maximum quantity of trade effluent which it is proposed to discharge in any one day; and

— the maximum proposed rate of discharge.

When an undertaking generates a range of effluents from its operations, a separate application will be required for each discrete point of discharge. Provided the proposed discharge does not contain a "special category effluent" as defined in section 138 of the Act, the sewerage undertaker may accept or reject the application without further reference.

Conditions of Consent

A major concern of the sewerage undertaker is its *own* liability for discharges from its treatment works under current UK and EU legislation, notably the Urban Waste Water Directive, 91/271/EEC, implemented through the 1994 Regulations for Urban Waste Water Treatment, SI 194/2841 (for England and Wales) and SI 1994/2842 (for Scotland). Consequently, the composition and volume of the effluent that it receives must be compatible with the ability of its sewage works to treat it commercially and satisfy the discharge and waste disposal criteria imposed. The disposal of sewage slurry is a particular problem, for the Urban Waste

Water Directive will result in its generation in greater quantities (through increased processing of raw sewage) and prohibit its dumping at sea, yet disposal on agricultural land will be limited by the measures resulting from the EU's "nitrate" and drinking water Directives.

Although the undertaker may not specify that pre-discharge treatment plant is installed by its customers, the terms of a consent may be such that, in order to meet the criteria set, such plant is necessary. Under section 121(1), the consent may include conditions with respect to:

— which receiving sewer(s) the discharge is made to;

— the nature or composition of the effluent;

— the maximum daily rate; and

— the maximum hourly rate.

In addition, a number of other conditions may be specified, including, *inter alia*:

— the periods of the day when discharge is permitted;

— an exclusion relating to *all* condensing waters;

— the elimination or diminution of any specific component prior to discharge; and

— the temperature and pH at the time of discharge.

Contravention of consent conditions is an offence which attracts the same penalties as those for discharging effluent in the absence of a consent. Charges for discharge are generally based upon the "Mogden Formula", details of which are given in Table 4-3 on page 183.

Appeals and Variation to Consents
For all applications "duly made" to the sewerage undertaker, the applicant has a right of appeal to the Director General of Water Services (OFWAT) against the refusal of a consent, the failure to grant a consent within two months or in respect of any condition attached to such a consent (section 122, WIA 1991).

In the first two circumstances, the Director General may grant a conditional or unconditional consent and for the third he may, after reviewing *all* the consent conditions (not just those under appeal), annul any specific condition or substitute "any other set of conditions, whether more or less favourable to the appellant". Any such direction is considered in law as if it was made by the relevant sewerage undertaker. There is also a further recourse to the High Court on points of law.

Sewerage undertakers may vary the conditions of a consent within certain limits (section 124) but they have no powers to revoke consents (c.f. powers of the Environment Agency, referred to elsewhere). Variations may not be made within two years of the date on which the consent was set, unless the variation is made with the consent of the owner *and* the occupier of the trade premises in question (section 124(3)) or if the undertaker considers it necessary to do so "to provide proper protection for persons likely to be affected by the discharges".

Public Involvement
Unlike the provisions for controlled waters, below, there is less opportunity for the involvement of the general public, who have no rights to be informed of an application for a consent, or in relation to the granting of consents, or appeals. However, all consents, variations, agreements and directions by the sewerage undertaker or the Director General must be placed on a public register held by the sewerage undertaker. These do not contain details of any samples taken but this may be justified in part by the absence of the right to private prosecution for breaches of consent, except by "persons aggrieved" or with the consent of the Attorney-General.

Further restrictions are imposed on the use of information recorded in the registers and section 206(1) WIA 1991 prohibits the disclosure of *any* information furnished under section 196, section 204 and Chapter II of Part IV of the Act, except under specific circumstances. This effectively prevents "common interest groups" from publishing any information legally retrieved from the public registers.

Special Category Effluent

Additional controls are imposed on discharges which are defined under section 138 WIA 1991 as "special category effluent", which may arise if:

— prescribed substances are present in the effluent, or are present in prescribed concentrations; or

— the effluent is generated by a prescribed process, or from a process using prescribed substances or using prescribed substances in excess of prescribed amounts.

Effluent from processes subject to central control (i.e. Integrated Pollution

Control) is *not* classified as "special category effluent", even though it may fulfil the same compositional criteria, since the IPC authorisation process itself addresses these issues.

The concept of "special category effluent" allows the Secretary of State to give effect to EU Directives on pollution caused by the discharge of dangerous substances to the aquatic environment (76/464/EEC) and on the prevention and reduction of environmental pollution by asbestos (87/217/ EEC), and to reduce discharges of "Red List" substances to the North Sea, as agreed by the UK at the North Sea Conferences of 1984, 1987 and 1990. These obligations are effected through the Trade Effluent (Prescribed Processes and Substances) Regulations 1989, SI 1989/1156, as amended by SI 1992/339. The Regulations define two groups of effluent:

— Schedule 1, in which the effluent contains "Red List" substances, listed in Table 4-4 (page 184), in concentrations which exceed "background" levels; and

— Schedule 2, relating to effluent produced from listed processes, where it contains concentrations of asbestos or chloroform in excess of "background" concentrations.

Where "special category effluent" criteria are met, the sewerage undertaker has a duty to refer the application to the Environment Agency for a determination on whether the relevant discharge should be prohibited or whether any specific conditions should be imposed (section 120 WIA 1991). Provided the undertaker does not intend to refuse the application, the referral to the Agency must be made within two months and they themselves must make the determination of the application within a further two months. Other aspects of the procedures concerning "special category effluent" are contained in sections 127 and 130.

Processes Subject to Integrated Pollution Control

Whilst the granting of an authorisation to operate a "Part A" process under Part I EPA 1990 and the regulation of the attendant concentrations and volumes of effluent is the responsibility of the Environment Agency or SEPA, a discharge from these processes cannot be made to a sewer until the appropriate consent has been obtained from the relevant undertaker. The criteria employed for assessing the effluent from IPC processes are based upon the same EU Directives and international agreement as "special category effluent", although in this case the relevant enabling legislation is contained within the Environmental Protection (Prescribed Processes and Substances) Regulations 1991, SI 1991/472, as amended (see Tromans[1] for comprehensive list of amendments).

Pre-treatment of Trade Effluent

An alternative to the direct discharge of trade effluent to the sewerage system is to undertake some form of pre-treatment. This may be a direct requirement of the Environment Agency (to meet IPC criteria), an indirect requirement of the sewerage undertaker in order to meet consent criteria, or the decision of the organisation concerned that this is the best option for reducing its effluent charges. A number of physical, chemical and biological techniques are available and even relatively unsophisticated processes, such as primary sedimentation, can significantly reduce the content of the hazardous material suspended or in solution within the effluent. However, such processes are not without their own capital and operational costs and in general will be subject to the requirements of the Waste Licensing Regulations 1994, SI 1994/1056, as amended, or those of Integrated Pollution Control (see Chapter 13).

PROTECTION OF CONTROLLED WATERS

Range of Instruments Employed

The statutory control of water pollution has a long history within the UK and the format of the "general pollution offence" of section 85 of the Water Resources Act 1991 (WRA) is not dissimilar to that of section 2 of the Rivers Pollution Prevention Act 1876, viz:

> "Every person who puts or causes to put or to fall, or knowingly permits to be put or to fall or to be carried into any stream, so as either singly or in combination with other similar acts of the same or any other persons to interfere with its flow, or to pollute its waters ... shall be deemed to have committed an offence."

Howarth states (*Utilities Law Review* [1990] 105) that despite the principle criminal offence relating to the pollution of a watercourse being one of strict liability, as determined in *Alphacell v Woodward*, the criminal law pre-1989 was inappropriately formulated to protect the water environment. "Causing or knowingly permitting any poisonous, noxious or polluting matter or any solid waste matter to enter any controlled waters" has invariably been understood to apply to distinct pollution incidents with discrete escapes occurring over a relatively short time period from

---

[1]   *The Environment Acts 1990-1995, 3rd Edition*, S Tromans, M Nash and M Poustie, Sweet & Maxwell, 1996, pages 787-789.

identifiable point sources, and many incidents, such as the run-off of fertiliser or herbicide, escaped prosecution.

Significant changes in the mechanisms of control were introduced as a result of the Water Act 1989 and truly preventative measures began to be incorporated into the legislative process alongside the more traditional "command and control" instruments employed earlier. The Act extended the criminal law from the direct act of causing pollution to a range of causative activities which often precede pollution. The legislation relating to this new "precautionary" approach is in three main forms:

— regulation of the possession of potentially polluting substances (section 110 Water Act 1989, now section 92 Water Resources Act 1991);

— regulation of land use in areas designated as "water protection zones" (section 111 Water Act 1989, now section 93 Water Resources Act 1991);

— restriction of the use of nitrate fertilisers in "nitrate sensitive areas" where the resultant pollution can contaminate drinking water supplies (section 112 Water Act 1989, now section 94 Water Resources Act 1991).

Whilst these measures undoubtedly reflected the change in attitude towards water pollution, it should not be overlooked that very similar powers existed in section 31(4) and (5) of the Control of Pollution Act 1974, although they were never exercised.

The role of the NRA must be acknowledged, both in its attitude to the enforcement of the legislation and in its development of water quality objectives under its powers in sections 82-84 of the Water Resources Act 1991. Although it might be argued that some of these measures were prompted by EU initiatives, the NRA was proactive in these and UK requirements and in the development of an integrated, forward-looking policy towards the improvement of water standards.

In addition to these strictly legislative measures for the prevention of pollution, the use of advisory instruments, such as Codes of Practice and education, and of financial instruments such as subsidies and taxes has also played an important role.

Statutory Water Quality Objectives

Central both to the establishment of discharge consents and to the preventative measures in sections 93 and 94 of the Water Resources Act

1991, is the concept of statutory water quality objectives. The traditional British approach to the control of water pollution has been to concentrate on the environmental impact of pollutants, rather than the use of uniform emission standards or limit values as in other Member States. The benefits of this approach were argued by the UK in relation to the Dangerous Substances Directive, 76/464/EEC, but a *formal* water quality classification was not drawn up until 1978. Furthermore, it was not until after the decision by the European Court of Justice in *Commission v Belgium* that the UK government was forced to introduce a mechanism for establishing statutory water quality objectives in the Water Act 1989, in order to replace the existing administrative measures. However, it was 1994 before the formal measures were brought in establishing the first statutory water quality objectives, through the Surface Waters (River Ecosystem) (Classification) Regulations 1994 (SI 1994/1057).

These provisions, now included in sections 82-84 of the Water Resources Act 1991, require that the Secretary of State establishes standards for the classification of waters and establishes water quality objectives for each stretch of controlled waters. The water classification Regulations made under section 82 are based upon mandatory standards laid down in EU Directives, viz:

— *Inland Waters:* Directive 57/440 Surface Waters for Drinking – Surface Waters (Classification) Regulations 1989, SI 1989/1148;

— *Bathing Waters:* Directive 76/160 Bathing Waters – Bathing Waters (Classification) Regulations 1991, SI 1991/1597;

— *Dangerous Substances:* Directive 76/464 Dangerous Substances in Water and its "daughter" Directives – Surface Waters (Dangerous Substances) (Classification) Regulations 1989 and 1992, SI 1989/ 2286 and 1992/337,

and are incorporated in the water quality objectives where appropriate. Although nature conservation is not currently included as a goal of the statutory water quality objectives, it is intended that this will be added "once a generally acceptable means of setting objectives designed to promote conservation can be agreed" (*Hansard HL*, vol. 508, col. 183, 23 May 1989).

Within this framework, the Environment Agency and SEPA are under a duty to achieve and maintain the statutory water quality objectives "so far as is practicable". Although the water quality objectives are integral to both the setting of discharge consents and the establishment of water protection and nitrate sensitive zones, no direct reference is made to them in Chapters

II and III of Part III of the Act. Their importance results from the duty placed upon the Agencies to maintain these standards, an important corollary of which is that it effectively obliges it to develop a national policy on water pollution.

Regulation of the Possession of Potentially Polluting Substances

Under section 92 WRA 1991, the Secretary of State may make provisions which prohibit, or permit only under prescribed conditions, a person from having in his custody or control "any poisonous, noxious, or polluting matter", in order to prevent or control the entry of such materials into any controlled waters. While this powerful instrument has may potential applications in the control of environmentally harmful materials such as oils and chemicals, to date it has only been used in the Control of Pollution (Silage, Slurry, Agricultural Fuel Oil) Regulations 1991, SI 1991/324, as amended by SI 1996/2044, which makes it an offence, *inter alia*, to contravene the standards set. These Regulations state performance standards rather than giving explicit design standards and thus permit a degree of discretion. However, their requirements are quite specific and leave little doubt as to what is to be achieved.

While there is a specific offence related to the incorrect storage of *agricultural* fuel oil in quantities over 1,500 litres, there are no parallel provisions relating to the storage of oil for *industrial* applications and reliance is placed on the non-statutory guidance notes. The setting of statutory design standards for industrial oil storage is a simple, straightforward way of avoiding serious pollution incidents, which currently account for ~25% of all substantiated incidents in England and Wales and result in an annual expenditure of £500,000 for clean-up by the Environment Agency alone.

It seems incredible that the powers to introduce such Regulations were available under the Control of Pollution Act from 1984 and, despite government promises to introduce measures "at an early point", no action was taken until recently. However, a consultation paper has now been issued by the DoE proposing controls very similar to those for agricultural fuel oil and covering all industrial, commercial and institutional premises storing mineral oils used for power or heat generation, synthetic lubricating and hydraulic oils, and waste oils derived from these products.

Some sites such as those subject to IPC and individual, above-ground tanks serving domestic premises will be exempt, as will tanks holding less than 1,500 litres. From the draft, the DoE appear unwilling to include petrol storage facilities, despite their acknowledged risk as a "significant polluter".

The paper states that bringing petrol within the Regulations would be "a major extension of control" and would affect 17,000 retail sites, as well as 9,000 other non-retail sites operated by haulage companies and other fleet owning organisations.

Although Regulations made under section 92 of the Water Resources Act 1991 clearly have a strong preventative element, they perhaps have a closer affinity to the Duty of Care Regulations in section 34 of the Environmental Protection Act 1990 than to the other preventative measures of sections 93-94 of the Water Resources Act 1991. Furthermore, such Regulations are directed towards the control of pollutants rather than the improvement of water quality and as such are made without reference to local conditions.

Protection of Specific Areas

The powers contained in sections 93 and 94 of the Water Resources Act 1991 provide a mechanism for protecting specific, sensitive areas and for combating non-point discharges such as pesticide or fertiliser run-off. A particularly useful feature is the ability of the Secretary of State to select *any* area for particular protection and thus establish a "local law" within a given zone with regard to water pollution. There is also the facility to make different provisions for different persons and for different circumstances.

Although it has been suggested that there is no reason nitrate pollution could not have been tackled through the water protection zones mechanism, the measures in these two sections of the Act differ in three fundamental aspects and as such their drafting as separate issues is perhaps more satisfactory. These differences are:

— water protection zones are restricted to prohibiting and limiting activities, whereas nitrate sensitive areas may require positive action to be taken (section 94(3)(c));

— a mechanism for financial compensation is detailed in section 94(3)(b) in respect of the obligations arising from the designation of the land as a nitrate sensitive area, but no *formal* mechanism exists in relation to water protection zones.;

— the Minister of Agriculture, Fisheries and Food makes the designation of nitrate sensitive areas, rather than the Secretary of State for the Environment (in England) in the case of water protection zones. Both require the consent of the Treasury and, depending upon the terms of the order, the operation of a nitrate sensitive area may involve both MAFF and DoE.

Water Protection Zones

Although there has been strong opposition by agricultural interests to both water protection zones and nitrate sensitive areas, to date only the latter have been used in relation to agricultural pollution. Both sections 93 and 94 are concerned with the protection of *areas* which are particularly vulnerable to water pollution, rather than the control of polluting *substances*. The problems associated with the establishment of the first water protection zone – the River Dee catchment area – give an indication of the issues to be addressed in such measures. The vulnerability of the River Dee catchment area has long been known and results from two factors:

— industrial pollution upstream from major population centres; and

— the lack of bank-side storage facilities of the four water companies abstracting water from the river, thus making the supply of water vulnerable in the event of a major spillage.

A risk assessment modelling exercise was undertaken by the NRA in order to identify the potentially polluting activities and a consultative document was issued containing the following proposals:

— the requirement of NRA's consent for the storage of chemicals within the catchment zone;

— the need for a quantitative risk assessment to be undertaken in cases where a potential threat had been identified, and a demonstration that the risk was "as low as reasonably practicable (ALARP)";

— precautionary measures to be taken where the risk was shown not "ALARP".

It was estimated that the scheme would require companies in the Wrexham and Chester area to spend at least £4 million on precautions to prevent spillage.

Nitrate Sensitive Areas

There has been significantly greater activity in the designation of nitrate sensitive areas than water protection zones. This has been prompted by a number of underlying EU Directives – Quality of Surface Water Abstracted for Drinking, 75/440/EEC; Drinking Water, 80/778/EEC; Protection of Waters affected by Nitrate Pollution from Agricultural Sources, 91/676/EEC; and Urban Waste Water Directive, 91/271/EEC – and the decision against the UK in the European Court of Justice following the failure in 28 regions of the UK to meet the target of 50 mg/litre set by the Drinking Water Directive, 80/778/EEC (*Commission v United Kingdom*, case 337/89).

Under sections 94 and 95 of the Act, it is possible to have three types of nitrate sensitive area although, in practice, designations can be a combination of all three. The three basic options are:

— *voluntary areas, section 95(2) and (3):* Management agreements may be entered into voluntarily by farmers in return for compensation;

— *mandatory areas without compensation, section 94(3)(a) and (4)(a):* Specific activities may be required, prohibited or restricted. Consents may be required and contraventions sanctioned by criminal offences;

— *mandatory areas with compensation, section 94(3)(b):* Here, provisions may be included for paying compensation to farmers affected by the resulting obligations,

although in practice, nitrate sensitive areas have been introduced in two forms:

— *nitrate sensitive areas (NSAs)*, participation in which is voluntary and for which the participant farmers receive financial compensation;

— *nitrate vulnerable zones (NVZs)*, which are mandatory and for which compensation is not given.

DISCHARGES TO CONTROLLED WATERS

While the above preventative measures represent an important part of the overall strategy in the protection of controlled waters, a major part of the enforcement activities of the Environment Agency is directed towards the regulation of direct discharges. Whereas the emphasis of the controls imposed on discharges to sewers is on the protection of the assets and infrastructure of the system and their operation, the regulation of controlled waters is concerned with the quality of the receiving waters as a result of both direct discharges and other polluting events. Although the unrestricted flow of rivers and streams and the pollution of the river bed are aspects of these controls, in practice they do not play a major part.

The formulation of the pollution-related offences within the 1991 Water Resources Act is of practical importance to the enforcement strategy adopted by the Agency and significant changes have occurred as a result of statutory legislation and its interpretation in the courts, notably in *Wychavon v NRA* and *Attorney-General's Reference (No 1 of 1994)*. As a consequence of section 31(2)(e) of the Control of Pollution Act 1974, there were two distinct offences associated with the pollution of controlled waters – the breach of a discharge consent (section 32(1)) and pollution through specific incidents (section 31(1)). However, this distinction was removed in the Water Act 1989, making it possible for the regulator to prosecute on the basis of *either* a breach of a consent *or* the "general pollution offence" of "causing or knowingly permitting". This change introduced a degree of flexibility to prosecution policy and in view of the evidential problems in proving a breach of consent – primarily as a result of the requirement for tripartite sampling – the general offence was more frequently used. Nevertheless, the choice of which party to prosecute, particularly in cases involving the repair and maintenance of sewerage systems by contractors, and which limb of the "causing" and "knowingly permitting" offence to employ, continued to be problematic. These issues appear to be becoming resolved as a result of the ruling in *Attorney-General's Reference (No 1 of 1994)* and the changes introduced in section 111 of the Environment Act 1995, q.v.

The principal pollution offences under the Water Resources Act 1991 are contained within Chapter II of Part II, and section 85 establishes five separate but not necessarily exclusive offences, viz:

— causing or knowingly permitting *poisonous, noxious or polluting matter*, or *any solid waste* to enter *any* controlled waters (section 85(1)) – the "general pollution offence";

— causing or knowingly permitting pollution of controlled waters by *any matter* other than trade or sewage effluent, in contravention of a section 86 prohibition notice or Regulation (section 85(2));

— causing or knowingly permitting any trade or sewage effluent to be discharged into controlled waters, or through a pipe into the sea outside the seaward limit of controlled waters [of England and Wales] (section 85(3));

— causing or knowingly permitting any trade or sewage effluent to be discharged in contravention of a section 86 prohibition notice or Regulation, from a building or from any fixed plant:

— onto or into any land;

— into any waters of a lake or pond which are not inland fresh waters (section 85(4)); and

— causing or knowingly permitting *any matter whatever* to enter inland freshwater so as to tend, either directly or in combination with other matter which he or another person causes or permits [note: absence of "knowingly"] to enter those waters, to impede the flow of the waters in a manner leading, or likely to lead to *substantial* aggravation of:

— pollution due to other causes; or

— the consequences of such pollution (section 85(5)).

As with other "high profile" environmental offences, these carry severe penalties (up to three months' imprisonment, a fine of up to £20,000 or both on summary conviction; two years' imprisonment, an unlimited fine or both on indictment). In contrast to waste offences, the practice of the courts has been to award high fines rather than to impose custodial sentences.

The principal defence to section 85 offences is that the discharge was made under and in accordance with one of the statutory provisions listed in section 88, e.g. an IPC authorisation, a waste management licence or any local statutory provision which confers the power to make the discharge. Other defences are contained in section 89 and include, *inter alia*:

— the discharge was made in an emergency in order to avoid danger to life and health, *and* all reasonably practicable steps were taken to prevent/ minimise the discharge *and* its polluting effect, *and* the Agency was informed as soon as reasonably practicable (section 89(1));

— the trade or sewage effluent was from a vessel (section 89(2));

— the discharge was permitted by a relevant person to come from a mine abandoned prior to 31st December 1999 (section 89(3), (3A-3C));

— the deposit was a solid waste from a mine or quarry, provided that the relevant consent was held, no other site for the deposit was available, and all reasonably practicable steps were taken (section 89(4)).

Specific provisions are made for the purpose of determining the liability of sewerage undertakers in relation to discharges made from sewers and sewerage works (section 87). Even where the sewerage undertaker did not cause or knowingly permit a discharge which results in an infraction of the legislation, it is nevertheless *deemed* to have caused the discharge *if* this was the result of matter in the sewage which it was bound to receive into the sewer or sewerage works (section 87(1A)). Where two sewerage undertakers are involved in such an incident, it is the "upstream" undertaker *only* who is deemed to have caused the offence (section 87(1B), (1C)).

Provided the undertaker "was *bound* ... to receive [the effluent] into the sewer" the law considers that he is responsible for ensuring that the operations, for which he has the operational control, do not cause pollution. Only in cases in which the discharges are not lawfully made into its sewers will the undertaker have a defence against the strict liability of these provisions (section 87(2)) – see *NRA v Yorkshire Water Services*.

In addition to section 85, further offences are created within section 90 with respect to the cutting of vegetation and the removal of accumulated deposits from the bottom of streams, rivers, etc. where this is undertaken without the consent of the Environment Agency and results in these materials remaining within the water or in suspension within the water.

Consents for Discharges to Controlled Waters

Within the Water Resources Act 1991, the term "discharge consent" means "a consent ... for any discharge or description of discharges as is given for the purposes of section 88(1)(a) ... either on application for a consent, or by virtue of paragraph [6] of schedule 10 to this Act, without such an application having been made." Thus, under section 91(8) the Environment Agency may issue a consent in the absence of an application where it considers that a discharge would be a contravention of section 85(3) or a prohibition under section 86.

A separate consent is required for each discharge and the applicant is expected to give details of the location of the discharge and other relevant information (e.g. its nature, composition, temperature, flow, quantity). This notice is made publicly available through local newspapers and the London Gazette, and local authorities and relevant water undertakers are given copies of the application. An application under Schedule 10, para. 1(7) may be made to the Secretary of State to grant a certificate of exemption from these and the public register provisions (section 190) where he considers the information to be contrary to the public interest or to unreasonably prejudice commercial information. However, publicity is not mandatory if the Environment Agency considers that the discharge will have "no appreciable effect" on the receiving waters and some guidance on this is given in DoE Circular 17/84. This suggests a number of tests, the most important of which is that there is "no appreciable effect" where there is less than a 10% increase in "all relevant parameters", unless some significant environmental amenity is affected.

The system of consents for the discharge of substances to controlled waters has recently been modified by the introduction of the Control of Pollution (Applications, Appeals and Registers) Regulations 1996, SI 1996/2971, which replaced three sets of Regulations: the Control of Pollution (Consents for Discharges, etc.) (Secretary of State's Functions) Regulations 1989, SI 1989/1151; the Control of Pollution (Discharges by the NRA) Regulations 1989, SI 1989/1157; and the Control of Pollution (Registers) Regulations 1989, SI 1989/1160. The new Regulations simplify the procedure for advertising applications for consents and modifications, and mirror those for IPC authorisations. Time limits and procedures for appeals against Agency decisions on consents, revocation and enforcement notices, and exclusion of information from public registers are laid down. In addition, the modifications abolish the public's right to make representations to the Secretary of State to call in a consent application.

In addition to the *application* for a consent to the Environment Agency (Schedule 10, para. 1), the Agency may *issue* a consent in the absence of an application if it appears to them that a person has caused or permitted effluent or other matter to be discharged contrary to sections 85(3) or 86 of the Act (Schedule 10, para. 6). In the case of discharges made by the Environment Agency itself, the application is made directly to the Secretary of State (Schedule 10, para. 5).

Charging Scheme

The charging scheme introduced by the NRA in July 1991, under its powers of section 131 WRA 1991, differed in a number of fundamental aspects from that for trade effluent. It was based upon the cost-recovery of the regulator's *actual* costs in relation to the administration, regulation and monitoring of discharges. The system is uniform across England and Wales and is based upon the product of a national cost rate and each of three banded weighting factors from the *consented* discharge volume, discharge content and category of the receiving waters (Table 4-5, pages 185-186). The present scheme cannot be regarded as an effective economic instrument for pollution control, since there is no specific surcharge for "Red List" substances and the receiving water weighting factor operates in a counter-productive manner, favouring discharges made to the most sensitive waters (i.e. groundwater) and discouraging discharges to the least sensitive (i.e. estuarial waters).

Consent Conditions

A former feature of discharge consents was that they were not limited to discharges made by a particular person and were specific only to the discharge itself (Schedule 10, para. 2(6)). This reflected the position for trade effluent discharges and enabled the same consent to be used by new owners, tenants or lessees.

However, paragraph 21 of Schedule 23 to the Environment Act 1995 introduced important changes relating to the way that consents to discharge to controlled waters are held. After 1st October 1996, the discharge consent can only be relied upon by a *person* who has given notice prior to that date to the Environment Agency that they intend so to do. In addition, the transfer of a discharge consent must be notified to the Agency within 21 days and an offence is committed where this is not undertaken.

These modifications create a system of *personal* discharge consents, in place of the former scheme whereby a discharge consent was available to *anyone* discharging pursuant to it, and not just to the holder. Potential problems may arise where there are several dischargers relying upon the same consent, e.g. on a small industrial estate.

Whilst the trade effluent offence relates to the occupier or owner of the premises, the controlled waters provision applies to "a person" and, in combination with these modifications to discharge consents and the "knowingly permitting" offence, the liability of the owner is extended to the activities of *all* those using his site and the associated discharge facilities – contractors, tenants and licensees. This is particularly important in view of the need only to demonstrate constructive knowledge, following the *Schulmans* case described below.

The Agency may grant an application unconditionally, conditionally attaching "such conditions as it may think fit", or refuse it (Schedule 10, para. 2(1)). A non-inclusive, non-specific list of the type of condition which might be applied is given in paragraph 2(5) and, in conjunction with section 111 of the Environmental Protection Act 1995, this provides the Agency with a powerful means of monitoring and controlling discharges.

In addition to the above general application for a consent, section 90A WRA 1991 makes specific provisions for consents for the deposit of solid refuse from a mine or quarry (section 89(4)(a)) and the removal of deposits from the bed of a river or stream (section 90(1)).

Enforcement Notices

Although "enforcement notices" have been available for the control of processes subject to IPC, these were not available for the regulation of water pollution until section 90B was introduced into the WRA 1991 under the 1995 Act. Whilst these are not exactly a *compliance* measure, using Hawkins' terminology,[1] enforcement notices do provide a half-way house alternative to prosecution, in cases of actual or likely contravention of discharge consents.

An enforcement notice may be served on the *holder* of a consent and must state, *inter alia*:

---

[1]   *Environment and Enforcement*, K Hawkins, Clarendon Press, 1984, pages 3-4.

— the matters constituting the actual or anticipated contravention;

— the steps which need to be taken; and

— the time limit for compliance with the notice.

Failure to comply with a notice is subject to severe penalties (section 90B(3)) but where the Agency is of the opinion that such procedures would afford an ineffectual remedy, under section 90B(4) it has the option of taking proceedings in the High Court for the purpose of securing compliance. However, it is necessary to show that the defendant is the appropriate person against whom to take action and, in the absence of an injunction, there would be a continuing non-compliance (*Bradford Metropolitan City Council v Brown*).

Revocation and Variation of Consents

The Environment Agency has a *duty* to review from "time to time" the consents granted under paragraphs 2 and 5 of Schedule 10, and under paragraph 6 has power to:

— revoke the consent;

— modify the conditions within the consent; or

— impose conditions on a previously unconditional consent.

In addition, the Secretary of State *may at any time* direct the Agency to undertake any of the above measures, where it is necessary for him to do so:

— to enable the government to give effect to Community or international obligations;

— for the protection of public health, or fauna and flora dependant upon the aquatic environment; or

— in consequence of any representations or objections made to him or otherwise.

A variation or revocation by the Agency cannot be made sooner than the minimum time stated within the consent (generally two years) without the consent of the discharger. This applies even in cases in which the discharger was in breach of a consent or the discharge contains a new pollutant not covered in the consent conditions. Where a direction is made within the time limit, on the grounds of public health or fauna and flora protection, the Agency must compensate the consent holder.

Appeals

Under section 91 WRA, there is a right of appeal in respect of any of the regulatory functions of the Agency relating to discharge consents, including the refusal of an application, the imposition of specific conditions or time limitations, their modification or revocation, or the issue of an enforcement notice. The Secretary of State may, under section 114 of the Environment Act 1995, delegate his functions of determining appeals under a number of environmental provisions, including sections 43, 91, 92, 161C and 191B(5) WRA, to *any person* he appoints to act on his behalf, and to refer such matters to that person.

The powers of the Secretary of State, or his delegate, for hearing appeals are dependent upon which aspect of the consent is under appeal and these are detailed in sections 91(2A) to (2K).

ANTI-POLLUTION WORKS AND OPERATIONS

Discretionary powers are now available to the Environment Agency through section 161 of the Water Resources Act which permits it to undertake "works and operations" to prevent polluting matter entering controlled waters and to remedy/mitigate the effects resulting from pollution, including the restoration of the fauna and flora dependent upon the aquatic environment in question.

When first introduced in the WRA 1991, there was a reluctance on the part of the NRA to use these powers since:

— a large outlay was required for the majority of incidents;

— funding was not available from central government for:

    — financing the initial outlay; or

    — any shortfall caused where the polluter was impecunious or could not be found or identified; and

— there was the possibility of a conflict in the NRA's role, if it was both undertaking clean-up operations and also acting in a regulatory capacity.

These shortcomings were overcome by a series of modifications through Schedule 22 to the Environment Act 1995 which, *inter alia,* gave powers to the Environment Agency:

— to undertake investigations to establish the source of contaminants in controlled waters, the person who had caused or knowingly permitted them to be present and the place from which it was likely that they entered the waters;

— to issue a "works notice" to the person who was, or in its opinion was, responsible for "causing" or "knowingly permitting" the polluting matter to be present. Such notices may require specific action to be taken, viz:

— removing or disposing of the source of the contamination;

— remedying or mitigating any pollution caused; and

— restoring the waters, *including the fauna and flora*, as far as is reasonably practicable.

By putting the onus on the alleged polluter, many of the difficulties in the existing financial and operational procedure have been overcome. An appeal against a "works notice" may be made to the Secretary of State, if made within 21 days of the service of the notice, and he has the power to confirm the notice, with or without modification, or to quash it.

Non-compliance with a "works notice" is an offence under section 161D(1), and carries the same sanctions as failure to comply with an enforcement notice, *supra*. In addition, failure to comply with *any* of the requirements of the notice may result in the Agency undertaking the necessary work and recovering its costs or expenses.

"CAUSING" AND "KNOWINGLY PERMITTING"

The terms "causing" and "knowingly permitting" are frequently employed in UK legislation and in the present context their most important usage is in section 85 WRA 1991 in relation to *offences* related to water pollution and in section 78F(2) EPA 1990, as amended, where it is the *primary test* for allocating responsibility in the case of contaminated land. It is also used in EPA 1990 in connection with the deposit of waste (where the offence is *knowingly* causing or knowingly permitting), although to date there has been little contention in this area.

"Causing"

Most of the relevant case law relates to "causing" in the context of water pollution, where *Alphacell v Woodward* is the leading authority. However, the issues involved were considered more recently in *Attorney-General's Reference (No 1 of 1994)* and, in addition to reiterating the judgment in *Alphacell*, the case also clarified a number of issues which have been problematic in its application.

Causation is generally a mixed question of fact and law (as in the *Ann Stathatos* case), and in *Alphacell* the House of Lords decided as a question of law that the wording of the relevant statute implied that knowledge and fault were not relevant to causation. Many of the cases post-*Alphacell* concern questions of fact relating to whether the defendant had "caused" pollution, although in *R v CPC (UK) Ltd* it was noted that identifying, and where necessary delimiting, the relevant question of fact are matters of law.

In *Alphacell*, it was held in relation to the Rivers (Prevention of Pollution) Act 1951 that the subsection of the Act contemplated two things – "causing" and "knowingly permitting": "causing" involves some active operation or chain of operations involving as a result the pollution of the stream; "knowingly permitting" constitutes a failure to prevent the pollution, which failure must be accompanied by knowledge. The word "cause" is to be given its common sense meaning and the concept of *mens rea* was inapplicable to "causing", there being no need to read "knowingly" into section 2(1) of the Act. Consequently, the absence of negligence is irrelevant, although where acts of third parties or natural forces amounting to Acts of God are involved, a riparian owner *may* have a defence under section 2(1) to "causing". Alphacell were found guilty of "causing", essentially as a result of the *location* and *design* of their operations. As long as their activity was intentional, all that needed to be shown was a causal link between that activity and the discharge.

The present position regarding "causing" was summarised by Lord Justice Taylor in *Attorney-General's Reference (No 1 of 1994)* in relation to section 107(1)(c) of the Water Act 1989. From a consideration of *Alphacell*, *NRA v Yorkshire Water Services*, *Price v Cromack* and *Wychavon*, he stated that the following propositions emerge clearly:

— it was a question of fact in each case whether the defendant had caused pollution;

— the word "knowingly" was not to be implied as a qualifying word in the relevant section of the Act;

— the word "causes" was to be given its plain, common sense meaning;

— the word "causes" involved some active participation in the operation or chain of operations resulting from the pollution;

— "mere tacit standing by and looking on" per Lord Widgery in *Price v Cromack* was insufficient to amount to causing.

With regard to this last point, in *Attorney-General's Reference (No 1 of 1994)*, a charge was brought against a sewerage undertaker under the general pollution offence – section 107(1)(a) in the 1989 Act – where it was held that the failure to maintain the pumping system, negligently and/or in breach of a defendant's statutory duty, constituted a positive act or chain of operations sufficient to constitute "causing" within the meaning of the Act. Their Lordships suggested that, while a question phrased in terms of "failure to maintain the system" (i.e. phrased "passively") implied an omission, if it were rephrased as "is running a system in an un-maintained state sufficient to constitute 'causing'?", then the answer should be made in the affirmative.

In addition, it was held that section 107(1)(a) of the Act could be committed by more than one person "where one or more persons executed different and separate acts, and either each of the separate acts contributed to the matter entering the waters or without either of the acts, the material would not have entered the waters". This is of importance, since it addresses an issue, left undecided in *Alphacell*, as to whether a conviction should be upheld if the activities of a defendant were to be regarded as only *a* cause, rather than *the* cause of the pollution (Lord Pearson, at 845). In *R v CPC (UK) Ltd*, it was held that there was no need for the defendant's actions to be the sole cause of pollution and *Attorney-General's Reference (No 1 of 1994)* extended this to include the acts or omissions of more than one person for the same incident of "causing". Although the context of the judgment was in relation to the operations of a sewerage undertaker, of the three questions of law addressed, it is perhaps significant that unlike the other two this did not specifically refer to sewerage undertakers and was primarily concerned with the general pollution offence, section 107(1)(a) of the 1989 Act. This would tend to suggest that their Lordships were considering the broader situation, although further judicial guidance will be needed to clarify this point.

With regard to the broader issues of causation from a number of potential sources, in *Wilsher v Essex Area Health Authority* it was held that the onus of proving causation rested upon the plaintiff and, where there were a number of different factors, causation could not be attributed to a single factor or factors in the absence of evidence to that effect. Their Lordships also noted that it was doubtful whether the Court of Appeal was entitled to resolve a conflict between experts which the judge had left unresolved.

"Knowingly Permitting"

There are two elements to the offence of "knowingly permitting" – the failure to prevent pollution and the knowledge on the part of the defendant, both of which must be satisfied to secure a successful prosecution. Proof of knowledge or *mens rea* is essential and consequently the offence cannot be characterised as one of strict liability. There are clearly evidential problems surrounding the degree of the defendant's knowledge, in addition to uncertainties as to what such knowledge should encompass and, as a result, the regulators appear to have a preference for the charge of "causing". Consequently, much of the case law has been directed towards the consideration of what is, and what is not, "causing" and most judicial statements on "knowingly permitting" in relation to water pollution offences have been made *obiter*, at the conclusion of these cases. Until recently it has been necessary to consider the meanings of "knowingly" and "permitting", either individually or in combination, in other areas of law such as in motoring offences where permitting was often used in the context of giving a person permission or authority to undertake an act, rather than to allow a polluting action to occur.

In *Alphacell*, Lord Salmon stated that the creation of an offence in relation to permitting pollution was probably included in the section (of the Act) so as to deal with the type of case in which a man knows that contaminated effluent is escaping over his land into a river and does nothing at all to prevent it. A more detailed judicial consideration was given to "knowingly permitting" in the context of section 85 of the Water Resources Act in *NRA v Schulmans Incorporated Ltd* and this has provided a better understanding of the phrase, although there are nevertheless some issues still to be explored, *infra*.

Knowledge
In *Alphacell*, where Lord Wilberforce stated that:

" 'Knowingly permitting' ... involves a failure to prevent pollution, which failure, however, must be accompanied by knowledge."

In the *Schulmans* case, the defendants were charged with "knowingly permitting" under section 107(1) of the Water Act and section 4(1) of the Salmon and Fresh Water Fisheries Act 1975, and Leggatt LJ set out the elements of knowledge that would need to be established for a conviction on either charge. These were the defendant's knowledge that:

— a spill had occurred;

— the spill had entered the drainage system;

— the drainage system discharged into the brook; and

— that unless something was done, the spill would soon enter the brook,

and, for the offence under the 1975 Act only,

— the extent of the pollution.

Furthermore, the case also determined that the defendant bears the evidential burden of proof to show that he did not have the requisite knowledge, although the extent of the knowledge required was not defined.

Permitting
In addition to a knowledge of the factors surrounding the pollution incident, the defendant must be in a position to prevent the continuation of the pollution. An important defence in relation to "knowingly permitting" is that no offence will be committed if the defendant could not have prevented the entry or discharge of the polluting material. The courts recognise that there are finite limits to a defendant's ability to prevent pollution but it remains unclear where the boundaries of reasonableness are drawn, particularly in view of the court's attitude to the importance of preventing pollution. Tromans[1] points out that "reasonable steps" does not necessarily equate to any steps which may be scientifically demonstrated to have a remedial or mitigating effect, and may include the exercise of contractual rights to exert legitimate pressure on another party to cease a polluting activity.

Note should also be taken of the comments of Earl Ferrers relating to "knowingly permitting" in the context of contaminated land, *infra.*

WATER LEGISLATION IN SCOTLAND

In Scotland, the principal legislation relating to the pollution of water is contained in Part II of the Control of Pollution Act 1974. Unlike the legislation relating to England and Wales, the provisions for controlled waters and discharges into and from sewers are contained within the same Act, under sections 30B and 30H respectively. The 1974 Act has been subject to a number of amendments since it came into force and addresses most of the pollution issues covered by the Water Industry Act 1991 and the Water Resources Act 1991, including: water quality objectives (section 30C); pollution offences (section 30F); precautionary measures (section 31A); nitrate sensitive areas (section 31B); "works notices" (section 46A); and public registers (section 41).

A consolidated version of Part IA (relating to water pollution resulting from abandoned mines) and Part II (as discussed above) of the 1974 Act is contained in Appendix 4 of Tromans' annotated environmental statutes.[2]

---

[1] *Contaminated Land,* S Tromans and R Turrall-Clarke, Sweet & Maxwell, 1994, page 81.
[2] *The Environment Acts 1990-1995, 3rd Edition*, S Tromans, M Nash and M Poustie, Sweet & Maxwell, 1996.

CONTAMINATED LAND

Corporate Liabilities

In this "stakeholder society", many different groups have an interest in contaminated land, ranging from the "meddlesome busybody" to the "entirely responsible and respected body with a genuine concern for the environment" (Mr Justice Otton's description of Greenpeace in *R v HMIP and MAFF*). In addition to the owner of the land, the possible presence of contamination may affect, *inter alia*:

— occupiers (owners/tenants/lessees);

— owners/occupiers of adjacent land;

— downstream riparian owners;

— employees/those using land;

— contractors/sub-contractors;

— lenders/mortgagees/insurers;

— parties to corporate transactions;

— developers of a site;

— regulators;

— consultants/legal advisors;

— the general public;

— local and national pressure groups,

as the result of statutory provisions, contractual agreements or common law rights. There is a significant body of statutory legislation which may be applied to the different aspects of contaminated land (Table 4-6, pages 187-188) but, in relation to the present discussion, the most pertinent is that which relates to liabilities associated with the resultant pollution of controlled waters and clean-up of land designated as contaminated. In his article "Current Developments and Trends in the Law and Administration of Water Resources" ([1991] 3 *JEL* 69), Burchi notes the link between the use of land resources and the control of water pollution and gives examples of the development of controls in other jurisdictions on the activities which have the potential to influence water quality.

In addition to legislation specific to these issues, there is also statutory legislation and common law rights in which the knowledge of a situation imposes liabilities relating either to a "knowingly permitting" type of offence or to the precautions which need to be imposed to protect the health of relevant persons who might be affected by the presence of the contamination.

As discussed earlier, within Chapter III of Part III of the Water Resources Act 1991 there are a number of essentially preventative measures to control the effects of on-going industrial and agricultural operations. Part II of the Environment Act 1995 modified the Environmental Protection Act 1990 by removing the unused section 61 and section 143 provisions and adding section 78A to 78YC to form a new Part IIA which relates to the clean-up and remediation of contaminated land. This poses a significant threat to land owners in particular for, although the primary responsibility for remediation is borne by the person(s) who caused or permitted the substances or any substances responsible for the contamination to be present (section 78F(2) and (3)), if "after reasonable enquiry" the original polluter cannot be found, then this falls upon the owner or occupier. In many instances of "historical pollution" this will be the case, since it will be difficult to identify with any certainty the original polluter.

The use of "causing" and "knowingly permitting" in Part IIA of the amended 1990 Act differs from that in other legislative measures such as section 85 of the Water Resources Act 1991, since:

— these terms refer to an on-going situation, rather than to an isolated incident or event;

— the circumstances being addressed with regard to contaminated land are the *presence* of a pollutant in, on or under land, whilst for controlled waters it is the *entry* of a pollutant into those waters which is of concern;

— they only act as a "trigger" for the identification for an "appropriate person" (section 78F) and, if this test fails "after reasonable enquiry", the responsibility reverts to the owner or to the "occupier for the time being".

A useful clarification of the meaning of "knowingly permitting" was given by Earl Ferrers, Minister of State for the Environment, who stated "the test of 'knowingly permitting' would require both knowledge that the substances in question were in, on or under the land, and the possession of the power to prevent such a substance being there" (*House of Lords Hansard*, 11 July 1995 col. 1497). Following *Pepper v Hart*, in certain limited circumstances it is permissible to refer to parliamentary debate to establish the meaning of a statute.

Other important features of the provisions are:

— the liability imposed for the escape of contamination onto the land of others (section 78K(1)) differs from that under the rule of *Rylands v Fletcher* following Lord Goff's ruling in *Cambridge*;

— the "pollution" of controlled waters has a meaning in the Act (section 78A(9)) different from that in section 85 Water Resources Act 1991 as interpreted by the rulings in *NRA v Egger* and *R v Dovermoss*;

— the "secondary" effects of chemical or biological reactions, which formed the basis of the action in *Gertsen*, are included in the effects of contamination under the statutory provisions of section 78F(9).

It is important for organisations to bear in mind that the definition of "remediation" in section 78A(7) includes *all* of the stages involved in a clean-up operation, from the initial assessment through to the post-remedial monitoring (but *not* the identification by the LA). However, under section 78H(5)(d) the local authority need not serve a "remediation notice" if it is satisfied that "appropriate things are being, or will be done", although a "remediation statement" must be prepared and published by the organisation.

Contaminated Land and the Environment Act 1995

Although the 1995 Act is often described as a means of dealing with contaminated land, it should be borne on mind that not all land subject to the presence of contaminants will come within its definition of "contaminated land" or "special sites". Furthermore, *direct* action may only be initiated by local authorities or the Environment Agency/SEPA, as appropriate, and access to this legislation by "aggrieved third parties" must be through these official bodies. Pending further initiatives from the EU on civil liability for environmental damage, the common law provides the only means by which third parties may take action themselves.

It seems ironic that an Act, which on one hand attempts to rationalise the approach to waste management through the incorporation of the 83 WRAs within the Environment Agency, fosters a disparate approach to the complex issue of contaminated land by placing the majority of the responsibility in this area in the hands of the various local authorities. While these may be operating within the same guidelines, the vigour with which they pursue their duties will be dependent upon local influences and the funding and local expertise which are available.

Part IIA of the amended Environmental Protection Act 1990 places the primary responsibility for identifying contaminated land with the local authorities, who have a duty under section 87B(1) to inspect their area "from time to time". The responsibilities of the local authority relate to the contamination of land and water *within* their area and, under section 78X of the 1995 Act, this includes pollution resulting from *outside* their area. Similarly, the combined effects of two or more sites may be taken into consideration.

There have been a number of delays to the implementation of the Part IIA provisions of the Act, *inter alia* as a result of the many suggested amendments following the consultations on the draft guidance, *infra*, and from a review of these proposals after the May 1997 general election. With regard to the latter, the Labour Party policy document *In Trust for Tomorrow* contained two features which might be included in the revised guidance, viz:

— whether to introduce a "foreseeability" defence in relation to the liability for contaminated sites; and

— whether to introduce "completion certificates" for remediated sites which would give land owners or occupiers some degree of immunity against future claims.

It now seems likely that new proposals for this guidance will not be available until late 1997 (HC Written Answers, 21 May 197, Cols. 84-5) and, allowing for their introduction by means of the negative resolution procedure, they will not come into effect before early 1998.

Contaminated Land within the 1995 Act

Within the Act, three categories of land are envisaged:

— "contaminated land", which is land responsible for causing *significant* harm, or with the potential to do so, and for which the local authorities have the regulatory responsibility;

— "special sites", which are land designated as such under section 78C and the attendant Regulations (to be issued) and come within the remit of the Environment Agency/SEPA. A working draft of the "special site" Regulations is contained in Appendix A of the Consultation Document on Contaminated Land issued in September 1996; and

— land which falls within neither category and is not covered by the Act and also land which is excluded by the Act from these categories.

The definition of "contaminated land" is given in section 78A as being land which appears to the authority to be in such a condition, by reason of substances in, on, or under it that either:

— significant harm is being caused, or there is a significant possibility of such harm being caused; or

— pollution of controlled waters is being caused or is likely to be caused.

"Harm" means harm to the health of living organisms, interference with the ecological systems of which they form a part and in the case of man includes harm to his property. The pollution of controlled waters does not have to be "significant" but this is tempered by the cost-benefit approach required by section 78E(4) and (5). Under section 78A(8), controlled waters are "affected by contaminated land if, and only if, it appears to the enforcing authority that the contaminated land in question is in such a condition by reason of substances in, on, or under the land, that pollution of those waters is being, or is likely to be caused."

Guidance on the Contaminated Land Provisions

Under section 78YA, the Secretary of State has the power to issue guidance on the contaminated land provisions, and the document *Consultation on the Draft Statutory Guidance on Contaminated Land, Volumes 1 and 2* was issued in September 1996. The final version will be issued in a joint DoE/Welsh Office Circular and will provide *statutory* guidance, having as its main contents three annexes, viz:

— Annex A: Statutory Guidance

— Annex B: Procedural Description of Part IIA, EPA 1990

— Annex C: Bibliography of Government Publications on Contaminated Land.

The guidance given will be quite detailed and Annex A will comprise the following chapters:

I: The Inspection of Contaminated Land – section 78A(2) and section 78B(2);

II: The Definition of Contaminated Land – section 78A(2), (5) and (6);

III: The Remediation of Contaminated Land – section 78E(5);

IV: The Exclusion from, and Apportionment of, Liabilities for the costs of Remediation of Contaminated Land – section 78F(6) and (7); and

V: The Recovery of Costs of Remediation – section 78P(2).

Within the document, the guidance is subject to an hierarchy of authority and that issued under sections 78A, 78B and 78F is *mandatory*. As a consequence, this material is subject to the parliamentary negative resolution procedure and if, within 40 days of the draft guidance being laid before Parliament either House votes against it, then it may not be issued.

The second tier in the hierarchy of guidance is that issued under sections 78E and 78P and, whilst it is not mandatory, the local authorities must "have regard" to it. The final tier is descriptive and is designed to assist the local authorities in their interpretation of the guidance.

In addition to the above statutory guidance, Regulations will be issued on a number of related issues, including:

— Land required to be designated as a special site;

— Remediation notices;

— Appeals against remediation notices;

— Compensation for granting of rights;

— Remediation registers,

and the overall policy intentions in each of these areas are given in Annex D of the Consultation Document.

At the time of writing, the consultation process was still in progress and a number of the significant amendments to the draft had been urged by the Commons Environmental Committee, following substantial criticisms by a number of groups including the Local Authority Association, the United Kingdom Environmental Law Association and the Royal Institute of Chartered Surveyors (Session 1996/7, 2nd Report, *Contaminated Land*). The proposed amendments include: the introduction of a one year gap between the preparation of the LA strategies and the completion of initial inspections so as to avoid blighting land; clean-up liabilities being determined by compulsory arbitration; the means of addressing sites which cause water pollution; and closing the "statutory gap" which will curtail local authorities' powers to deal with less polluted sites causing a statutory nuisance.

As noted earlier, a further issue for consideration is whether to introduce a "foreseeability" defence and "completion certificates" (see *ENDS Report* 268 [1997] 35).

In addition to this general guidance, the Environment Agency/SEPA may give specific guidance to any local authority in relation to any particular "contaminated land" (section 78V). Whilst the local authority shall have regard to such guidance, it may disregard it if it is inconsistent with that issued by the Secretary of State under this part of the Act. Similarly, the Secretary of State may issue guidance to the appropriate Agency in regard to the exercise or performance of its powers.

Local authorities also have a duty to consider whether land should be designated as a "special site", i.e. land designated as such through section 78C(7) or 78D(6). Alternatively, the Agency may also notify local authorities (section 78C(4)) of land which they consider as requiring designation as a "special site".

"Special Sites"

The designation of land as a "special site" will be made on the basis of Regulations (to be issued) and will result in the relevant provisions being enforced by the Environment Agency or SEPA rather than by the local authority. The consultation document includes an extract from the working draft of the "special site" Regulations, which indicates that land requiring to be designated as a special site will include:

— contaminated land affecting controlled waters which:

  — are used for drinking water;

  — are situated in a major aquifer and are being contaminated by prescribed substances;

  — do not meet the criteria of the Surface Waters (Dangerous Substances) Regulations 1989 and 1992, SI 1989/2286 and SI 1992/337, respectively;

  — result in harm or interference being caused, or which may be caused, to a European Site, within the meaning of SI 1994/2716;

— land which is contaminated by reason of prescribed substances being in, on, or under it;

— land occupied for the purposes of the Ministry of Defence;

— land comprising or forming part of a site in which there is in force a nuclear site licence under the Nuclear Installations Act 1965;

— land which is contaminated as a result of waste acid tars which were stored on that land in lagoons or bunds (i.e. sealed areas designed to contain spillages);

— land on which prescribed activities have been undertaken *at any time*, including processes subject to a Part I EPA authorisation, the purification of petroleum and the manufacturing or processing of explosives;

— land adjoining or adjacent to land in the above category which is contaminated by reason of substances which appear to have escaped.

Under section 78C(9), different provisions may be made for different cases, circumstances, areas or localities (c.f. the Secretary of State's powers in section 93(4)(e) Water Resources Act 1991 re: water protection zones).

In addition, a different appeals procedure will apply – appeals against the decisions of local authorities are through the Magistrates' and higher courts. For special sites, appeals against the Agencies' decisions rest with the Secretary of State, against whose decision there may be no further appeal, as in the case of IPC authorisations (see *ENDS Report* 226 [1993] 44).

Procedure for Special Sites

Although the enforcing agency is the Environment Agency/SEPA, the local authorities nevertheless have an important role in the identification of special sites and the preliminary consultative process. Under section 78C(1), a local authority may at any time decide that land should be designated as a special site and must give notice of that decision to "the relevant persons", who are defined in section 78C(2) as:

— the potential recipient of the notice;

— the owner of *any* land which will be involved in the remedial work (e.g. for access);

— any person who appears to be in occupation of the whole or part of the land; and

— the appropriate agency.

Alternatively, the Agency itself may suggest to the local authority that land should be designated as a special site but, at this stage, it is for the LA to decide whether the land is to be so designated (section 78C(4) and (5)). "Appropriate persons" must then be informed within 21 days of such a decision. There is no requirement to inform all those persons that the land has been considered where the special site designation has been rejected. However, the Agency must be informed of *any* decisions taken by a local authority. The Agency has a further 21 days to consider the local authority decision and the notice of designation takes effect either following this period if no decision is made by the Agency, or within this period if the Agency concur with the LA assessment (section 78(6)).

Where the Agency disagrees, under section 78D the matter must be referred to the Secretary of State, who may confirm or reverse the decision with respect to the whole or part of the land to which it relates. There are no time constraints within which the Secretary of State must make his decision.

Once the decision has been taken on the designation of a special site, a remediation notice must be issued and the procedure is essentially the same as for "contaminated land", except that the Environment Agency becomes the "enforcing authority" and appeal is to the Secretary of State.

There are provisions in section 78Q for situations in which the appropriate agency considers that "contaminated land" should be treated as a special site or the special site status is no longer appropriate. However, for as long as the land is a special site, the Agency has the authority to monitor its condition.

Land Excluded from the Provisions of the Act
In addition to land falling outwith the definitions of "contaminated" and "special site", the provisions of Part IIA EPA 1990 do not apply where powers are available under other statutory provisions (section 78YB-YC), including:

— the clean-up powers under section 27 EPA 1990, in relation to processes subject to Integrated Pollution Control;

— situations in which a current waste management licence is held, unless the contamination is unrelated to the activities controlled by that licence, e.g. pre-existing contamination or that resulting from outside the licensed site;

— where action may be taken under section 59 EPA 1990, in relation to unlawful deposits and fly-tipping.

Furthermore, these powers cannot be used to prevent discharges being made under an appropriate consent under the Water Resources Act 1991, or in the case of harm or pollution attributable to radioactivity. The statutory nuisance powers of Part III EPA, as discussed below, cannot be applied where the nuisance arises as a result of "any land being in a contaminated state" (section 79(1A)). The statutory nuisance definition of land in a "contaminated state" is in section 79(1B), which states that land is to be considered as such if, and only if, by reason of substances in, on, or under the land:

— harm is being caused or there is a possibility of harm being caused; or

— pollution of controlled waters is being, or is likely to be, caused.

This differs from the definition of "contaminated land" in section 78A(2) and, without the qualification "significant" (in relation to "harm" and "pollution"), disapplies the statutory nuisance provisions to a wider range of conditions than those covered in Part II of the Act. In addition, whilst the term "contaminated land" is subjective, being dependent upon the assessment of the local authority, "land in a contaminated state" is defined objectively.

Limitations on Serving Remediation Notices
In addition to the above exclusions, section 78H introduces further restrictions on the enforcement agency serving a remediation notice. Perhaps the most important is that imposed by section 78E(4) and (5) which requires the potential cost of the remediation and the seriousness of the pollution to be taken into account. This is considered in the draft statutory guidance, *infra*.

A remediation notice is not required when the enforcing authority undertakes the work itself using the powers in section 78N, or when the authority itself is the relevant person on whom a notice should be served. In addition, the enforcing authority has discretion *not* to serve a remediation notice where it is satisfied that the necessary measures are being, or will be, undertaken.

Where no remediation notice is served by virtue of the cost-benefit analysis provisions in section 78E(4) and (5), the enforcing authority must prepare and publish a "remediation declaration" which records:

— the authority's reasons for requiring action to be taken; and

— the grounds on which it is precluded from serving a notice.

In the case of the other restrictions above (section 78H(5)(b),(c) or (d)), a "remediation statement" must be prepared and published, which records:

— details of the remediation undertaken, or to be carried out;

— the name and address of the persons involved; and

— the expected time-scale for the work.

The person undertaking the work, which may be the enforcing authority, is responsible for the preparation and publication of this statement.

Strategy for the Identification of Contaminated Land

The Act places a duty on local authorities to inspect their area from time to time (section 78B(1) and (2)) and the draft statutory guidance requires that a formal written strategy is published within 15 months of the issue of the guidance and is kept under review. The Environment Agency or SEPA are to be supplied with a copy of the strategy, which must relate to specific local circumstances, taking into account historical and present day contaminative uses of land and the potential "receptors" of this contamination. The term "receptor" refers to the "target" for the contamination and may be a living organism, a group of living organisms, an ecological system, or some piece of property which:

— is one of the types of receptor listed in Table 4-7 (page 189);

— in the case of living organisms or property, is, at least from time to time, in, on, or under the land or other land and is being, or could be harmed, by that contaminant (*sic*);

— in the case of an ecological system is being, or could be, interfered with by that contaminant.

The strategy should also "seek appropriate timescales" for the inspection of different parts of the local authority's area and give priority to the higher risk sites.

Assessment of Risk from Contaminated Land

In common with an increasing amount of environmental legislation, such as the control of special wastes, the action taken by the regulatory body – the local authority in this case – is governed by legal provisions which themselves are reliant in part on a "scientific" interpretation of the situation. Here, the assessment undertaken by the LA to determine whether the land appears to be contaminated will be made on the basis of an assessment of the risks to man and to the environment.

Risk is defined as the product of the probability or frequency of the occurrence of the hazard and the magnitude of its consequences. Critical to any such analysis of risk is the *source-pathway-target* relationship, for the presence of a potentially harmful substance alone is insufficient to result in a finite probability of harm. There must be a *target* which may be at risk from that substance (the *source*) and a means (the *pathway*) by which it may reach the target. A linkage which forms the basis for the determination that land is contaminated is termed a "significant pollutant linkage" and the pollutant responsible is a "significant pollutant".

The purpose of the guidance note is to provide a method for reviewing each of the factors which will trigger that "contamination" definition (section 78A(9)), viz:

— harm to human health: acute effects/chronic effects/other physical damage;

— harm to eco-systems;

— harm to property.

Table 4-7 on page 189 indicates the conditions whereby harm is to be judged as "significant" for different receptors and Table 4-8 (pages 190-191) illustrates the conditions for there being a significant possibility of significant harm for different specified effects.

The guidance indicates that the investigation of a potentially contaminated site will constitute a three-stage process: a desk-top survey, followed by a visual inspection and then an intrusive investigation. However, before it proceeds to the second stage, the local authority should be satisfied that a significant pollution linkage is likely to be present, and a stage three investigation should only be undertaken where the presence of both a receptor and a reasonable possibility of the presence of pollutants and potential pathways have been established.

There are other conditions which may preclude the undertaking of an assessment by the local authority, such as the provision of detailed information by other sources. However, an important practical restriction on action by the local authority is that *there is no provision for any recovery of its costs at the preliminary identification stage.* A remediation notice cannot require an investigation to be taken which would enable the local authority to determine whether the land was contaminated or not. In addition, before authorising or carrying out an inspection of land, the local authority must consider whether the land would constitute a special site, in which case the inspection should be carried out by the appropriate Agency.

Such examinations will give the local authority (or the Agency in the case of special sites) an indication of the possible risks posed by the land in question and what action to take, which may be:

— to undertake no further action if the land is not designated as "contaminated"; or

— to initiate the consultation part of the procedure for the issue of a remediation notice under section 78H; or

— to request advice from the Agency, if it considers the land should be designated as a "special site"; or

— to initiate remedial action without further consultation (section 78N).

In the last case, the local authority has powers to undertake the work itself and then to seek to recover its costs. However, in most cases of contaminated land, the consultative process outlined below will be followed.

The standard to be adopted for remediation is "suitable for use" and where possible the aim should be to use best practicable techniques to remove the factors which lead to the designation of the land as contaminated and to remedy the effects of significant harm or pollution to controlled waters. Part of the remediation process will be a cost/benefit assessment to determine whether the benefit gained by the proposed work will be outweighed by the costs incurred in carrying it out. Other factors to be considered are the effectiveness, the durability and the practicability of the remediation.

Procedure for the Issue of a Remediation Notice

Having identified a particular piece of land as "contaminated", the local authority must first consult those who are likely to be involved in the remediation work. Section 78H(1) of the 1995 Act specifies these as:

— the potential recipient of the notice;

— the owner of *any* land which will be involved in the remedial work (e.g. for access);

— any person who appears to be in occupation of the whole or part of the land; and

— any other person, as prescribed.

As discussed, there are a number of restrictions on the service of a notice and additionally there must be a three-month period for consultations to take place prior to any notice being served.

Providing these conditions are met, the local authority has a *duty* to require the remediation of the contaminated land by serving a remediation notice on those identified as "appropriate persons" (see below). There is a right of appeal against a remediation notice under section 78L but this must be made within 21 days of service. The magistrate (or Secretary of State, in the case of special sites) has jurisdiction to quash the notice entirely or to confirm it, conditionally or unconditionally.

Failure to comply with a remediation notice is the only offence associated with these contaminated land provisions (section 78M) and, where land is defined as industrial, trade or business premises (section 78M(6)), it is subject to a fine up of to £20,000, *plus* a penalty of £2,000, regardless of the size of the fine, for each day on which the failure continues after conviction and before the enforcing authority undertakes the work itself.

Section 78M(1) provides a defence for non-compliance on the grounds of "reasonable excuse" and section 78M(2) for situations in which a number of persons are responsible for the *remediation* and the *sole* reason for non-compliance is the refusal or inability of one or more of these parties to bear their part of the costs. The defence of "reasonable excuse" will be applicable in situations in which the defendant has no control of the circumstances surrounding the alleged offence, as in *Wellingborough Borough Council v Gordon*. The test applied is whether there was some "overwhelming or even difficult situation ... which the defendant was not able to control and which led to the breach" although, after *Saddleworth UDC v Aggregate and Sand*, it is clear that the lack of finance will not be taken into consideration.

As with the "works notice" procedure for the clean-up of water pollution, if the local authority considers that proceedings under section 78 would provide an *ineffectual* remedy, it has the option of taking the action to the High Court in order to seek compliance.

The Allocation of Responsibility for Remediation

The allocation of responsibility is a complex task since the contamination may comprise a number of components, released either diffusely or from a number of discrete points, by a number of potential polluters, over a substantial period of time.

The framework for the allocation of responsibility is contained in section 78F, with section 78J relating to the pollution of controlled waters, section 78K concerning the migration of pollutants from other sources and section 78X covering persons acting as insolvency practitioners. These provisions will be augmented by guidance issued by the Secretary of State, under section 78F(7), and the draft guidance envisages a four-step process.

For each significant pollution linkage, the enforcing authority must:

— identify the potentially liable "appropriate persons";

— categorise them into the correct liability group, A or B;

— apply the appropriate exclusion tests; and

— apportion the costs between the remaining members of the liability group.

The draft statutory guidance designates as an "appropriate person":

— *any* person who "caused or knowingly permitted" the contaminants themselves or any subsequent reaction products, to be present in, on or under the contaminated land. These are referred to as "Class A" persons.

— where no Class A person has been found "after reasonable enquiry", the owner or occupier for the time being, and such persons are referred to as "Class B" persons. The term "owner" is defined in section 78A(9) but no guidance is given on the meaning of "occupier".

The draft statutory guidance notes the statement of Earl Ferrers that, in relation to banks or other lenders, there is no judicial decision which supports the contention that a lender, by virtue of the act of lending money only, could be said to have "knowingly permitted" the contamination of the land (*House of Lords Hansard*, 11 July 1996 col. 1497).

In establishing liability, the initial requirements are for the local authority to identify, *for each significant pollutant*, the persons who would be appropriate persons for remediation action. Collectively, the appropriate persons for any significant pollution linkage are referred to as the "liability group" for that linkage. For each significant pollution linkage, one of the following sets of circumstances will apply:

— *More than one person can be found who has caused or knowingly permitted the presence of the significant pollution forming part of the significant pollution linkage.* These Class A persons form the liability group for that linkage and guidance is given:

　　— in Part E of Chapter IV of the guidance on whether they should be treated as appropriate persons;

　　— in Part G of Chapter IV of the guidance on the proportions they are liable to pay;

　　— in Part H of Chapter IV of the guidance on the effect of other significant pollution linkages.

— *Only one such person can be found.* In this case, that Class A person will himself constitute the liability group for the significant pollution linkage. Guidance in Part H of Chapter IV of the guidance *may* be relevant if there are other significant pollution linkages relating to the land in question.

— *No such persons can be found after reasonable enquiry.* Here the Class B person(s) constitutes the liability group and Part F gives guidance on whether these are to be regarded as appropriate persons. Parts G and H of Chapter IV of the guidance may also be appropriate.

— *No appropriate Class A or Class B person can be found after reasonable enquiry.* Companies that have been dissolved and persons who have died come into this category.

Orphan Linkages

The term "orphan linkage" is used to denote the condition where no occupier or owner can be found, or where the occupier or owner is exempted by statutory provision, *infra*. In such cases, the costs of remediation may have to be met by the local authority.

The Exclusion Tests

In applying the exclusion and apportionment tests, three principles are to be employed:

— the financial circumstances of any member of a liability group should have no bearing on the decision, regardless of the terms of the "hardship rules", the availability of insurance cover, or other means of transferring responsibility. The rationale behind this is to avoid the "deep pocket" approach to remediation;

— the authority need only obtain such information as is reasonable, having regard to access to this information, its costs and potential significance;

— where an agreement on the apportionment of costs between parties involved is in place, in most cases the authority should make its determination to give effect to this agreement.

Class A Exclusions
The conditions under which members of a Class A liability group might be excluded from liability are contained within Part E of Chapter IV. This procedure involves the application of the six tests of exclusion summarised below and, after these have been made and any exclusions applied, *at least*

one member of the liability group should remain to bear the responsibility for *each* significant pollution linkage.

Test 1: "Excluded activities". This excludes those identified as having limited responsibility in relation to the "causing or knowingly permitting" of contamination. Such activities include, *inter alia*: providing or withholding financial assistance to another person; carrying out any action necessary for the purposes of underwriting an insurance policy in relation to the contamination of land; providing legal, financial, scientific or technical advice to another person.

Test 2: "Payments made for remediation". This excludes those who have already paid some other members of the liability group to undertake adequate remediation;

Test 3: "Sold with information". This applies where a Class A person has sold the land or let it on a long lease (more than 21 years in England and more than 20 years in Scotland) *and* has ensured that the purchaser or lessee had the information as to the presence of those pollutants and thus had the opportunity to take that into account in agreeing the price. The guidance states that in transactions since 1990 between large commercial organisations, permission from the seller for the purchaser to carry out his own survey "should normally be taken as sufficient evidence that the purchaser had the necessary information"!!

Test 4: "Changes to substances". In this case, although the exempted persons were responsible for the presence of a given substance on site, on its own this would not have caused the significant pollution linkage (SPL). The actual cause of the SPL was the result of a chemical or biological reaction with another substance introduced at a subsequent date, or was due to physical changes to the initial substance as a result of the activities of another member of the liability group.

Test 5: "Escaped substances". This test excludes from liability those who would otherwise be liable as the result of the escape of a substance, where it can be shown that another Class A person was actually responsible for the escape.

Test 6: "Introduction of pathways or receptors". Here the exclusion is on the basis of the subsequent introduction by others of the relevant pathways or receptors forming part of the significant pollution linkage.

Class B Exclusions
The purpose of these exclusions is to exclude from liability those who do not have an interest in the capital value of the land in question. The

excluded persons are those who:

— occupy the land under a licence which has no marketable value; or

— are liable to pay rent equivalent to the rack rent of the land they occupy *and* hold no beneficial interest in the land other than any tenancy to which the rack rent relates (in England and Wales); or

— are liable to pay a rent equivalent to the full market value for the land and hold no interest in the *dominum utile* over the land (in Scotland).

Apportionment of Liability

Having identified the members of the liability group who are to bear the costs of remediation, the final step is to apportion these costs. Remediation will be undertaken to achieve a particular purpose with regard to one or more of the defined significant pollution linkages, and the authority must determine whether each remediation action is:

— referable solely to the significant pollution linkage in a single significant pollution linkage – a "single-linkage action";

— referable to the significant pollutant in more than one significant pollution linkage – a "shared action".

Only the latter is subject to the apportionment procedure of Part H of Chapter IV, for which there are two categories of action:

— a "common action", which addresses together all the significant pollution linkages to which it is referable and which would have been part of the remediation package for *each* of those linkages if each had been addressed together;

— a "collective action" which addresses together all the significant pollution linkages to which it is referable but would *not* have been part of the remediation package for *every one* of those linkages if each had been addressed together.

For a Class A liability group, the principle behind the apportionment is the relative degree of responsibility of each member of the group in relation to the significant pollution linkage in question. This is taken into account by considering, *inter alia*, the contribution of each member of the group to "causing" or "knowingly permitting" and the degree of control they exercised in relation to the quantities of pollutant involved, the time involved and the area of land. Overall, the principle of just and equitable settlement is to be applied.

Class B liability is based upon the capital value of the land of each member of the group, using the day immediately before the service of the notice of contamination as the datum and disregarding the existence of any contamination.

Cost Recovery

Chapter V of the guidance sets out the circumstances under which the enforcing authority should seek to recover the costs of remediation it undertakes itself, the amount of these costs and any hardship which might be caused through imposing such costs. For Class A persons, local authorities would be given powers for the recovery of unrecovered costs by means of "charging notices". The issue of such a notice empowers the authority to take control of the premises which consist of or include the contaminated land, thus giving them security for the costs of remediation undertaken by them.

Public Registers

There is a requirement for local authorities and the Environment Agency/ SEPA to maintain public registers of all statutory notices, references made from other agencies and other relevant matters in connection with their own functions in relation to contaminated land. As a consequence, the majority of the information on "contaminated land" will be held on *local* registers, with the Agencies holding that pertaining to "special sites".

The provisions in section 78R-T follow very much the pattern adopted elsewhere in UK environmental legislation (see Chapter 7), although in the case of "remediation statements" it is the duty of the "responsible person" to prepare and publish these.

Unlike the "section 143" registers, which were based upon contaminative land *use*, the section 78R registers are based upon the appropriate agency's *current* assessment of *specific* sites, which in fact may present a serious risk. Although the designation "special site" is not necessarily a permanent one, the information will remain on the registers after the completion of the remedial work. The confidentiality of the information is nevertheless subject to the four-year rule. In this case, however, this is of benefit to the land owner, for it records the information relevant to the clean-up of the site, including post-remediation monitoring. However, section 78(3) makes it clear that an entry on the register does not constitute a statement by the body maintaining the register to the effect that such work was in practice undertaken.

STATUTORY NUISANCE

The Scope of Statutory Nuisance

Statutory nuisance has formed part of UK law since 1848 and, whilst the initial application was directed towards sanitation and public health, its scope has been extended to other areas such as noise and dust. The Noise and Statutory Nuisance Act 1993 and the Environment Act 1995 have further increased its scope, although the controls on "offensive trades" (blood boiling and drying, bone boiling, fat extracting and melting, fellmongering, glue making, rag and bone dealing, size making, tallow making and tripe boiling) from sections 107 and 108 of the Public Health Act 1936 have been repealed by the Repeal of Offensive Trades or Businesses Provisions Order 1995, SI 1995/2054.

It is also worthwhile noting that in the Environment Protection Bill the possibility of including light as a source of nuisance was considered (as it was in the draft IPPC provisions) and this perhaps may be a future potential inclusion. See also the paper by M M Taylor " 'And God Divided the Light from the Darkness' – Has Humanity Mixed Them Up Again?", [1997] 9 *ELM* 32.

The link between statutory nuisance and common law nuisance was demonstrated in *National Coal Board v Thorne*, in which Watkins J stated that:

"A nuisance ... [within the meaning of the Public Health Act 1936] ... must either be a public or a private nuisance as understood by common law."

Until recently, the regime in Scotland was contained in the Public Health Scotland) Act 1897 and Part II of the Control of Pollution Act 1974. However, under section 107 and Schedule 17 of the Environment Act 1995, these provisions were repealed and the statutory nuisance legislation within Part III of the Environmental Protection Act 1990 was made applicable to Scotland.

The problems of applying common law remedies to environmental situations are discussed in the next chapter, and the role of statutory nuisance is to provide individuals or local authorities with relatively quick and inexpensive access to the courts on specific issues. In conjunction with clean air, statutory nuisance forms the title to Part III of the Environmental Protection Act 1990 and there are important links with Part IIA of the Act on contaminated land and Part II of the Control of Pollution Act 1974 (COPA) for noise nuisances.

Although the noise provisions of sections 58 and 59 of COPA 1974 are now covered by the 1990 Act, sections 60 and 61 of COPA 1974, relating to noise from construction sites, remain in force and are important means of control in this area. In addition, new domestic noise controls were introduced through the Noise Act 1996 and, following the Noise Act 1996 (Commencement No. 1) Order, SI 1996/2219, section 10 of the Act is brought into force, empowering local authorities to seize and remove any equipment used in the emission of noise from premises.

Local Authority Action on Statutory Nuisance

Under section 79 EPA 1990, every local authority has a duty to inspect its area from time to time to detect any source of statutory nuisance which ought to be dealt with. Subject to certain restrictions in subsections (1A) to (6A), this applies to the nine general areas outlined in Table 4-9 (page 192). The duty applies to statutory nuisances which are experienced *within* its area and the local authority has the ability to act against sources of nuisance which arise outside its area, although summary action is through the Magistrates' Court whose jurisdiction includes the location of the source of the nuisance.

With its origins in the Public Health Act of 1936 and before, much of the language describing these nuisances is arcane and the definitions in section 79(7) must be read in conjunction with the extensive case law in this area, bearing in mind their present day context. Following the ruling in *Betts v Penge UDC*, it is not necessary to read the two limbs of "prejudicial to health or a nuisance" conjunctively. An activity need not be "prejudicial to health" in order to constitute a statutory nuisance and it is sufficient to show an interference with personal comfort, although the nuisance must arise on neighbouring property (*National Coal Board v Neath BC*).

"Prejudicial to health" means injurious or likely to cause injury to *health* but does not include the likelihood to cause an *accident*. In *Coventry City Council v Cartwright*, the court held that the accumulation of household waste and building materials did not constitute a statutory nuisance where it was inert (i.e. not putrescible/unlikely to attract vermin, etc.) and there was no possibility of an associated health risk. In *Cunningham v Birmingham City Council*, Mr Justice Pill held that the proper test in assessing whether or not premises were "prejudicial to health" was objective rather than subjective, and it was not necessary to consider the health of *individual* occupiers.

The meaning of "premises" includes land and vessels (other than those powered by "steam reciprocating machinery") but, unlike the 1936 Public

Health Act, nuisance *at* workplaces is excluded, since this is now covered by health and safety legislation.

As noted in *National Coal Board v Thorne*, the same criteria apply to statutory nuisance as those in common law and the main factors to be taken into consideration in determining whether to issue an abatement notice are its nature and location, the time and duration of the nuisance, and the utility of the activity giving rise to the nuisance.

The "Person Responsible"

Action in statutory nuisance is against the "person responsible" who, as stated in section 79(7):

— is the person to whose act, default or sufferance the nuisance is attributable;

— in relation to a vehicle, *includes* the person in whose name the vehicle is registered ... and any other person who is for the time being the driver of the vehicle;

— in relation to machinery or equipment, *includes* any person who is for the time being the operator of the machinery or equipment.

Where more than one person is responsible for a statutory nuisance, section 80 EPA 1990 applies to *each* of those persons whether or not any one of them is responsible for what would by itself amount to a nuisance (section 81(1)). With regard to street noise, section 80A applies to *any of the persons* responsible (section 81(1A and 1B)).

These definitions of the "person responsible" should be viewed in the light of *Carr v London Borough of Hackney*, in which the court held that the council was no longer the "person responsible" for the nuisance since it was prevented from carrying out works by a third party. Where it is necessary for third parties to grant access to those upon whom the abatement notice has been served, then the refusal of access has the potential:

— to form the basis of a defence for failure to comply with the notice; and

— to transfer the onus of the "responsible person" onto the party refusing access. However, the "reasonable excuse" defence of section 80(4) may be available if the third party were put to considerable inconvenience.

It will be noted that the provisions for contaminated land *require* that the necessary access is given in order to undertake the remediation work and provide for the payment of compensation of such access (section 79G).

Procedure for the Abatement of a Statutory Nuisance

There is a strong similarity between this and the contaminated land provisions discussed earlier. Where a local authority is satisfied that a statutory nuisance exists or is likely to occur or recur within its area (section 80(1)), it must serve an "abatement notice" which may impose all or any of the following conditions:

— the abatement of the nuisance, prohibiting or restricting its occurrence or recurrence (section 80(1));

— the execution of such works as may be necessary.

The abatement notice is served on the person(s) responsible for the nuisance and, if these cannot be found or the nuisance has not yet occurred, on the owner or occupier of the premises. Where the nuisance results from structural defects, service is on the owner of the premises (section 80(2)(b)) and, in relation to noise in the street from unattended vehicles, machinery or equipment, the notice is served either upon the owner or is affixed to the vehicle, etc. if the owner cannot be found (section 80A(2)(b)).

Appeals

A person served with an abatement notice has 21 days within which to appeal to magistrates (section 80(3)) although, as the articles by Jones[1] and by Graham[2] point out, there is a paucity of guidance on the key issues of:

— the rules governing appeals against abatement notices;

— the rules of evidence which are applicable; and

— whether the court decides the appeal on the basis of the facts existing when the notice was served or at the time of the appeal.

Appeal against an abatement notice is covered by Schedule 3 to the EPA 1990 and the Statutory Nuisance (Appeals) Regulations 1990, SI 1990/ 2276, as amended by SI 1990/2483 and SI 1995/2644. In comparison with a prosecution for the contravention of an abatement notice, appeal

---

[1]   "Statutory Nuisance Appeals with Special Reference to Smells", D Jones, [1995] *JPEL*, September, 797.

[2]   "Statutory Nuisance: What are the rules governing appeals?", T Graham, [1996] *JPEL*, March, 199.

proceedings permit a greater scope for disputing the nuisance and the grounds for appeal include, *inter alia*:

— the abatement notice is not justified under the terms of section 80 of the Act;

— there has been a substantive or procedural error in the service of the notice;

— the local authority has acted unreasonably in refusing alternative requirements or their requirements are unreasonable and unnecessary;

— "best practicable means" (BPM) were used to mitigate the nuisance (for industrial, business or trade premises).

The Regulations on street noise (SI 1995/2644), incorporating the provisions of the Noise and Statutory Nuisance Act 1993, list the following grounds for appeal, in addition to BPM:

— the nuisance from these sources was already subject to a consent under the 1993 Act's provisions, and the abatement notice had imposed more onerous conditions;

— the notice should have been served on the "person responsible" and not on the appellant, or served on such a person in addition to the appellant, where this would have been "equitable".

Offences

Failure to comply with an abatement notice is an offence, triable only in a Magistrates' Court and on conviction is subject to a fine plus a daily penalty for the continuing non-compliance. Alternatively, the local authority may abate the nuisance itself and recover its expenses (sections 80(4) and 81(3) and (4) EPA 1990). Provisions relating to the recovery of expenses and the payment of expenses by instalments are contained within sections 81A and 81B, although these two sections do not apply in Scotland.

The defence of "best practicable means" is available in the circumstances listed in section 80(8) and (9) and is defined in section 79(9). "Practicable" means reasonably practicable, having regard, *inter alia*, to local conditions and circumstances, to the current state of technical knowledge and to financial implications. In *Wivenhoe Port v Colchester Borough Council*, the court accepted that profitability was a factor and that the installation of dust abatement equipment would render the process uneconomic but held that, to establish the BPM defence, the onus of demonstrating practicability lay with the defendant. There are a number of codes of practice in relation to noise which establish guidelines against which this form of nuisance may be judged.

It is also a defence to show that there was a "reasonable excuse" for carrying out the activity which resulted in the contravention. In *Lambert (A) Flat Management v Lomas*, it was held that the relevant provision under COPA 1974 was designed to provide a defence where there was some special difficulty in complying with the abatement notice. In addition, special defences apply to actions relating to noise on construction sites, under sections 60 and 61 COPA 1974 and under the noise provisions of section 80(9) EPA 1990.

Action in the High Court

Where a local authority is of the opinion that proceedings under section 80(4) would afford an *inadequate* remedy (c.f. the wording *ineffectual* in section 78M(5) EPA 1990 in relation to contaminated land and in section 161D(4) WRA 1991 for controlled waters), then it may take action in the High Court to secure the abatement, prohibition or restriction of the statutory nuisance (section 81(5)).

A defence provided in section 81(6) to actions against noise nuisance on construction sites is that the noise was authorised under a "section 60 notice" or a "section 61 consent" issued under COPA 1974.

In *Hammersmith London Borough Council v Magnum Associated Forecourts*, it was held that this remedy was available *in addition* to summary proceedings and was not a bar to relief through on-going summary remedies. Thus, after the service of an abatement notice, a local authority may initiate action in the High Court to expedite the abatement of the nuisance and interlocutory relief may be sought, following *American Cyanamid Co v Ethicon*. Furthermore, it was held in *Lloyds Bank v Guardian Assurance* that the jurisdiction of the High Court is not affected by proceedings under statutory nuisance and, while an *individual* may not seek a common law remedy which is stricter than any abatement notice which had already been served, it is possible for a local authority to use section 81(5) proceedings to strengthen a weak abatement notice.

Local authorities may exercise similar powers under section 222 of the Local Government Act 1972 and in *Wyre Forest v Bostock* it was held that these powers are available concurrently. However, in *Vale of White Horse District Council v D C and R J Allen*, the relationship between the section 222 powers of the 1972 Act and the statutory nuisance provisions of EPA 1990 were considered in relation to an alleged nuisance from a pig farm in

Oxfordshire. Mr Justice Bell held that section 222 of the Local Government Act did not bring a separate entitlement to bring an action in statutory nuisance and the provisions in Part III of the Environmental Protection Act 1990 provided a "self-sufficient code" for dealing with such problems. A local authority's entitlement to seek an injunction only arose if the specific conditions set out in section 81(5) of the Act were met and, after a detailed consideration of the relevant reports, minutes and resolutions of the local authority, it was held that this criterion had not been satisfied. While the local authority had considered whether proceedings in the High Court would be more convenient and were more likely to lead to a satisfactory solution to the problem, this was not the correct legal test.

With regard to bringing proceedings under section 222, Mr Justice Bell concluded that the local authority had not determined that such proceedings were "expedient for the promotion or protection of the interests of the inhabitants in their area".

Action by Individuals

Where action on a statutory nuisance is not taken by a local authority, there is a restricted right for "aggrieved persons" to initiate action in a Magistrates' Court, in cases where a nuisance exists or although abated is likely to recur on the same premises (section 82 EPA 1990). In *R v Carrick District Council ex parte Shelley and Another*, a local authority was held to have failed in its statutory duty when it resolved not to take any action in regard to complaints of pollution of the local beaches but merely to monitor the situation.

Only a local authority has a right to commence preventative action prior to the existence of a nuisance. In *Attorney-General (Gambia) v N'Jie*, Lord Denning defined the "person aggrieved", stating:

"The words 'person aggrieved' are of wide import, and should not be subjected to a restricted interpretation. They do not involve of course, a mere busybody who is interfering in things that do not concern him; but they do include a person who has a genuine grievance because an order has been made which prejudicially affects his interest."

Although prior to the introduction of the 1990 Act there was no formal requirement for the aggrieved person to give notice of such action, in *Sandwell Metropolitan Borough Council v Bujok* their Lordships expressed disapproval where the defendant was not given an opportunity to remedy the situation. However, under section 82(6) and (7) it is now necessary to give three days' notice in the case of noise from premises or from vehicles/equipment/machinery in the street, and 21 days' notice in other cases, before bringing proceedings under section 82(2).

As with other statutory nuisance offences, the defences of "best practicable means" and "reasonable excuse" are available (section 82(8) to (10)). On conviction, the court may order either or both of the following:

— a requirement for the defendant to abate the nuisance within a given time period and to execute any works as are necessary;

— a prohibition on the recurrence of the nuisance and a requirement to execute any such works as are necessary to prevent its recurrence,

and additionally may impose a fine. Failure to comply with any of the court's requirements may result in an additional fine plus a daily penalty for any continuing non-compliance. Furthermore, the local authority may be directed by the court to undertake any work which should have been done by the defendant. Costs may be awarded in favour of the complainant, where it is proved that the alleged nuisance existed *at the time of the complaint*, whether or not it existed at the time of the hearing. Although there is no reference to the payment of compensation to "persons aggrieved" within the Act, such payments may be made under the general powers of the Powers of the Criminal Courts Act 1973, where a magistrate may require a person to pay compensation of up to £5,000 to the victim "for any personal injury, loss, or damage resulting from the offence". However, in *R v Liverpool City Council ex parte Cooke*, Lord Justice Leggatt noted that the provisions of the 1973 Act "were not themselves tailored to the requirements of statutory nuisance" and a compensation order can only relate to damage resulting "from an offence".

Although Part III of the EPA 1990 created an offence of non-compliance with an abatement notice issued by the court, it did *not* create a specific offence in respect of being responsible for the nuisance. Since no offence is committed until the expiry of such a notice, then no compensation may be awarded in relation to the period prior to the expiry.

Construction Noise

As noted above, specific provisions for the control of construction noise are contained within sections 60 and 61 of the Control of Pollution Act 1974 and these apply to works of the type described in section 60(1), viz:

— erection, construction, alteration, repair or maintenance of buildings, structures or roads;

— breaking up, opening or boring under any road or adjacent land in connection with construction, inspection, maintenance or removal of works;

— demolition or dredging work; and

— any work of engineering construction.

This broad description encompasses many operations and it is likely that most waste management businesses will at some time engage in such activities.

There are two basic methods for the controls of noise from these processes. The local authority may be approached not less than 28 days in advance of the intended works and a "section 61 consent" obtained. Such a consent will detail the works to be undertaken and the measures for minimising the noise, which may include specific conditions. *Any* person who knowingly carries out works in contravention of *any* conditions of such a consent commits an offence under Part III of the 1974 Act.

Alternatively, the local authority may serve a "section 60 notice" in relation to works that are being or are going to be carried out on any premises. The notice is to be served on the person who appears to the LA to be carrying out the works *and* on other such persons who appear to be responsible for, or to have control over, the carrying out of the works. Under section 60(3), the notice may stipulate:

— the plant or machinery which is, or is not, to be used;

— the hours during which work may be undertaken;

— the levels of noise which may be emitted from the premises, or at any specified point on those premises, and also the times relating to such noise emissions.

The local authority must have regard to any relevant Codes of Practice issued under Part II of the Act, and to the need for ensuring that best practicable means are employed to minimise the noise (section 60(4)). However, the desirability of such conditions to the recipients of the notice regarding the methods, plant or machinery must be taken into consideration. Contravention of a section 60 notice is an offence, although it is a defence to prove that the alleged contravention amounted to the carrying out of the works in accordance with a section 61 consent.

It is clearly preferable for an organisation to make prior arrangements with the local authority through a section 61 consent, where there is a possibility of discussing its content, than to be subject to a section 60 notice which is not open to negotiation.

There is clearly scope within these provisions for the local authority to take action against the principal or any of his contractors or their sub-contractors. On large construction projects, the principal may require his main contractor to apply for the section 61 consent, although this will not exclude him from action under these provisions. However, if different types of work are to be undertaken, e.g. civil works and electrical/mechanical engineering, it may not be practical for the main contractor to seek a section 61 consent on behalf of all those working on site.

FURTHER READING

Water

Building a Cleaner Future, video produced by the Environment Agency and CIRIA (Construction Research and Information Association), with the support of the BOC Foundation for the Environment

"Causing, Knowingly Permitting and Preventing Water Pollution", W Howarth, [1990] *Utilities Law*, Summer, 105

"Environmental Pollution Control and Strict Liability in Anglo-Australian Penal Laws", J K Bentil, [1986] *JPL* 255

Environment and Enforcement, K Hawkins, Clarendon Press, 1984

International Law and the Environment, P W Birnie and A E Boyle, OUP, 1992

The Law of Sewers and Drains, 8th Edition, J F Garner and S H Bailey, Shaw & Sons, 1995

"Poisonous, Noxious or Polluting: Contrasting Approaches to Environmental Regulation", W Howarth, [1993] 56 *MLR* 171

Pollution Prevention Pays, video produced by NRA and re-issued by the Environment Agency

"Protection of the Water Environment through Private Court Action", A Mumma, [1992] *Water Law*, 51

Water Pollution Law, W Howarth, Shaw & Sons, 1988

Wisdom's Law of Watercourses, 5th Edition, W Howarth, Shaw & Sons, 1992

Statutory Nuisance

Noise Control: the law and its enforcement, 2nd Edition, C N Penn, Shaw and Sons, 1995

"Oh, Noisy Bells, be Dumb: Church Bells, Statutory Nuisance and Ecclesiastical Duties", S Thomas and T G Watkin, [1995] *JPEL* 1097

"Report of the United Kingdom Environmental Law Association Working Group on the Statutory Nuisance Provisions of the Environmental Protection Bill", [1990] 2 *LMELR* 9

"Statutory Nuisance Appeals with Special Reference to Smells", D Jones, [1995] *JPEL*, September, 797

"Statutory Nuisance: What are the rules governing appeals?", T Graham, [1996] *JPEL*, March, 199

Contaminated Land

Contaminated Land, S Tromans and R Turrall-Clarke, Sweet & Maxwell, 1994

"Contaminated Land and the Environment Act 1995 Working Draft Guidance: Part I: The Germ of an Idea", P Kellett and D Hughes, [1996] *ELM* 217

"Environmental Pollution Control and Strict Liability in Anglo-Australian Penal Laws", J K Bentil, [1986] *JPL* 255

"Paying for our Past – Will We?", Sir Hugh Rossi, [1995] 7 (1) *JEL* 1

"The Regulatory Lacuna: Waste Disposal and the Clean Up of Contaminated Sites", N Atkinson, [1991] 3 (2) *JEL* 265

General

The Environment Acts 1990-1995, 3rd Edition, S Tromans, M Nash and M Poustie, Sweet & Maxwell, 1996

Environmental Law, J D Leeson, Pitman Publishing, 1995

Occupational Health and Safety Law, 2nd Edition, R Barrett and R Howells, Pitman Publishing, 1995

"Strict Liability Offences: A Radical Analysis of Recent Decisions", A Reed, [1995] *ELM* 156

Table 4-1: Range of Environmentally-Related Legislation
Applicable to a Typical Company

Control of Pollution Act 1974

Health and Safety at Work Act 1974

Control of Pollution (Amendment) Act 1989

Environmental Protection Act 1990

Environment Act 1995

Clean Air Act 1993

Food and Environmental Protection Act 1985

Planning(Hazardous Substances) Act 1990

Noise and Statutory Nuisance Act 1993

Wildlife and Countryside Act 1981

Wildlife and Countryside (Amendment) Act 1985

Planning (Listed Buildings and Conservation Areas) Act 1990

Town and Country Planning Act 1990

Planning and Compensation Act 1991

Occupiers' Liability Acts 1957 and 1984

Salmon and Freshwater Fisheries Act 1975

Land Drainage Act 1991

Water (Consolidation) (Consequential Provisions) Act 1991

Water Resources Act 1991

Water Industry Act 1991

Deregulation and Contracting Out Act 1994

Finance Act 1996

Table 4-2: Categories of Water Pollution Incident

Category	Incident	Description
1.	Major	One or more of the following: — potential or actual persistent effect on water quality or aquatic life; — closure of potable water, industrial or agricultural abstraction necessary; — extensive fish kill; — excessive breach of consent conditions; — extensive remedial measures necessary; — major effect on amenity value.
2.	Significant	One or more of the following: — notification to abstractors necessary; — significant fish kill; — measurable effect on invertebrate life; — water unfit for stock; — bed of watercourse contaminated; — amenity value to public, owners or users reduced by odour or appearance.
3.	Minor	Suspected or probable pollution which on investigation proves unlikely to be capable of substantiation or to have no notable effect.

Table 4-3: The Mogden Formula for Trade Effluent Charges 183

Charges for discharges of trade effluent to sewers are normally calculated on the basis of the "Mogden Formula", which takes into account the volume and content of the discharge. Although its actual form may vary between sewerage undertaker, it is generally in the form:

$$\text{Cost, } C = R + V^* + B \times [O_t/O_s] + S \times [S_t/S_s]$$

where

$$V^* = [V + V.B], \text{ or } V \times M, \text{ or } M$$

where

C   = Total charge in pence per cubic metre of trade effluent

R   = Reception and conveyance cost per cubic metre of sewage

V   = Volumetric and primary treatment cost per cubic metre of sewage treated

VB = Additional cost per cubic metre where there is biological treatment

VM = Treatment and disposal charge for sea outfalls

M   = Cost, per cubic metre of sewage, of providing and operating effective marine outfalls

B   = Biological oxidation cost per cubic metre of settled sewage (including the cost of secondary sludge disposal)

S   = Treatment and disposal cost of primary sludges per cubic metre of sewage

O_t = The Chemical Oxygen Demand (COD) in mg/1 of the trade effluent after settlement for a specified period (usually one hour)

O_s = The COD (mg/1) of average strength settled sewage

S_t = The total weight of suspended solids (mg/1) of the trade effluent

S_s = The total weight of suspended solids (mg/1) of average strength crude sewage.

Although a similar formula is used by most undertakers, the constants within it are significantly different, and charges vary quite widely across the country, unlike those for controlled waters which do not take into account local factors.

Table 4-4: "Red List" Substances

Mercury and its compounds

Cadmium and its compounds

Gamma-hexachlorocyclohexane

DDT

Pentachlorophenol

Hexachlorobenzene

Hexachlorobutadiene

Aldrin

Dieldrin

Endrine

Polychlorinated biphenyls (PCBs)

Dichlorvos

1,2-dichloroethane

Trichlorobenzene

Atrazine

Simazine

Tributyltin compounds

Triphenyltin compounds

Trifluralin

Fenitrothion

Azinphos-methyl

Malathion

Endosulfan.

Table 4-5: Charging Scheme for Controlled Waters   185

The charging scheme for discharges to controlled waters is based upon the formula:

$$\text{Charge, } C = R \times (V \times C \times RW)$$

where:

R   = national unit cost rate
V   = banded weighting factor based on consented discharge volume
C   = banded weighting factor based on consented discharge content
        [bands classified A (most Polluting) to G (least)]
RW = banded weighting factor based on category of receiving water

Content of discharge classified by bands	Factor (C)
A = Pesticides, herbicides, fungicides; polyhalogenated biphenyls; poly-nuclear aromatic hydrocarbons; aliphatic, aromatic, heterocyclic and halogenated hydrocarbons; alcohols (except methanol, ethanol, butanol, propanol and glycols); aromatic nitrogen compounds; phenolic compounds (except total and monohydric phenols); esters; ethers; ketones; aldehydes (except formaldehyde); viruses; effluents where consent requires toxicity tests (other than rapid bacterial toxicity tests)	14
B = Metals, metalloids; cyanides; sulphides; total and monohydric phenolic compounds; methanol, ethanol, butanol, propanol; glycols; carboxylic acids; organic nitrogen compounds (except those in Band A, urea and quaternary ammonium salts); bacteria; effluent where consent requires rapid bacterial toxicity tests	5
C = Sewage and organic trade effluent with numeric consent conditions (except those specified in Bands E or G)	3
D = Sewage with no numeric conditions; trade effluent not specified in other bands	2
E = Site drainage from trade premises; storm and emergency discharges at treatment works, pumping stations and from drainage systems; direct cooling water other than that specified in Band G; trade effluents from prevention of interference with mining and quarrying (if not in Band F)	1
F = Surface water; trade effluent from prevention of interference with mining, etc for which only conditions are volume, suspended solids, iron, pH and chloride; any effluent not identified elsewhere	0.5
G = Cooling water where only conditions are volume, temperature, pH, chlorine; water abstracted from controlled water and discharged after use in a trade, subject to limits in the increase of concentrations of BOD, suspended solids, ammonia	0.3

Table 4-5 (continued)

Volume of discharge (m³/day)	Factor (V)	Volume of discharge (m³/day)	Factor (V)
0-5	0.3	> 1000-10,000	3
> 5-20	0.5	> 10,000-50,000	5
> 20-100	1	> 50,000-150,000	9
> 100-1000	2	> 150,000	14

Type of receiving water	Factor (RW)
Estuarial	1.5
Surface	1
Coastal	0.8
Ground	0.5

Table 4-6: Legislation Associated with Contaminated Land

Statute	Area of Control	Enforcement Powers	Regulatory Body	Defendant	Notes
Water Resources Act 1991, s161.	Pollution of controlled waters — surface — ground.	Preventative action. Remedial Action. Cost recovery. *Discretionary power.*	NRA	Person responsible for 'causing' or 'knowingly permitting'.	Anticipatory power.
Environmental Protection Act 1990, s27.	Harm resulting from s23(1)(a).	Remedy *actual harm.* Recover costs.	Environment Agency/ SEPA	Recipient of enforcement/ abatement notice.	
Environmental Protection Act 1990, s59.	Unlawful deposition of waste within WRA area. Unlawful deposit in s33 EPA.	Removal of waste. Eliminate/reduce consequences of deposition. Recovery of costs.	WRA/LA	Any person/occupier. May appeal to Magistrate.	'Innocent occupier' defence.
Environmental Protection Act 1990, s78A-78YC.	'Contaminated Land' and 'Special Sites' as defined in the Act and Regs.	Investigate/assess/ designate/clean-up/ monitor. *Duty to inspect. Duty to serve a Remediation Notice.*	LA / Environment Agency/ SEPA	'Appropriate persons' as defined by the Act: polluter/occupier/ owner.	Not yet in force. Excludes land subject to IPC control or Waste Management Licence.
Environmental Protection Act 1990, ss80, 81.	Any premises re: health/nuisance (inc. land). Any accumulation or deposit. Any other enactment.	Inspection. Abatement notice. Action and cost recovery. *Duty to inspect.*	Local authority	Person responsible for the nuisance, or owner/occupier.	'Best Practicable Means' defence. Excludes statutory nuisance caused by contamination.

Table 4-6 (continued)

Statute	Area of Control	Enforcement Powers	Regulatory Body	Defendant	Notes
Town and Country Planning Act 1990, ss215-219.	Vacant sites, open land, seriously injured amenity value within authority's area.	Serve notice of action to be taken.	Local authority	Owner or occupier. May appeal to Magistrate.	
Building Act 1984, s76.	Action by local authority if EPA 1990 action would cause undue delay.	Serve notice of action that LA will take, re: abatement of statutory nuisance.	Local authority		
Occupiers Liability Acts 1957 and 1984.	Common duty of care to visitors of site.			Occupier with 'sufficient degree of control'.	Includes lawful visitors and trespassers. Defence of *volenti non fit injuria*.
Health & Safety at Work Act 1974.	General duty to ensure health, safety and welfare of employees.	Criminal sanctions.	HSE	Employer.	
Criminal Justice & Public Order Act 1994.	'Damage to the land itself'.	Criminal sanctions.	Police		Aimed at 'travellers' but equally applicable to other situations.

TABLE A

TYPE OF RECEPTOR	DESCRIPTION OF HARM
Human beings	Death, serious injury, cancer or other disease, genetic mutation, birth defects, or the impairment of reproductive functions. Disease is to be taken to mean an unhealthy condition of the body or some part thereof.
Any living organism or ecological system within any habitat notified under section 28, declared under section 35 or designated under section 36 of the Wildlife and Countryside Act 1981, any European Site within the meaning of Regulation 10 of the Conservation (Natural Habitats etc) Regulations 1994 or any habitat or site afforded policy protection under paragraph 13 of Planning Policy Guidance Note 9 on nature conservation or Planning Guidance (Wales): Planning Policy (that is, candidate Special Areas of Conservation, potential Special Protection Areas and listed Ramsar sites).	Harm which results in an irreversible or other substantial adverse change in the functioning of the habitat or site. (In determining what constitutes a substantial adverse change, the local authority should have regard to the advice of English Nature, Scottish Natural Heritage or the Countryside Council for Wales, as the case may be, and to the requirements of the Conservation (Natural Habitats etc) Regulations 1994.)
Property in the form of livestock, of other owned animals, of wild animals which are the subject of shooting or fishing rights or of crops.	Death, disease or other physical damage such that there is a substantial loss in their value. For this purpose, a substantial loss should be regarded as occurring when a substantial proportion of the animals or crops are no longer fit for the purpose for which they were intended. In many cases, a loss of 10% of the value can be regarded as a benchmark for what constitutes a substantial loss.
Property in the form of buildings, where 'building' has the meaning given in section 336(1) of the Town and Country Planning Act 1990, that is, " 'building' means any structure or erection, and any part of a building ... but does not include plant or machinery comprised in a building".	Structural failure or substantial damage. For this purpose, substantial damage should be regarded as occurring when any part of the building ceases to be capable of being used for the purpose for which it is or was intended.

Table 4-8: Conditions for Significant Possibility of Significant Harm, for Different Effects within "Table A" of the draft Statutory Guidance

TABLE B

DESCRIPTIONS OF SIGNIFICANT HARM TO RECEPTORS	CONDITIONS FOR THERE BEING A SIGNIFICANT POSSIBILITY OF SIGNIFICANT HARM
Effects on the health of humans from the intake of, or other exposure to, a contaminant.	If the intake by, or other exposure of, the humans involved as receptors in the pollutant linkage in question, over all or part of their lifetimes, of, or to, the pollutant in that linkage would be of an amount which would be unacceptable when assessed in relation to appropriate, authoritative and scientifically based information on the toxicological properties of that contaminant (or, where such information is normally compiled by reference to a chemical class of contaminants, of that class). Such an assessment should take into account the relative contribution of the pollutant linkage in question to the aggregate intake of the relevant substance(s) by the humans concerned. Toxicological properties should be taken to include carcinogenic, mutagenic and teratogenic and other similar properties.
All other effects specified in Table A on human beings (particularly by way of explosion or fire).	If the level of risk of significant harm (as defined in relation to human beings in Table A), assessed in relation to appropriate, authoritative and scientifically based information relevant to the pollutant linkage in question, is unacceptable. Such an assessment should take into account the levels of risk of effects of the kind in question which have been judged unacceptable in other contexts.

Table 4-8 (continued) 191

DESCRIPTIONS OF SIGNIFICANT HARM TO RECEPTORS	CONDITIONS FOR THERE BEING A SIGNIFICANT POSSIBILITY OF SIGNIFICANT HARM
All effects specified in Table A on any habitat or site mentioned in that Table.	If significant harm (as defined in relation to habitats and sites in Table A) is more likely than not to result from the pollutant linkage in question. An assessment for this purpose should take into account the relevant appropriate, authoritative and scientifically based information for the pollutant linkage in question, particularly in relation to ecotoxicological effects of the pollutant.
All effects mentioned in Table A on property in the form of livestock, of other owned animals, of wild animals which are the subject of shooting or fishing rights or of crops.	If significant harm (as defined in relation to such property in Table A) is more likely than not to result from the pollutant linkage in question. An assessment should be made for this purpose, taking into account the relevant appropriate, authoritative and scientifically based information for the pollutant linkage, particularly in relation to ecotoxicological effects of the pollutant.
All effects mentioned in Table A on property in the form of buildings, where 'building' has the same meaning as in that Table.	If significant harm (as defined in relation to such property in Table A) is such that it is more likely than not that such significant harm will result from the pollutant linkage in question during the maximum expected economic life of the building. An assessment should be made for this purpose, taking into account the relevant appropriate, authoritative and scientifically based information for the pollutant linkage in question.

Statutory nuisances and inspections therefor

79.—(1) Subject to subsections (2) to (6) below, the following matters constitute "statutory nuisances" for the purposes of this Part, that is to say—

(a) any premises in such a state as to be prejudicial to health or a nuisance;

(b) smoke emitted from premises so as to be prejudicial to health or a nuisance;

(c) fumes or gases emitted from premises so as to be prejudicial to health or a nuisance;

(d) any dust, steam, smell or other effluvia arising on industrial, trade or business premises and being prejudicial to health or a nuisance;

(e) any accumulation or deposit which is prejudicial to health or a nuisance;

(f) any animal kept in such a place or manner as to be prejudicial to health or a nuisance;

(g) noise emitted from premises so as to be prejudicial to health or a nuisance;

(ga) noise that is prejudicial to health or a nuisance and is emitted from or caused by a vehicle, machinery, or equipment in the street;

(h) any other matter declared by any enactment to be a statutory nuisance.

Chapter 5

THE COMMON LAW AND WASTE-RELATED OPERATIONS

INTRODUCTION

Since 1989, nine major pieces of primary legislation have been introduced specifically to deal with "environmental" issues and against this background the continued utility of common law remedies is frequently questioned. There is no unequivocal answer and while some authors hold that:

"The private law of nuisance ... remains one of the most effective weapons in the armoury of the citizen",[1]

and

"The common law continues to play an important role in providing a form of redress for those suffering health and property damage, notwithstanding a comprehensive set of environmental legislation dealing with pollution control",[2]

others are less optimistic as to its future:

"The common law of nuisance remains necessary where the plaintiff seeks damages or where for some reason the public body is unable or unwilling to act, but we are witnessing here, as in other areas of tort, the steady ousting of private law by public law."[3]

Nevertheless, there are a number of situations for which the common law provides a satisfactory, and often the only, remedy and while its use by the regulatory agencies may be limited, it is essential for a waste manager to appreciate fully the potential liabilities it imposes on his operations and the circumstances under which it may be of benefit to him in relation to the activities of third parties.

Since the development of common law proceeds on an incremental, case-by-case basis, it is less structured than statutory provisions and has a greater potential for change as different aspects of a given area receive

---

[1]   C Pugh, in *Whose Environment is it Anyway?*, Law Centres Federation, London, 1990.
[2]   Andrew Bryce, *Legal Times*, Environmental Supplement, 16 October 1996.
[3]   *Winfield and Jolowicz on Tort, 13th Edition*, Sweet & Maxwell, London, 1989.

attention by the courts. Indeed, Tromans and Turrall-Clarke[1] note:

> "Any attempt to extract clear principles from the common law relating to environmental problems is an exercise certain to lead to frustration."

However, the decisions reached are not without reference to current or future statutory provisions (note Lord Goff's comments in *Cambridge* regarding statutory civil liability for historical pollution) or to the public policy considerations of judgments which might "open the floodgates" to a large number of cases (as in certain areas of economic loss in negligence).

The present chapter considers the common law from the point of view of its use in relation to waste-related activities and for a more detailed review the reader is directed towards the standard reference texts on the law of tort. Before considering the relevant branches of common law, the remedies available and the limitations in its application will be discussed, and within this framework its advantages and disadvantages will become apparent, and its potential applications identified.

THE ROLE OF THE COMMON LAW

Availability to Environmental Issues

There are two important factors concerning the availability of common law to waste-related issues which distinguish it from statutory provisions, namely:

— there is no concept of "waste" within the common law; and

— common law is only concerned with actions which result in harm to persons or property.

The first factor is important, for by not according a special status to an item by classifying it as "waste", any action which is brought must be based upon the effect that item has upon persons or property, or the consequences of the operations and activities associated with its handling or use. In the United States, the rule in *Rylands v Fletcher* (q.v.) has developed into a general rule of strict liability for damage caused by "ultra-hazardous operations" but, as Lord Goff notes in *Cambridge*, the Law Commission and the UK courts have been unwilling to proceed down this path. By contrast, in Scotland the rule of *Rylands v Fletcher* was described by Lord Fraser of Tullybelton in *RHM Bakeries (Scotland) v Strathclyde Regional Council* as having "no place in Scots law, and the suggestion that it has, is an heresy which ought to be extirpated".

---

[1]   *Contaminated Land*, S Tromans and R Turrall-Clarke, Sweet & Maxwell, 1994.

The second factor has implications both on the type of damage covered by common law and the persons who may bring an action. Being constrained by personal and property interests, the common law excludes virtually all issues associated with "the unowned environment" and, except for the discretionary granting of a *quia timet* injunction, it is generally concerned with balancing the competing individual rights once the polluting event has occurred. Thus, it seldom acts in a preventative manner and when dealing with remediation it can only address those aspects associated with personal or property issues. For example, following a pollution incident, as in *Marquis of Granby v Bakewell UDC*, the court may award the plaintiff a "pecuniary sum which would make good, as far as money could do so, the loss which he had suffered as a natural result of the wrong done to him", and in this case the calculation was based upon:

— the number of fish killed and their value to the fishery;

— the number of fish needed to re-stock the river, taking into account the value of:

— replacement fish when turned into the river;

— the destruction of fish food in the river; and

— the locality in which the fish were poisoned.

However, the fauna and flora which are not associated with the plaintiff's claim will be excluded. Furthermore, when an award is made in relation to environmentally-related damage, there is no compunction on the successful plaintiff to employ it to remedy the damage incurred.

Limitations on Bringing an Action

Within statutory legislation on the environment, there are now few restrictions on non-statutory bodies taking enforcement action and, given access to the relevant environmental information, this provides a powerful tool for individuals and groups with specific concerns in this area. However, the opportunities within the common law are more limited, although the availability of the environmental registers established under statute may provide useful evidence.

A person may only bring an action in private nuisance in relation to the unreasonable interference in his use or enjoyment of his *own* land, or of some right he has in relation to it. Following *Malone v Lasky*, it was held that only owners of freehold premises, lessees, and licensees with a right of exclusive occupation could bring an action in private nuisance, and other groups such as lodgers, hotel guests and the immediate relatives of the owner were potentially excluded. This ruling was relaxed in *Khorasandjian v Bush*, in which the court held that a daughter residing in her parents' home could bring an action in private nuisance, although a subsequent decision of the Court of Appeal in *Hunter v Canary Wharf Ltd* interpreted these requirements more restrictively. When *Hunter* was subsequently considered by the House of Lords, their lordships held that "*Khoransandjan v Bush* must be over-ruled in so far as it held that a mere licensee could sue in private nuisance".

Within public nuisance, the interference complained of must "materially affect the comfort and convenience of life of a *class of Her Majesty's subjects*". Unlike private nuisance, a proprietary interest in land is *not* required but the plaintiff must show that he has suffered special damage over and above that suffered by the community as a whole. Although there are no guidelines regarding the numbers of persons who must be affected, in *Attorney General v PYA Quarries*, Denning LJ stated:

> "Public nuisance is a nuisance which is so widespread in its range or so indiscriminate in its effect that it would not be reasonable to expect one person to take proceedings on his own responsibility to put a stop to it, but that it should be taken on the responsibility of the community at large."

An interest in property is a component of negligence, as demonstrated in *Bruton and NRA v Clarke*, a civil action for the recovery of costs following a pollution incident, in which His Honour Judge Mellor ruled that the NRA could not sue in negligence for economic loss where no property interests of its own had been damaged.

Group Actions

It will be appreciated that in actions concerning pollution damage (as opposed to the judicial review of planning or other decisions), the necessity of an interest in property or land, or in personal injury, will significantly restrict the involvement of common interest groups and pressure groups. As noted earlier in relation to the *Hunter* case, groups of local residents may bring a common law action but national and international groups will have difficulty unless one of their members is affected. However, one organisation which has been particularly successful in pursuing such actions is the Anglers Conservation Association (ACA) which since its inception in the 1940s has initiated over 5,000 cases, yet lost only two (*The Guardian*, 10 June 1995).

In addition to actions resulting from "direct" pollution damage, there is the possibility of health-related claims based upon the alleged effects of emissions to the environment. While these may be individual or group actions, in view of the "dilute and disperse" approach to emissions which was quite common in the UK until recently, it is unusual for such claims to exist in isolation. There is a high degree of commonality, in both the sources of pollution responsible and the legal principles involved, between these and actions arising on the basis of occupational health, or on safety-related claims. This link was highlighted in *Margereson and Hancock v J W Roberts Ltd* where, in a landmark decision on a negligence claim for personal injury resulting from the operation of an asbestos factory, it was held that a duty of care was owed to residents in its immediate vicinity. Consequently, if a company allows a pollutant to escape it can be liable for causally-related disease.

As noted in Chapter 1, there are a number of problems in determining at what stage an organisation is considered in law to be aware of the deleterious effects of its activities, and it is difficult to give a satisfactory answer, since each case will be determined on its own technical and legal factors. It is important to emphasise to organisations the importance of ensuring that they maintain a current awareness of all the environmental effects of their business, possibly through the introduction of an environmental management system. However, to fulfil the "foreseeability" objectives, such a scheme would need to have the capability of tracking developments of medical knowledge in known and suspected problem areas, and also following the improvements in analytical techniques which permit a greater knowledge of all emissions to the environment. Only by an awareness of all the potential environmental effects of its operations, including heat, light, noise and vibration, and ionising/non-ionising radiation, can an organisation expect to introduce the appropriate controls as and when required.

Standards of Proof

Unlike criminal actions, in which the standard of proof is that of "beyond reasonable doubt", civil cases need only be proved "on the balance of probabilities". While this is of assistance to the plaintiff in a civil case, there are a number of other factors which add to the uncertainty of the outcome, not least of which is the use of imprecise standards for judging the behaviour of the parties concerned. In statutory legislation, there is the potential for unambiguous standards of performance, such as the definition of specific performance criteria within authorisations and in discharge consents, although problems can arise in non-specific or "general" pollution offences which are based upon undefined parameters such as "environmental harm" and "pollution" (see discussion in Chapter 4 on the cases of *Eggers* and *Dovermoss*), and measures using nineteenth-century terminology of "poisonous, noxious or polluting matter".

Nevertheless, these problems seem trivial in comparison with many of the concepts within the common law, such as "reasonableness", "proximity", "hyper-sensitive" and "foreseeability". While such uncertainties permit a degree of judicial freedom which it may be expeditious to exercise in some circumstances, such as in strict liability cases, it has been argued in the article by Wilkinson, "Negligence after Murphy: Time to Re-think" ([1991] 50 (1) *CLJ* 58), that the use of such imprecise concepts leads to "sloppy thinking" and arbitrary decisions.

However, there are certain areas of common law associated with individual rights, e.g. trespass and riparian rights, which are actionable *per se* and it is only necessary to prove an infringement of these rights, and "harm" need not be shown. This makes their use an extremely powerful tool in environmental cases when it can be demonstrated that these rights have been infringed.

COMMON LAW REMEDIES

Although the common law provides a number of potential remedies, it should be borne in mind that some are at the discretion of the court and should not be considered as alternatives. In the context of environmental matters, the common law provides for the award of damages to the plaintiff or the granting of an injunction requiring the defendant to undertake, or refrain from undertaking, a specific activity. In addition, there is the possibility of abatement (or "self-help") action, although this is not an option available to or approved by the courts, whose involvement is invariably *post facto*.

The appropriate remedy to be sought is dependent upon the nature of the environmental problem and while an isolated, major incident may be remedied by an appropriate award of damages, smaller levels of pollution continuing over a period of time may require action to prevent their build-up, and injunctive relief may be more appropriate.

Following the Limitation Act 1980, as amended by the Latent Damage Act 1986, actions in tort must be brought within six years of the date when the cause of action accrued, although for personal injuries (and defamation) the period is three years. Where the tort is actionable *per se*, as in trespass and riparian rights, the time period commences at the moment the act was committed, whether the injured party is aware of it or not.

In nuisance and negligence, the time runs from when the damage occurred, although there are clearly problems in a number of environmentally-related areas in which the damage is not immediately apparent. For such "latent damage", if greater than six years have elapsed, the period of limitation becomes three years from the "starting date", i.e. the earliest date on which the plaintiff had the knowledge and the right to bring an action. Knowledge here includes that which the plaintiff might reasonably have been expected to acquire or ascertain, with appropriate expert advice where necessary. Where personal injuries are not involved, there is a maximum period of 15 years within which to bring an action in negligence.

Damages

Damages are the principal remedy for loss in tort and are normally awarded to compensate a plaintiff for his loss or injury, on the basis of *restitutio in integrum*, and the aim of the award is, as far as is possible, to place the plaintiff in the position he would have been in prior to the wrongful act. While this is relatively straightforward with regard to damage to property and to personal injury (rather than illness), it is more difficult to apply where the pecuniary element cannot be defined precisely, such as in relation to pain and trauma and to environmental impairment. The problems of assessing environmental damage are particularly acute in cases of maritime pollution, in view of its widespread effects and the range of potential claimants. Although generally covered by international conventions and statutory legislation, the issues raised are similar to those in common law and the paper by Jacobsson and Trotz[1] provides a detailed consideration of these. In addition to compensatory damages, the court may award contemptuous, nominal or exemplary/punitive damages and in these cases the intention is clearly non-compensatory. However, in almost every case, the award made by the court relates to *past* losses suffered by the plaintiff and, although there remains the possibility of equitable damages in respect of *future* losses, such payments are not a favoured option since they effectively legitimise a future unlawful act of the defendant through payments made in advance.

Equitable damages may only be awarded in lieu of an injunction in exceptional circumstances, where the plaintiff's right is:

— small;

— capable of being estimated in monetary terms; and

---

[1] "The Definition of Pollution Damage in the 1984 Protocols to the 1969 Civil Liability and the 1971 Fund Convention", M Jacobsson and N Trotz, [1986] *J Maritime Law and Commerce*, 17, 467.

— where it would be oppressive to grant an injunction.

In *Pride of Derby*, an alternative solution was imposed, for while the court did not award damages in lieu of the two year suspension of the injunction restraining each of the defendants from polluting the river, it placed the defendant under an undertaking to indemnify the plaintiff against all damage arising out of the suspension of the injunction.

Compensatory Damages – Land and Property
In environmental cases, the principal of *restitutio in integrum* may be applied in a number of different ways and the plaintiff may be awarded:

— the costs of the clean-up required to restore the land or property to its value prior to the pollution damage;

— the expenditure incurred by the plaintiff in procuring alternative assets as a replacement for those damaged; or

— the difference in value of the property, etc. before and after the pollution incident.

The approach adopted by the courts was noted in Chapter 1 in relation to *Earl of Harrington v Derby Corporation* where, as a remedy for the river pollution from a number of sources/causes, the plaintiff claimed:

— an injunction restraining the defendant from polluting the river and causing a nuisance; and

— damages in respect of:

  — the silting up of a lake;

  — the loss of a waterwheel and the expenses incurred in the replacement of this source of power with a pump and engine house;

  — pollution of a well and the expenses of obtaining a new supply of water;

  — depreciation to a house on the river bank and to the castle of one of the plaintiffs.

With regard to the damages claimed, while these were allowed in respect of the provision of a new water supply and source of power and injury to the house and fishing, they were *not* awarded in respect to the loss of amenity relating to the castle and the silting up of the lake. Furthermore, the court held that there was no limitation period for an incident involving continuing pollution:

"If ... one damage is done today and another subsequently, there is nothing to prevent a fresh action *toties qoties* fresh damage is inflicted."

An insight into setting the quantum of damages is given in *Cambridge Water Company v Eastern Counties Leather plc and Hutchings and Harding Ltd* where, although the plaintiff's claims were not upheld, Mr Justice Kennedy stated his opinion on the matter "against the possibility that this case goes further". The pollution of the borehole at Sawston Mill by organochlorides had necessitated that the plaintiff consider a number of options and both parties put forward to the court *technical* arguments concerning the feasibility of these options and whether CWC were justified in selecting the chosen option of sinking a new borehole, with its attendant costs.

The judge rejected the defendant's argument that the damages should be based upon the actual cost of the abandoned borehole, increased by an appropriate inflation correction and treated it as if it were a redundant asset. He considered instead that the costs of sinking a new borehole, subject to certain adjustments, were an appropriate basis for an award.

Compensatory Damages – Personal Injury
Unlike common law actions relating to accidents resulting from, *inter alia*, the failure of health and safety provisions, most environmental claims are the result of the general debilitating effects caused by exposure to toxic emissions and as a result the nature of the claims is somewhat different. However, there are some instances in which direct physical injury is suffered as a result of environmental emissions, as in *Gertsen & ors v Municipality of Metropolitan Toronto & ors*. In this case, the build-up of methane from a negligently constructed and managed landfill resulted in an explosion which caused damage to property and injury to one of the plaintiffs, Floris Gertsen. Both defendants were found to be negligent in a number of areas and, in addition to damages for nuisance and damage to property, Mr Gertsen was given an award in respect of personal injuries and loss of earnings. As with property damage, such claims are subject to scrutiny and expert testimony on both sides, and here Mr Justice Lerner noted of the plaintiff "he did not minimise his complaints. He was prepared to attribute his further loss of hearing, haemorrhoids, and heart problems, to this explosion, although his counsel was more realistic."

More typical of environmental actions are cases such as *Margereson and Hancock v J W Roberts* and *Whittaker v BBA*. Both concerned asbestos-related illness and they highlight the risks to business which are associated with such claims. In *Whittaker*, the plaintiff began to suffer from the symptoms of mesothelioma late in 1993, although his exposure to asbestos was the result of a few months' employment with the defendant, between February 1943 and July 1944. Despite his age, total damages of £88,488.10 were awarded, based upon general damages directly associated with the illness of £35,000, a dependency claim of £46,692 and other miscellaneous damages.

Awards to the plaintiffs in *Margereson and Hancock* were of £65,000 and £50,000 respectively, the second plaintiff bringing her claim under the Fatal Accidents Act on behalf of her husband's estate, as allowed under the Law Reform (Miscellaneous Provisions) Act 1934. One of the plaintiff's legal advisors suggested that exemplary damages (q.v.) might have been appropriate, although, as now, they were not available for such cases. However, the defendant's parent company, T & N plc, did suffer a substantial financial penalty, for on the day of the judgment shares in the owning company fell by 12 pence, reducing its market value by £70 million.

Contemptuous Damages and Nominal Damages
While the term "damages" is generally associated with the award of large sums to the plaintiff,

> *"... Monster, Monster, dread our fury,*
> *There's the judge, and we're the Jury,*
> *Come, substantial damages !"*
>
> W S Gilbert, *Trial by Jury*, 1875

there are occasions on which only a token payment is made. In cases in which the court has formed a low opinion of the plaintiff's legal claim, or where his conduct morally, if not legally, justified the defendant's action, then the court will award a derisory sum, referred to as contemptuous damages. In addition, there is a possibility that costs, which are at the judge's discretion, will not be awarded.

Nominal damages are awarded in cases where the plaintiff's legal right has been infringed such as in torts which are actionable *per se*, e.g. riparian rights or trespass to land, but no damage has resulted. The plaintiff may also be deprived of the payment of his costs or may be required to pay the costs of both sides, although this is unlikely in cases where he was completely successful in his claim and no misconduct was attributed to him.

Exemplary or Punitive Damages
Common law retains the possibility of an award of exemplary or punitive damages which exceed the losses suffered by the plaintiff, and these have the objective of deterring the defendant and others from committing a tort which results in their financial gain. Following *Rookes v Barnard*, their use has been restricted to classes of tort which were subject to the award of

exemplary damages prior to 1964, and where there has been:

— oppressive, arbitrary or unconstitutional action by servants of the government; or

— where the defendant's conduct was calculated to make a profit in excess of any damages payable.

Although claimed in the actions resulting from the Camelford incident, when a drinking water supply was negligently contaminated – *AB & ors v South West Water Services Ltd* and *Gibbons & ors v South West Water Services Ltd* – it was held that exemplary damages in cases of public nuisance fell outside the categories in *Rookes v Barnard*. With regard to breaches of Community law, in *Factorame (No 5)* it was held that these were of the character of breaches of statutory duty and as such could only result in compensatory damages, unless there was express statutory provision for punitive damages. The Law Commission has recently recommended that within the law of tort a wider availability of exemplary damages might be appropriate, and this could find a ready application in environmental cases where such an award would provide an incentive to organisations to consider the wider implications of their actions.

Injunctive Relief

The issue of an injunction is an equitable remedy available at the discretion of the court and, while there is no reason why it should not be employed to prevent the continuation or repetition of any tort, it is generally sought against nuisance, continuing or repeated trespass, or interference with contract. Injunctions may be used to prohibit the commission or continuance of a wrongful act or the continuance of some wrongful omission. For an injunction to be granted, the alleged act or omission must be continuing at the date of the commencement of the (legal) action (though not necessarily at the date of the court hearing) with a threat that the activity will continue.

This is a discretionary remedy and the court will take into account the seriousness of the alleged activity and the balance of competing interests between the plaintiff and the defendant, i.e. the court will assess the "social utility" of the activity in question and will compare its public importance with the alleged interference of the plaintiff's rights.

Before examining the effectiveness of injunctions in practice, it is necessary to consider the forms which might be issued.

Perpetual and Interlocutory Injunctions
In most cases, an injunction is issued at the end of the trial when the court has considered the balance of interests between the plaintiff and defendant,

and this is referred to as a perpetual injunction. However, if it can be shown that there is a serious question to be tried, as in *Laws v Florinplace Ltd*, the plaintiff may seek an interlocutory injunction before the start of the proceedings. In this case, the court must decide whether the balance of convenience lies in granting or refusing it (see *American Cyanamid Co v Ethicon Ltd*). The granting of an interlocutory injunction does not pre-judge the final verdict and the plaintiff may be required to give an undertaking to pay any damages resulting from the injunction, should the court find for the defendant.

Mandatory Injunctions

In most cases, injunctions are prohibitory and require the plaintiff to discontinue an act or omission. However, the court may also order a defendant to undertake positive action to remedy the consequences of his actions. However, such mandatory injunctions are only awarded where the plaintiff can show there is a very strong probability that serious damage will occur in the future. The general principles for such an award were outlined in *Redland Bricks Ltd v Morris*, and are:

— damages will not be an adequate remedy for the harm caused;

— the behaviour of the defendant in his dealings with the plaintiff and the court, and the cost of remedying earlier activities, will be important factors for the court to consider;

— if a mandatory injunction is issued, the court must be careful to specify clearly what has to be done, in order that contractors can be given clear instructions for undertaking the work.

"Quia Timet" Injunctions

A *quia timet* ("because he fears") injunction may be sought by a plaintiff in order to prevent or restrain the defendant from undertaking some threatened action, which if carried out would cause him substantial damage and for which money would be neither an adequate nor a sufficient remedy. However, the power to grant a *quia timet* injunction is seldom exercised, since the plaintiff must show that damage is both inevitable and imminent. Furthermore, a court will not issue an injunction to compel a defendant to undertake an action which he would do without its intervention.

Abatement

In English law, there is a long history of abatement or "self-help" as a remedy for certain torts such as trespass, goods wrongfully taken and property wrongfully on a plaintiff's land. However, there are a number of practical and legal reasons for exercising extreme caution before undertaking such a course of action. It has been held that self-help "many times occasions tumults and disorders" and embarking on this type of action may also destroy any right to a subsequent action in nuisance.

There are also problems in applying these ancient remedies – which evolved for the removal of cattle from land, lopping protruding roots and branches, etc. – to present day situations. In *Arthur and Another v Anker*, Sir Thomas Bingham stated:

> "[He] did not feel constrained to undertake heroic surgery to seek to apply that medieval remedy [distress damages fesant] to twentieth century facts [wheel clamping]",

although a *limited* right to legal self-help was acknowledged in *Co-operative Wholesale Society v British Railways Board*, in which Lord Justice Beldam held:

> "To deny an occupier the right to the cost of removal of a potential source of danger to his property, which the *court* had held was expenditure justifiably and reasonably incurred in the circumstances, could deter action being taken to prevent danger to visitors or workmen using the premises."

However, the court held that the right of abatement should be confined to cases where the security of lives or property required immediate and speedy action, or where such action could be exercised simply without recourse to litigation and where it would give no rise to argument or dispute. Where a "simple and speedy" application to a court could be made, the remedy of "self-help" was held to be neither appropriate nor desirable.

In general, before abatement is attempted the offending party should be given an opportunity to remove the nuisance, unless this is impracticable and, in undertaking any action, the least damaging option should be taken. Furthermore, it was held in *Midland Bank plc v Bardwell Property Services Ltd and John Willmott (GB) Ltd* that no cause of action arises until there is actual physical damage, and damages cannot be awarded in anticipation of future problems.

Where damage results from water-borne contamination, the common law rights associated with water are a further consideration and some guidance may be given by *Home Brewery Co Ltd v William Davis & Co Ltd (Leicester)*. Although an occupier of land is under no obligation to accept water resulting from natural, unchannelled flow from higher, adjacent land, he may only take *reasonable* steps to prevent its ingress. Any unreasonable measures which give rise to reasonably foreseeable damage to the higher land may result in an action for nuisance.

COMMON LAW ACTIONS IN PRACTICE

In 1867, the Royal Commission on the Pollution of Rivers stated in its Third Report:

> "It [bringing a common law action] is an expensive remedy. For the same money which is spent over a hard fought litigation against a single manufacturer, a Conservancy Board armed with proper powers, might for years keep safe from all abuse, a long extensive river with hundreds of manufactories situated on its banks."

While the situation now is clearly different from that in the mid-nineteenth century when only ~15% of the population had recourse to actions in nuisance as a result of the property-related criterion, common law actions remain a lengthy and expensive process. In *Graham v ReChem International Limited*, a total of 198 days of the court's time, spread over thirteen months, were taken in an action in nuisance and negligence on the alleged effect of the airborne emissions from a waste incinerator on farming operations. Similarly, in *Bruton and NRA v Clarke*, despite the defendant having pleaded guilty, the complexities of calculating damages in this water pollution case took two weeks to determine.

It is becoming apparent that, in addition to the legal complexities of common law actions, the uncertainties associated with environmental issues add a further complicating factor and often need detailed technical consideration. Useful indicators of the utility of common law actions are:

— the number of occasions in which it is employed in comparison with statutory provisions;

— the profile of the typical plaintiff (i.e. commercial organisation/ national or international pressure group/"common interest group" with legal aid); and

— the paucity of "landmark" cases relating specifically to the environment in each of the major classes of tort discussed below.

TRESPASS

Reference has already been made to the potential utility of this tort in relation to environmental pollution, since it is actionable *per se* and requires no proof of damage. Consequently, the plaintiff need only show that there has been an interference to his rights and from the above discussion it is clear that an injunction, rather than damages, would be the appropriate remedy. However, despite the simplicity of this tort, it is generally considered as being "under-developed" in relation to environmental actions and, apart from its use at the turn of the century in *Jones v Llanrwst UDC*, it has had few subsequent applications in relation to pollution.

Trespass is "an unjustifiable interference with the plaintiff's possession of land" and requires *direct* interference with the plaintiff's personal or proprietary rights, and *intention* or *negligence* on the part of the defendant. Potentially, trespass may be applied to situations involving the pollution of land by contaminated water (as in *Jones v Llanrwst*) or solid matter, vertical or horizontal intrusion upon the sub-soil (as in *Cox v Glue*) or interference with air space (as in *Woollerton & Wilson Ltd v Richard Costain Ltd*).

In *Jones v Llanrwst*, faecal matter from the defendant's drains passed into the river and accumulated on its gravel banks, which were owned by the plaintiff. "Intent" was satisfied by the *intentional* discharge of sewage into the river, and "directness" by the *proximity* of the outfall to the plaintiff's land and the consequent inevitability that it would discharge sewage onto it. However, despite this much cited "successful" application of trespass, in view of the public utility of the defendant's activities, the injunction restraining them from "causing sewage to flow untreated into the river, and solid or excrementitious matter ... to be a nuisance to the plaintiff or his tenants" was suspended for eighteen months to allow remedial work to be undertaken.

The importance of the inevitability component of trespass was demonstrated in *Esso Petroleum Ltd v Southport Corporation* where, as a result of the jettison of 400 tonnes of oil from a tanker, there was damage to the foreshore and the owners of the tanker were sued for negligence, nuisance and trespass. Lord Radcliffe rejected the claim for trespass, indicating that, unlike *Jones v Llanrwst* and *Smith v Great Western Railway Company*, there was no certainty as to the final destination of oil which was

> "... jettisoned at sea, committed to the action of wind and wave, with *no certainty* as far as it appears, how, when or under what conditions it may come to shore",

Lord Tucker adding that, where trespass was alleged under such conditions, the action should be against the ship's master and not its owners.

Since the case was heard (in 1956), there have been significant advances in mathematical modelling techniques and it should now be possible to predict the probability (i.e. a measure of the certainty) of the oil coming ashore at the relevant time. As the law stands, the use of trespass for marine pollution is limited and likewise the inevitability component has prevented its use for most airborne emissions. However, with regard to the latter, it was held in the Canadian case of *McDonald v Associated Fuels* that an action in trespass would have succeeded where carbon monoxide was negligently blown into a house during the delivery of sawdust fuel. Although the trespass itself was not intentional, the act whereby it entered the house was.

Trespass has been applied successfully to the interference of air space by tower cranes on building land adjacent to the plaintiff's land (*Woollerton & Wilson Ltd v Richard Costain Ltd*) although, in this particular case, the injunction was suspended until the works were completed.

RIPARIAN RIGHTS

The owners or occupiers of land adjoining a river or stream enjoy a number of "riparian rights" for which the common law provides a number of specific and powerful remedies for any breach. While such rights assist landowners by providing a useful supplement to other statutory and common law remedies, it should not be forgotten that they may also be used *against* the landowner by other downstream riparian owners.

The principle requirement for the existence of riparian rights is the ownership or occupancy of land which is in actual contact with the river or stream, either laterally or vertically. There is no distinction between the rights on navigable or tidal rivers and those on non-navigable rivers – see *North Shore Railway v Pion*. It is important that the course of the river is natural rather than man-made, although non-natural riparian rights may be achieved through an easement or by prescription. While certain riparian rights relate to the bed and banks of the watercourse, it is more pertinent to consider those which relate to the use and flow of the running stream.

Riparian proprietors own the *alveus* (the river bed) up to the mid-point of the river (*medium filum fluminis*), although they may not undertake any action which produces a sensible effect on the river, its purity or its flow. (Compare this with the problems encountered by the NRA in *NRA v Biffa Waste Services Ltd.*)

While they do not own the water itself, riparian owners are entitled to receive it in its natural state, subject only to *reasonable* use for *ordinary purposes*, as in *Chasemore v Richards*. This does not apply to water percolating thorough underground strata "which has no certain course and no defined limit, but oozes through the soil in every direction in which rain penetrates". However, as demonstrated in *Ballard v Tomlinson*, an action in nuisance can arise from the contamination of percolating waters once these are extracted for the plaintiff's use.

Riparian rights were concisely summarised by Lord McNaghten in *Young & Co v Bankier Distillery*, viz:

> "A riparian proprietor is entitled to have the water of the stream on which his property lies, flow down as it has been accustomed to flow down to his property, subject to the ordinary use of the flowing water by upper proprietors, and to such further use, if any, on their part in connection with their property as may be reasonable in the circumstances. Every riparian owner is thus entitled to the water of his stream, in its natural flow, without sensible diminution or increase, and without sensible alteration in its character or quality."

The invasion of riparian rights is treated similarly to trespass and, in *Nicholls v Ely Sugar Beet Factory*, it was held that it was unnecessary to prove pecuniary loss and that injury to this legal right carried with it the right to damages. Following *Young & Co*, it is only necessary for the plaintiff to demonstrate a "sensible alteration" to the quality or quantity of the river, and in this case it was the hardness of the water that was changed as a result of mine working operations and this rendered it unsuitable for the plaintiff's distillery. In *Cook v South West Water*, it was held that, although the defendant had a licence to discharge effluent, this licence did not make reference to the discharge of detergents and thus did not provide a defence to an action for the infringement of riparian rights.

The pollution of a river by sources other than those of the defendant cannot be used as a defence to a suit to restrain pollution by the defendant (*Crossley v Lightowler*) and the defendant need only be shown to be contributing to the pollution. In *Young & Co*, Lord McNaghten stated that "any invasion of this (riparian) right causing actual damage or calculated to found a claim which *may ripen into an adverse right* may entitle the party ... to the intervention of the court." However, in *Cambridge* at the first instance, Kennedy J reviewed this judgment and stated:

> "I cannot think that it is right that a contributor *whose addition is insignificant* must be held liable because his mite is associated with a clear case of pollution by another. I suspect there can be no one rule to meet every case and that every case must be seen on its own."

While all of the above undoubtedly assists the riparian owner, in order to succeed in an action it is nevertheless necessary for the plaintiff to overcome a number of hurdles. He may take water for "ordinary purposes" which includes domestic usage and the supply of water for cattle, and for "extraordinary purposes" provided that the water is substantially undiminished in volume and unaltered in character. (It would be difficult to argue that the distilling of whisky in *Young & Co* satisfied these criteria.) Furthermore, the owner's use of water must relate to operations *within* the tenement, as held in *McCartney v Londonderry and Lough Swilly Railway Company Ltd,* where although the intended use of the water was reasonable from the point of view of the railway company (and would only have prevented the plaintiff's mill from operating for three minutes each day), it was in excess of their rights and an infringement of those of the plaintiff.

The absence of an absolute quality standard is not particularly beneficial, for whilst there need only be a "sensible alteration", this must be against some initial benchmark. This is also important when an upstream owner claims a prescriptive right to pollute. Over the twenty-year period necessary for prescription, the pollution must be known to the plaintiff and must remain essentially the same: in *Hulley v Silversprings Bleaching and Dyeing Company Ltd*, it was held that a progressive increase in the volume and concentration of contaminants was "destructive to the *certainty* and *uniformity* essential for prescription".

NEGLIGENCE

Negligence is defined as the breach of a legal duty to take care which results in damage, undesired by the defendant, to the plaintiff. Since it is a fault-based system, negligence is often applied where other common law remedies are unavailable although, in many cases, the plaintiff will sue in negligence in addition to trespass, nuisance or the rule in *Rylands v Fletcher.*

The principle features of the tort of negligence are the need to prove that:

— a duty of care was owed by the defendant to the plaintiff;

— the defendant has breached that duty of care; and

— the breach has given rise to a foreseeable loss.

Furthermore, in *Marc Rich & Co v Bishop Rock Marine*, it was held that:

"It was settled law that the elements of foreseeability and proximity as well as considerations of fairness, justice and reasonableness applied to all cases of negligence, whatever the nature of the harm sustained by the plaintiff."

Considering the frequency with which negligence is used in other areas such as health and safety, it has been used surprisingly little in relation to environmental problems. It is tentatively suggested that this might reflect the difficulty in determining the limits of a polluter's duty of care, in view of the widespread effect of a typical incident, for as Lawson J noted in *British Celanese v A H Hunt (Capacitors) Ltd*, "no-one owes a legal duty to the whole world". It is perhaps notable that in the relatively few successful applications of negligence in this area – *Gertsen v Municipality of Toronto, McDonald v Associated Fuels, Willis v FMC Machinery and Chemicals Ltd, Tutton v A D Walter* – the proximity of plaintiff and defendant and knowledge by the defendant of the plaintiff's activities were readily demonstrated.

With regard to the range and scope of activities which may give rise to an action in negligence, there have been a number of important developments and the significance of *Margereson and Hancock v J W Roberts* has already been noted. In *Hunter & ors v Canary Wharf Ltd*, it was held that the deposit of dust on homes resulting from construction activities was capable of giving rise to an action in negligence. However, a landowner was generally entitled to build on his land as he wished and, accordingly, would not be liable in nuisance because a large building he had erected had interfered with television reception. More importantly, a recent commercial court decision considered the extent to which it was possible to recover losses from the spillage of a hazardous chemical (*Losijska Plovidba v Transco Overseas Ltd*). The context of this case was an attempt to strike out certain points of claim and, against this background, the court established a number of important points:

— temporary contamination of property as a result of a polluting activity does constitute a physical damage;

— from the moment the plaintiff suffers damage of this sort, then the expenses of mitigating damage are fully recoverable.

Furthermore, there is the possibility that positive steps to mitigate the dangers of on-going pollution may constitute recoverable damage, once quantified, and may therefore be an exception to *Murphy*.

Although more pertinent to health and safety incidents, there have also been developments associated with "nervous shock" resulting from incidents, the House of Lords ruling in *Page v Smith* that there is no difference in negligence between "psychiatric" and "physical" injury suffered by the *primary* victim of an accident. However, *secondary* victims' claims are viewed more restrictively and a number of controls have been introduced on policy grounds – see *Alcock v Chief Constable of*

South Yorkshire Police. Furthermore, the Scottish courts have held that employees who witness accidents are owed no special duty of care (*Robertson and Rough v Forth Road Bridge Joint Board*).

With regard to the various limbs to the tort of negligence, *supra*, proof of the breach of duty is the least ambiguous. The requirement of "fairness, justice, and reasonableness" permits a high degree of judicial interpretation, and the concepts of duty of care and foreseeablilty have undergone a number of changes over the years. As with other torts requiring foreseeability – nuisance and the rule in *Rylands v Fletcher* – the term is critical for it embodies both the legal view of what is deemed as foreseeable and on what basis this is judged, and the state of knowledge available at the relevant time on which the decision is made.

In *Margereson and Hancock*, it was held that the starting point for the consideration of a duty of care was Lord Lloyd's statement in *Page v Smith* that:

> "The test in every case ought to be whether the defendant can reasonably foresee that his conduct will expose the plaintiff to the risk of personal injury."

With regard to environmental issues, it is important to note Mr Justice Holland's comment that "there is nothing in law that circumscribes the duty of care by reference to the factory wall".

Standards of foreseeability will be dependent upon the facts of the case and in *Margereson and Hancock* it was held that the potential harm of asbestos dust should have been *in the defendant's "corporate mind"* long before the birth of the first plaintiff in 1925. In *Cambridge* it was held that a *reasonable supervisor* would not have been in a position to have foreseen the consequences of the spillages of PCE prior to 1976. However, in *Graham v ReChem*, the benchmark for knowledge of the health-related effects of certain chlorinated compounds was a *scientific paper* written in 1977.

In addition to these developments in the scope of the duty of care, there have been important changes in the applicability of negligence to economic loss, i.e. purely financial loss such as that resulting from negligent statements or advice, where there is no direct physical injury to the plaintiff or damage to his property. Following the ruling in *Anns v Merton LBC*, awards in respect of economic loss were made in an increasing number of areas and the judgment was cited in no less than 189 cases over a period of 13 years. However, following *Murphy v Brentwood*, it was held that pure economic loss could only be recovered in tort where there had been reliance on negligent advice, as in *Hedley Byrne v Heller and Partners*, or a special relationship of proximity imposing on the tortfeasors a duty of care to safeguard the plaintiff from economic loss, as in *Junior Books v Veitchi*.

The provision of professional advice is of relevance to waste management operations where reliance is placed upon professional advice from, *inter alia*, surveyors, engineers, lawyers and "environmental consultants". This type of relationship *may* also exist under certain circumstances between organisations and the regulatory agencies, as in the (pre-*Murphy*) case of *Scott-Whitehead v National Coal Board & ors*, where the regional water company was held to be liable in nuisance for not informing a farmer of the increased salinity of water he was using for irrigation.

Whilst advice given by "environmental consultancies" may probably fall within the *Hedley Byrne* criteria, there are potential problems in view of the wide spectrum of activities encompassed by the term "environmental consultant", the absence of a single professional body for the regulation of their activities and the quite restricted time envelope within which they often operate, e.g. often immediately prior to contract signature for the purchase of land. The terms and conditions of their appointment and the scope of their professional indemnity cover are clearly of great importance.

There is a developing case law in this area of professional advice and in *Smith v Eric S Bush* it was held, in relation to a surveyor's duty, that a duty of care will arise when:

— it is reasonably foreseeable that if the advice is negligent, the recipient is likely to suffer loss;

— there is a sufficiently proximate relationship between the parties; and

— it is just and reasonable to impose the liability.

With regard to the second factor, this could include situations in which the surveyor is aware that reliance is being placed on his advice by third parties. A further concept of particular relevance to contaminated land was introduced in *Roberts v J Hampson & Co*, by which a surveyor would be expected to "follow the trail of suspicion" where he had doubts or uncertainties regarding certain aspects of his commission. An important limitation to the application of *Hedley-Byrne* was raised in *Nitrigin Eireann Teoranta v Inco Alloys*, where it was held that this only applies to professional relationships and does not include advice given by the manufacturers of specialist equipment.

NUISANCE AND THE RULE IN *RYLANDS v FLETCHER*

Private Nuisance

The private law remedy of nuisance is based upon unreasonable interference with the plaintiff's use and enjoyment of land or some right over or in connection with it. In general, a claim in nuisance must satisfy three criteria:

— it must not arise on the premises of the plaintiff's occupation;

— it must arise outside the plaintiff's land and then proceed to the affected land or its use; and

— it must be a continuing wrong.

While the application of negligence to environmental issues has been somewhat restricted, there has been a long history of the use of nuisance as a remedy for problems in this area. In assessing liability in nuisance, the court will consider both the defendant's use of his own property and the effect this has on the plaintiff's proprietary rights. This balancing of competing factors is judged on considerations of the "reasonableness" of both parties and much will depend upon the circumstances of each case. Similarly, the standards adopted for "reasonableness" may change over time and reliance may not always be placed on earlier cases.

Reasonableness of the Defendant's Activities

The primary consideration in nuisance is whether the defendant's use of his property is reasonable or not, for if he is using it reasonably "there is nothing at law can be considered a nuisance" – *Saunders Clark v Grosvenor Mansion Company Ltd and D'Alles Sandy*. Nuisance may arise as a result of an activity which is being undertaken on the defendant's land, or of the condition of the land or property itself. Furthermore, liability may arise as a result of man-made or natural processes on land – see *Leakey & ors v National Trust for Places of Historic Interest or Natural Beauty*.

In addition, it is possible for an occupier of the land to "adopt" a nuisance created by a third party or act of nature, provided he has actual or constructive knowledge of the state of affairs and fails to take reasonable steps to abate it (*Sedleigh-Denfield v O'Callaghan*). However, in *Page Motors v Epsom and Ewell Borough Council*, it was held that the occupier's means and resources should be taken into account in determining what might reasonably have been done.

The locality in which the alleged activity is taking place will be one of the factors considered by the court, for as Pollock J stated "that may be a nuisance in Grosvenor Square, which would be none in Smithfield Market" (*Bamford v Turnley*). Further substance is given to this view in *St Helen's Smelting v Tipping* where Lord Westbury drew the distinction between personal discomfort and material damage to property. Atmospheric pollution from the defendant's copper smelter damaged the plaintiff's trees and it was held that the convenience of the locality for the particular trade in question did not absolve the defendant from liability for material damage. However, liability for personal discomfort must also take into account the nature of the locality and the trade and commercial operations which exist for the benefit of the inhabitants of the town and the public at large. *Andrea v Selfridge & Co Ltd* extended this concept to demolition, excavation and building works, where it was held that provided these were undertaken with reasonable care and skill using proper scientific means of avoiding inconvenience, a nuisance was not committed.

Planning Permission

Planning permission, once granted, can change the character of a neighbourhood at a stroke, as demonstrated in *Gillingham BC v Medway (Chatham) Dock Co Ltd*. When planning permission for a development or a change of use is granted, any subsequent questions of nuisance involving non-physical damage must be judged with reference to the neighbourhood incorporating the development. Coupled with the *Ryford Houses* case (*ENDS Report* No 169, 30), which found that a local authority cannot be found liable in negligence to third parties for ill-judged planning decisions, this severely restricts the courses of action open to residents' groups. However, not every planning decision authorises any nuisance which inevitably flows from the granting of that permission, and non-strategic decisions such as that in *Wheeler v J J Saunders*, a case concerning smells emanating from pig-weaning houses, are excluded. In this case it was held that *Gillingham* could only be applied to major developments which altered the character of the neighbourhood, or with wide consequential effects such as required balancing of competing public and private interests before permission was granted.

Statutory Authority

In certain circumstances, the activities of public and private bodies which are operating under statutory authority may *not* give rise to an action in nuisance, as in *Smeaton v Ilford Corporation*, although much will be dependent upon the exact wording of the relevant statute(s). Some clarification of the liabilities of bodies acting under statutory authority is given in *Department of Trade v North West Water*, although in practice the courts are unwilling to grant an injunction which would result in the suspension of a public utility's essential services – see *Prices' Patent*

Candle Co Ltd v LCC – or where this would place impossible demands on the defendant, as in *Pride of Derby*. In *Hasley v Esso Petroleum Ltd*, although the court upheld the plaintiff's claims that the noise and smell emanating from the oil depot were unreasonable, it found that an immediate injunction would have had significant consequences on both defendant and the consumers of its services, and the order was suspended for six weeks. English courts, however, have not gone as far as those in the US, where in the case of *Madison v Ducktown Sulphur, Copper and Iron Co* an injunction was refused on the grounds that the resulting loss to a community consequent on unemployment would be unacceptable.

Prescription

A defendant may attempt to rely upon the fact that he has acquired a prescriptive right to undertake his operations, and twenty years will legalise a private nuisance, though not a public one. However, it is necessary for the plaintiff to be aware of the activity during this period and unlawful activities such as a breach of discharge consent are not included. Furthermore, as demonstrated in *Sturges v Bridgman*, the *particular* activity giving rise to the nuisance and not the general business activity of the defendant must have been undertaken over the full period required for prescription.

Duration of the Nuisance

In general, it is necessary for the nuisance to be a continuing activity, although the requirements of continuity will depend upon the facts of the case. Single events have sometimes led to successful claims in nuisance, as in *Spicer v Smee* in relation to faulty electrical wiring and in *British Celanese v A H Hunt* for the escape of inadequately stored metal foil, but in these cases "it must be proved that the nuisance arose from the *condition* of the defendant's land or premises or property or activities thereon that constituted a nuisance" – *SCM (United Kingdom) Ltd v W J Whitehall & Son Ltd*. However, in the more recent judgment of *Crown River Cruises Ltd v Kimbolton Fireworks and Another*, it was held that "the holding of a fireworks display in a situation in which it was inevitable that for *15 to 20 minutes* debris would fall upon nearby property of a potential flammable nature created a nuisance which was actionable at the suit of the property owner who suffered as a result."

Building works commonly give rise to actions in nuisance, although in *Harrison v Southwark and Vauxhall Water Co Ltd* it was held that the continuous noise from a temporarily installed water pump was actionable only if reasonable precautions were not taken to prevent nuisance (see also *Andrea v Selfridge*).

Foreseeability

In his judgment in *Cambridge Water Company v Eastern Counties Leather plc*, Lord Goff stated that "it is still the law that the fact that the defendant has taken all reasonable care will not of itself exonerate him from liability (in nuisance)... but it by no means follows that the defendant should be held liable for damage of a type he could not reasonably foresee." The leading case in foreseeability is *Overseas Tankship (UK) Ltd v Miller Steamship Co Pty (The Wagon Mound (No 2))*, from which it is now settled law that foreseeability of harm is a prerequisite for the recovery of damages in both private and public nuisance.

The Role of the Plaintiff

In order for nuisance to be actionable, there must be proof of damage to the plaintiff and since many issues with a claim in nuisance have a strong subjective element – noise, smell, dust, etc. – the court must determine whether the activity complained of has resulted in an unreasonable interference of the rights of the plaintiff or whether he is unusually sensitive in this respect. In *Heath v Major of Brighton*, the complainant sought an injunction to restrain noise from a power station but since there was no proof of damage or annoyance to others, the request was denied. Winfield and Jolowicz[1] note that a man cannot increase the liabilities of his neighbour by applying his own property to special uses, whether for business or pleasure. However, once the nuisance is established, the remedies available will extend to delicate and sensitive operations. In *Attorney-General v Gastonia Coaches*, the distinction was made between the background level of noise and smell resulting from a maintenance depot, which was not actionable, and that above this *de minimis* level, which was.

In general, a plaintiff "coming to a nuisance" has the same rights as an existing plaintiff who suffers the imposition of a "new" source of nuisance (*Bliss v Hall*), although the nuisance is judged on the locality doctrine discussed, *supra*. This was extended in *R v Exeter CC ex parte J L Thomas & Co Ltd*, where the court held that a planning authority may grant planning permission for a new development, despite the possibility of complaints by new occupiers as a result of the existing incompatible use.

Public Nuisance

A public (or common) nuisance is an act or omission which materially affects the reasonable comfort and convenience of "a class of Her Majesty's

---

[1]   *Winfield and Jolowicz on Tort, 14th Edition*, Sweet & Maxwell, 1994, Chapter 14.

subjects". Whereas private nuisance is always tortious, public nuisance is a crime, although where a member of the public suffers damage over and above that suffered by others, it may also be tortious. The distinction between public and private nuisance is illustrated in *Tate and Lyle Industries Ltd and Another v Greater London Council and Another*, in which the plaintiff was subject to additional dredging costs as the result of the construction of a new jetty in the Thames by the defendant. The claim in private nuisance was dismissed because the plaintiff's own jetty was unaffected and they had no rights of property of the river bed. However, the silting caused by the defendant's jetty resulted in an interference to public rights of navigation and the plaintiff's expenditure on dredging was sufficient to bring an action in public nuisance.

The question of the number of persons affected which constitutes a public nuisance is dependent upon the facts of the case and, in *Attorney General (on the relation of Glamorgan CC and Pontadawe Rural District Council) v PYA Quarries Ltd*, Romer LJ held that:

> "It is not necessary to prove that *every member of the class* has been injuriously affected; it is sufficient to show that *a representative cross-section of the class* has been so affected ...",

Lord Denning adding

> "Public nuisance is a nuisance which is so widespread in its range, or so indiscriminate in its effect that it *would not be reasonable to expect one person to take proceedings on his own responsibility* to stop it, but that it should be taken on the responsibility of the community at large."

Actions in public nuisance generally proceed by indictment, although it is possible that the Attorney General might bring a relator action for an injunction or, under more restrictive conditions, a local authority can act through section 222 of the Local Government Act 1972. Where a local authority chooses this course of action, there is no requirement for cross-undertakings in damages unless it can be shown that there are special circumstances justifying such an imposition and even then it is a matter for the court's discretion (*Coventry City Council v Finnie and Another*).

The Rule in *Rylands v Fletcher*

While the tort of nuisance is concerned with a continuing activity, following the judgment in *Rylands v Fletcher*, a case law has developed which imposes, *inter alia*, a strict liability upon the defendant responsible for isolated escapes, the major components of which were summarised by Blackburn J as:

"The person who for his own purposes brings onto his land and collects there anything likely to do mischief if it escapes, must keep it at his peril and if he does not do so is *prima facie* answerable for all the damage which is the natural consequences of its escape."

The original case concerned the flooding of the plaintiff's mine as a result of the construction of a reservoir on the defendant's land but the rule has been applied subsequently to a wide range of activities, and of relevance to its "environmental" applications are the leakages and spillages of dangerous chemicals, oil or water, the escape of gas from landfill sites, explosions and noxious fumes. In *Rylands v Fletcher* the damage arose as a result of the activities of a contractor employed by the defendant.

As noted earlier, in the United States the rule has developed into a general rule of strict liability for damage caused by ultra-hazardous activities but in English law its use has become quite restricted. In *Cambridge Water Company v Eastern Counties Leather plc*, Lord Goff noted that "it is more appropriate for strict liability in respect of operations of high risk to be imposed by Parliament, than by the courts", since:

— the relevant activities can be identified; and

— precise criteria can be laid down establishing the *incidence* and *scope* of such liability,

and "those concerned can know where they stand". However, although the Environment Act 1995 has introduced mechanisms for the clean-up of contaminated land, these may only be undertaken *directly* by the regulatory bodies and the EU measures imposing civil liability for environmental damage are still at an early stage.

In view of its significance, the *Cambridge* case will first be reviewed and the implications and other factors on the application of the rule in *Rylands v Fletcher* will then be discussed.

The "Cambridge Water" Case
The operations giving rise to the action took place prior to 1976 and involved the repeated spillage of small quantities of organochlorine solvents (perchloroethylene – PCE, and trichloroethlyene – TCE) used in connection with the tannery business of English Counties Leather (ECL) in Sawston. It was estimated that a minimum of 3,200 litres of solvent was spilled in the relevant period – early 1950s to mid 1970s – and this seeped through the floor of the building into the soil below, collecting in pools at the base of the chalk aquifer. This solvent gradually contaminated the waters flowing through the aquifer into the surrounding land and was

present in the drinking water which was abstracted by the Cambridge Water Company (CWC) at Sawston Mill, which they had purchased in 1976. It is important to note that the abstraction operations commenced *after* the polluting activity (i.e. the spillage of solvent) had ceased and it was not until 1983 that Sawston Mill was taken out of supply, in response to the Department of Environment criteria for "wholesome" water in Circular 20/82, 15th August 1982, which was based upon the EEC Directive on Drinking Water Quality, 80/778/EEC. (Subsequent changes were made through SI 1989/1147, which *increased* the maximum permitted levels of PCE and TCE to the original World Health Organisation Guideline levels, on which the Directive was based.)

An action in nuisance, negligence and *Rylands v Fletcher* was commenced against both Eastern Counties Leather and Hutchings and Harding Ltd, another but much smaller user of PCE at Sawston. At the first instance, it was held that both defendants failed to establish that the PCE which had been stored on their land was harmless and the plaintiff succeeded on this limb of the rule. However, it was held that, since Sawston was an industrial village, the storage of solvent did not constitute a non-natural use of the land and the plaintiff failed on this limb. In addition, it was held that the contribution of Hutchings and Harding Ltd to the pollution was *de minimis* and would have been insufficient to merit the award of damages if the claim had been successful.

The Court of Appeal only briefly considered *Rylands v Fletcher*, stating that there was no need to address the relevant issues if a claim in nuisance could be made out. There was agreement that no duty of care existed regarding the spillage of the solvent and, since the damage was not foreseeable, negligence could not be established. Great reliance was placed upon *Ballard v Tomlinson*, where it was decided that "where nuisance is an interference with a natural right incident to ownership, then the liability is a strict one".

In the House of Lords, Lord Goff stated that the rule in *Rylands v Fletcher* should be considered as an off-shoot of nuisance and as such was subject to the requirements of reasonable foreseeability. However, the court considered that "the PCE had passed beyond the control of ECL" *after* such damage had been foreseeable to the defendants and as such they could not be held liable under *Rylands v Fletcher*. In addition, although detailed consideration was not given to the non-natural use of land, Lord Goff commented, *obiter*, that the storage of chemicals in substantial quantities should be regarded as "an almost classic case of non-natural use", in direct contradiction of Mr Justice Kennedy's first instance ruling.

Foreseeability
Prior to *Cambridge,* foreseeability was not a component of the rule in *Rylands v Fletcher* but, following Lord Goff's ruling, *Rylands v Fletcher* was held to be an extension of nuisance applied to cases of isolated escapes and as such was subject to the same considerations of foreseeability (q.v.). The issue of the PCE "passing beyond the control of ECL" is problematic since, at the time of the House of Lords ruling, techniques *were* available by which the solvent could be removed from underground sources, albeit over a long time period, and these were considered in the first instance hearing. (The air stripping technique, rejected by CWC, is currently in use to reduce pollutants beneath AEA Harwell under similar circumstances.) Although not part of the House of Lords' considerations, it is clear that, while the *contamination* of the aquifer might have been foreseen pre-1976, the *changes in the drinking water acceptability criteria* could not.

Now that foreseeability is an established requirement of *Rylands v Fletcher*, it will no doubt receive more detailed consideration in subsequent cases. While some authors suggest that *Cambridge* has effectively closed the door on claims arising from "historical" pollution of land, it has a possible application in relation to current owners of sites contaminated as a result of their own activities, who do not take precautions to prevent the migration of any gases generated or the leachate produced.

"Non-Natural Use of Land" and Common Benefit
An early restriction was placed on the rule in *Rylands v Fletcher* by the judgment in *Rickards v Lothian* in which it was held that:

> "It is not every use to which land is put that brings into play that principle. It must be *some special use bringing with it increased danger to others*, and must not be the ordinary use of the land, or such a use as is proper for *the general benefit of the community.*"

With regard to the "non-natural use" of land, two approaches concerning the meaning of "natural" have emerged, viz:

— that which *exists by nature* and is *not artificial*, following Lord Cairns in *Rylands v Fletcher*; and

— that which is *ordinary* and *usual*, following Professor Newark's approach in "The Boundaries of Nuisance" ([1949] 65 *LQR* 480).

The courts have tended towards the latter definition, although bearing in mind the contradictory views expressed at different stages of *Cambridge* and Lord Goff's *obiter* comments, there is clearly a need for further consideration to clarify the meaning. This would also need to consider the concept of "common benefit" since this has been used as a defence where the source of danger is maintained for the mutual benefit of plaintiff and defendant, as well as being a component of the "non-natural use" concept.

Other Aspects of the Rule in Rylands v Fletcher

The judgment in *Read v Lyons* clarified the necessity for the *escape* to occur "*from* a place where the defendant has occupation or control over land, *to* a place outside his occupation or control". However, the court's finding that the rule is inapplicable to personal injuries has not been followed, since it is anachronistic for proprietary interests to receive a greater degree of protection than personal security.

With regard to the "accumulation on land", this must be a deliberate act of the defendant and spontaneous or natural accumulations – vegetation, water, animal life – are excluded. The position of statutory bodies is less certain, for while Sellars LJ held in *Dunne v North Western Gas Board* that "a nationalised industry could not be said to accumulate ... for its own purposes", in *Smeaton v Ilford Corporation* Upjohn LJ stated "whatever may be the law ... as regards use of land for domestic purposes ... different considerations apply when a local authority collects, even though under a duty to do so, large quantities of sewage which they are bound to dispose of." Furthermore, it could also be argued that privatised utilities are "operating for their own purposes". In relation to this phrase, Winfield and Jolowicz[1] state that the rule applies where the defendant has a franchise, such as the right to use land founded on a statute or upon private permission for laying pipes to carry gas or cables for electricity. Similarly, licensees using the land by permission of the tenant or occupier are also liable under the rule.

---

[1]   *Winfield and Jolowicz on Tort, 14th Edition*, Sweet & Maxwell, 1994, Chapter 15.

FURTHER READING

"Affirmative Action in the Law of Tort: The Case of the Duty to Warn", J Logie, [1989] 48 (1) *CLJ* 115

"The Boundaries of Nuisance", F H Newark, [1949] 65 *LQR* 480

Clerk and Lindsell on Torts, 17th Edition, Sweet & Maxwell, 1995

Contaminated Land, S Tromans and R Turrall-Clarke, Sweet & Maxwell, 1994

"The Definition of Pollution Damage in the 1984 Protocols to the 1969 Civil Liability and the 1971 Fund Convention", M Jacobsson and N Trotz, [1986] *J Maritime Law and Commerce*, 17, 467

Delictual Liability, J M Thomson, Butterworths, 1994

"Economics and the Environment: A Study in Private Nuisance", A I Ogus and G M Richardson, [1987] 36 (2) *CLJ* 284

Environmental Law, 3rd Edition, D Hughes, Butterworths, 1996

"*Locus Standi*: An Essential Hurdle in Judicial Review of Environmental Action", J Upson and D Hughes, [1994] *ELM* 136

"*Murphy v Brentwood DC*: The Water Law Implications", S Ball, [1990] *Water Law*, November, 102

"Negligence after Murphy: Time to Re-think", D Wilkinson, [1991] 50 (1) *CLJ* 58

Pollution and Personal Injury: Toxic Torts II, C Pugh and M Day, Cameron May, 1995

"Private Law and the Environmental Nuisance in Context", J Steele, [1995] 15 *Legal Studies* No 2, 236

Salmond and Heuston on Torts, 21st Edition, Sweet and Maxwell, 1996

"Television, Tower Blocks and Nuisance", B Harvey and A Robinson, [1996] *UKELA Journal*, vol. 10/1, 24

Toxic Torts, C Pugh and M Day, Cameron May, 1992

Water Pollution Law, W Howarth, Shaw and Sons, 1988

"Water Rights Diluted", A Ogus, [1994] 6 (1) *JEL* 150

Whose Environment Is It Anyway?, Law Centres Federation, 1990

Winfield and Jolowicz on Tort, 14th Edition, Sweet & Maxwell, 1994

Chapter 6

WASTE HOLDER LIABILITY

INTRODUCTION

Within the ambit of the term *waste producer* defined with reference to the EU Framework Directive and current UK legislation (see Chapter 8), it is necessary to examine the extent to which the resultant liabilities extend to the corporate organisation and specific individuals within it. In addition, consideration must also be given as to whether a given pollution incident will be attributed to a single defendant or, as indicated in Chapter 4, the waste producer may be one of several defendants involved in the same "concurrent causative conduct" – see *Attorney-General's Reference (No 1 of 1994)*.

Where a business is conducted as a sole trader, the sole trader is personally liable for his own acts, both in criminal and civil law. Likewise, the members of a partnership are personally liable for those acts undertaken in the course of the business. However, a company – whether it is a private limited company, a public limited company or a company limited by guarantee – is a separate legal body, which is distinct from its officers and its shareholders. Whilst a company can be guilty of an offence, as in *Director of Public Prosecutions v Kent and Sussex Contractors*, it is usually necessary to show that the company itself had the *actus reus* and the *mens rea* of the crime. Since it is a legal rather than a physical entity and can only act thorough people, it is necessary to examine the extent to which the actions and intentions of individuals may be attributed to the company, and the recent judgment in *Meridian Global Funds Management Asia Ltd v Securities Commission* has clarified this issue.

A company's rights and obligations are determined either by the primary rules of attribution, expressed in its constitution or implied by law, or by the general application of the general principles of agency or vicarious liability. Where this does not resolve the intention of a specific aspect of statutory legislation, the question of attribution for that particular substantive rule is a matter of its construction. If a court decides that the substantive rule was intended to apply to a company, it then has to decide how the rule was intended to apply and whose act or knowledge or state of mind was for that purpose intended to count as the act, knowledge or state of mind of the company.

The concept of "the directing mind and will" of a company has been used as a convenient test of attribution of the activities of a person within a company and on this premise a number of propositions may be made, viz:

— a company will be guilty of an offence if it arises from the "directing mind and will" of that company;

— an employee or an independent contractor may be guilty of an offence, without any associated liability being placed upon the company, providing that party is not associated with its "directing mind and will"; and

— the position of a director or other official as "directing mind and will" may, subject to specific statutory provisions, also involve criminal liability on their part where an offence is committed by the company.

However, in *Meridian*, their Lordships stated that it is not possible to apply this test of "the directing mind and will" in every case and, as will be discussed later, only the last of the above propositions is unaffected by this ruling, since it is subject to specific statutory provisions.

THE "DIRECTING MIND" OF THE COMPANY

The term "the directing mind and will" of a company derives from the speech of Viscount Haldane LC in *Lennard's Carrying Co Ltd v Asiatic Petroleum Co Ltd*, in which an attribution rule had to be derived for the substantive provision in section 502 of the Merchant Shipping Act 1894. In the *Meridian* case, Lord Hoffmann stated that it was a coincidence of the facts of the *Lennard's* case that "left Viscount Haldane's speech open to the interpretation that he was expounding a *general* metaphysic of companies". The anthropomorphism put forward by Lord Justice Denning in *H L Bolton (Engineering) Co Ltd v T J Graham & Sons Ltd* regarding the directing mind "distracted attention from the purpose for which Viscount Haldane had said he was using the notion ... namely to apply the attribution rule derived from section 502 to the particular defendant in the case."

Consequently, whenever a servant of a company has authority to do an act on its behalf, knowledge of that act will not necessarily be attributed to the company. It is a question of construction in each particular case as to whether the particular rule required the knowledge that an act had been done, or the state of mind with which it was done, should be so attributed.

In *NRA v Alfred McAlpine Homes East*, Simon Brown LJ noted the importance of distinguishing between circumstances in which a company is liable under the offence section of an Act, and where it is entitled to invoke a defence section. An example of the latter is *Tesco Supermarkets*

Ltd v Natrass, in which the manager of a large supermarket chain was held not to be identified with the mind or will of that organisation, in accordance with the defence available in section 11(2) of the Trades Description Act 1968. However, such a defence was unavailable in *Tesco Stores Ltd v Brent London BC* (in relation to section 11, Video Recordings Act 1984) and in *NRA v Alfred McAlpine Homes East* (in relation to section 85 Water Resources Act 1991).

With regard to the range of persons who might come within the ambit of "the directing mind and will", in *Seaboard Offshore Ltd v Secretary of State for Transport* it was held that this might include those persons who, by virtue of the constitution of the company or otherwise, are entrusted with the exercise of its powers. Potentially, this could encompass directors, whose powers and authority are defined by the company articles, or even "influential" shareholders, whose power and influence is defined by the shareholders' agreement. Furthermore, in *El Ajou v Dollar Land Holdings plc and Another*, it was held that, even if a director of a company plays no active part in its management but he individually exercises powers on its behalf, then he will be treated as its directing mind and will.

There have been recent developments in relation to corporate liability in the area of health and safety which are of relevance to environmental legislation. In *R v British Steel* it was held that, subject to the defence of reasonable practicability, section 3(1) of the Health and Safety at Work Act 1974 imposed absolute criminal liability and a corporate employer could not avoid liability on the basis that the company at "directing mind and will" or senior management level was not involved, having taken all reasonable care to delegate supervision.

British Steel, using sub-contractors on a "labour only" basis (i.e. equipment and supervision by British Steel) for the repositioning of a 7.5 tonne steel platform, were involved in the fatal accident of one of the sub-contractors. Whilst the defendants agreed on a *prima facie* breach of section 3(1) of the Act, they relied upon the "so far as is reasonably practicable" provision of the subsection, and on *Tesco v Natrass*. The court held that the absolute nature of the offence was decided in *R v Board of Trustees of Science Museum* and in *R v Associated Octel* and the words "so far as is reasonably practicable" simply referred to the measures necessary to avert the risk. In particular, the court noted the comments of Stuart-Smith LJ in *Octel*, who stressed that section 3(1) was framed "to achieve a result". As a consequence of this decision, it is not necessary to determine whether particular employees are part of senior management or not. It will be noted that the *British Steel* case is a further example of a court carrying out the process of interpretation, as in the *Meridian* case.

It is interesting to note that in *R v Board of Trustees of Science Museum*, no members of the public suffered *actual* harm as a result of the poor maintenance of the cooling system but they were put *at risk* of contracting legionnaire's disease. The courts appear to take a serious view of legionella and Hounslow Magistrates' Court fined a catering company £80,000 for a similar offence, where "members of the public were put at risk of contracting a potentially very serious, and in some cases, fatal disease".

The above arguments apply equally well to environmental provisions which are designed to create absolute liability and with a particular objective in mind, i.e. "to achieve a result". Many provisions are of this nature, e.g. section 85 of the Water Resources Act 1991, and, in these cases, the existence of an environmental management system, such as ISO 14000 or EMAS, or evidence of management care will not provide a defence if the duty is breached, although it may go in mitigation. If the duty involves the exercise of reasonable care, or a "due diligence" defence exists, then proper care by senior management may be argued as a defence. It has been suggested that, in relation to waste management within the Environmental Protection Act 1990, the statutory duty of care in section 34, supported by the Code of Practice, provides a means of fixing criminal responsibility more easily on those "above the hierarchical line" for lapses of those "below the line", without the need to consider vicarious liability.

CRIMINAL AND CIVIL LIABILITY OF DIRECTORS AND SIMILAR OFFICERS

Scope of the Term "Director"

Despite the criminal and civil liability and the attendant possibility of fines, imprisonment or disqualification imposed on individual company directors, there is a high level of ignorance of these issues in most boardrooms. A 1994 survey by the Institute of Directors indicated a deterioration in the situation since 1993, with 24% of directors admitting to be "very unknowledgeable" of environmental law and 34% being "quite unknowledgeable".

As indicated in *Seaboard*, "the directing mind and will" of the company is not associated solely with the person holding the title of director, and Tromans and Irvine[1] have examined the range of company officials who might fall within the ambit of the term. English law does not recognise any distinction between executive and non-executive directors, although in

---

[1]   *Directors in the Dock*, S Tromans and G Irvine, Technical Communications (Publishing) Ltd, 1994, Chapter 5.

practice it would not be reasonable to attribute to a non-executive director the detailed knowledge of a company's business that an executive director might have. Nevertheless, there are circumstances in which non-executive directors, shareholders and members of "environmental advisory boards" may be personally liable for environmental offences. The position of shadow directors has been considered in *Re: Hydrodam (Corby) Ltd (in liquidation)*.

With regard to shareholders, many statutory provisions contain a clause such as that in section 157(2) of the Environmental Protection Act 1990, viz:

> "Where the affairs of the body corporate are managed by its members, subsection (1) above [relating to directors, secretaries and similar officers] shall apply in relation to acts or defaults of a member in connection with his functions of management as if he were a director of the body corporate."

Waite[1] noted that there are four circumstances in which a director might be liable:

— primary liability;

— liability as an accomplice;

— conspiracy; and

— statutory liability.

In the above categories, a distinction must be drawn between primary liability, in which the director commits the *actus reus* of the offence as a principal, as in *R v Daily Mirror Newspapers Ltd*, and categories in which his involvement is more indirect. A number of statutory provisions, such as section 85 of the Water Resources Act 1991, are worded such that any "person" who commits an act shall be guilty of an offence and, in these circumstances, a director or manager of a company who performs the act will be guilty of that offence, whether or not he was performing it for the benefit of the company, as in *Dellow v Busby*.

With regard to acting as an accomplice, anyone who assists a principal to commit an offence by aiding, abetting, counselling or procuring the commission of the offence will be held to have the same criminal liability as the principal. Smith and Hogan[2] state that:

---

[1]   "Criminal and Civil Liability of Company Directors", A Waite, [1991] 3 (3) *LMELR* 74.
[2]   *Smith and Hogan – Criminal Law, 8th Edition*, J C Smith, Butterworths, 1996, Chapter 7.

— " 'procuring' implies causation but not consensus;

— 'abetting' and 'counselling' imply consensus but not causation;

— 'aiding' requires assistance, but neither consensus nor causation."

In cases of strict liability and of secondary parties who aid, abet, procure or counsel, it is necessary that the party who commits the offence has the *mens rea* in the sense of knowing the essential matters that constitute the offence.

In the case of conspiracy, where a director resolves to commit an illegal act in the name of the company, there is no conspiracy between him and the company until another natural person is involved – *Rothwell v McDonnell* and *Knuller (Publishing, Printing and Promotions) Ltd v DPP*. Furthermore, under section 1(2) of the Criminal Law Act 1977, for strict liability offences *mens rea* is a requirement of conspiracy.

Statutory Liability

There are now over 200 statutory provisions in which directors and other senior officers of a company are considered, in certain circumstances, as statutory principals to offences committed by their companies. Most of the recent "environmental" statutes contain such provisions, which typically take the format of section 157, Environmental Protection Act 1990:

> "Where an offence under any provision of this Act, committed by a body corporate is proved to have been committed with the consent, connivance of, or to be attributed to any neglect on the part of any director, manager, secretary, or other similar officer of the body corporate, or any person purporting to act in any such capacity, he as well as the body corporate shall be guilty of that offence and shall be liable to be proceeded against and punished accordingly."

While the ability to prosecute senior officers has been used relatively sparingly in some areas of legislation, with regard to environmental offences there has been a growing tendency for the regulatory agencies to address formally the culpability of these persons. A superficial examination of the situation would tend to suggest that, for water-related offences, substantial fines are imposed on companies and their officers although few custodial sentences are awarded. In contrast, for waste-related offences, fines are in general much lower but a not inconsiderable number of company officials have been given custodial sentences. A further important difference between these two regimes is the significance of "relevant offences" in relation to the licensing requirements for certain waste management activities, *infra*.

From the wording of the offence, such as section 157(1)EPA 1990, it is evident that the prosecution has three criteria to meet:

— the company must be guilty; and

— the defendant must be a director or similar officer of that company; and

— the offence must have been committed with the consent, connivance or neglect of the defendant.

In section 741(1) of the Companies Act 1985, a director is defined as "any person occupying the position of director, by whatever name called" and the discussion above indicates the range of officers who might be associated with "the directing mind" of a company. In fact, the judicial interpretation given to the persons included in section 157(1) EPA 1990 and other similar provisions has been in effect to equate them to "the directing mind of the company". The words "or purporting to act in such capacity" cover the situations in which the appointment is defective or irregular, as in *Dean v Hiesler*, or in which there is a *de facto* or a shadow director, *supra*.

Having ascertained that the company itself was guilty and the defendant was a director, it is necessary to examine the other preconditions of liability – consent, connivance and neglect.

In *Huckerby v Elliott*, both consent and connivance were considered and for the former it was held that there must be both knowledge and prior approval:

> "It would seem that where a director consents to the commission of an offence by his company, he is well aware of what is going on, and agrees to it."

The meaning of "consent" was considered in *Attorney General's Reference (No 1 of 1995)* where the Appeal Court held that the *mens rea* that had to be proved against a company director (in this case charged with consenting to the company accepting a deposit without an authorisation or licence from the Bank of England) was that he knew the material facts which constituted the offence by the company and agreed to its conduct in its business on the basis of those facts.

Connivance does not require positive knowledge but there has to be some knowledge amounting to more than ignorance, inattention or negligence:

> "Where [the director] connives at the offence committed by the company, he is well aware of what is going on, but his agreement is tacit, not actively encouraging what happens, but letting it continue and saying nothing about it."

"Neglect" is the widest of the three terms and in *Re: Hughes*, the court held this to imply

> "failure to perform a duty, which the person knows or ought to know."

It is difficult to interpret this definition, since the leading case on the duties of a director dates back to 1925 – *Re: City Equitable Fire Insurance Company Ltd* – when the situation was considerably different. However, Tromans and Irvine[1] suggest that the following would need to be determined in order to ascertain these duties:

— the nature of the company's business;

— the manner in which the company's work was distributed between directors and other officials, and whether this distribution:

    — was reasonable in the circumstances; and

    — was consistent with the company's written constitution – its articles of association,

and with regard to the expertise required of a director to undertake his specific tasks:

— he is not expected to be an expert unless appointed as such;

— he must exercise reasonable care and skill but is not liable for errors of judgment;

— he is entitled to rely upon outside experts but cannot by so doing abdicate the need to exercise his judgment.

The Definition of "Manager"

The meaning of *manager* was examined in *R v Boal* in relation to section 23 of the Fire Precautions Act 1971 and the Court of Appeal held that the intention of the legislation was:

> "To fix with criminal liability only those who are in a position of real authority, the decision makers within the company who have the power and responsibility to decide corporate policy and strategy. It is to catch those responsible for putting proper procedures in place, it is not meant to strike at underlings."

---

[1] *Directors in the Dock*, S Tromans and G Irvine, Technical Communications (Publishing) Ltd, 1994, Chapter 4.

Although the defendant in *Boal* was fourth in the hierarchy of the company and at the relevant time was standing in for his immediate superior, the Appeal Court held that he was not a manager, since he had no control over policies or strategy. It has been suggested that, applying the reasoning of *Tesco*, an employee who successfully distances himself from liability as a co-defendant with the company may be unwittingly placing himself in a position of sole responsibility as "another person" should the initial charge fail against the company alone.

The ruling in *Boal* was reinforced in *Woodhouse v Walsall Metropolitan Borough Council* where the general manager of a waste disposal company operation was found guilty under section 87(1) of the Control of Pollution Act 1974 of an offence under section 85 committed by the company, on the grounds that his responsibilities involved the day-to-day operation of the site. However, the High Court allowed an appeal and held that to be convicted of such an offence, in addition to being in a position of authority, a person must also have actual powers of decision-making in relation to corporate policy and strategy. Under certain circumstances, it is possible for directors to devolve their decision-making power but this must be accompanied by the devolution of authority and the provision of adequate resources.

Delegation of Responsibilities

In *Boal* and *Woodhouse*, although the defendants were senior officials within their respective companies, it was held that they were not liable under the relevant part of the Acts since they did not have the actual power of decision-making in relation to corporate policy and strategy. However, the courts do recognise that some of a director's duties "may properly be left to some other official, and the director is, in the absence of grounds for suspicion, justified in trusting that official to perform such duties honestly" – *Re: City Equitable Fire Insurance Company Ltd.*

The extent to which he may delegate is dependent upon the facts and the circumstances of each case but the director must allocate adequate resources to the delegatee in order for him to undertake the allotted tasks, in addition to monitoring them and, where necessary, taking intervening action.

An example of such delegation, albeit from another jurisdiction, is *Her Majesty the Queen v Bata Industries Ltd & ors*, in which it was held that the Chairman of the Board, Thomas G Bata Jnr, was entitled to rely upon the President and the Vice President (Operations), both of whom were found guilty of failing to take all reasonable care to prevent the incident (a polluting discharge). The chairman "did not allow himself to be wilfully blind to problems, or to be orchestrated in his movements when at the plant". An interesting feature was the Appeal Court's ruling that the company was not to indemnify the directors for the fines, on the grounds that indemnification would allow corporate officials to turn a blind eye to their responsibilities. However, this aspect of the ruling was subsequently reversed. Note also that this is not the position in the UK for, *inter alia*, marine oil pollution.

Vicarious Liability of Directors

In general, a company director cannot be liable for the criminal acts of the company's servants or employees, after *Mallon v Allon*, although exceptionally he may be vicariously liable for torts committed by the company if he had extensive control over its conduct at the relevant time in connection with the tortious activity.

CORPORATE LIABILITY FOR ACTIONS OF OTHERS

In addition to liability resulting from the actions of persons associated with "the directing mind and will" of a company, it is necessary to consider the position relating to others empowered to undertake its activities. In *Meridian*, Lord Hoffmann stated that it is necessary for a company to appoint:

> "... servants and agents whose acts, by a combination of the general principles of agency and the company's primary rules of attribution, counted as acts of the company. And having done so, it would make itself subject to the general rules by which liability for the acts of others could be attributed to natural persons, such as estoppel or ostensible authority in contract, and vicarious liability in tort.

> Any statement about what a company had or had not done, or could or could not do, was necessarily a reference to the rules of attribution, primary and general, as they applied to that company."

It is within such a framework that a company's liability for actions of others will be determined and, where this approach does not provide a solution, it is necessary for the court to "fashion a special rule of attribution for the particular substantive rule", as in *British Steel* and *Meridian*.

Vicarious Liability

The doctrine of vicarious liability is based upon the policy that the employer should pay for damage or injuries caused when something is being done for his benefit and this may include actions which he has expressly prohibited. However, the vicarious liability of an employer is in addition to the personal liability of the worker who committed the wrongful act, and is not an alternative to it. The worker may be sued both by the injured party and, where appropriate, by the employer under the Civil Liability (Contribution) Act 1978.

Vicarious liability does not arise unless the court considers that a tort has been committed by an employee and, in determining this, it will take into account the training given to him and the resources which have been allocated. Where the level of responsibility is not matched by such provisions, as in *Jones v Manchester Corporation*, the employer may be held personally, rather than vicariously, liable.

In civil law, a company will generally be liable for the acts of its employees, provided that:

— the employee was acting under a contract of service;

— the tort was committed "in the course of employment".

With regard to the former requirement, in *Ready Mixed Concrete (South East) v Minister of Pensions and National Insurance*, McKenna J held there to be three conditions necessary to establish that a contract of employment existed, viz:

— the worker agreed to provide his own work and skill in the performance of service for the employer; *and*

— there was an element of control exerciseable by the employer; *and*

— the other terms of the contract must not be inconsistent with the existence of a contract of employment.

Although a substantial body of case law has developed relating to specific contractual terms which may be inconsistent with there being a contract of employment, there is no single factor which is regarded as decisive and much is dependent upon the facts of the case.

With regard to the meaning of the phrase "in the course of employment", in *Limpus v London General Omnibus Company* the employer was held to be liable where the employee undertook an act he was authorised to do but in a wrongful, improper and unauthorised manner. Whereas in the older cases it was held that this excluded situations in which the employee was undertaking something he was not employed to do – e.g. a bus conductor driving the bus "at a considerable pace" (8 mph) in order to prepare it for its next journey, or where the employee deviates from his allocated tasks and goes off on a frolic of his own" (*Joel v Morison*) – a much broader interpretation is now given. This includes actions which were for the benefit of the employer, even if he had expressly prohibited them, as in *Rose v Plenty* (use of a minor to assist with the delivery of milk) and in *Smith v Stages* (travel from workplace in uninsured vehicle).

Consequently, even where an employee is careless (lighting and discarding a match when delivering petrol) or foolish (injury from horseplay), providing he was acting in connection with what he was employed to do, then the employer will be vicariously liable. The situation is similar when acting with the employer's actual or ostensible authority, though circumstances involving an action which the employer would be presumed not to have authorised are excluded. In general, the concept of vicarious liability does not apply in criminal law, although, as noted above, the situation is different in relation to corporations which have no physical existence and must operate through agents and employees. If a strict duty is imposed by criminal law and the person on whom it is placed is not allowed either to delegate responsibility for performance of that duty or to bring evidence that another person is the actual wrongdoer, the effect will be virtually the same as under the common law of vicarious liability. The recent *Meridian* case has clarified the position regarding the extent to which the company is liable for the actions of persons within the organisation.

Self-Employed Workers and Loaned Employees

Over the past few years, the overall employment situation has changed considerably from the time when the principal authorities on the employer/employee/independent contractor relationship were decided and there are now "good reasons for both workers and employers to avoid the 'employee' label" (*Lane v Shire Roofing Co (Oxford) Ltd*). Lord Justice Henry noted that from the workman's point of view, being self-employed brought him into a more benevolent and less prompt tax regime. From the employer's point of view, the protection of employees' rights contained in the employment protection legislation of the 1970s brought certain perceived disincentives to the employer to take on full-tome long-term employees.

However, there were good policy reasons in the health and safety field to ensure that the law properly distinguished between employees and independent contractors. In *Lane* tests were considered which might be applied to distinguish employees from independent contractors and it was held that in some circumstances the element of control would provide the solution. However, this might not be decisive in relation to "skilled workers" who had discretion to decide how their work was to be done and here the question was broadened to "whose business was it – the workman's or the employer's?" The answer to this might involve a determination of where the financial risk lay and whether the workman "had an opportunity of profiting from sound management in the performance of his task".

Lord Justice Nourse noted the distinction between the situation in *Ferguson v Dawson*, in which an employer engaged men on "the lump" (and the men were clearly employees whatever their tax status) and where a specialist contractor was employed to perform some part of a general building contract (where the individual concerned was clearly an independent contractor).

With regard to loaned employees, there is a strong presumption that liability will remain with the permanent or general employer unless there is clear evidence that overall control over the method of working has passed to the temporary or special employer. Much will depend upon the facts of the case (*Mersey Docks and Harbour Board v Coggins and Griffiths Ltd*) but the factors to be considered will be very similar to those outlined in the *Lane* case. However, although the contract between the two employers will determine who bears the loss in any action, this will not influence which of them is vicariously liable to the injured party.

Independent Contractors

The term "independent contractor" is used to distinguish a person who contracts to perform a particular task for another and is not under the other's control regarding the manner in which he performs the task, from an employee. In general, the natural or legal person who engages the independent contractor is not vicariously liable for torts committed under the contract. However, an employer may be sued for damage caused by his independent contractor where he himself was in breach of a statutory duty owed to the plaintiff. Examples of this are:

— *Torts ratified by the principal or where the contractor is employed to undertake an illegal act.* In these circumstances, the principal and the contractor are joint tortfeasors.

— *Where the principal is negligent in the selection of contractors or fails to give them proper instructions.* With regard to the former, he may be liable if he employs incompetent contractors or contractors with inadequate resources to undertake the task. An example of the latter is *Robinson v Beaconsfield Rural Council*, where the council engaged a contractor to clear cesspools but gave no instructions on the disposal of the resultant waste, which was deposited on the appellant's land.

— *Where strict liability is imposed by law.* In cases where a "non-delegable" duty has been imposed upon an employer, then he remains liable under that duty, regardless of whether he or an independent contractor undertakes the operation. Strictly speaking, no duty is delegable (see *Casssidy v Ministry of Health*, per Lord Denning at 363) but, if it merely involves a requirement "to take reasonable" care, then this is discharged in the selection of a competent contractor. However, if the duty is "to provide that care is taken" or "to achieve a result", then the duty is not performed unless care *is taken* or the result *is achieved.*

While the first two examples do not place any additional burdens upon an employer as a result of the environmental effects of his activities, the third is of particular importance in this area. "Non-delegable" duties may arise in both common law and in statute law and in each it is a question of law whether the duty in a given case is non-delegable. As noted earlier, many environmental statutes are designed to create strict liability or to achieve a result, and consequently the employer cannot delegate the responsibility for performing such duties to an independent contractor. Whilst he may make the contractor liable through the terms of the contract for the *financial* consequences of his activities, the existence of a contract may also initiate action against the principal where it can be shown that he was "knowingly permitting" the contractor's polluting activities. Tromans and Turrall-Clarke[1] point out that failure to exert legitimate pressure on another party to cease a polluting activity through the exercise of contractual rights may result in such an action, as in *London Borough of Tower Hamlets v LDDC.*

The House of Lords recently considered the position of independent contractors in relation to the Health and Safety at Work Act 1974. In *R v Associated Octel Co Ltd*, their Lordships held that section 3 of the Act was not concerned with vicarious liability but imposed a duty on the employer himself with reference to a certain kind of activity, viz the employer's conduct of his undertaking. It was indifferent to the nature of the contractual relationships by which the employer chose to conduct it. If an employer engaged an independent contractor to carry out work which formed part of his undertaking, he had to stipulate whatever conditions were needed to avoid risks to people's health and safety and which were reasonably practicable.

Referring to *R v Mara*, the question was simply whether the activity could be described as part of the employer's undertaking. Whether the activity

---

[1] *Contaminated Land*, S Tromans and R Turrall-Clarke, Sweet & Maxwell, 1994, pages 79-81.

which had caused the risk amounted to part of the employer's conduct of his undertaking was in each case a question of fact and should therefore properly be left to the jury.

Examples of common law liabilities within the above categories include:

— withdrawal of support from neighbouring land;

— operations affecting the highway, other than in the course of its normal use; and

— strict liability.

With regard to contractors' activities associated with waste management, strict liability offences are perhaps of most relevance. In addition to the rule in *Rylands v Fletcher*, some areas of nuisance impose strict liability and, in *Matania v National Provincial Bank*, it was held that "where an act ... involves a special danger of the nuisance being complained of, then ... the employer of the contractor will be responsible if there is a failure to take the necessary precautions that the nuisance shall not arise" (in this case, dust and noise from building operations). Hughes[1] notes that some commentators argue that occupiers are generally liable for nuisances arising from acts of their independent contractors but states that there is no consensus on this point.

In addition to nuisance, there is a class of "extra hazardous acts ... which in their very nature, involve in the eyes of the law, special danger to others" (*Salsbury v Woodland*), such as acts resulting in fire and explosions and for these the employer cannot escape liability by delegating their performance to an independent contractor. In such cases, he has a duty not merely to take care but to ensure that care is taken, and this is held to include activities with an inherent safety content (installation of an electric cable), and those which through the absence of taking precautions can have disastrous consequences (use of flash photography).

In the Scottish case, *MTM Construction Ltd v William Reid Engineering Ltd*, it was held that where a contractor engaged a sub-contractor to undertake works which necessitated an inherently dangerous operation, and the sub-contractor engaged a sub-sub-contractor to do part of that work, the sub-contractor was not liable for the negligence of the sub-sub-contractor. The principle, that a person employing an independent contractor to undertake inherently dangerous work was responsible for the contractor's

---

[1] "Companies' Environmental Liabilities for Acts of Vandalism", D Hughes, [1995] 44 (6) *Env. Information Bulletin* 13.

negligence, rendered the principal himself liable and hence barred him from invoking the same principle against his sub-contractor.

Use of Consultants

The complexities of waste management are such that it is almost inevitable that at some stage advice will be required from "experts" such as consultants, lawyers, surveyors and architects. The information provided by these professionals may be of critical importance in decisions relating to the allocation of funds and resources, or the acceptance of responsibility/ liability for operational and other ventures.

Unlike the other issues of corporate liability discussed earlier, which were concerned solely with the actions of an organisation in relation to third parties, situations in which consultants are involved are more complex. Consultants are engaged to undertake a broad spectrum of activities, from data collection, sampling and analysis to the provision of comprehensive advice to be used by the client and possibly by third parties. As a result, in addition to the client itself, there is a wide range of potential claimants on the consultant, including directors and officers, third parties, regulatory agencies and those involved in the client's transactions – lenders, insurers, purchasers, etc. However, the present discussion will be limited to the relationship between the client and the consultant and how this influences the client's liabilities.

The Role of the Consultant

The role of a professional in this context was summarised by Bingham LJ in *Eckersley v Binnie and Partners*, who stated that:

> "He must bring to any professional task he undertakes no less expertise, skill and care than any other competent member of his profession would bring, *but need bring no more*. The standard is that of the *reasonably average* ... it is the standard prevailing at the time of his acts or omissions which provides the relevant yardstick. He in not ... to be judged by the wisdom of hindsight." [emphasis added]

A corollary to this ruling is that any consultant who holds himself out to have knowledge and expertise above "the reasonably average" will be expected to exercise a correspondingly higher degree of skill and care. Contracts with consultants normally contain a clause to the effect that work will be performed with the standard of skill and care possessed by a reasonably competent member of the consultant's profession and, in the absence of such a provision, a term to that effect will be implied under section 13 of the Supply of Goods Act 1982. This was demonstrated with reference to the position of a director in *Williams v Natural Life Health Foods* as discussed below.

Where the consultant himself employs a specialist, he cannot accept the specialist's advice unquestioningly and may be under a duty to warn the client of any danger or problem which may arise, of which a consultant of ordinary competence ought to be aware.

With regard to the liabilities of the client to third parties for the consequences of a consultant's activities, the position of the consultant will be no different from that of an independent contractor, as discussed earlier.

Terms of Contract and Associated Liabilities
There are two major areas of liability which may arise between the client and a contractor or consultant, viz:

—   tortious liability, generally in negligence; and

—   contractual liability.

Tortious Liability
While a contractual relationship may exist between two parties, it is possible that they owe each other concurrent duties of care both pursuant to the contract and to the general law of tort. There has been an on-going debate on whether such concurrent duties exist and, as relatively recently as 1986, Lord Scarman stated:

> "Their Lordships do not believe there is anything to the advantage of the law's development in searching for a liability in tort where the parties are in a contractual relationship."

However, a number of recent judgments have supported the view that concurrent duties do exist. In *Arbuthnott & ors v Fagan and Feltrim Underwriting Agencies Ltd & ors, and other related actions* the court rejected the argument that a contractual relationship automatically excluded the tortious rights and remedies, and held that the question to be asked was whether, on interpreting the terms of the contract, the parties can be said to have agreed that tortious remedies were to be limited or excluded.

Although the remedies available in tort and in contract are generally similar, the limitation periods under the general law of tort are more generous than those under the law of contract. In *Holt and Another v Payne Skillington*, it was held that, where a duty of care in tort arose between two parties to a contract, wider obligations could be imposed by the duty of care in tort than those arising under the contract.

In *Williams v Natural Life Health Foods* the court held that, while a company director is normally entitled to the limited liability of a company when acting on the company's business, where it can be shown that he has expressly directed or procured the commission of a tort or has assumed a personal responsibility to the plaintiff, then he may be sued in person. Although this case related to a franchising operation, in which its publicity emphasised the expertise of the managing director and major shareholder, it clearly has parallels in the environmental sphere where various professionals give advice to third parties.

Contractual Liability
While an excursion into contract law is beyond the scope of the present discussion, the importance of the terms and conditions of a contract cannot be over stressed, since these are issues over which the client has direct control and to which he has recourse in the event of subsequent problems.

The existence of a contract enables a client to recover as damages the physical and financial losses which result from the consultant's or contractor's breach, subject to any valid limitation on liability providing they arise naturally or from breach of contract or were in contemplation of the parties when the contract was made (*Hadley v Baxendale*). While it is not possible to transfer the liability to the contractor for certain classes of offence, this does not necessarily preclude the recovery of fines as damages (*Osman v J Ralph Moss*).

Where circumstances permit the use of sub-contractors, the situation is the same as with the client/contractor relationship, where the consultant may sub-contract the performance of the work but may not always delegate the responsibility for undertaking it. A particular problem arises where consultants employ a laboratory for specific tests or analyses, and here the client has no direct contractual relationship with the sub-contractor. In such circumstances, a client seeking a remedy against the sub-contractor may have to resort to tortious liability in negligence, although proof of a duty of care may be difficult where the laboratory has no knowledge of the consultant's brief, other than the request for their specialist services. One possible solution is to provide within the contract the power for the contractor or consultant to employ third parties as agents for the client, thus establishing a direct contractual relationship between the client and the third party.

Many contractors and consultants operate to standard terms and conditions (STC) and it is important to negotiate an agreed form which meets the client's requirements and protects his interests. Particular areas of concern will be:

— exclusions or limitations on liability;

— indemnity for actions of contractors;

— use of third parties by contractors (as discussed above); and

— confidentiality of results.

Exclusions of liability for consequential loss and damage, and limitations on the amounts payable in these circumstances are governed by section 2(2) of the Unfair Contract Terms Act 1977, which precludes limits on liability for a contractor's negligence except where this satisfies "the requirement of reasonableness".

The burden of proof for demonstrating "reasonableness" lies with the contractor and section 11(1) of the Act provides that the test of reasonableness is satisfied if the condition is fair and reasonable having regard to the circumstances which were, or ought reasonably to have been, known to or in the contemplation of the parties at the time the contract was agreed. With regard to limiting the liability to a specific amount, section 11(4) states that here the test of reasonableness shall have regard to:

— the resources available to the person relying on the clause; and

— whether insurance cover is available for this situation.

The former point is illustrated in the recent case of *St Albans City and District Council v International Computers Ltd*, where the court held that a clause limiting ICL's liability to £100,000 was void. Although the award made to the plaintiff was reduced on appeal, the court upheld the judge's decision that the defendant's standard contractual terms and conditions which sought to limit its liability for loss to £100,000 were unreasonable and not enforceable under the Unfair Contract Terms Act 1977.

The relationship between a sub-contractor and an employer was considered in the Scottish case of *British Telecommunications plc v James Thompson & Sons (Engineers) Ltd*. The court held that if a sub-contractor in a building contract was aware that the employer had undertaken to insure against, *inter alia*, the risk of negligence on the part of the sub-contractor – in this case, a statutory obligation – then he was entitled to assume not merely that he need not himself insure but that he was not under a duty of care to the employer with regard to loss or damage caused by his negligence.

Should one party to a contract intend the other to be mistaken as to the terms of the agreement by making false and misleading statements to divert the other's attention from discovering the mistake, that party is not entitled to insist on the performance of the contract "to the letter" and might be bound by the agreement the other party thought was being made (*Commission for the New Towns v Cooper (Great Britain) Ltd*).

The activities of both contractors and consultants may involve site work and, where intrusive investigations are undertaken, there is a potential for damage such as severing services – power, water, sewerage – or of mobilising contaminants through breaking through containment barriers/ providing a pathway for the egress to a watercourse. It is therefore important that the client is indemnified against such actions and the recent case of *Barclays Bank v Fairclough Building Ltd* demonstrated the importance of two specific contractual terms, viz:

— to execute work "in an expeditious, efficient and workman-like manner"; and

— to comply with any statutory provisions applicable to the work.

The court held that since these were strict contractual obligations, then:

— the defences of contributory negligence were not available to the contractors; and

— these express obligations were not co-extensive with tortious duties and did not depend upon failures to take reasonable care.

Once it has been established that strict contractual obligations are in place, then notwithstanding that a breach might create parallel liability in tort, defences of contributory negligence cease to apply.

In view of the potential for civil and criminal actions arising from the activities of the client and the access of both the regulators and the general public to certain classes of information relating to the environment, it is important that, wherever possible, any data, information or reports which are generated by any party, including the client himself, do not prejudice his position. This is particularly important in relation to investigations of "unknown" situations, e.g. contamination of land and water, and the general surveys of the "environmental effects" of an organisation as required by certain environmental management systems. This and other related issues will be considered more fully in the next chapter on environmental information.

FURTHER READING

"Asbestos Hazards: Past, Present and Future", A Dalton, [1995] *Occupational Health Review*, September/October, 34

"CDM Regulations – Why Clients Need to Protect Themselves", A Poole, [1995] 6 (3) *Construction Law* 91

"Companies' Environmental Liabilities for Acts of Vandalism", D Hughes, [1995] 44 (6) *Env. Information Bulletin* 13

"The Company Behind Bars", A and S Smith, [1995] *Health and Safety at Work*, February, 8

Contaminated Land, S Tromans and R Turrall-Clarke, Sweet & Maxwell, 1994

"Contracts for Works to be Carried Out: Clauses on Health, Safety and the Environment", D Levine, *UKELA Journal*, Winter 1995/6, 24

"Criminal and Civil Liability of Company Directors", A Waite, [1991] 3 (3) *LMELR* 74

Directors in the Dock, S Tromans and G Irvine, Technical Communications (Publishing) Ltd, 1994

"Environmental Risks Past, Present and Future in the United Kingdom: Does the Polluter Pay or do his Insurers?", M S Mendelowitz, [1995] 83 *Journal of the Insurance Institute of London*, 64

A Guide to Risk Assessment and Risk Management for Environmental Protection, Department of the Environment, HMSO, 1995

"Liability for Independent Contractors", G Williams, [1956] *CLJ* 180

Profiting from Pollution Prevention – the 3Es Methodology, HMIP and Business in the Environment, 1996

Smith and Hogan – Criminal Law, 8th Edition, J C Smith, Butterworths, 1996

Use of Risk Assessment within Government Departments, Health and Safety Executive, HMSO, 1996

Chapter 7

SUPERVISION, COMPLIANCE AND ENVIRONMENTAL INFORMATION

SUPERVISION AND REGULATORY COMPLIANCE

The supervision of waste-related activities is not restricted to the "environmental" agencies and a wide range of enforcement agencies is involved in the planning and supervision of this area of business. There is strong link between these activities and the issues surrounding the exchange of environmental information considered later in this chapter and companies would be wise to establish formal procedures relating to the conduct of employees and their contact with the regulatory agencies. This is particularly true for large organisations where there may be several managers with environmental responsibilities. It is to the advantage of both parties to restrict the number of contact points, for in that way it is clear who the key individuals are, what their areas of responsibility are and what are the limits to their authority.

Waste management operators may receive visits from the representatives of any of the relevant agencies, including:

Environment Agency/ SEPA	: waste processes under Part I EPA 1990; : controlled waters; : waste regulation;
Water company (private)	: discharges to foul sewer;
HSE	: health and safety;
H M Customs & Excise	: landfill tax;
Police	: packaging and labelling regulations (for Department of Transport);
Local authorities	: statutory nuisance; : contaminated land.

In view of the different provisions under which these bodies operate, the range of powers available may differ – from those authorised by the local authority to enforce the litter provisions and who cannot compel an offender to release his name, to those of H M Customs and Excise who have the power of arrest. Consequently, it is important that the limits of the officer's/inspector's authority are ascertained at the outset of his visit and that the conduct of the visit is constrained within these *vires*.

However, this part of the chapter will focus on the powers of those empowered to enforce the legislation contained in "environmental" statutes, i.e. primarily those of the Environment Agency/SEPA, the local authorities and those acting on their behalf.

THE APPOINTMENT OF INSPECTORS

The functioning of environmental statutes is dependent upon formal contact between the regulatory agencies and those subject to the legislation, and substantial powers are given to inspectors of these bodies and to those appointed to operate on their behalf. Prior to the formation of the Environment Agency and SEPA, the appointment and the relevant powers of the inspectors of HMIP, NRA and the Waste Regulation Authorities were contained in a number of statutory measures. However, Schedule 24 to the Environment Act 1995 repealed these individual provisions and new powers were created under sections 108 to 110 of the Act for those acting on behalf of the "enforcing authorities". In addition, statutory guidance and a Code of Practice on Enforcement were issued by the Environment Agency.

All those responsible for investigating offences must have regard to the codes of practice made under the Police and Criminal Evidence Act 1984 ("PACE"), particularly Code B dealing with the search of premises and seizing of property, and Code C dealing with the detention, treatment and the cautioning and questioning of suspects.

POWERS OF ENTRY

Persons with Powers of Entry

While the former "powers of entry" provisions within the 1990 Act were specific to the exercise of the powers of *inspectors*, the provisions of the 1995 Act follow the pattern of the Control of Pollution Act 1974 and the Water Resources Act 1991, which empowered *any person* designated in writing for the purpose by either of the Ministers or by the Authority. The new powers of entry are contained in section 108 and Schedule 18 of the 1995 Act and are conferred upon "*a person* who appears suitable to *an enforcing authority*", with the additional requirement that the authorisation is in writing. The authorisation may also state the terms under which the powers under section 108(4) may be exercised. This is a much broader definition than before and there is apparently no restriction on "a person" (undefined) including a legal person (e.g. an environmental consultancy) as well as a natural person.

The term "enforcing authority" encompasses the Secretary of State, the Environment Agency, SEPA or a local enforcing authority, the latter relating to a local authority within the meaning of Part IIA of the EPA 1990 in its capacity as enforcing authority in relation to that part, and a local authority for the purposes of Part IV of the 1995 Act (section 111(15)).

Within this broad framework, section 108(1) defines the purpose of the powers given to authorised persons as:

— determining whether any provision of the pollution control enactments relevant to that authority is being, or has been, complied with;

— exercising or performing one or more of the pollution control functions of that authority; and

— determining whether and, if so, how such a function should be exercised or performed.

The term "pollution control enactments" refers to the enactments and instruments relating to the pollution control functions of the enforcing authority, and "pollution control functions" include the functions conferred or imposed on the Environment Agency or SEPA by or under the wide range of legislative instruments listed in Table 7-1 (page 285). Note, however, that this list does *not* include those measures relating to the functions of the Drinking Water Inspectorate and those under Part VI EPA 1990 concerning the release of genetically modified organisms (GMOs), since neither of these functions was transferred to the Environment Agency or SEPA under section 2 of the 1995 Act.

These new measures assist significantly the operation of the Environment Agency and SEPA. Although most existing staff remained within their present areas of expertise, there will be occasions, such as pollution incidents, which demand immediate action in a number of areas. Furthermore, each regulated business will have a single "account manager" to contact as part of the "first-stop shop" philosophy and these managers will have the authority to take action in any of the matters referred to them.

In addition to authorising persons to undertake the three strictly "regulatory" duties listed above under section 108(1), the Environment Agency or SEPA may also authorise powers of entry in relation to persons preparing a report or undertaking an assessment, following a request from the Minister, under section 5(3) or 33(3) of the Act.

Powers for Gaining Entry

It is now obligatory for an inspector or other designated person to produce evidence of his designation and other authority *before* he exercises his powers (Schedule 18, para. 3). (In the past, such authority only needed to be shown on demand.) However, there may be occasions on which entry is refused or the premises are permanently or temporarily unoccupied. It may also be deemed necessary to gain entry without giving prior warning to the occupier. Under such circumstances, a justice of the peace or a sheriff (in Scotland) may issue a warrant to enter the premises provided he is satisfied, on the basis of sworn information in writing, that:

— there are reasonable grounds for the exercise of the power; *and*

— one or more of a number of the conditions in paragraph 2(2)(a)-(e) of Schedule 18 are fulfilled.

The term "premises" is given a wide definition in section 108(15) and includes any land, vehicle, vessel or mobile plant. Under section 5 and Schedule 1 of the Interpretation Act 1978, "land" is taken to include any buildings and structures on it.

The designated person may be accompanied by a constable and force may be used to gain entry "if need be" (section 108(4)(b)(i)). However, he owes a duty to an occupier who is temporarily absent to leave the premises "as effectively secured against trespassers as he found them". Furthermore, the enforcing authority must make full compensation to any person (i.e. including adjacent landowners) who has sustained damage as a result of the acts or omissions of the designated person in exercising the powers in section 108(4)(a), (b) and (5). However, as noted earlier, provided the actions of the designated person were done in good faith and on reasonable grounds, he will not be liable in any civil or criminal proceedings.

Scope of Powers of Entry

The powers of entry in the Act are listed in section 108(4) and supplementary provisions are included in Schedule 18. An important feature of the new Act is the purposes for which these powers may be used, since it extends significantly the earlier provisions. In *J B & M Motor Haulage Ltd v London Waste Regulation Authority*, it was held in relation to section 93 of the Control of Pollution Act 1974 that, where the relevant authority sought to use the power under section 93 (which related to the power of authorities to obtain information), it must reasonably consider that it needed the information on the basis of admissible evidence of the commission of an offence and that the person on whom a notice was served was or may have been connected with that offence. This ruling effectively prevented inspectors from entering premises on "fishing trips". The 1995 Act reverses this restrictive approach and permits entry at any reasonable time providing the inspector has "reason to believe it is necessary for him to enter" (section 108(4)(a)). In *Hicks v Faulkener*, it was held that "reason to believe" meant "a reasonable and *bona fide* belief in the existence of such a state of things as would amount to a justification of the course pursued. ... It is not essential in any case that facts should be established ... as evidence for a jury."

However, despite these wide powers, following the judgment in *Dudley MBC v Debenham Stores*, unless the enforcement agency adopts the requirements of the code of practice and other necessary provisions of the Police and Criminal Evidence Act 1984, there is the possibility that evidence uncovered which could support a prosecution may not be admissible. Although this case concerned trading standards offences, it is equally applicable to environmental enforcement. Mrs Justice Smith stated:

> "It would be wholly artificial to draw a distinction between the entry of an officer for the purpose of seeing whether there was any evidence of a contravention ... and where there was already a suspicion in his mind that an offence had been committed."

It was "fair and right, and within the law, that the relevant part of the code (of practice) should apply from the start."

Entry to residential premises is subject to special conditions (section 108(6)) and, except in an emergency, in any case in which entry is required or heavy equipment is to be taken onto these premises, seven days' notice must be given to the person who appears to be the occupier. If he does not give his consent, then a warrant must be sought under Schedule 18.

Investigative Powers

The authorised person may take with him any other authorised person, including a constable if any *serious obstruction* is anticipated, and any equipment or materials as might be required. Investigative powers include the taking of photographs, recordings and samples from the three environmental media in, on or in the vicinity of the premises. The Secretary of State may make regulations concerning the sampling procedures to be used (section 108(9)) and the admissibility of results obtained is covered in section 111, discussed below. Under section 108(5), experimental borings "and other works" may be taken *on the premises* and monitoring equipment may be installed, kept and maintained there.

An important power is the ability to direct that the whole or any part of the premises is left undisturbed for as long as is necessary, in order to undertake an examination or investigation (section 108(4)(d)). Likewise, anything within the premises may be subject to such a direction. It is clear that action of this type could lead to significant disruptions in operational activities and the phrase "for as long as is reasonably necessary" is of critical importance. It is significant that the element of reasonableness relates to the time spent on the investigation and not to the decision to undertake the investigation in a particular manner.

There are also substantial powers in section 108(4)(g), (h) for the examination of "articles or substances" found on the premises which appear to be linked to a pollution event – actual or potential – although the person with responsibility for the premises may request to be present. Unlike in Part II EPA 1990, "substances" is not defined and, in view of the increasing commonality between waste legislation and that pertaining to hazardous chemicals, it is unfortunate that this section has not been drafted more precisely. (Under the CHIP Regulations, SI 1994/3247, "substances" means chemical elements and their compounds, whereas "preparations" refers to mixtures of substances.) In addition, "articles and substances" may be subject to any process or test or may be dismantled but not so as to destroy or damage them unless necessary.

Stop and Search Powers

The Environment Agency sometimes becomes involved in vehicle "stop and search" operations in conjunction with the police and with other agencies such as the Health and Safety Executive and the Benefits Agency. A narrow interpretation of section 5 of the Control of Pollution (Amendment) Act 1989 might suggest that this provision is not a firm basis for such activities, although to date such a challenge has not been subject to judicial consideration. The Head of Waste Regulation within the Environment Agency has stated (*Wastes Management* [1997] February, page 10) that the Agency is required, under the EU Regulations on the Transfrontier Shipment of Waste, 259/93/EEC, to monitor as well as to enforce European and international waste movements. In relation to monitoring, Article 30 of these Regulations specifically mentions spot checks of *internal* waste movements.

Powers of Questioning

Questioning may take one of the three forms summarised in Table 7-2 (page 286) and employees should be made aware of these and their implications in relation to both themselves and their company. On routine visits unconnected with a pollution incident, questioning is likely to be informal and, although the information so gained could possibly be used in a prosecution, the chance of this happening is remote. However, it is not unknown for an inspector on an informal visit to a site to observe a situation which demands questioning on a more formal basis. In such cases, the existence of company standing orders/guidelines stipulating the conduct of questioning – e.g. ensuring that legally-permitted representation (presence of a senior manager or legal advice, as appropriate) is available – will assist both the individual and the company.

When questioned under a formal caution under the Police and Criminal Evidence Act 1984, there is a right to silence and to the presence of legal advice. Any confession obtained may be used against the individual, the company, or both. Environmental and other provisions also allow inspectors and others to conduct "obligatory" questioning, as in section 108(4)(k) of the 1995 Act, and here the conditions are significantly different. No caution need be given since the person involved is obliged by law to answer and, although legal advice cannot be made available, a non-legal person such as a senior manager may be present. (Hence the utility of company standing orders to clarify the persons who should be present to represent the interests of the individual and the company.) While use of a confession cannot be made in the prosecution of the person giving the information, it may form the basis of an action against the company.

Issues concerning formal and obligatory questioning were considered in *R v Page*, in relation to whether a false statement made to a trading standards officer was a statement to which criminal sanctions applied. It was argued that the offence (of making a false statement) could only be committed where the interviewee was acting under mandatory requirements and that, if he had been told under caution that he need not answer, then the relevant provision was not applicable. However, the court held that because the wording of section 21(1)(c) of the Trade Descriptions Act 1968 included the words "without reasonable cause" (in relation to questioning) and the defendant had been told that he need not give the information, then by choosing to give a false statement he put himself within the scope of the offence. This reasoning applies equally well to similar environmental provisions.

Self Incrimination

An important component of the new provisions of the 1995 Act is that, under section 108(12), no answer given by a person in pursuance of a requirement imposed under section 108(4)(j) is admissible in evidence against that person in any criminal proceedings. Upton and Harwood[1] contend that if a director or senior manager was providing evidence on behalf of his company, then under this provision that information could not be used against him or the company.

However, as highlighted by *R v Hertfordshire Council ex parte Green Environmental Industries Ltd*, in this context there is a distinction between these section 108 powers which are available to an inspector when making an investigation, or in a potential emergency, and those available to the Agencies under section 71(23)(b) in which the request for information is by means of a notice in writing.

In the former case, the law gives a certain degree of protection against self-incrimination, since the interviewee may have no immediate access to representation and may be denied the benefit of a formal interview. However, this is not the case where there are more formal processes for the requisition of information and the person involved may have the benefit of representation and the questioning will be subject to the PACE provisions.

In relation to questioning by DTI inspectors in the events leading to the "Guinness" trial, the European Court of Human Rights affirmed in *Saunders v United Kingdom* that the use by the prosecution of statements given under legal compulsion during a statutory examination (into corporate fraud) was an infringement of the applicant's right not to incriminate himself.

Legal Professional Privilege

Under section 108(13), none of the powers relating to entry, etc. may be used to compel the production by *any person* of *a document* which was subject to legal professional privilege. As will be discussed later, privilege applies to the *advice* given by a solicitor or barrister and not to specific *facts*, although the courts have been reluctant to order the release of information appended to legal advice. However, in view of the strictly numerical nature of much of the information surrounding environmental compliance, this might be an area for future challenge. It requires no legal knowledge to ascertain whether a given condition within a consent or authorisation has been met – the manager or his technical advisor is probably better qualified than a lawyer in this context – and it might be regarded that the involvement of a lawyer to determine solely whether an infraction had occurred was an abuse of privilege. Section 108(4)(k) appears to have been drafted with this in mind.

---

[1]   "The Stunning Powers of Environmental Inspectors", W Upton and R Harwood, [1996] *JPL* August, 623.

Since section 108(13) relates to *documents*, inspectors may still demand answers from relevant persons regarding *facts*, such as whether specific breaches of a consent had occurred or particular operating conditions were adhered to. An interesting situation arises in relation to the questioning of directors, managers and similar officers who under other circumstances might be subject to individual criminal liability, such as section 157 EPA 1990, but under mandatory questioning would not. This imposes a "Catch 22" type of situation on the regulators on whether to ask the question of this class of person, particularly in a one-man business or small organisation, and also on the directors, etc. regarding the frankness of their replies, balancing their loyalty to the company against their risk of prosecution.

Emergency Situations

After the occurrence of a pollution incident, it is essential that immediate action is taken to minimise its effect and to prevent the situation from deteriorating. This is an area in which statutory provisions are demonstrably more flexible than common law remedies, since account may be taken of both the actual and the potential harm to the "unowned environment" as well as to property interests.

With regard to the powers of entry, the term "emergency" is defined in section 108(15) and means a case in which it appears to the authorised person that:

— there is an imminent risk of serious pollution of the environment or serious harm to human health; *or*

— circumstances exist which are likely to endanger life or health, *and*

that immediate entry is necessary to verify the existence of that risk, to assess its cause or to effect a remedy.

The powers to deal with such situations are contained in section 109, which applies to *any* premises and empowers an authorised person to seize the article or substance causing the danger and render it harmless, destroying it if necessary. In view of the scope of this power, any action undertaken must be accompanied by the production of a signed report detailing the action which was taken, as soon as possible. In addition, a signed copy must be given to the responsible person on the premises and to the owner. Where the owner cannot be determined after reasonable enquiry, his copy is given to the responsible person on the site.

For more serious and widespread pollution incidents involving the disruption of water supplies or sewerage services to an area, the Secretary of State has powers under section 208 of the Water Industry Act 1991 and section 207 of the Water Resources Act 1991 to give such directions to relevant undertakers as appear to be requisite or expedient.

Offences

Enforcement of the powers of entry is dealt with in section 110 which creates an offence of intentionally obstructing an authorised person in the exercise or performance of his duties. This offence existed elsewhere within EPA 1990 (e.g. sections 23(1)(f) and 69(9)(c)) and, although on one hand it would appear to strengthen the hand of inspectors, the qualification of "intentionally" places on them the burden of demonstrating *mens rea*.

As noted in relation to the "Directive" definition of waste, the courts have interpreted *intent* as being synonymous with *aim* and, in *R v Mohan*, *intention* was defined as "a decision to bring about, in so far as it lies within the accused's power [a proscribed result], no matter whether the accused desired that consequence of his act or not". With regard to the term "obstruct", in *Hills v Ellis* McCullough J held (in relation to police powers) that "wilfully obstruct" meant "doing deliberate actions with the intention of bringing about a state of affairs which, objectively regarded, amount to an obstruction ... i.e. making it more difficult for the police to carry out their duty." This ruling with its emphasis on "doing deliberate actions" does not assist the inspector greatly, since inaction can sometimes be as obstructive as more positive behaviour, although there may be some mileage in section 108(4)(l) which requires "any person to afford [the authorised person] such facilities and assistance with respect to any matters or things within that person's control ... as are necessary to enable the authorised person to exercise any of the powers conferred on him ..."

There are three categories of offence relating to obstruction, viz:

— a failure to comply with *any* requirement of section 108 (section 109(1));

— a failure or refusal to provide facilities or assistance or information, or to permit any inspection, reasonably required (section 109(2)); and

— the prevention of any other person appearing before an authorised person or answering any questions required under section 108 (section 109(3)).

There is a defence of "without reasonable cause", although this is available only in so far as relevant circumstances are beyond the control of the defendant, as in *Wellingborough Borough Council v Gordon*.

SAMPLING

The taking of samples, which subsequently results in an action being initiated against a company, is sometimes mistakenly assumed to be the prerogative of the regulator, yet successful prosecutions may be based upon samples taken by third parties, as in *Greenpeace v Albright and Wilson*, or by the company itself, as in *NRA v Pasminco*. "Samples" are a further form of environmental information to be controlled and, in view of a regulator's powers to demand relevant information, unless covered by privilege organisations should consider why (and how) such analytical information should be brought into being.

In general, analytical results may be challenged on either legal or scientific grounds and, although this possibility has been reduced by section 111 of the 1995 Act, there is scope for a challenge regarding the latter, if it can be shown that:

— the sample taken was not representative of the bulk concentration or related only to a short period of time;

— degradation of the sample occurred during storage, such as that resulting from the pick-up of contaminants from or reaction with the storage container, storage at the wrong temperature, or delay before analysis;

— there were inaccuracies in the analysis itself due to:

— use of an inappropriate technique;

— lack of quality control or recent calibration;

— interference of results by other components;

— limitations on accuracy of technique;

— high background concentrations.

Much case law on sampling concerns the water environment and a detailed review of this has been undertaken by Mumma.[1] Although a number of these principles apply to the sampling of the other environmental media, it should be stressed that the (legal) validity of a given sample is dependent upon the wording of the Act in question, which may apply specific conditions upon the person or organisation who undertook the sampling.

---

[1] "Use of Compliance Monitoring Data in Water Pollution Prosecutions", A Mumma, [1993] 5 (2) *JEL* 191.

Sampling by a Company

Many companies undertake routine sampling, unrelated to regulatory requirements, as a means of checking compliance, or they may be required to do so as a condition of an IPC authorisation or a discharge consent. The former may comprise part of an environmental management system which demands records to be maintained and the latter may additionally require such information to be passed on to the regulating body to be subsequently placed upon a public register.

A company has little option but to comply with the data-gathering requirements of the regulatory body, particularly in view of the amendments in section 111 of the Environment Act 1995, *infra*, and runs the risk of a prosecution either by the regulator itself or by a third party using the register as evidence. In *D A Wales v Thames Water Authority*, Thames Water itself had placed the information on a public register, which was subsequently used against it by a third party.

However, unless requested by an inspector or another authorised person, a company has no obligation to supply the regulator with additional, unspecified, samples taken on the occasion of a spillage/incident, provided it is aware of the identity of the pollutant. Following the argument in *Scott-Whitehead & ors v National Coal Board*, a discharger cannot be expected to know the concentration of the components within, or the flows of, the receiving medium. Consequently, such additional samples may not be of benefit to the company but could be used in its prosecution.

Use of Samples by Third Parties

Where statute permits private prosecution by parties other than the regulator, this may be undertaken on the basis of information held on public registers or samples taken by the parties themselves. (Note, however, that under sections 196 and 206 of the Water Industry Act 1991, sewerage undertakers are not obliged to disclose their sampling data.)

Although third parties do not have the regulator's power to enter premises in order to sample, prosecutions have been made on the basis of samples taken at a point other than the statutorily specified location, as in *Greenpeace v Albright and Wilson*. In the past, where a sample was taken by a person who was "not acting for the Authority", the results *could* be admissible in the absence of the tripartite sampling requirements imposed on the regulator under section 171 of the Water Industry Act 1991 and section 209 of the Water Resources Act 1991. However, this is not now relevant in view of section 111 of the 1995 Act.

While this might appear to weight the odds against a company, there are a number of courses of action which are open to it. Any attempt by a third party to obtain a sample by trespass on the company's land may be challenged as improperly obtained evidence, although the chances of success are not high. However, the scientific validity of the sample or analytical procedure might be questioned, since only the company possesses knowledge of the operational conditions at the relevant time. Furthermore, unlike sampling by the regulator, there are no restrictions on attempts to frustrate the ability of a third party to obtain a valid sample by ensuring that any samples taken are not representative of the operational situation, e.g. dilution or diversion of effluent streams, providing such action does not contravene any consents or authorisations.

With regard to the use of data from public registers, there was the potential issue of it being regarded as hearsay evidence but, following the Civil Evidence Act 1995, the rules on the admissibility of hearsay evidence have changed. As a result of cost considerations, the majority of the data on the registers is based upon "routine" rather than "legal" samples and as such may not be admissible as evidence, although this too changed with the introduction of section 111 of the 1995 Environment Act. However, samples taken by the regulator will be admissible under section 24 of the Criminal Justice Act 1988 and the discharger's own data would be regarded as a confession under sections 76 and 82 of the Police and Criminal Evidence Act 1984.

Sampling by the Regulator

With regard to the legal validity of a sample, in the past this was dependent upon the regulator taking a "tripartite" sample, according to section 209 of the Water Resources Act 1991 or section 171 of the Water Industry Act 1991. In *NRA v Harcross Timber and Building Supplies Ltd*, the Divisional Court held that the Wantage magistrates had rightly ruled non tripartite samples taken by the NRA as inadmissible, since section 148(1)(a) of the Water Act 1989 – the predecessor to the current provisions – applied to samples taken from the receiving water as well as those from the effluent. Further consideration on the procedures for taking a legal sample was given in *Attorney General's Reference (No 2 of 1994)*, with particular reference to the meanings of "on taking a sample" and "then and there".

These and other difficulties associated with the use of automatic sampling devices are addressed in section 111 of the Environment Act 1995, which introduced a number of important changes, viz:

— the restrictive provisions of section 171(4) and (5) WIA 1991 and section 209(1), (2) and (4) WRA 1991 were repealed (subsection (1));

— there are now few, if any, restrictions upon the admissibility of evidence for *any* proceedings, including, *inter alia*, monitoring data and "information so provided or obtained or recorded by means of *any* apparatus" (section 111(2));

— the omission of information from a record, where this is part of a licence condition, is now admissible as evidence that the condition has not been observed (section 111(4)).

Tromans[1] notes that the interpretation of this last provision is uncertain and it is less evident as to what is required than in its earlier form in section 25(2) EPA 1990. Section 111(4) states:

"Where by virtue of a condition of a relevant licence, an entry is required to be made in any record as to the observance of any condition of the relevant licence, and the entry has not been made, the fact shall be admissible in any proceedings as evidence that *that condition* has not been observed."

The words "that condition" could relate either to the entry of information or the fulfilment of the licence condition and clearly the latter interpretation would give the regulators a very powerful tool to assist enforcement.

These provisions will add significantly to the powers of the regulatory authorities and may alter their prosecution strategy from "general" pollution offences to those associated with discharge consents. Furthermore, it would be unusual if, on the periodic reassessment of consent conditions, the regulators did not make use of section 111(4) and require a substantially greater degree of sampling to be undertaken by the company itself. Not only would this "self-regulation" concentrate the "corporate mind" on achieving the consent limits but it would take pressure off the resources of the regulator. In view of the wording of this subsection, such a move would produce a "win-win" situation for the regulator and a "lose-lose" one for the regulated.

Automatic Sampling and Computer Statements

The use of automatic sampling devices has proved problematic in the past and in *R v CPC (UK) Ltd* it was held that, although the equipment generated an analysis relating to the water flow in question, since no discrete "sample" came into existence section 209 did not apply, and the evidence

---

[1]   *The Environment Acts 1990-1995, 3rd Edition*, S Tromans, M Nash and M Poustie, Sweet & Maxwell, 1996, page 636.

was admissible. Clearly, the new provisions will change the need for such exercises in semantics and, more importantly, section 111(3) will place the burden of proof regarding the accuracy of *any* apparatus on the defendant. Since section 111(2) relates to any apparatus, this could be applied to both "in-house" equipment and that of the regulatory agency, both of which would be presumed to be accurate. There is a potential area of conflict where these are not in agreement and it will clearly be of benefit to a company to maintain full records of the calibration of their equipment and to be aware of the potential for sources of discrepancy between the types of sampling equipment or procedures used.

LIABILITY OF THE REGULATORY AGENCIES AND THEIR INSPECTORS

The relationship between the regulatory agencies and their "customers" is such that a high degree of reliance is placed upon their assessment of a particular situation and, in certain circumstances, action may be taken against the regulator or an individual inspector. This was considered in *Scott-Whitehead v National Coal Board & ors*, where it was held that the second defendant, the Southern Water Authority, owed a duty of care to warn the plaintiffs of the risk of dangerous levels of salinity in the water extracted under licence for spray irrigation. However, Stuart-Smith J thought that a duty to check the water every day as to its suitability for the various purposes for which it was used would be a "wholly unwarrantable burden" on the authority.

Scott-Whitehead was decided in 1976 and, in view of subsequent changes in the law of negligence, the application of this ruling with its reliance on foreseeability as the sole test of liability must now be questioned. More recently, a local food authority was held liable for the economic loss, estimated at £39,522, sustained as a result of the negligence of one of its environmental health officers in requiring unnecessary work to be undertaken to secure compliance with the Food Act 1960 (*Welton v North Cornwall District Council*). Their Lordships considered the fairness, reasonableness and justice and all the material aspects of policy in reaching their conclusion, and stated that the officer was acting both outside the power of the Act and outside the informal enforcement practice of the local authority. In the scale and detail of the directions he gave and the degree of control the officer exerted, he conducted himself "in a manner which was exceptional". In the view of Lord Justice Rose, in such a situation a duty of care might well be imposed upon police officers and others.

In *R v Lambeth LBC ex parte Wilson*, where a local authority made an "eleventh hour" decision not to contest an application for judicial review in a case involving a homeless person, it was held that individual officers involved were personally liable for wasted costs, under section 4 of the Courts and Legal Services Act 1990. (See *Symphony Group plc v Hodgson* for a review of the case law in this area.) The court considered that this exceptional power to award a non-party costs should be applied on the basis of a three-fold test:

— had the person of whom the complaint had been made acted improperly, unreasonably or unjustly;

— if so, did such conduct cause the applicant to incur unnecessary costs; and

— if so, was it in all the circumstances just to order the person to compensate the applicant for whole or part of the relevant costs.

In addition, the circumstances surrounding the case, such as any financial or managerial shortages or constraints on the officer's time, should be taken into consideration.

There are a number of cases in which the powers of the regulatory agencies have been questioned by the courts. The misuse of statutory powers was considered in *R v National Rivers Authority ex parte Haughey*, where the court noted that the licensing system under the Salmon and Fresh Water Fisheries Act 1975 was in place to regulate the numbers of those who fished and not for the purposes of inquiring into whether the use of any particular instrument specified in the licence would be unlawful.

Of greater importance, perhaps, is *R v Carrick District Council ex parte Shelley and Another*, where a local authority was held to have failed in its statutory duty when it resolved not to take any action in regard to complaints of pollution of the local beaches but merely to monitor the situation. Potential applications of this judgment extend beyond cases of statutory nuisance under Part III of the 1990 Act and such action or threatened action could be one means by which "common interest groups" might exert pressure on local authorities in relation to their contaminated land duties under Part IIA of the Act.

FURTHER DEVELOPMENTS

It was noted at the beginning of this chapter that much of the practical enforcement of the legislation arises as a result of the day-to-day activities of the inspectors and other representatives of the regulatory agencies. A useful insight into their work is given in Hawkins' analysis of the regulation of water pollution prior to the establishment of the NRA,[1] in which he concludes that pollution control is done in a moral, not a technological world (c.f. Hughes' more recent comments, Chapter 1, page 4). More importantly, he classifies strategies of enforcement as *compliance* or *sanctioning*, which are in turn associated with *conciliatory* or *penal* styles of enforcement. *Compliance* strategies seek to prevent harm rather than punish wrongs and are directed towards securing conformity to a rule or standard, with recourse to the legal process as a last resort. By contrast, *sanctioning* is concerned with the application of punishment for breaking a rule and doing harm, and this has an essentially binary outcome – punishment or nothing.

At the time of this study, enforcement in the water industry was based upon *compliance* but, following the establishment of the NRA, there was a distinct change in attitude, with a significant rise in the number of prosecutions and a very high rate of success (Table 7-3, page 287). Not all of the "environmental agencies" at the time followed this policy and the establishment of the Environment Agency and SEPA may result in a further change in direction. The Environment Agency's management statement stresses the need to reflect the principles of the Deregulation and Contracting Out Act 1994. In particular, the statement sets out the following guidance on enforcement procedures:

— an enforcement officer who seeks remedial action must beforehand promptly send the party concerned notice of the action required and reasons why it should be taken, as well as details of timescales;

— all recipients of formal enforcement notices should also be advised how an appeal may be undertaken;

— a reasonable period will be allowed before enforcement action can be taken;

— before formal enforcement action is started, a notice must be sent to the person concerned, explaining why enforcement is under consideration and seeking representations;

— the Agency will be required to seek out ways of resolving disputes before any formal action or prosecution is instituted.

Against this apparently cautious approach, the 1995 Act provides for a wide range of future modifications. Section 108(15)(m) allows for future EU legislation, introduced through section 2(2) of the European

---

[1] *Environment and Enforcement*, K Hawkins, Clarendon Press, 1984.

Communities Act 1972, to be included in relation to the "pollution control functions" of the Environment Agency or SEPA. Furthermore, section 108(4)(m) provides a "catch-all" whereby the Secretary of State may introduce by regulations *any* power of entry in order to carry out the purposes of the Environment Agency or SEPA, as defined in subsections (1) and (2). There is also an intriguing provision in section 65 of Schedule 22 allowing the Secretary of State "to add, whether generally or in such circumstances as may be prescribed by regulations, any person specified in the regulations, or any description of persons so specified, to the persons who are authorised persons" in relation to the duty of care in section 34 of the 1990 Act.

Until the Environment Agency and SEPA become established, it will not be possible to determine how the above provisions or policy will be interpreted but, in view of the numerical superiority of former NRA employees in the new Agencies, it will be surprising if the culture of their organisation does not become dominant.

ENVIRONMENTAL INFORMATION

> *"Minister, two basic rules in Government:*
> *– never look into anything you don't have to; and*
> *– never set up an enquiry unless you know in advance of its findings."*
> *The Complete Yes Minister*, Jonathan Lynn and
> Anthony Jay, BBC Books

Many of the above statutory powers are concerned with the generation and provision of environmental information and in addition to the regulatory bodies there are many groups and individuals with an interest in "information relating to the environment". The Department of the Environment Booklet *Environment Facts – A Guide to Using Public Registers of Environmental Information* lists over fifty sources of such data, most of which are available for inspection by the public at no cost. Taken in conjunction with the Environmental Information Regulations 1992, the rights relating to disclosure of information in the course of litigation and the moves towards "open government" such as the 1994 voluntary code of practice to provide greater access to government information, it would appear that the management of environmental information should be a priority issue for most organisations. This is reinforced by reference to the issues surrounding the *Brent Spar*, where Greenpeace was first alerted to the intention for the deep-sea disposal of Shell's oil storage platform after scrutinising their Best Practicable Environmental Option (BPEO) proposals.

However, the actual position is more complex and it is not necessarily the nominal *availability* of information which is of importance, but the *accessibility* of data relevant to the particular situation and the ability to interpret and apply the facts obtained. In some circumstances, there are restrictions on the further disclosure of information obtained from public registers, as in section 206 of the Water Industry Act 1991, and in others the person or group acquiring the data may not have the *locus standi* for it to be used as the basis of a court action. In the example above, Greenpeace had no official standing to challenge HMIP's decision regarding the BPEO for the disposal of the oil storage platform, although they achieved their objectives through other means – in part by customer-focused economic action.

This area of environmental control is at a relatively early stage of development and there are few people with the necessary skill and knowledge to access and interpret the available data sources. More than 75% of the information in the registers in the DoE's listing is available only in printed form and is held at a limited number of locations, necessitating for some a lengthy journey, possibly to a remote sewage works in order to access information relating to discharge consents, during the periods deemed as "reasonable hours" when the registers are made available (generally "normal office hours"). There have been other practical problems, such as the wide range of charges imposed by different regions of the same body and difficulty in interpreting the raw data recorded.

THE DEVELOPMENT OF ACCESS TO ENVIRONMENTAL INFORMATION

The development of statutory measures for access to information has strongly reflected the political and commercial climate within the UK and only relatively recently have EU initiatives become a factor. Ball and Bell[1] point out that there has been a culture of secrecy surrounding environmental information which has its origins in the activities of the Alkali Inspectorate who, empowered by the Alkali Act 1863, instituted a policy of keeping the industry's information private unless its availability was permitted by the owner of the information or was required by statute. Under the provisions of the Official Secrets Act 1911, information held by the government, including that relating to environmental issues, could not be disclosed and these restrictions were not removed until the recommendations of the Franks Committee in 1972 were implemented in the Official Secrets Act of 1989.

---

[1]   *Environmental Law, 3rd Edition*, S Ball and S Bell, Blackstone Press, 1995, Chapter 7.

Many of the early environmental statutes, such as the Rivers (Prevention of Pollution) Act 1961, continued the restrictive approach of the Alkali Inspectorate to the release of industrial information and, where public registers were established, as with the Alkali Act 1906 and the Notification of Installations Handling Hazardous Substances Regulations 1982, they were generally restricted to a listing of premises subject to the legislation.

The Royal Commission on Environmental Pollution (RCEP) has considered the public access to environmental information on a number of occasions and reviewed the arguments of bodies such as the CBI for its restriction, viz:

— the possible adverse effect on the viability of industrial operations through breaches in commercial confidentiality;

— the misuse, or misinterpretation of data by environmental groups or individuals;

— the allegedly disproportionately high costs of establishing and maintaining the registers.

However, the RCEP considered that the public had a right to know the potential risks resulting from environmental pollution and that a more transparent approach to the regulation of industrial processes was required in order to re-establish public confidence in the system of controls. It has been pointed out that industry does not have a right to pollute and, although individuals may have private rights in relation to land, water and property, the environment as a whole is "unowned".

Nevertheless, there has been a reluctance by successive governments to permit greater freedom of information and in addition there have been significant differences in the approach used in different contemporary measures. Although section 28(7) of the Health and Safety at Work Act 1974 prevented inspectors of the Industrial Air Pollution Inspectorate from disclosing information concerning atmospheric pollution, under section 41 of the Control of Pollution Act 1974 the water authorities were placed under a duty to establish "registers containing prescribed particulars" relating to water (although it was not until mid-1985 that the relevant part of this Act was implemented).

Subsequent legislation brought more information into the public domain, with the Environment and Safety Information Act 1988 providing access to certain enforcement notices and the Environmental Protection Act 1990 including a wide range of information in a number of its Parts (I, II, IV, VI, VIII) – according to the requirements of the control imposed, including *inter alia* authorisations and the relevant applications, enforcement notices, convictions and monitoring data. However, there was still an official reluctance with regard to some of the potentially sensitive areas and the original drafting of Part VI restricted public access to information on Genetically Modified Organisms (GMOs) to the advertisement of applications for consents. It is also instructive to read in *The Dirty Man of Europe* by Chris Rose about the blatant official manipulation of figures relating to the discharges from sewage works during this period, i.e. prior to the privatisation of the water utilities.

The Influence of European Legislation

Within the EU, there have been a number of important developments relating to rights of access to information and the Maastricht Treaty, signed on 7th February 1992, contains a declaration stating:

> "The Conference considers that transparency of the decision-making process strengthens the democratic nature of the institutions, and the public's confidence in the administration."

This was followed by further commitments to improving access to information, culminating in the approval of a code of practice concerning public access to Council and Commission documents (Council Decision 93/731/EEC), which provided, *inter alia*, that:

> "The public will have the widest possible access to *documents* held by the Commission and Council. 'Document' means any written text, whatever its medium, which contains *existing* data, and is held by the Council or Commission."

These provisions contained a clause which permitted Community institutions to refuse access to documents under certain circumstances and, on the same day that this was approved, the Council adopted its own rules of procedure (Decision 93/662/EC), which pursued a more *restrictive* approach, viz:

> "The deliberations of Council shall be covered by the obligation of professional secrecy, except in so far as the council decides otherwise."
> (Article 5(1).)

These two Decisions were considered by the European Court of Justice in *Carvel and Another v EU Council*, in relation to the refusal of an application by *The Guardian* for access to certain documents. The court held that the EU Council had failed to exercise its discretion in compliance with the relevant law so as to balance the interests of citizens seeking information against its own interests in preserving the secrecy of its deliberations.

A further successful challenge to a refusal of access to documents by the Commission was made in *Worldwide Fund for Nature v Commission of the European Community*, case T-105/95. The Commission had refused WWF access to documents relating to the building of a visitor centre in Mullagmore, Eire, on grounds of protection of the public interest and the Commission's confidentiality requirements. However, the Commission did not state precisely why these grounds for refusal were applicable and the ECJ held that a blanket assertion of public interest was inadequate. Furthermore, it stated that the Commission had not attempted to balance the citizens' interest in gaining access to these documents and its own interest in protecting the confidentiality of its proceedings.

One important aspect of EU legislation in this area has been the introduction of the Freedom of Access to Environmental Information Directive, 90/313/EEC, a measure which itself took over five years between the draft proposal and its adoption in 1990, with a further delay before its implementation in 1992. This is discussed in greater detail below.

While some Directives contain specific requirements for the establishment of public registers, the whole process of legislation through the implementation of Directives by each Member State is dependent upon the feedback of information to the Commission and this has indirectly promoted measures for the exchange of information. Although some Directives included provisions for reporting details of their implementation to the Commission, it was not until 1991 that comprehensive measures were introduced for standardising and rationalising reports on the implementation of environmental measures, through Directive 91/692/EEC. This complemented the prior establishment of the European Environment Agency and the setting up of the European environmental information and observation network. Until the introduction of these measures, the EU Commission had to place great reliance upon the complaints procedure as a means of highlighting the non-compliance of measures by Member States.

As noted in Chapter 1, there is now a greater emphasis on the sustainable development aspects of waste management and the introduction of procedures through the European Waste Catalogue and the UK National Waste Classification Scheme will have the effect of bringing further information into the public domain. Although some of the impetus for the introduction of civil liability for damage to the environment has been lost, were this to be introduced in combination with *locus standi* for "common interest groups", then there would be further pressure for the disclosure of environmental information as a result of any ensuing court actions.

Developments Within the UK

In 1994, as part of its Citizens' Charter initiatives, the government produced a Code of Practice on Access to Government Information. Subject to the following fifteen classes of exemption,

— defence, security and international relations;

— internal discussions and advice;

— communications with the Royal Household;

— law enforcement and legal proceedings;

— immigration and nationality;

— effective management of the economy and collection of tax;

— effective management and operation of the public service;

— public employment, public appointments and honours;

— voluminous or vexations requests;

— publication or prematurity in relation to publication, i.e. information which is or will soon be published, or where disclosure would be premature in relation to a planned announcement or publication;

— research, statistics and analysis;

— privacy of an individual;

— third party's commercial confidence;

— information given in confidence;

— statutory and other restrictions,

the Code commits departments and public bodies which are under the jurisdiction of the Parliamentary Commissioner for Administration (the Ombudsman) to a number of policies, including the publication of facts and analyses *which the government considers relevant and important* in framing major policy proposals and decisions, explanatory information, materials on departments' dealings with the public, and giving reasons for administrative decisions to those affected.

It promises to release, in response to specific requests, information relating to their policies, actions and decisions. However, there is no commitment that pre-existing *documents*, as distinct from *information*, will be made available (unlike the EU provisions, above) and no requirement to acquire information where this is not in the possession of the department.

These provisions are clearly a far cry from the Freedom of Information Act demanded by some and those provisions currently in existence relating to Community institutions, *supra*, and in other Member States (see OJ (1993) C156/5). These have resulted, *inter alia*, in the publication of "Customers' Charters" by the regulatory agencies – *Pollution Prevention – Our Common Concern*, HMIP, March 1994 and *Our Statement of Service Standards*, NRA, January 1994 – and certain policy changes which make available, at the end of a consultation period, the responses received on all consultative documents. There remains, however, the possibility for a respondent to request that all or part of a response remains confidential.

While not providing any new rights to environmental information, the Environment Act 1995 does indirectly assist in the more efficient application of existing systems. The creation of a single Environment Agency will provide an opportunity for the rationalisation and integration of the information systems of its constituent bodies, particularly if it is to satisfy Lord de Ramsay's[1] expectation of a "first-stop shop" for its "customers".

Another important provision of the Act is in section 111, which relates to the admissibility of evidence in relation to certain pollution offences. This could have a significant effect on the approach adopted by the regulators with regard to the generation of monitoring data and the use of automatic sampling devices, as discussed earlier.

Information Technology

Many of the early environmental management systems were hard-copy based and this format limits both the amount of data which can be incorporated into the system and also the ease with which it can be accessed or disseminated. However, as greater use is made of information technology, such restrictions will be overcome. Similarly, any initiatives by the regulatory bodies to encourage formal communications to be made in a computer-compatible format will significantly assist the maintenance of, and access to, public registers.

Table 7-4 on pages 288-289 lists a number of sources of environmental information which now can be accessed through the Internet.

---

[1]   "The Garner Environmental Law Lecture 1995", Lord de Ramsay, *UKELA Journal*, Winter 1995/6, 7.

However, such as move is not without its own problems, as the use of computer based/generated information creates additional legal problems. The *presumption* of accuracy of, *inter alia*, automatic analytical equipment in section 111(2) of the Environment Act 1995 represents a change in emphasis from section 69(1)(b) of the Police and Criminal Evidence Act 1984 (PACE), which states that a statement contained in a document produced by a computer is not admissible unless it is shown "... that at all material times, the computer was operating properly".

Other important issues in the area of electronically held information include: how to denote that a computer print-out is an "original document" (*Glencore International AG and Another v Bank of China*, where the Court of Appeal considered that marking the document "original" would suffice); whether the *retrieval* of information from a computer is the "use of data" under the Data Protection Act 1984 (*R v Brown (Gregory)*); whether digital images are equivalent to photographs (*R v Fellows* and *R v Arnold*); and the breach of copyright through the inclusion of material on the Internet (*Shetland Times v Jonathan Wills and Another*). However, more traditional methods of "print, type and ink writing" have also been subject to judicial consideration in *Co-operative Bank v Tipper*, where it was held that alterations made in pencil to a bank guarantee rendered the deed unenforceable.

In addition, under PACE a statement contained in a computer-generated document is not admissible unless it can be shown, *inter alia*, that there are no reasonable grounds for believing the statement is inaccurate because of improper use of the computer and the courts interpret this in terms of the extent to which human intervention is involved in its production, as demonstrated in the "poll tax" cases of *Camden LBC v Hobson and Another* and *R v Coventry Justices ex parte Bullard and Another*, and those of *John Eric Spiby* and *Hilda Sheppard*.

CORPORATE ENVIRONMENTAL INFORMATION

The presence (or absence) of environmental information is a vital component of corporate liability and organisations would be unwise to ignore this aspect of their environmental management systems, from the point of view of both current and future liabilities. In view of the current restrictions on the accessibility of information, there are few companies within the UK that have an integrated system for managing the generation and dissemination of environmental information. Nevertheless, there is no reason for industrial concerns to be complacent. Despite these shortcomings, legal and technological developments will improve the accessibility of environmental information and cause both the regulators and commercial organisations to reassess and optimise the systems they have in place for its generation, storage, retrieval and control.

A prerequisite to any consideration of the management of information is the establishment of the *mechanisms* responsible for its existence and those involved in its acquisition from the company or producer (i.e. external consultant) by a regulator or third party. Once such a matrix is established, it is then possible to institute the appropriate controls.

The primary test in any such categorisation is whether the generation of the information is associated with any mandatory requirements. While the majority of the following discussion will relate to legislative requirements, it should not be forgotten that bodies such as insurers and lenders may also require an accurate analysis of a company's liabilities (e.g. with regard to contaminated land) and the consequences of an inadequate or inaccurate assessment *may* have greater financial implications than a prosecution in the courts.

Within the category of mandatory information, there are a number of sub-groups, viz:

— operational and other data to be supplied on a routine basis to the regulator;

— information given directly to inspectors of the regulatory bodies, e.g. while on a routine visit or in response to an alleged incident;

— that subject to the Environmental Information Regulations; and

— information relating to litigation, to be made available during discovery.

There is clearly some overlap between the above groups but the purpose of such an analysis is to identify *routes* for information transfer, not to label specific documents. It is, however, necessary to be aware of the contradictory requirements of *different* legislative provisions regarding the *same* data. This is well illustrated with reference to "Duty of Care" Transfer Notes, which under Regulation 3 of the Environmental Protection (Duty of Care) Regulations 1991, SI 1991/2839, are required to be retained for *two* years, whereas under section 2(3)(a) of Schedule 5 to the Finance Act 1996, in relation to the landfill tax, "registerable persons" must maintain such records for up to *six* years. Furthermore, the associated Order on "qualifying material" demands that the Transfer Notes contain additional information relating to this material which is not required under waste management legislation.

DATA ON PUBLIC REGISTERS

The Explosives Act 1875 contains an early example of the establishment of public registers and these were open to all ratepayers within the local authority area, licensees and persons registered under the Act, who on payment of one shilling were permitted to inspect and take copies or abstracts of the entries. An interesting provision was the imposition of a penalty payment of one pound by the local authority if it failed in this duty.

Details relating to aspects of waste management may be included in a number of different registers (Table 7-5, pages 290-291) and, in addition to planning controls, the most important registers will be those concerning operational activities: current waste management licences, waste carriage and activities subject to IPC. Although the scope of each of these is different, there are features which are common to all and these will be discussed using the information requirements of sections 64 to 66 of Part II of the Environmental Protection Act 1990 and the Waste Management Licensing Regulations 1994, since these represent the major provisions relating to information on waste.

An important point is that it is the duty of the regulator to establish and maintain the register and the holder of the information does not play an active role in placing an entry on it. However, *any* formal communications with the regulator have the *potential* for inclusion, unless a successful application is made for exemption under one of the prescribed categories discussed below.

Commercial Confidentiality

The issue of commercial confidentiality has been one of the major objections raised by industry against free access to environmental information and is based upon fears that, by "back-calculation" from effluent compositions or by scrutiny of authorisations, permits and consents, competitors and others might gain an insight into a company's process conditions. In their *Tenth Report*, the RCEP concluded that the emphasis given to commercial confidentiality was disproportionate and misconceived. While some environmental legislation (e.g. section 49 of the Clean Air Act 1993) and other general legislation is couched in the terms of *trade secrets*, viz:

> "... information disclosing the identity of a packer of a package, or the identity of the person who arranged with the packer of a package for the package to be made up, shall be treated as a trade secret ..." (section 64(2), Weights and Measures Act 1985, c72),

the majority of current measures use the more broadly applicable term "commercial confidentiality". This is defined in section 66(11) EPA 1990 thus:

> "Information is ... commercially confidential, in relation to any individual or person, if it being contained in the register would prejudice *to an unreasonable degree* the commercial interests of that individual or person" [emphasis added],

and the issue of confidentiality may be raised either by the *person* supplying the information (section 66(2)) or by the *holder* of the register (section 66(4)). The regulatory agency is the primary arbiter of whether information is to be so treated and, if a determination is not made within 14 days of the application, then it is deemed to be confidential. Appeals against a regulator's decision may be made to the Secretary of State, who additionally may direct that information classified as confidential *is* included on the registers, if this is in the public interest.

Information may be treated as confidential for a period of four years after which the person supplying the original information may request a continuation for a further four years (section 66(8)). Where information is excluded from the register on the grounds of commercial confidentiality, a statement to that effect must be recorded on the register (section 64(2)).

Though not directly related to confidentiality, there are two other time-related aspects of these registers which are of importance. In relation to waste licences, the waste regulatory body has a duty to maintain details relating to both current and "recently current" licences, i.e. licences which have been terminated or surrendered within the previous 12 months, or rejected licence applications within 12 months of the date of rejection. In addition, there is no requirement to keep monitoring data on the register for more than four years or any information which has been superseded by later information (Reg. 11(2), Waste Management Licensing Regulations 1994, SI 1994/1056). These provisions overcome the potential problems of the storage of large amounts of data, although computer-based systems should have a significantly greater capability for storage. However, it is too soon after the implementation of the Regulations to determine whether the regulators will avail themselves of this provision.

Information Affecting National Security

A further potential exclusion from public registers is information which, in the opinion of the Secretary of State, "would be contrary to the interests of national security". The procedures for exclusion of such information are necessarily different from those relating to commercial confidentiality and there are two mechanisms for identifying information in this category. The Secretary of State may direct the regulatory body as to what specific information is to be excluded from the registers or what classes of information are to be referred to him for a determination (section 65(2)). Alternatively, a person may give notice to the Secretary of State of *any* information which appears to him to require this classification, although he must also notify the relevant authority. This section implies no link between the person notifying the Secretary of State and ownership of the information, thus allowing third parties, such as other government agencies, to intervene.

Exclusion under section 65 is not given lightly and, according to *Hansard* (HL vol. 522, col. 380), requires "cogent and specific evidence". The exclusion, once given, remains as long as is deemed necessary by the Secretary of State and, unlike commercial confidentiality, there is *no* register entry to indicate an exclusion, for it is felt that even the acknowledgement that such information exits would itself be contrary to national security.

ENVIRONMENTAL INFORMATION REGULATIONS

As a result of the EU Directive on the Freedom of Access to Environmental Information, 90/313/EEC, the government passed the Environmental Information Regulations 1992, SI 1992/3240, to allow access for any natural or legal person within the Community to "information relating to the environment" which is held by "public authorities". Although initially welcomed as "a powerful instrument for extending access to environmental information well beyond that which is held in public registers – including information going back many years", there have been significant problems in their application in view of the lack of detail in the wording and the absence of a procedure for an aggrieved party following the refusal of information. Since there has been only one judicial consideration of these Regulations to date, many of the initial uncertainties remain and the reader is directed towards the paper by Hughes[1] and the submission to the Lords by UKELA[2] for a fuller consideration of the issues involved.

The Directive is addressed towards "information concerning the environment" and the UK Regulations interpret this as meaning if, *and*

---

[1] "Freedom of Access to Information on the Environment: Directive 90/313/EEC, and the DoE Consultation Paper", D Hughes, [1992] 4 *LMELR* 75.

[2] *The Implementation and Effectiveness of Directive 90/313/EEC on the availability from public authorities of information on the environment,* United Kingdom Environmental Law Association, 21 February 1996.

only if, the information relates to:

— the state of water, air, soil, fauna, flora and natural sites;

— activities (including those which give rise to nuisances such as noise) or measures *adversely* affecting or likely to affect these; and

— activities or measures designed to protect these, including administrative measures and environmental management programmes.

Hughes points out that microbial and bacteriological life forms do not fit neatly within the environmental media listed and the restriction to *adverse* effects excludes substances whose ultimate impact is not foreseen. In addition, climatic changes and effects on man following environmental incidents, such as the water pollution at Camelford, are not included.

The other limb of the applicability test is concerned with information held by "public authorities". The DoE consultation paper included a list of organisations which *might* be covered by the Directive but this excluded BNFL and the privatised water and sewage companies. Within EU case law, there has been a clarification following *Foster v British Gas, Doughty v Rolls Royce plc, Griffin v South West Water Services Ltd* and *National Union of Teachers & ors v Governing Body of St Mary's Church of England (Aided) Junior School & ors*, as to what constitutes an "emanation of the state" but it is not clear whether an "emanation of the state" is synonymous with "public authorities" or "bodies with public responsibility for the environment under the control of public authorities". It is unfortunate that in the sole UK case considering this aspect of the Regulations, *R v British Coal ex parte Ibstock*, this point was not pleaded by British Coal while others with less potential for success were argued (and dismissed).

Some organisations, uncertain as to whether they fall within the Regulations, have taken the view that it is easier to act as though they fall within its ambit and to rely upon the many caveats which may be applied to prevent disclosure, than to claim inapplicability of the Regulations to their organisation. There are two distinct classes of information for which there are exceptions to the right of access – information which *must* be treated as confidential and information which is *capable* of being treated as confidential. Mandatory confidentiality is conferred on information falling within Regulation 4(3) and includes:

— situations in which the provision of information would constitute a breach of any statutory provision or rule of law, subject to Regulation 3(7), *infra*, or would involve a breach of any agreement;

— personal information, where no consent has been given for its release;

— material supplied by a third party, not in relation to the Regulations, and where no consent has been given for its release; and

— information likely to result in damage to the environment if released (e.g. the location of an endangered species).

Regulation 3(7) effectively overrides other legislative provisions which impose a restriction or prohibition on the disclosure of information, providing all the requirements of these Regulations are met. While this clearly lifts a number of restrictions, the condition relating to the breach of *any* agreement (undefined) is potentiality open to a broad interpretation.

Further limitations to access are imposed in the area of discretionary confidentiality (Regulation 4(2)) where information is confidential only if the relevant authority determines it to be so. This includes:

— information relating to matters affecting international relations, national defence or public security;

— information which is or has been *sub judice* or the subject of any legal or other proceedings, whether actual or prospective;

— information relating to the "confidential deliberations" of any relevant person, or to the internal communications of a body corporate or other undertaking or organisation;

— incomplete documents or documents in draft;

— commercial confidentiality and intellectual property.

The application of Regulation 4(2) was considered in *R v London Borough of Tower Hamlets ex parte Tilly*, in relation to the request of the applicant (Miss Tilly) for judicial review in respect of a report on contaminated land commissioned by the London Borough of Tower Hamlets. The initial application was refused on the grounds that the document was in draft and under Regulation 4(2) the Borough were not obliged to disclose it. A copy of the *final* report was supplied to the respondent, whereupon she alleged that this version was materially different from the draft and sought leave for judicial review for the provision of the draft. The court rejected this application on the grounds that the final report had been disclosed and evidence from the authors of the report, the Institute of Public Health, stating that it did not consider that the final report to be materially different from the draft.

Regulation 3 states the obligations imposed on relevant persons to make environmental information available – making arrangements for responding to requests, reply within two months, stating details of any refusal – although a charge may be made and there is no requirement to make it available "except in such form, and at such times as may be reasonable". Furthermore, "manifestly unreasonable" requests or those "formulated in too general a manner" may be refused. A number of commentators have highlighted the apparent illogicalness of this provision, for if it is not known what information exists it is extremely difficult to know what may be asked for and a literal interpretation of Regulation 3(3) "... could drive a coach and horses straight through the Regulations".[1]

Some clarification on the application of the Regulations was provided in *R v British Coal ex parte Ibstock*, although the circumstances of the case – whether Ibstock was entitled to costs involved in litigation relating to a planning decision, on the grounds that it had a right to this "environmental information" under SI 1992/3240 – serve to emphasise the difficulties experienced by complainants. Although British Coal did not argue the point relating to the applicability of the regulations to themselves, *Ibstock* did clarify a number of important issues, viz:

— the presence of hazardous materials within the ground is "information relating to the state of the environment" within Regulation 2(2);

— "historical" activities of the Ministry of Defence (waste dumping in 1947) could not be regarded as "national defence/public security" issues in 1994;

— the name of a supplier of information was not to be regarded as "personal details" and could be included in such information.

In addition, Mr Justice Harrison noted that a "responsible corporation would have given the information without resort to judicial review, or would have given the reason why the information was not given."

Guidance on the scope of information which may be requested is given in *Forrester v British Railways Board*, an action resulting from a child's fatal fall from a train, in which it was held that the defendant could not be ordered to make available to the plaintiff documentation that included all of its fatal and non-fatal accident reports, nor its reports on incidents concerning the door-locking mechanisms, design, maintenance and safety.

---

[1] "A Right to Know: the Environmental Information Regulations 1992", W Birtles, [1993] *JPEL* 615.

The width of the request was described as "staggering" and "oppressive". However, Mr Justice Aldous did suggest that the plaintiff's expert should look at two recent, independent reports which set out statistics and contained recommendations.

A review of Directive 90/313/EEC is being undertaken by the Commission and the House of Lords Select Committee on the European Communities has been hearing evidence on its operation within the report prepared by the United Kingdom Environmental Law Association (UKELA) presented to the Committee made three major criticisms of the UK Regulations:

— the government widened the scope of some of the exemptions from disclosure provided by the Directive in the Environmental Information Regulations 1992;

— there was a failure to give clear guidance on what costs it was reasonable for public bodies to charge for the information; and

— they created difficulties by declining to draw up even a non-exhaustive list of the bodies subject to the Regulations.

In contrast, evidence from the Department of the Environment indicated there were few problems with the operation of the disclosure regime but they admitted that there were no central monitoring arrangements for the scheme. The DoE received backing from the Confederation of British Industry (CBI) but environmental groups listed a number of complaints including being denied information by a combination of high prices, obstructive officials, excessive exemptions and the lack of an effective appeals mechanism.

DISCLOSURE OF INFORMATION DURING LITIGATION

Of the many parties to whom environmental information might need to be disclosed, litigants form one of the more important groups. In civil proceedings, all parties to an action must give discovery of all relevant documents that are, or have been, in their possession, custody, or power. The scope of such disclosure is apparent from the meanings of these terms:

— *documents:* anything on which information is recorded in a tangible or intelligible form, and includes papers, computer-based data, tape recordings, photographs, films and videos;

— *possession:* physical possession;

— *custody:* documents a party has, but may not own or possess;

— *power:* an enforceable right to documents, even if not in the party's possession or custody.

Examples of documents which might be used against a company during the course of litigation are:

— independent environmental audits, such the "preliminary reviews of environmental effects" as required by some environment management systems;

— board minutes, including as part of *general* business decisions on forthcoming prosecution/litigation;

— consultants' reports, prepared as a brief for litigation but photocopied and distributed "for comment";

— internal memoranda such as a marketing strategy, which include references to litigation proceedings;

— files of unactioned complaints.

In view of the above, it would be prudent for a company to formulate a policy relating to environmental information: its creation, use and retention; to use selectively legal professional privilege; and to ensure that the company's practices and procedures do not result in privilege being inadvertently waived. While systems such as ISO 14,000 and EMAS have a requirement for the management of environmental information, their objective is not the minimisation of corporate liability.

The procedure whereby the court orders a party to produce documents is contained in Order 24, Rule 23 of the Rules of the Supreme Court and this was considered in *Wallace Smith Trust Co Ltd (in liquidation) v Delloitte Haskins & Sells (a firm) and Another*. The general principles underlying discovery remain those set out in *Compagnie Financiere et Commerciale de Pacifique v Peruvian Guano Co*, although Lord Justice Neill added that these might need to be re-examined in the near future. The court held that, in deciding whether to order a party to produce any documents for inspection by the other party, the court should examine the facts of the particular case and, in particular:

— the central issues in the action;

— the nature of the documents; and

— the information the documents were likely to contain.

In *Regina v W (G), Regina v W (E)*, it was held that, where a third party applied under the Criminal Procedure (Attendance of Witnesses) Act 1965 to set aside a witness summons requiring a large number of documents to be disclosed, the judge could accept the assertion of the possessor of the documents that they were irrelevant to any issue in the case. Alternatively, if this claim was implausible or suspect, he could look at the documents himself or it was quite proper in the exercise of his discretion to accept the assurance of an independent competent member of the Bar that the documents requested were irrelevant.

In *Mahon & ors v Rahn & ors*, it was held that there was no implied undertaking in criminal proceedings, such as existed in civil proceedings, that documents disclosed by the prosecution to the defendants would not be used by the defendants in subsequent civil proceedings without the leave of the court.

Disclosure of Information by Employees

Within a company, it is often the employees rather than the board who are aware of the day-to-day environmental consequences of its operations, yet as the law stands they may be inhibited from disclosing such information, either by specific clauses within their contracts of employment, as in relation to workers of the new NHS Trusts, or through implied terms of employment – obeying the lawful and reasonable orders of an employer (*Laws v London Chronicle*) and refraining from undermining the trust and confidence which exists between them (*Woods v W M Car Services*).

There are, however, some statutory provisions under which information may be (or must be) disclosed. The Employment Protection (Consolidation) Act 1978 provides certain rights for safety representatives in relation to their sphere of activity and the mandatory questioning by Environment Agency Inspectors under the various provisions of the EPA 1990 provides for reactive, if not pro-active, disclosure.

It is doubtful whether it would be "lawful and reasonable" for an employer to restrict an employee from disclosing information which was in the public interest and, in the case of *Re: A Company's Application*, Mr Justice Scott held that the employee's duty of confidence did not prevent him from disclosing information to the relevant regulatory authority.

The issues of employee protection are beyond the scope of the present discussion and are considered in more detail by Homeswood and Lewis.[1]

---

[1] "Enforcing Environmental Law – Whistle Blowing and Employee Protection", S Homeswood and D Lewis, [1993] *UKELA Journal*, Winter, 58.

While the UK does not have the equivalent of the Whistleblowers Protection Act 1989 and other such provisions of US law, there has been support for the proposed Public Interest Disclosure Bill which would allow individuals a certain degree of protection for exposing malpractice, provided that:

— they did not act in bad faith;

— they believed on reasonable grounds that the information was accurate;

— they took reasonable steps to raise the matter internally first; and

— they informed the relevant authority and did not act for personal gain or payment.

Such a measure would concentrate the minds of senior managers with respect to the views of their employees, whose formally-recorded concerns might be regarded as information which might be used on disclosure during litigation or as an expression of concern which might be taken to the appropriate authorities.

An interesting corollary is the decision of the European Court of Human Rights in *Goodwin v United Kingdom*, in which it was held that a court order requiring the applicant, a journalist, to reveal his source of information and the fine imposed upon him as a result of his refusal was a violation of his right to freedom of expression under Article 10 of the European Convention on Human Rights. In reaching its decision, the court considered whether the interference of the plaintiff's freedom of expression was "prescribed by law" and "pursued a legitimate aim" and, in addition to assessing the particular circumstances, laid down general principles on whether the interference was "necessary in a democratic society".

Legal Professional Privilege

Under certain circumstances, communications between a legal advisor and his client are regarded as privileged and as such an inspector from a regulatory agency cannot compel their production, as in section 108(13) of the Environment Act 1995, and they may be withheld in relation to an order for discovery in an action in the High Court.

Whilst legal professional privilege is an essential tool in the minimisation of corporate environmental liability, it is only useful within certain limits. As discussed above, it would be unwise to withhold privileged information from a party which is entering into a contractual relationship on the basis of being made aware of the entire situation. In addition, in situations in which a regulator is unable to take copies of a privileged document, he has powers under section 108(4)(j) of the 1995 Act to require a person whom he has reasonable cause to believe to be able to give relevant information, to give answers to his questions and to sign a declaration of the truth of his answers. Since it is the *advice* which is privileged and not the *facts* (see *Lyell v Kennedy*), questioning under these powers has the potential for eliciting the required information.

There are two forms of privilege:

— "advice privilege", which may apply whether or not litigation is in prospect and covers communications between a lawyer acting in a professional capacity and the client, provided the communications are confidential and are for the purpose of seeking or giving advice; and

— "litigation privilege", which relates to communications between a lawyer and a client, a non-professional agent (i.e. non-lawyer) or a third party, for the sole or dominant purpose of seeking or giving legal advice relating to litigation or for obtaining evidence to be used in it.

Although there is established UK case law in the general area of legal professional privilege, this has not been considered in relation to environmental issues. However, guidance may be obtained from cases in other jurisdictions (*R v McCarthy Tétrault* and *Gregory v NMR*) and Table 7-6 on page 292 summarises the conclusions reached by Stewart et al[1] in relation to environmental reports.

As noted earlier, it is the facts which are privileged but in practice the courts have been reluctant to authorise discovery of attachments to legal advice where this might permit the nature of the contents of the document giving the advice to be inferred. In *Belabel v Air India*, it was held that, where the broad purpose of the communication was the attainment of legal advice, in this case a conveyancing transaction, then the document was privileged. A useful test of privilege, given in *Waugh v British Railways Board*, was whether the intended supply of the information to the lawyer was the reason for its existence.

In civil proceedings, a party cannot refuse to disclose a document merely because it is confidential and confidentiality agreements signed with consultants give little protection against discovery. In *New Victoria Hospital v Ryan*, Tucker J held that legal professional privilege was not available unless the parties were advised by a solicitor or a barrister. Although such advice may be given by both external and in-house lawyers

---

1   [1993] *Environmental Liability*, 137.

(*Compton (Alfred) Amusement Machines v Customs and Excise Commission (No 2)*), care must be exercised with regard to the latter. It is essential that the company lawyer is acting in his professional capacity only and is not including in his advice recommendations on general management issues.

It should be noted that following *R v Secretary of State for the Home Department ex parte Gardian and Another*, save in exceptional cases, an appellant in judicial review proceedings is not entitled to discovery of material which was not before the lower court, unless there is new evidence that could not have been made available at first instance by reasonable diligence.

Although legal professional privilege is recognised as a general principle within EU law (*A M & S v Commission*), this is subject to two conditions:

— the communication must be for the client's "right of defence"; and

— the lawyer must be in private practice (i.e. not an in-house lawyer).

Legal privilege is not conferred solely by marking documents "without prejudice" and does not cover communications between the client and non-legal advisers, such as engineers and specialist consultants. Furthermore, it is a powerful tool and must not be inadvertently waived as a result of "mixing" discussions/communications/documentation regarding privileged issues with non-privileged ones, e.g. including both within the same board minute without appropriate qualification/restriction on distribution or passing privileged documents to third parties. A possible exception to the latter is the so-called "common interest privilege", as described in *Buttes Gas and Oil Company v Hammer*, where litigation privilege may exist for several unrelated parties, providing they have a common interest in the litigation.

Privilege is clearly an essential consideration in any contentious situation and, in view of the qualifying conditions, it is important that it is considered from the outset. Where circumstances are such that a non-privileged investigation reveals a potential source of litigation, it would be prudent to halt it as soon as this is suspected and to seek legal advice. In the environmental context, the potential use of legal professional privilege is a means of ensuring that clean-up and remediation operations are undertaken within the company's agenda rather than that of a third party and ensuring that such actions may be presented in order to receive approbation, not opprobrium.

FURTHER READING

Powers of Inspectors

Customer Charter: Our statement of service standards, Environment Agency, May 1996

Enforcement Policy Statement, Environment Agency, May 1996

Environment and Enforcement, K Hawkins, Clarendon Press, 1984

"The Garner Environmental Law Lecture 1995", Lord de Ramsay, *UKELA Journal*, Winter 1995/6, 7

"The Stunning Powers of Environmental Inspectors", W Upton and R Harwood, [1996] *JPL* August, 623

"Use of Compliance Monitoring Data in Water Pollution Prosecutions", A Mumma, [1993] 5 (2) *JEL* 191

Information

"Access to Environmental Information", Chapter 7, *Environmental Law, 3rd Edition*, S Ball and S Bell, Blackstone, 1995

"Confidentiality and Environmental Audits", N Stewart, C Pugh and D Oudkerk, [1993] *Environmental Liability*, 137

The Dirty Man of Europe, C Rose, Simon and Schuster, 1991

"Enforcing Environmental Law – Whistle Blowing and Employee Protection", S Homeswood and D Lewis, [1993] *UKELA Journal*, Winter, 58

"Environmental Reporting: what it is, who does it, and why", S Tromans, [1996] *Environmental Assessment*, September

Environment Facts – A Guide to Using Public Registers of Environmental Information, Department of Environment, 1995

"Examining the Applicability of the Environmental Information Regulations 1992: A Strange Case", A Charlesworth, [1995] 7 *JEL* 297

"Freedom of Access to Information on the Environment: Directive 90/313/EEC, and the DoE Consultation Paper", D Hughes, [1992] 4 *LMELR* 75

Freedom of Access to Information on the Environment: Guidance on the Implementation of the Environmental Information Regulations 1992 in Great Britain, Department of the Environment, 1992

"Groups Hit Out Over Access to Information Regime", *ENDS Report* 256, May 1996, 29

The Implementation and Effectiveness of Directive 90/313/EEC on the availability from public authorities of information on the environment, submission by the United Kingdom Environmental Law Association to the House of Lords European Communities Committee – Sub-Committee C, 21 February 1996, UKELA

"Lords Hear Complaints about Access to Information Regime", *ENDS Report* 255, April 1996, 29

"Public Access to Environmental Information: A Means to What End?", J Rowan-Robinson, W Walton and J Rothnie, [1996] 8 (1) *JEL* 19

"Science and the Law – Giving Scientific Evidence in the Courtroom", R Malcolm, *Institute of Chemical Engineers Environmental Protection Bulletin*, No. 42

"Trial of an Expert Witness", S Tromans, [1996] *Environmental Assessment*, September

UK Waste Law, J H Bates, Sweet & Maxwell, 1997

Part III, Rivers (Prevention of Pollution) (Scotland) Act 1951, c66

Rivers (Prevention of Pollution) (Scotland) Act 1965, c13

Part I, Health and Safety at Work etc. Act 1974, c37

Parts I, IA and II Control of Pollution Act 1974, c40

Control of Pollution (Amendment) Act 1989, c14

Parts I, II and IIA Environmental Protection Act 1990, c43

Chapter III of Part IV Water Industry Act 1991, c56

Part III and sections 161 to 161D Water Resources Act 1991, c57

Section 19 Clean Air Act 1993, c11

Radioactive Substances Act 1993, c12

Regulations under section 2(2) European Communities Act 1972, c68

Table 7-2: Questioning by the Regulator

Form of Questioning	Relevant Legislation	Right to Silence	Use of Statements	
			Against Interviewee	Against Organisation
Informal	None	n/a[#]	Possible but unlikely	Possible
Formal, under caution	PACE 1984	Yes	Yes	Yes
Obligatory	s108(4)(j) Environment Act 1995	No	No	Yes

* Although legal advice may not be available, a non-legal person (e.g. a senior manager) may be nominated to be present.

Since informal questioning is not governed by any legislative provision, there is no formal associated right of silence and legal representation.

Table 7-3: NRA – Pollution Incidents

1989 Pollution Incidents

Incident type		Description	Percentage
1	Major	> 50 fish kill	<1%
2	Significant	1-50 fish kill	30%
3	Minor	No noticeable fish kill	70%

TOTAL = 25,000-30,000

Year	No. of Cases #	Total Fines (£)
1989	140	114k
1990	452	424k
1991 *	536	1051k
1992	435	1091k
1993	339	820k

* In this year there were 250 formal cautions

Total number of cases *reported*. Substantiated cases ~75%

Table 7-4: Environmental Information which can be Accessed by the Internet

Site	Address
UK Environment Agency	http://www.environment-agency.gov.uk
Health and Safety Commission	http://www.open.gov.uk/hse/home.htm
Department of the Environment	http://www.open.gov.uk/doe/doehome.htm
Ministry of Agriculture Fisheries and Food	http://www.open.gov.uk/maff/maffhome.htm
European Union homepages	http://www.cec.lu
European Environment Agency	http://www.eea.dk/
US Environmental Protection Agency	http://www.epa.gov
United Nations Environment Programme	http://www.unep.no/ or http://www.unep.no/newdraft/unep/
Alphabetical list of environmental information on www	http://www.lib.kth.se/~lg/envsite.htm
Environment on the www	http://www.ovam.be/internetrefs/english.htm
Environmental Routenet	http://www.csa.com/routenet/newaccess.html
Information for Industry	http://www.ifi.co.uk
Geotechnical and geo-environmental software directory	http://www.ibmpcug.co.uk/~bedrock/gsd
Contaminated land information	http://www.contaminatedland.co.uk/

Table 7-4 (continued)

Site	Address
ISO Infocentre – Information on ISO 14,000	http://www.iso14000.com/
EcoTradeNet – Information on clean technology	http://www.ecotradenet.com
Environmental Bankers Association	http://www.envirolink.org/orgs.ebo.whyarewhere.html
London Transport	http://www.londontransport.co.uk
Institute of Environmental Management	http://www.iem.org.uk
Environment Council	http://www.envirocom.com/tec/index.htm
Friends of the Earth	http://www.foe.co.uk
Greenpeace	http://www.greenpeace.org
RECOUP – information on recycling	http://www.tecweb.com/recoup/index.htm
Legacy – UK solicitors' web site	http://www.legacy.co.uk
Air and Waste Management Association	http://www.awma.org
Envirolink	http://www.envirolink.org

Table 7-5: Information Disclosure Required by Legislation

Legislation	Disclosure Requirements	Access	Notes
Integrated Pollution Control Part I, ss20-22, EPA 1990.	Information on emissions to all media, from 'Part A' processes, inc. authorisations and monitoring. Chemical Release Inventory – database on above.	Environment Agency and SEPA Divisional offices.	Exclusions on grounds of national security and confidentiality. Also from FoE Internet site: http://www.foe.co.uk/cri
Local Authority Air Polln Control Part I, ss20-22, EPA 1990.	Information, as above, on 'Part B' processes.	LA offices.	Unlike IPC registers, there is no information on water and waste.
Industrial Major Accident Hazards SI 1984/1902 as amended.	Eleven items of information re: these installations given to local communities potentially affected.	County emergency planning departments.	Information available on request.
Waste Part II, ss64-66, EPA 1990.	Licences, applications, notices and appeals relating to deposit and carriage of controlled waste.	Environment Agency and SEPA, County and Metropolitan Councils.	Exemptions relate to national security and confidentiality.
Licensed Dumping at Sea Food and Environmental Protection Act 1985, and EPA 1990, Part VIII, ss146-7.	Information (applications, etc.) re: licensed dumping at sea.	Registers of all licences to dump at sea held by MAFF.	Licences cover sewage sludge (until 1988), mine waste (until 1999).
Water Water Resources Act 1991, s190 and Water Industry Act 1991, s195.	Water Quality Objectives, applications, consent certificates and samples.	Environment Agency and SEPA Regional Offices.	Registers open to public at no cost.
Pesticides Food and Environmental Protection Act 1985.	Details of licences issued under the Act.	Relevant government department.	Information disclosure requirements on the pesticide industry.
Public Notices concerning Safety and Environmental Information Environmental and Safety Information Act 1988.	Maintenance of registers giving details of notices served under other Acts where there are safety or environmental implications.	Local authorities, fire authorities, and some government departments.	Covers Fire Precautions Act 1971, Health and Safety at Work Act 1974, Part III Food and Environmental Protection Act 1985.

Table 7-5 (continued)

Legislation	Disclosure Requirements	Access	Notes
Planning Registers Town and Country Planning Act 1990, s69.	Contains all planning applications and decisions, and any conditions attached.	County, London Metropolitan, Borough and District Councils.	Section 188 of EPA 1990 also requires planning authorities to maintain enforcement registers.
Environmental Assessment Town and Country Planning (Assessment of Environmental Effects) Regulations 1988.	Environmental impact statements must be lodged for public viewing.	County, London Metropolitan, Borough and District Councils.	
Contaminated Land Environmental Protection Act 1990, as amended, s78.	Details of remediation notices, statements and declarations.	Local authorities.	Not yet in force. Form of information to be prescribed by the Secretary of State.
Genetically Modified Organisms Environmental Protection Act 1990, Part VI, s122.	Particulars relating to applications for consents, consents and convictions.	Secretary of State for the Environment, Transport and the Regions.	Health and Safety Executive maintains similar registers covering the contained use of GMOs.

Table 7-6: Legal Professional Privilege and
              Environmental Reports, after *Stewart et al* *

(i)   an environmental report prepared by a third party (e.g. an environmental consultant) will not be covered by legal advice privilege;

(ii)   an environmental report prepared *by a solicitor* is covered by legal advice privilege if the report constitutes or is prepared for the purposes of giving legal advice;

(iii) an environmental report prepared by a third party (e.g. an environmental consultant) may be governed by litigation privilege if it was prepared after litigation was commenced or contemplated, for the sole or dominant purpose of such litigation;

(iv) an environmental report prepared by a non-lawyer third party will not be covered by advice privilege (i.e. where no litigation is pending or reasonably contemplated);

(v)   a report prepared within the company will not be covered by advice privilege unless it is prepared at the outset as material (or part of material) genuinely to be submitted to lawyers for the purpose of obtaining legal advice and assistance (though the submission itself may be to in-house lawyers);

(vi) in practice it is likely to be easier for communication with outside lawyers to satisfy the requirements for advice privilege, especially where the in-house lawyers are quite heavily involved in general management issues.

---

* [1993] *Environmental Liability*, 137.

Part II

PRACTICAL WASTE MANAGEMENT

Chapter 8

THE DEFINITION OF WASTE

"The definition of 'waste' in the Directive is imprecise and open-ended, and it is clear that the Member States have found difficulty to apply it to the various situations which may occur in practice."
Advocate General Jacobs, in *Euro Tombesi & ors*

INTRODUCTION

In Chapter 1, the utility of the concept of "waste" was explored and it was suggested that, although in the past the term had been imprecisely applied to a range of essentially unwanted substances, there was a continued need for its use in a number of areas. However, the effectiveness of any legislation relating to waste is dependent upon the ability to formulate a rigorous but workable definition, and the objectives of the legislative measures in question have an influence on the degree of specificity demanded of the definition. While some instruments such as those related to the "landfill tax" need to be quite broad in their scope, others relating to specific waste streams must be more closely targeted. However, this balance is not easily achieved and the case of *Thanet District Council v Kent County Council*, discussed later, illustrates the problems which may be encountered if too prescriptive a definition is used.

There are a number of different forms in which the definition may be introduced, including *inter alia*:

— inclusive definitions: "waste is ...";

— exclusive definitions: "waste is not ...";

— lists of substances relating to an inclusive, or an exclusive, definition;

— actual or theoretical "tests" to be applied to substances to determine whether they constitute waste.

In practice a combination of these may be required and this may involve an hierarchy of definition/classification, viz:

— does the material fall within the general definition of waste; and if so

— within which sub-group of this definition does it fall; and then

— within which category of the sub-group does it fall.

In addition, there may be further qualifications which limit the classes of substance to which the definition of waste applies or grant exemptions for those substances which are within the scope of the definition but are not subject to certain of the associated controls.

In the licensing of waste management operations, it is common for certain activities to be exempted from the licensing requirements. In such measures, however, it is generally the *activity* which is subject to the exemption and, provided the materials concerned meet the criteria of the "waste" definition, then they will continue to be classified as such.

Consistency between the different definitions of waste used within the regulatory framework is an important feature and Figure 1 opposite shows the interrelationships between different classifications. Whilst in general such legislative measures relating to waste *per se* achieve a substantial degree of *horizontal* consistency (i.e. between different definitions within the legislation), *vertical* consistency (relating to different stages within the life-cycle of a given waste) is less readily achieved. There is often a mismatch between the terminology applied to "waste" at its point of production and the classification of landfill sites for the acceptance of such wastes. The provisions currently in place include:

— the *definition* of a substance as a waste, under section 75(2) of the Environmental Protection Act 1990, as amended, the Waste Management Licensing Regulations 1994, SI 1994/1056, and the Special Waste Regulations 1980, SI 1980/1709 as amended by SI 1988/1790, where appropriate;

— the *description* of waste, as required by the Duty of Care provisions under section 34 of the 1990 Act;

— the *licensing* of waste carriers, under the Controlled Waste (Registration of Carriers and Seizure of Vehicles) Regulations 1991, SI 1991/1624, which impose no requirements or limitations concerning the wastes that a carrier is likely to have on his vehicles;

— in relation to special wastes, the *classification* of the waste being carried under the Classification, Packaging and Labelling Regulations, SI 1996/2092;

— the *conditions of the licence* for the landfilling of wastes, required under SI 1994/1056. Waste Management Paper 4, issued under sections 35(8) and 75(4) of the Environmental Protection Act 1990 and which the Environment Agency has a duty to have regard to, suggests two possible methods for the classification of landfill sites – by the type and

Figure 8-1: The Inter-Relationship of Waste Categories

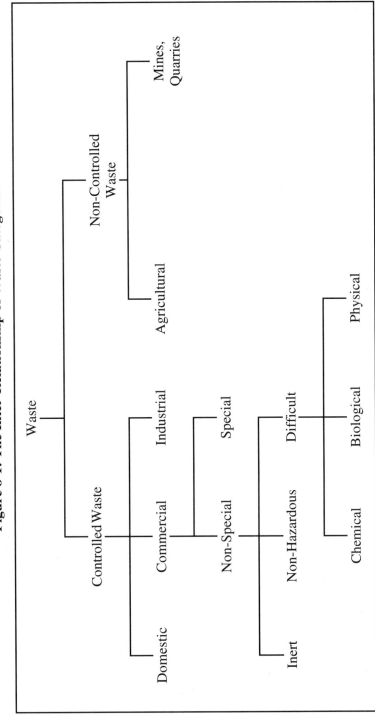

range of wastes they can accept; and by the extent to which they are designed to contain pollutants – and additionally includes the WAMITAB (Waste Management Industry Training and Advisory Board) classification of landfill facilities in relation to the "competence certification" it offers for the managers of such sites;

— the so-called "landfill tax", which imposes a levy on all wastes disposed of at licensed landfill sites, uses a definition of waste different from that in other environmental legislation;

— the classification of wastes within the proposed National Waste Classification system.

In addition, when contaminated land was disposed of at a landfill site, the former Waste Regulation Authorities individually imposed their own acceptability criteria, generally based upon "Kelly's Tables" (a system originally to assist in the classification of contaminated soils from a health and safety perspective, in relation to assessing the risks to construction and site workers), the guidelines drawn up by the ICRCL (Interdepartmental Committee for the Redevelopment of Contaminated Land – and intended for the classification of land for redevelopment of brown field sites, *not* the material from them for landfill) or some variant of either of these.

Having identified the potential conflicts associated with the categorisation of waste during its life-cycle, consideration will now be given to the criteria employed to classify a substance as waste, and the implications of doing so.

PRIOR TO THE IMPLEMENTATION OF THE WASTE FRAMEWORK DIRECTIVE

The Deposit of Poisonous Waste Act 1972 was the first statutory measure in which consideration was given to the control of "waste", although the majority of "ordinary" wastes were excluded since there was a presumption that only wastes *not* prescribed in the Schedule of the Deposit of Poisonous Waste (Notification of Removal or Deposit) Regulations 1972, SI 1972/1017, were subject to section 3 of the Act.

In contrast, the Control of Pollution Act 1974 considered a broader range of waste materials which fell within the non-exclusive definition of section 30, which stated that waste *included*:

— any substance which constitutes a scrap material or an effluent or other unwanted surplus substance arising from the application of any process; and

— any substance or article which required to be disposed of as being broken, worn out, contaminated or otherwise spoiled.

In addition there was a presumption that anything discarded, or otherwise dealt with as if it were waste, was regarded as waste unless the contrary was proved. As with other waste provisions, certain classes of substances were excluded from its control, including explosive substances as defined by the Explosives Act 1875.

The above definition of "waste" and the "presumptive" clause were retained in section 75 of the Environmental Protection Act 1990 and, although the range of *substances* constituting "waste" was essentially the same as in the Control of Pollution Act 1974, the number of *operations* coming within the control of the Act increased significantly.

In common with the 1974 Act, waste subject to control under the 1990 Act is referred to as "controlled waste", which under section 75(4) means " 'household', 'industrial', and 'commercial' waste, or any such waste". In *Thanet District Council v Kent County Council*, Farquharson LJ rejected the submission that the *ejusdem generis* principle could be used to expand the term "any such waste" to include other wastes having shared characteristics with those defined in the Act and the associated Regulations. It was held that "any such waste" meant that controlled waste was to be defined as household, industrial and commercial waste or any combination or permutation of these three classes of waste.

Definitions of the individual terms "household", "industrial" and "commercial" waste are given in:

— section 75(5) to (8) of the 1990 Act, as amended;

— the Collection and Disposal of Waste Regulations 1988, SI 1988/819; and

— the Controlled Waste Regulations 1992, SI 1992/588, as amended by SI 1994/1056,

and are reproduced in Tables 8-1 to 8-3 on pages 327-330. Non-statutory guidance is given in Department of the Environment Circulars 14/92 (on controlled wastes) and 11/94 (on wastes in general).

As noted in *Thanet*, these definitions act exclusively and substances not so defined are not controlled wastes. In addition to listing types and sources of waste, the 1992 Regulations also contain further exclusions of wastes *not* to be treated as "household", "industrial" and "commercial" waste, and the definitions of specific types of waste – clinical waste and construction waste. Provision is made for the application of Part II of the 1990 Act to litter and refuse and Schedule 2 lists the types of household waste for which a charge may be made for collection.

Under section 30(1) of the Control of Pollution Act 1974 (COPA) and section 75(1) of the Environmental Protection Act 1990, waste was defined in terms of its characteristics and the burden of proving that a substance or object was not waste effectively lay with its current holder. Case law focused on either the action resulting in the offence:

— the meaning of the word deposit (*R v Metropolitan Stipendiary Magistrates & ors ex parte London Waste Regulation Authority*),

or the characteristics of the substance or object in question that resulted in its classification as waste, viz:

— its intended use (*Long v Brook*);

— its purpose (*Kent CC v Queenborough Rolling Mills*; or

— its inherent value (*Nottinghamshire CC v Berridge Incinerators*).

In view of the change in the definition of waste resulting from the implementation of the EU Waste Framework Directive, a detailed analysis of these cases will not be given at this stage and reference will only be made where they are relevant to the current definition.

THE EU WASTE FRAMEWORK DIRECTIVE

The EU Waste Framework Directive is now the primary source of the definition of "waste" in the legislation of the UK, other Member States and the European Economic Area (EEA). The original EU definition of waste was contained in Article 1(a) of the Waste Framework Directive, 75/442/ EEC and, apart from legislative measures relating to specific forms of waste, this definition with its subsequent revisions has been used in all other EU Regulations and Directives in which reference was made to waste. (Other waste definitions within EU legislation include: waste oils, 75/489/EEC as amended by 87/101/EEC; PCBs, 96/59/EC; titanium dioxide waste, 82/883/EEC; and radioactive waste, 92/3/EURATOM.)

The 1975 Framework Directive has been substantially revised and the current provision is Framework Directive 91/156/EEC, as amended by 91/ 692/EEC and Council Decision 96/350/EC. However, as indicated by the quotation at the beginning of this chapter, its interpretation and implementation has proved problematic throughout the EU.

Exclusions from the Framework Directive

In spite of a desire to encompass all wastes within a single legislative instrument, a number of substances are excluded from the Directive and these fall into two groups within Article 2(a) and (b), viz:

— gaseous effluents emitted into the atmosphere; and

— certain categories of waste, *provided they are already covered by other legislation*, viz:

— decommissioned explosives;

— radioactive waste;

— waste resulting from prospecting, extraction, treatment and storage of mineral resources and the working of quarries;

— animal carcasses and the following agricultural waste: faecal matter and other natural, non-dangerous substances used in farming;

— waste waters, with the exception of waste in liquid form.

Article 2 also permits specific measures to be introduced for the management of particular categories of waste.

Gaseous Effluents
With regard to gaseous effluents, it is important to distinguish between those that are being controlled as waste *per se* and those that are a secondary component of the waste being controlled. The DoE guidance in Circular 11/94 gives an even narrower interpretation of this term, suggesting that only gaseous emissions from waste disposal and recovery operations are covered by the Directive.

This exclusion will now prevent the use of Part II EPA for the control of waste gases, such as the venting of ozone-depleting gases from air conditioning systems (see *ENDS Report* No. 236, September 1993, p40). However, in this particular case, EU Regulation 3093/94 on Substances that Deplete the Ozone Layer presents a possible means of control, whereby ozone-depleting substances contained in industrial equipment must be recovered, if practicable, for destruction, recycling or reclamation.

With regard to the escape of gasses from solid or liquid waste, section 33(1)(c) of the 1990 Act provides a generally applicable means of control in relation to processes involved in the treating, keeping or disposing of controlled waste in a manner likely to cause pollution or harm to human health. Provided that the controlled waste subject to control is not itself gaseous, then any resultant gaseous emissions will come within this part of the Act, as in a recent case in which the Yorkshire Water subsidiary, Global Environmental, received a fine of £5,000 with costs of £22,000 from Leeds Magistrates' Court in relation to a release of malodorous fumes from its waste treatment plant.

Wastes Subject to "Other Legislation"
With regard to the second group of excluded substances, the term "other legislation" has been interpreted by the DoE as EU or national legislation which pre-dates the signing of the Directive (i.e. 18th March 1991) and not the date of its implementation. Table 8-4 (page 331) indicates the legislation within the EU and the UK which relates to the areas identified above. However, care must be taken in applying these exclusions and the scope of the "other legislation" must be examined carefully.

As indicated earlier, it is unusual for a given legislative instrument to encompass *all* the wastes referred to in its title and most contain exclusions and exemptions. From a strict interpretation of the Framework Directive, the phrase "covered by other legislation" would apply to those wastes defined within a specific measure, but exempted from it, but *not* to wastes named but excluded from such an instrument.

Decommissioned Explosives
Controls on the handling and disposal of decommissioned explosives have been in place since the Explosives Act 1875 and this has been augmented by a number of other regulations. Waste explosives are also excluded from the definition of waste by section 75(2) EPA 1990. In the context of explosives, "decommissioned" is taken to include *all* waste explosives.

Radioactive Waste
The position regarding radioactive waste is similarly unambiguous, since this is covered by Council Directive 80/836/EURATOM, in relation to safety standards for protection against ionising radiation, and by the Radioactive Substances Act 1993 in relation to radioactive waste. In addition, there are Exemption Orders covering waste from "closed sources" of radioactivity and from hospital premises. Consequently, radioactive wastes are excluded from the scope of the Directive.

Quarrying and Agricultural Wastes
The situation is less clear in relation to mining and quarrying, and agricultural wastes. Section 75(7)(c) of the Environmental Protection Act 1990 states that, subject to the introduction of specific provisions by the

Secretary of State through section 75(8), waste from any mine or quarry and waste from premises used for agriculture within the meaning of the Agriculture Act 1947 or the Agriculture (Scotland) Act 1948, are not to be regarded as "commercial waste" and hence shall not be "controlled waste".

In this context "agriculture" has quite a wide definition and includes:

> "Horticulture, fruit growing, seed growing, dairy farming and livestock breeding and keeping, the use of land as grazing land, meadow land, osier land, market gardens and nursery grounds, and the use of woodlands where that use is ancillary to the farming of land for other agricultural purposes ..."

The lack of any qualification as to the scope of the materials covered by section 75(7)(c) would tend to suggest that it relates to *any* wastes arising from these activities. Consequently, any wastes produced as a result of these activities are excluded from the controls of the waste management legislation, as highlighted by the case of polychlorinated biphenyls (PCBs). In most circumstances, any wastes containing 50 ppm or more of PCB would be classified as special wastes, but section 6.15 of Waste Management Paper 6 states explicitly that any such materials arising from agricultural operations shall *not* be regarded as waste.

However, it is the view of the Department of the Environment in Circular 11/94 that any "non-natural" waste arising from these operations (such as canteen waste, discarded machinery, pesticides and solvents) does not come within the ambit of the exclusions. This view is also shared by H M Customs and Excise in relation to the exemptions from landfill tax (q.v.). While this may be consistent with the requirements of the Directive, it raises two problems:

— it is inconsistent with UK primary legislation (section 75(7)(c) EPA 1990) and with the DoE's own advice in Waste Management Paper 6, *supra*; and

— it implies that the UK is in breach of EU law, through an incomplete implementation of the Directive.

It is expected that these will be overcome when further legislation is introduced to cover these areas.

Waste Waters
The disposal of certain waste waters into inland waters and the sea is covered by the Dangerous Substances Directive, 76/464/EEC, and *any* liquid discharged into controlled waters comes within the Water Resources

Act 1991. The Urban Waste Water Treatment Directive 91/217/EEC covers liquid waste which is:

> "... waste water from residential settlements and services which originates predominantly from human metabolism and from household activities; and
>
> waste water from premises used for carrying out any trade or industry",

which is discharged into the sewers, fresh waters, estuaries and coastal waters. However, liquid waste going to a landfill site *would* be covered by the Framework Directive.

Prior to 1st May 1994, waste water treatment plants were not regulated since, under COPA 1974, sewage (i.e. matter passing through sewers and drains) did not constitute controlled waste. However, due to a difference in the wording of section 75 EPA, it was initially thought that many on-site waste water treatment plants required a waste management licence to operate. This was subject to a significant amount of discussion by those concerned and the DoE, and the date from which the licences were required has been postponed on two occasions. However, the situation has been finally resolved and the DoE have concluded that waste management licences are not required where the disposal of effluent is already subject to a discharge consent.

The Definition of Waste under the Framework Directive

Under the English language version of Article 1(a) of the Framework Directive, "waste" means:

— any substance or object which falls into one of the sixteen categories in Annex I of the Directive; which

— the holder must discard, intend to discard, or be required to discard.

It is evident from the inclusion of categories Q1, Q14 and Q16 within Annex I of the Directive (reproduced in Table 8-5 on page 332) that virtually any substance or object may be considered as coming within this limb of the definition. As a consequence, the second limb assumes a far greater significance and will be the more important in relation to the interpretation of the meaning of waste. In contrast to the former UK definition of waste, the Directive is concerned with both the origin of the waste and the activities of the waste holder, who may be either the producer of the waste or the natural or legal person who is in possession of it.

In addition to the definition of waste, Article 1 of the Framework Directive also contains the meanings of a number of other pertinent, related terms:

— "producer": anyone whose activities produce waste (the "original producer") and/or anyone who carries out pre-processing, mixing, or other operations resulting in the change in the nature or composition of this waste;

— "holder": the producer of the waste, or the natural or legal person who is in possession of it;

— "disposal": any of the operations provided for in Annex II, A.

— "recovery": any of the operations provided for in Annex II, B;

— "collection": the gathering, sorting and/or mixing of waste for the purpose of transport;

— "management": the collection, transport, recovery and disposal of waste, including the supervision of such operations and the after-care of disposal sites.

Annex II, A and Annex II, B are reproduced in Tables 8-6 and 8-7 (pages 333 and 334). Although not defined, the term "discard" is critical to the definition of waste and Department of Environment guidance suggests that, in addition to the above two criteria, the following test should be applied:

— whether on account of it being so discarded, the substance or object no longer forms part of the "normal commercial cycle" or "chain of utility".

Whilst tacit approval for the use of such practical measures was given by the Advocate General in the joined cases c-304/94, c-330/94, c-342/94 and c-224/94, *Criminal Proceedings against Euro Tombesi & ors*, a problem in their application is that neither of these terms is itself defined within DoE Circular 11/94.

The European Waste Catalogue (EWC)

In addition to the desirability of a common definition of "waste" to be used within Member States, the Framework Directive states the need to derive a common terminology for describing waste, in order to improve the efficiency of waste management within the Community. Article 1(a) of the Directive states that the Commission, acting in accordance with the procedures laid down in Article 18, will draw up "a list of wastes, belonging to the categories listed in Annex I", which is to be periodically reviewed and revised if necessary. The result of this was Commission Decision 94/3/EEC, which establishes the European Waste Catalogue (EWC) "an harmonised non-exhaustive list of wastes". The Catalogue itself comprises the 20 major categories shown in Table 8-8 (page 335), each of which is subdivided into more specific headings. Every entry is associated with a six-figure code, specific to the waste category. The EWC does not play any part in the "primary" process of determining whether a substance is waste or not and its purpose is, *inter alia*, to enable the quantities of waste falling under each of its headings to be determined and recorded, and subsequently used in national and Community planning initiatives. The UK has rejected the use of the ECW as a means of classifying waste and has established the National Waste Classification Scheme, described below.

However, the European Waste Catalogue forms the basis for the Hazardous Waste List, 94/904/EC, which is a *mandatory* component in determining whether a "general" waste is also categorised as "hazardous" (see Chapter 9 on "special waste"). In the Hazardous Waste List, the different types of waste are fully defined by the six-digit code for the waste. (Although two and four-digit codes are also included in the list, these relate only to generic headings and subheadings, *not* specific waste types – Table 8-9, page 336.)

Advocate General's Opinion on the Meaning of Waste

An important interpretation of some aspects of the meaning of "waste" was given by the Advocate General in relation to the joined cases c-304/94, c-330/94, c-342/94 and c-224/94, *Criminal Proceedings against Euro Tombesi & ors*. These form part of a large number (i.e. 25) of cases currently pending before the Court concerning the Community legislation on waste, and concern a number of questions referred to the ECJ by Italian national courts, primarily in relation to whether residues, wastes for recovery and other substances capable of economic re-utilisation should be classified as "waste". In addition to written observations made by one of the accused, Sig. Anselmo Savini, submissions were also made by the Danish, French, Italian, Netherlands and United Kingdom governments.

It was the contention of Sig. Savini that the producer or holder of a substance does not discard or intend to discard it if he treats it as if it were part of the normal commercial cycle, and that substances appearing in commercial lists will almost invariably be capable of immediate use, either as raw materials or as end products. This opinion was in line with that of the Italian government who argued that the Community definition of waste places importance on a subjective element – the decision of the holder to discard the substance or object – and it was legitimate to employ "the possibility of use" as a basic criterion to exclude from the notion of waste, substances which have recognised properties and are normally traded on the markets.

In contrast, the Danish Government considers that the concept of waste includes all residual products, the term "residual" being defined as "not being the goal sought of the production process".

The French approach lies at the other end of the spectrum and is that waste, including residues, continues to be waste until it has been recovered.

In the Netherlands and the United Kingdom an "intermediate" view is taken, the former noting that "discard" is used in two contexts in the Directive – disposal and recovery – and there is no delineation between when a substance is to be regarded as "waste" and when it is a "secondary raw material". In addition, for a substance to be considered as a "secondary raw material", it must be transported directly from the producer to the person making further use of it, it must be used 100% in a production process and it must not be subject to processes comparable to current means of waste disposal and recovery.

As noted above, the UK view is that a substance is to be regarded as waste if it leaves the "normal commercial cycle" or "normal chain of utility" and is consigned to a "specialised recovery process" such as those in Annex II, B of the Directive. However, a case-by-case decision needs to be made.

The final view is that of the European Commission, which rejects the use of concepts such as "continuity of economic or utility cycle", i.e. the type of approach adopted by the DoE as described above, in favour of a case-by-case approach based upon a broad interpretation of the legislation.

The above conflicting interpretations were reviewed by Advocate General Jacobs, who suggested there is little to be gained by considering the normal meaning of the term "discard" since it has "a special meaning in Article 1(a) encompassing both the disposal of waste and its consignment to a recovery operation". Consequently, the term "waste" depends upon what is meant by "disposal operation" and "recovery operation", although it is acknowledged that these terms "are not exhaustively defined". He also notes that "the distinction between the recovery of waste and normal processing of raw materials is somewhat fragile".

Against this background, the Advocate General stated that the solution is not to lay down a comprehensive definition but to work by example and examine whether the holder of an object or substance consigns or intends to consign it to one of the operations in Annex II, B or to an analogous operation. Some practical day-to-day guidance is necessary and the approach of the UK and the Netherlands is in keeping with the Directive, although it is accepted that to some extent a case-by-case consideration is necessary.

With regard to the specific questions put before the ECJ, the opinion of the Advocate General is that the Community rules on waste as laid down in Directive 75/442/EEC (as amended by 91/156/EEC), Directive 91/689/EEC and Regulation 259/93 apply to any substances or objects which the holder discards or intends to discard or is required to discard, even where they are capable of re-use and may be subject to a legal transaction or quoted as being of commercial value on public or private commercial lists.

Furthermore, the term "waste" is not to be understood as excluding substances which are capable of economic re-utilisation. A residual substance, derived from a production process or a consumption cycle in a manufacturing or combustion process, constitutes "waste" and is subject to waste management controls if its holder discards it or intends or is required to discard it. A substance is discarded if it is disposed of or if it is subject to a recovery operation listed in Annex II, B of the amended Directive.

De-activation processes intended merely to render waste harmless – landfill tipping in hollows or embankments, and waste incineration processes – constitute disposal or recovery processes falling within the scope of the Community rules. The classification of a substance as a re-usable residue, without reference to its characteristics or purpose, is insufficient to remove it from the scope of the Community rules.

On 25th June 1997, the European Court gave its ruling on *Tombesi*, concurring with the Advocate General's opinion. The court held that national legislation which defined waste as excluding substances and objects which were capable of economic utilisation was not compatible with the relevant Community provisions. The system of supervision and control in these instruments was intended to cover all objects and substances discarded by their owners, even if they had a commercial value and were collected on a commercial basis for recycling, reclamation and re-use. The court reiterated the Attorney General's views on de-activation on other processes, *supra*, thus emphasising the importance of defining the characteristics or purpose of a waste.

IMPLEMENTATION OF THE WASTE FRAMEWORK DIRECTIVE WITHIN THE UK

The implementation of the Waste Framework Directive's definition of waste within UK legislation has been undertaken piecemeal, with the result that the Directive is still not yet fully implemented, and a "legal gap-analysis" is necessary to identify the scope of the terms "waste", "Directive waste" and "controlled waste".

A major problem with the implementation was that the existing definition of "waste" was contained within *primary* UK legislation – section 75(2) of the Environmental Protection Act 1990 – and as such would normally have only been able to be amended by subsequent primary legislation. However, the Secretary of State used his powers in section 75(8) of the 1990 Act to prescribe the description of "household", "industrial" or "commercial" waste (i.e. "controlled waste") in terms of "Directive waste", which was defined in terms of the Framework Directive. This was undertaken by means of *inclusive* provisions, by which any reference to waste in the relevant legislation, i.e. Part II EPA 1990, Part I COPA 1974, Town and Country Planning Act 1990, Town and Country Planning (Scotland) Act 1972, Part II COPA 1974 and Part III, Chapter II Water Resources Act 1991, included a reference to "Directive waste" (SI 1994/1056, Regulation 1 and Schedule 4, paras. 9(2), 10(3) and 11 respectively).

In addition, *exclusive* provisions were introduced, amending the Controlled Waste Regulations 1992 and the Collection and Disposal of Waste Regulations 1988, whereby for the purposes of Part II EPA 1990 and Part I COPA 1974, waste which was not Directive waste was not be treated as household, industrial or commercial waste (i.e. controlled waste) (SI 1994/1056, Sch. 4, Regs. 24(8) and 22(4)). Directive waste and controlled waste were not synonymous, since it was possible for a substance to be controlled waste yet not Directive waste.

Ultimately, primary legislation was changed through section 88 and section 95 of Schedule 22 to the Environment Act 1995 and the EU definition of waste was incorporated in section 75(2) of the 1990 Act.

By focusing on the actions of the *holder*, the new definition has rendered the presumptive evidential provision (section 75(3) EPA) otiose and its repeal through section 88(3) of Schedule 22, Environment Act 1995 has had the effect of reversing the burden of proof from the holder (in proving that a material was *not* waste) to the regulator (in proving a "requirement", "intent" or action of "discarding").

Table 8-10 on page 337 summarises the definitions currently in force in

UK legislation which are pertinent to determining whether a substance or object is waste or not. It must again be emphasised that while they overlap in relation to certain wastes, these terms are not synonymous.

THE UK NATIONAL WASTE CLASSIFICATION

The EU has long recognised the importance of a common terminology for waste and at national level the Department of the Environment has highlighted the potential advantages to be gained from a National Waste Classification Scheme: an ability to aggregate data, regionally and nationally, using a system of uniform descriptions and classifications; assistance to industry to provide descriptions to satisfy the requirements of the Duty of Care, and to waste regulators for waste management licensing; and as a means of reference for the implementation of the landfill tax requirements.

A review of the suitability of the European Waste Catalogue for this purpose was undertaken by consultants on behalf of the Department of the Environment and it was felt that the EWC listed mainly industrial wastes and did not deal adequately with other wastes or with the chemical composition of wastes. As a consequence, a different scheme was devised and this was based upon a six-field description, with fields (or "boxes") relating to:

— the industry producing the waste;

— the process producing the waste;

— the waste category, with

— the standard description;

— the main composition; and

— any detailed components;

— the properties of the waste, mainly relating to its potential to pollute;

— the physical form of the waste;

— a label for additional information.

While this might seem acceptable from the bean-counter's point of view, in addition to verging on the incomprehensible, the Consultation Draft Documents were circulated at an inopportune time when those who would have been required to implement the classification were in the midst of assimilating other complex waste legislation. Industry groups expressed concern at the very short notice given for the implementation of the system, in view of the time required to interpret the new scheme and the wide-ranging changes it would necessitate in relation to licences and documentation systems.

As a consequence, the system was introduced on a non-statutory basis from April 1996 "so that its use can be fully assessed" and no date has been set for its statutory implementation. However, under the DoE guidance on the new special waste Regulations, Annex C to DoE Circular 6/96, a knowledge of the national waste classification code is required for the completion of section B2 of the Consignment Note.

There is no doubt that a uniform, all-encompassing system of classifying wastes is required, for the reasons identified by the Department of the Environment, but it is perhaps time that the DoE took an holistic look at the impact of all the recent waste legislation on the waste producers and holders and considered how this increasing burden can be reduced.

THE APPLICATION OF THE EU WASTE DEFINITION IN UK LAW

The Meaning of "Waste"

In order to understand the meaning of the EU definition of waste, it is necessary to examine the *form* of the definition and the *meaning* of the component words.[1] Since the first limb of the definition does little more than give an open-ended list of the categories which *might* comprise waste, any decisions regarding what is and what is not waste must be made on the basis of the second part. For the purpose of the following discussion, it should be noted that this comprises four components – the "holder", "require", "intend", and "discard"[1] – and a change in *any one* of these may result in a change in the "status" of the material under consideration (i.e. between "waste" and "non-waste", or vice versa). The corollary of this is that, *unless* there is a change in any of these, then there can be no change in the "status" of the material.

"Holder"
The first point to note is that the definition is written in terms of the "holder" rather than the "producer" and this is the legal person to whom the other components of the second limb of the definition refer. Since a given item may pass through the hands of several holders between its production and final disposal or treatment, it is necessary to re-apply the test of the waste definition each time it changes hands.

---

[1]   The meaning of "waste" and associated liability implications are considered in the author's publication "Waste Holder Liability", [1996] 8 *ELM* 101.
[2]   Whereas in its original form, 75/442/EEC, the Waste Framework Directive used "dispose" in the definition of waste, in its revised form, 91/156/EEC, "discard" was used.

However, a weakness of this approach is that, if such logic is applied, it is possible to argue that a substance ceases to be waste when it is transferred to another holder who *intends* it to be put to a "beneficial" use, *before* it undergoes any processing to achieve that end. This would be contrary to the objectives of the Directive and certainly not within the spirit of the Duty of Care provisions.

Although the term "holder" is used and provides a useful shorthand form for all those persons concerned with the handling and treatment of waste, it should be noted that there is no such person as a "holder" within section 34 of the Environmental Protection Act 1990 and any charge brought against a holder under this section would be invalid.

"Require"

A requirement to discard waste can exist in the absence of intent or the action of discarding and by definition needs no *mens rea*. There are two possible contexts in which the word "require" can be used in relation to waste management, i.e. where it is necessary:

— to comply with or satisfy some legislation or regulation; and

— to meet some objective associated with the undertaking of a business or activity.

There is little ambiguity in the first usage and there are a number of examples which may be cited as an illustration: the herbicides simazine and atrazine have been banned for all but agricultural use and may not be retained by the holder; substances, such as asbestos, which due to their condition present an immediate health risk must be treated or removed; PCB-contaminated oils required to be destroyed under the PCB Directive.

With regard to the requirements of IPC authorisations, until the implementation of the IPPC Directive, the Environment Agency cannot stipulate the final destination of a waste material, although it is likely that the authorisation will be sufficiently detailed to designate the wastes generated by the process and the holder of such an authorisation would be, by definition, the producer of any wastes thus designated.

The second meaning of "require" applies to situations in which there are no statutory obligations to remove the waste but where it is necessary to do so as part of the activities involved in carrying on an undertaking, such as the removal of litter from an enclosed shopping mall. Although "required" was used on two occasions in *Gotech Environmental Services and Pitcairn v Friel*, the court did not rule on the meaning of the word and this serves only as an example of its accepted usage.

As stated earlier, the absence of *mens rea* is a feature which sets "require" apart from "intend" or actual "disposal" and emphasises that the resulting liability is imposed by external factors. In practice, the use of "require" as a primary indicator of waste holder liability would place a different emphasis on cases such as *Gotech*, where as sub-contractors the appellants were brought in specifically to strip asbestos, an action required of the main contractor (by virtue of a private law contractual obligation) in order to undertake the job, regardless of the condition of the asbestos, or which was required (by other statutory provisions) of the client had the asbestos posed an immediate health hazard.

The meaning of the verb "require" was considered in *R v Page* in relation to making a false statement under caution and Lord Justice Kennedy noted that it was an ordinary English word and could be used in different contexts, as it was in different sections of the Trade Descriptions Act 1968. While some of the statutory provisions appeared to envisage the person of whom the requirement was made doing something which he had no option but to do, this was not the situation elsewhere within the Act.

"Intend"

The original EU definition of "waste" in Directive 75/442/EEC did *not* include any reference to the intent of the holder and, while its subsequent inclusion in the revised Directive, 91/156/EEC, may have been intended to broaden the scope of the term "waste", its use in conjunction with "holder" (rather than "producer") has had the opposite effect, as in the case of recycled material.

This modification has implications on the application of *Vessoso and Zanetti*, in which the court agreed with Advocate General Francis Jacob's argument that "waste" must be objectively defined and cannot cease to be so classified simply because the current holder *intends* to recycle it. While the ambit of the term "waste" as decided in *Vessoso and Zanetti* is unaffected by the inclusion of the word "intent" in the definition of waste – as acknowledged in *Commission v Federal Republic of Germany*, case c-422/92, and in the Advocate General's opinion on the joined cases c-304/94, c-330/94, c-342/94 and c-224/94, *Criminal Proceedings against Euro Tombesi & ors* – the liability of the holder resulting from the classification of the material as "waste" is changed.

The intention to discard waste applies to situations in which there is no requirement to do so but in which, for reasons such as "good housekeeping" or the realisation of scrap/recycling values, the holder has taken a decision to dispose of the substance or article. There is clearly an element of *mens rea* and the courts have interpreted intent as being synonymous with aim (see *R v Mohan*). When "intend" is used in relation to committing a (non waste-related) criminal offence, the court is not bound to infer action merely because the result is the natural and probable cause of the action taken – see Criminal Justice Act 1967, section 8 and *R v Hancock and Shankland*. However, its usage in relation to the discarding of waste relates only to the *definition* of a material as waste, which is not criminal *per se*.

There are two factors to be considered when analysing the existence of intent in the context of waste management:

— the intention of the holder to discard the substance or object – the *animus dereliquendi*; and

— whether the material when discarded can be considered as waste.

Not all uses of a material, post-discarding, result in its classification as waste, providing such a "non-waste" use was the original intention of the producer. A recent example illustrating this is given in the cases of *Cheshire County Council v Armstrong's Transport (Wigan) Ltd* and *Meston Technical Services v Warwickshire County Council*. The *Cheshire* case concerned the use of demolition material as infilling in a new housing development and, although this material was taken off-site for crushing prior to its use, the court held that the material was not waste on account of the intended use of the material – "the respondents never regarded the concrete as waste to be disposed of". In *Meston*, the appellants sought to rely upon the *Cheshire* ruling but Lord Justice Pill stated that the former case rested upon the approach taken by the owners of the material as to its use, whereas in the present case the material – a waste varnish mix – was described by the producer as "obsolete material".

Intent will be determined on the facts of each case but unless there are specific indications of intent – obvious stockpiles of waste material for collection, "season ticket" Waste Transfer Notes or Consignment Notes – proof may be difficult. However, since evidence of intent is sufficient to trigger the liabilities resulting from the classification of a substance as waste, it is in the interests of waste producers to ensure that all documentation, generated both by themselves and by third parties, carries a description of the material which conveys the intent of its subsequent application. It has been the practice of a number of organisations, uncertain as to whether a particular substance or object was waste, to complete a Waste Transfer Note as a "precautionary" measure, but in the future such a practice will be construed as intent.

Another area for attention is the disposal of surplus equipment on a "sold as seen" basis, in order to avoid product warranties. In many cases this equipment could be purchased either for its scrap value or for subsequent use, and it would be prudent for vendors to examine their conditions of sale.

In addition to the above considerations, it should be noted that it is the *intent* of the waste producer to consign his waste to landfill that is the criterion upon which the levy of "landfill tax" will be made.

"Discard"

In view of the open-ended nature of the categories of waste in Annex I of the Directive, a much greater emphasis is placed upon the meaning of the word "discard". According to the UK Regulations, "discard" has the same meaning as in the Directive, although it is not formally defined in that document! Fluck[1] indicates that other Member States, such as France and Germany, distinguish between discarding and disposal, the former being a prerequisite to a material being designated as a waste. In addition, their usage of discard does not apply to a substance released to a third party for recovery. However, in *Commission v Federal Republic of Germany*, the European Court of Justice held that, by excluding certain categories of recyclable material, the Federal Republic of Germany had failed to fulfil its obligations under Directives 75/442 and 78/319.

In English there is a degree of overlap between these two words, as demonstrated in the judgment of Watkins LJ in *R v Metropolitan Stipendiary Magistrates & ors ex parte London Waste Regulation Authority*. This clarified the uncertainty resulting from *Leigh Land Reclamation Ltd & ors v Walsall Metropolitan Borough Council* regarding the meaning of deposit, by stating that:

> "An article may be regarded as disposed of if it is destroyed or if it is passed on from one person to another; the ordinary sense of the term, certainly in the context of the Act [i.e. COPA 1974], rests upon the notion of getting rid of something."

While this provided a useful interpretation of the meaning of disposal prior to the implementation of the Directive, the situation is now more complex as a result of its usage in the Framework Directive. In the 1975 version, waste was defined in terms of disposal by the holder, where dispose referred to:

— the collection, storing, transport and treatment of waste as well as its storage and tipping above or under ground;

— the transportation operations necessary for its re-use, recovery or recycling.

---

[1]   "The Term 'Waste' in EU Law", J Fluck, [1994] *EELR* 79.

Within this context, in *Vessoso and Zanetti* the European Court of Justice held that:

> "The concept of waste ... is not to be understood as excluding substances and objects which are capable of economic re-utilisation. The concept does not presume that the holder disposing of a substance or object *intends* to exclude all economic re-utilisation of the substances and objects by others."

The current version uses "discard" for the definition of waste and restricts "dispose" to "any operations provided for in Annex II, A". From a consideration of the English, French and German versions of the Directive, Fluck[1] suggests that the concept of discarding does not presuppose that an object is released to a third party or that the waste holder abandons title to it. He states that discarding does not mean getting rid of an object but "releasing an object from its original intended purpose in order to recover or dispose of it". While this supports the reasoning of Department of Environment Circular 11/94, Waite[2] contends that this approach is incorrect on the grounds that:

— the Directive treats discarding as a separate stage from disposal or recovery. Articles 4 and 8 infer that the material has already been identified as waste, independently of, and prior to, the disposal or recovery operation;

— the disposal and recovery operations listed in Annexes II, A and II, B relate to operations which may be carried out on other materials as well as waste, and are not sufficient in themselves to categorise a material as waste (but note the Advocate General's opinion, *infra*),

and he states that the crucial element in determining whether a material is waste is "the true purpose of the holder", i.e. his intentions. However, such an emphasis on intent does not take account of the other elements of the Directive's definition of waste, or its objectives stated in the preamble.

Taking these views into consideration, the meaning of "discarding" may be considered as the action or decision taken by a person when a substance or object is no longer of *direct* use in its present form to that person *and* to any other third party. The person taking such a decision may be the waste producer or the waste holder. This is compatible with other elements of the Directive's definition, the concept of waste in relation to the use of by-

---

[1] "The Term 'Waste' in EU Law", J Fluck, [1994] *EELR* 79.
[2] "Crucial Need to Understand the Meaning of Waste", A Waite in *Law and the Waste Industry*, Institute of Wastes Management/UKELA, [1994] 4.

products, and avoids "circularity" by the incorporation of the need, post-discarding, for subsequent disposal or recycling, without referring to these operations implicitly within the definition.

The Concept of Recovery

Fluck[1] notes that within the meaning of Article 1(f) and Annex II, B of the Directive, the concept of recovery does not include all post-discarding forms of further use of waste, but only:

— recycling, re-use, reclamation or other recovery processes with a view to extracting secondary raw materials (Article 3(1)(b)(i)); or

— re-extraction, regeneration, recovery, re-refining of oil or other re-uses of oil, and spreading on land (Annex II, B, R2-10).[2]

In contrast to "re-use", an operation in which the material is "used as intended" is *not* one of waste recovery and by-products produced *specifically* for marketing, or intermediate products produced *specifically* for further processing, are not waste. Furthermore, substances and objects which, without having been so produced, are intended or released for *direct* use or consumption, or raw materials for further processing, are also not waste.

The releasing of an object to another party and its further use for its original purpose is likewise not "recovery" but "use as intended".

The Meaning of "Deposit"

Although the word "deposit" is not a part of the definition of waste, in a number of cases it may be a component of the action of the disposal of waste, and in addition it forms part of the offence in section 33(1)(a) of the 1990 Act. Problems concerning the meaning of the word arose in relation to section 3(1) of COPA 1974, the forerunner of section 33 EPA 1990, when in *Leigh Land Reclamation v Walsall MBC*, Lord Bingham held that it was a colourable word and, in the context of COPA 1974:

"Its provisions and the conditions in the licence, are directed towards the mode of the final disposal and not the intermediate processes. For the purposes of this Act, waste is to be regarded as deposited when it is dumped on the site with no realistic prospect of further examination or inspection to reject goods of which deposit is not allowed under the licence."

---

[1] "The Term 'Waste' in EU Law", J Fluck, [1994] *EELR* 79.
[2] Note that these numbers relate to those in the recent amendment to the Directive, 96/350/ EC, and do not relate to those in Fluck's original text.

This judgment created a number of problems in the enforcement of the Act at both licensed and unlicensed sites. Unlicensed transfer stations gave particular problems, since it could be argued that there was no offence under section 3(1)(a) if any waste was placed down with a view to removing it later. This lead WRAs to seek alternative means of enforcement, either through section 3(1)(b) of the Act or by seeking injunctive relief by means of section 222 of the Local Government Act 1972.

In *Lancashire County Council v Dodd, Dodd and Dugdale*, the *Leigh* case was distinguished on its facts and "deposit" was held to have its ordinary natural meaning, which included both temporary and permanent disposal or setting down. However in *R v Metropolitan Stipendiary Magistrates & ors ex parte London Waste Regulation Authority*, the judgment of Watkins LJ went further and it was held that *Leigh* had been wrongly decided in relation to the meaning of "deposit". The disposal of an article has

> "no more to do with finding a 'final resting place' than has the word 'deposit' in section 3(1)(a)."

Department of the Environment Guidance

In conjunction with the introduction of the Waste Management Licensing Regulations in 1994, the Department of the Environment issued Circular 11/94 which was intended, *inter alia*, to provide guidance on the meaning of waste. Although in relation to the discharge of the Agency functions in relation to Waste Management Licensing and for the associated accreditation of "fit and proper persons" it is described as "statutory guidance" (since it is issued under sections 35(8) and 74(5) of the 1990 Act), the Circular itself is not approved by Parliament and as such it does not have the authority of a Statutory Instrument.

It has been noted[1] that, while it offers some policy considerations to be taken into account in determining what constitutes waste, the Circular is not an authoritative interpretation of the Directive. Furthermore, it should be regarded with caution, since difficulties may occur if the UK courts, paying regard to the guidance, follow a particular definition or line which turns out to be contrary to that adopted by other Member States or a ruling of the European Court of Justice.

There are a number of legal and practical reasons why such caution is necessary. From paragraphs 2.12, 2.13 and 2.14 of the Circular, it is clear that the Department's interpretation of the Directive places a strong emphasis on three aspects of the preamble to the Directive, viz:

---

[1]   *Environmental Law Monthly* [1994] May, 1.

— the protection of human health and the environment against the harmful effects caused by waste management operations;

— the provision of a "high level of environmental protection"; and

— the development of a common terminology and definition of waste.

While any interpretation by the ECJ will take into account the objectives expressed in the preamble, it will undertake this in the light of the Directive's definition of waste.

Until there is definitive case law on the meaning of waste, waste producers and holders will have a problem with the interpretation of the Directive in those areas in which the DoE guidance appears to diverge from the Directive. As Nash[1] points out, although the Circular is non-statutory, it will probably carry substantial weight in the lower courts and possibly with the Agencies, particularly since the established case law is of doubtful applicability. Unless one is prepared to take one's case all the way to the ECJ, it is possible that the elegant principles of European jurisprudence will get one nowhere, in the face of disagreement from the Agency or the local Magistrates' Court. However, until someone does, these points will never be clarified.

SPECIFIC ISSUES RELATING TO THE DEFINITION OF WASTE

The above discussion has indicated some of the problems which have been encountered in determining the meaning of "waste" following the implementation of the Waste Framework Directive. Many of these problems may be overcome by considering the *form* of the definition and the *meaning* of its components parts, and this may be achieved by applying the following principles:

— the EU definition, which is in the format "waste means ...", should be regarded as a test to be applied to a substance at any given point in time, rather than a label to be given to that substance;

— there are four components to the definition of waste – "require", "intend", "discard" and the "holder" and a change in one or more of these may change the status of a material from "waste" to "non-waste" or *vice versa*;

— the producer of the waste is the person in whose hands the material is when it becomes waste; and

---

[1]   "The 1994 Waste Management Licensing Regime and the New Definition of Waste", *Commercial Seminars*, 6 December 1994.

— "discarding" is the action or decision taken by a person, when a substance or object is no longer of *direct* use in its present form to that person or to *any* other third party;

— "recovery" is the carrying out of certain processes or operations which are necessary in order for a substance to be used for its former purpose or for a new purpose.

Use of Spent Solvents as Fuels

The Directive does not address the question of when a substance ceases to be "waste" and the listing of recovery processes in Annex II, B is concerned with the control of waste treatment (Article 8) and the permitting requirements of such operations (Article 10), with no reference to "de-classification". However, Article 3(1)(b)(ii) requires Member States to take appropriate measures to encourage the use of waste as a source of energy, and one of the listed recovery operations, R9, is "the use principally as a fuel or other means to generate energy". The English and French versions of the Directive, using the terms "principally as a fuel" and "*utilisation principale*", differ from the German text which has "the use as a fuel (except in the case of direct incineration)". The latter view reflects a reference in the Basel Convention to "direct incineration", in relation to the use of incineration for the purpose of disposal, and conveys the fact that recovery operations, as defined in Annex II, B, exclude processes where the purpose of incineration is essentially for disposal, i.e. their primary intention is the reduction of the volume of the waste rather than the exploitation of energy generation.

Applying the above to the "secondary liquid fuel" (SLF) example, two propositions may be put forward, viz:

— the blending and mixing operation yields a product, to agreed thermal and other criteria, for a specific operation. In its processed condition, it is intended to be used as a fuel and as such is not waste; or

— although the holder of the SLF intends it to be used as a fuel, Annex II, B precludes the incineration operation from being designated as a recovery process, since the primary intention is not the recovery of thermal energy but the disposal of solvent. As a consequence, the SLF must be regarded as a waste.

Clearly, the *ipse dixit* of the producer of the fuel is an inappropriate test of intent in these circumstances and reasoned arguments may be made to support either of the propositions. Consequently, the most satisfactory solution would be for the Secretary of State, using his powers under section

29(7), to prescribe where these and similar operations constitute the treatment of waste under Part II of the 1990 Act. This would avoid a case-by-case examination by the courts and would enable the full environmental consequences to be considered when reaching the decision.

Licensing of Effluent Treatment Plants

In contrast to SLFs, the need to licence effluent treatment plants (ETPs) is relatively straightforward. While a degree of ambiguity is introduced through the use of the undefined terms "waste in liquid form" (which comes within the ambit of the Directive) and "waste waters" (which does not), the major contention is whether the operation of these plants is covered by the relevant discharge consent or whether the consent relates only to the final discharge to sewers or controlled waters.

Although detailed arguments have been made regarding exemptions and exclusions from the Directive and whether ETPs fulfil a disposal or a recovery function, the issue may be simplified by a consideration of the point at which the effluent becomes waste, for if it is not waste, then the legislation is inapplicable.

Where an ETP is part of a sequence of processes for undertaking a specific operation, then it is clearly not the intention of the operator of the plant to discharge/discard the effluent in its untreated form, i.e. prior to the treatment plant. Consequently, the input material is not waste, although an output (of solid waste or "waste in liquid form") will be. This situation is analogous to that in integrated complexes in the chemical industry, for which it is accepted that the concept of waste excludes those "residues" which are subsequently processed in another part of the plant.

The Department of the Environment has now stated that operators of treatment plants need not apply for a waste management licence where the disposal of effluent is already subject to a discharge consent.

Recycled Materials

Scrapped steel products provide a good example of the application of the waste definition and the difficulties in employing the guidance criteria. A substantial percentage of steel products are recycled to form the feed materials for steelmaking processes but only in certain circumstances can a commercial cycle or chain of utility be demonstrated, e.g. where off-cuts, turnings, punchings, etc. from a manufacturing operation are returned "directly" to the furnace with no intermediate treatment (other than handling, storage and transport). In other cases, the producers of these unwanted ferrous materials cannot be said to consider them as the potential feed for a steelmaking process, and as such they should be regarded as waste until they have undergone processing which renders them suitable for "direct" use by the steelmaker.

The opinion of the Advocate General, *supra*, providing it is accepted by the ECJ, will provide the basis for determining the status of recycled materials and residues. In addition, at the time of writing, Mayer Parry Recycling Ltd has issued a summons on the Environment Agency challenging its interpretation of scrap material from a number of sources as "waste".

Power Station Fly-Ash and Gypsum from Stack-Gas Desulphurisation

These two products are generated in substantial quantities and as such their classification is important. Fly-ash has a long history of on-site disposal and the question arises as to its status when disposed of to a third party for the manufacture of building materials. In *Kent CC v Queenborough Rolling Mills* (under COPA), Mr Justice Pill held that in relation to classifying a material as waste, the issue in question was that its producer had discarded it to landfill 15 years previously and the fact that a third party has sorted and graded the material and put it to an economic use (as ballast infill) was immaterial. Similarly, in *Long v Brook*, it was held that (again under COPA) waste was defined from the point of view of the disposer.

Consequently, when the producer of the fly-ash determines *in advance of its production* that some will be used for building material manufacture, it should not be classified as waste. There are potential evidential problems here, in view of stockpiles of the material which is not thus used and the time factor in this particular market, i.e. the greatest production of fly-ash being in the colder part of the year when there is a greater demand for power, against the demand for building materials during better weather.

With regard to the use of gypsum from stack-gas desulphurisation, Fluck[1] suggests that, where it is not required to meet any particular standard and is used for landfilling open-cast mines, it is probably waste. However, where it can be used *directly* to replace natural gypsum for building materials, particularly if there is no need for additional working up, then it is not waste.

The introduction of the landfill tax has added another dimension to these issues, since the tax is applicable to on-site landfills if subject to Part II EPA

---

[1]   "The Term 'Waste' in EU Law", J Fluck, [1994] *EELR* 79.

1990 Waste Management Licensing. These provisions permit the establishment of "tax free" areas for *temporary* storage of material pending re-use, recycling, incineration or sorting, provided written agreement is first obtained from the H M Customs & Excise enforcement officer.

IMPLICATIONS OF THE WASTE FRAMEWORK DIRECTIVE

Allocation of Waste Holder Liability

Virtually all industrial operations result in the generation of waste and, where a number of parties are involved, it is often difficult to allocate responsibility. Following *Attorney General's Reference (No 1 of 1994)*, under the Water Resources Act 1991, two or more parties, although undertaking different functions, may each be held to have "caused" the same pollution incident. With regard to waste management offences, although only one party is likely to be involved in an action of depositing, treating, keeping or disposing of controlled waste, the inclusion of "knowingly causing" and "knowingly permitting" in section 33(1) EPA 1990 and the Duty of Care provisions in section 34 broaden the range of parties who may be considered to have some liability.

The prosecution of the various parties contributing to the same waste management offence would strengthen the "cradle to grave" responsibility for waste and would complement the Duty of Care provisions which are directed towards the holder of the waste acting in a given capacity – importer, producer, carrier, keeper, treater, disposer or broker – and cannot be delegated to a contractor, as noted by Lord Denning in *Cassidy v Ministry of Health (Fahrini, third party)*.

For offences of "causing", the contractual details of the work to be undertaken will assume a greater importance, for as Simon Brown LJ stated in *NRA v Alfred McAlpine Homes East*:

> "An employer is liable for pollution resulting from its own operations carried out under its essential control, save only where some third party acts in such a way as to interrupt the chain of causation."

Consequently, if the client/principal gives an independent contractor specific instructions or working procedures to follow, then the client/principal becomes part of the chain of causation and some liability may be attached to him. This is now a strong possibility, in view of statutory and other requirements for setting out work practices in relation to health and safety and the tendency to include procedures relating to the environment with these.

Use in a Prosecution

A possible defence to waste-related offences is that the material in question did not constitute a waste, within the meaning of the definition. With regard to the general definition of waste, i.e. the Framework Directive definition, reliance must be placed upon the meanings of the words "require", "intend" and "discard". However, it should be noted that, unlike the offence of "causing or knowingly permitting", these words are used to *define* the material which is the basis for the offence. Consequently, it is insufficient to prove, for example, that the holder did not *intend* to discard the waste, if the waste was in fact discarded. In order to rely upon such a defence, the holder must prove that *none* of the above three components of the second limb of the definition of waste was satisfied.

In this context, it is instructive to consider the position in which a substance was unintentionally discarded. Unless there was a statutory requirement for the holder to discard that substance, the holder would only be subject to satisfy the "intent" and "discard" criteria. If the offence was brought under section 33 EPA 1990, which relates to "*knowingly* causing or *knowingly* permitting", there is clearly a requirement for *mens rea* in relation to discarding, although something more than the *ipse dixit* of the waste holder would be required in evidence. Although the section 34 Duty of Care offence does not require *mens rea*, a possible defence of taking "all such measures applicable to him ... as are reasonable in the circumstances" is available. The evidence of documented and audited procedures might go some way towards establishing such a defence.

Waste Licensing Requirements

The Framework Directive places a requirement on Member States to establish a system whereby any establishment or undertaking which carries out the operations listed in its Annexes II, A and B must obtain a permit from a "competent authority". Such a system of permitting will be based upon those substances which fall within the ambit of the definition of "waste", although providing other requirements of the Directive are met, such as those within Articles 4, 5 and 7, there is no requirement for all wastes to come within the permitting regime. As a consequence, the UK system of waste management licensing does not encompass all wastes falling within the framework definition and there are a number of operations for which exemptions may be granted. However, these are *not* absolute exemptions and are conditional on satisfying the requirements of the Directive. Particular emphasis is placed on the need to ensure that waste is recovered or disposed of without endangering human health and without using processes which could harm the environment, taking into consideration:

— risks to water, air, soil, and plants and animals;

— the possibility of nuisance through noise or odours; and

— the potential for adversely affecting the countryside of places of special interest.

It should be borne in mind that it is the *processes* that are exempt from the permitting/licensing requirements and the respective substances are still subject to other waste management legislation, provided they satisfy the criteria of the waste definition.

WASTES FALLING OUTWITH THE SCOPE OF THE DIRECTIVE

Section 63 of the Environmental Protection Act 1990 gives the Secretary of State powers to make provisions, after consulting with such bodies as he thinks appropriate, for wastes falling outside the definition of controlled waste as a result of section 75(7)(c), i.e. mining, quarrying and agricultural wastes. In addition, an offence is created for depositing, or knowingly causing or knowingly permitting the deposit of, any such waste which, if it were a controlled waste, would be a special waste. The revision of this section 63(2) overcomes the "clumsy and inept draughtsmanship" of the earlier version noted by Tromans[1] and enables measures to be introduced to control waste streams from these excluded categories, where there is a significant potential to cause pollution. However, it is necessary for secondary legislation to be introduced for such measures to become effective and, as noted earlier, wastes such as PCBs have not been made subject to such controls.

In addition, the Secretary of State may use section 75(8) in order that waste of a description prescribed in the regulations is treated as being, or not being, household, industrial or commercial waste. However, this provision cannot be used to define sewage waste as commercial waste, although there is no exclusion on it being classified as household or domestic waste.

The Controlled Waste Regulations 1992 exclude sewage waste from the definition of industrial or commercial waste, provided it is within the curtilage of a sewage treatment works.

---

[1]   *Contaminated Land,* S Tromans and R Turrall-Clarke, Sweet & Maxwell, 1994, page 216.

FURTHER READING

"The 1994 Definition of Waste and the Waste Management Licensing Regulations", M Nash in *The 1994 Waste Management Licensing Regime and the New Definition of Waste*, Commercial Seminars, 6 December 1994

"The Challenges of Environmentally Sound and Efficient Regulation of Waste – The Need for International Understanding", J T Smith, [1993] 5 *JEL* 91

"Crucial Need to Understand the Meaning of Waste", A Waite in *Law and the Waste Industry*, Institute of Wastes Management/UKELA, [1994] 4

"Defining Waste", M Purdue, [1990] 2 (2) *JEL* 250

"Divisional Court Settles the Meaning of 'Deposit' ", D Laurence, [1993] *Wastes Management*, February, 8

"Fitting Definition to Purpose: The Search for a Satisfactory Definition of Waste", I Cheyne and M Purdue, [1995] 7 (2) *JEL* 149

Guidelines for the Segregating, Handling and Transport of Clinical Wastes, London Waste Regulation Authority, 1995

"High Court Injunctions: an alternative for WRAs", S Burns, [1993] *Wastes Management*, February, 12

"The Problematic EU Hazardous Waste List", R Hunter, [1995] *EELR* March, 83

"The Term 'Waste' in EU Law", J Fluck, [1994] *EELR* 79

"Waste Holder Liability", D N Pocklington, [1996] 8 *ELM* 101

Waste Management Legislation in the UK, J H Bates, Sweet & Maxwell, 1997

Table 8-1: Household Waste   327

Definition in section 75(5) EPA 1990

(5) Subject to subsection (8) below, "household waste" means waste from—
- (a) domestic property, that is to say, a building or self-contained part of a building which is used wholly for the purpose of living accommodation;
- (b) a caravan (as defined in section 29(1) of the Caravan Sites and Control of Development Act 1960) which usually and for the time being is situated on a caravan site (within the meaning of that Act);
- (c) a residential home;
- (d) premises forming part of a university or school or other educational establishment;
- (e) premises forming part of a hospital or nursing home.

Definition in Schedule 1, Controlled Waste Regulations 1992, SI 1992/588

SCHEDULE 1   Regulation 2(1)

WASTE TO BE TREATED AS HOUSEHOLD WASTE

1. Waste from a hereditament or premises exempted from local non-domestic rating by virtue of—
   - (a) in England and Wales, paragraph 11 of Schedule 5 to the Local Government Finance Act 1988 (places of religious worship etc.);
   - (b) in Scotland, section 22 of the Valuation and Rating (Scotland) Act 1956 (churches etc.).
2. Waste from premises occupied by a charity and wholly or mainly used for charitable purposes.
3. Waste from any land belonging to or used in connection with domestic property, a caravan or a residential home.
4. Waste from a private garage which either has a floor area of 25 square metres or less or is used wholly or mainly for the accommodation of a private motor vehicle.
5. Waste from private storage premises used wholly or mainly for the storage of articles of domestic use.
6. Water from a moored vessel used wholly for the purpose of living accommodation.
7. Waste from a camp site.
8. Waste from a prison or other penal institution.
9. Waste from a hall or other premises used wholly or mainly for public meetings.
10. Waste from a royal palace.
11. Waste arising from the discharge by a local authority of its duty under section 89(2).

Definition in section 75(6) EPA 1990

(6) Subject to subsection (8) below, "industrial waste" means waste from any of the following premises—

    (a) any factory (within the meaning of the Factories Act 1961);

    (b) any premises used for the purposes of, or in connection with, the provision to the public of transport services by land, water or air;

    (c) any premises used for the purposes of, or in connection with, the supply to the public of gas, water or electricity or the provision of sewerage services; or

    (d) any premises used for the purposes of, or in connection with, the provision to the public of postal or telecommunications services.

Definition in Schedule 3, Controlled Waste Regulations 1992, SI 1992/588

SCHEDULE 3   Regulation 5(1)

WASTE TO BE TREATED AS INDUSTRIAL WASTE

1. Waste from premises used for maintaining vehicles, vessels or aircraft, not being waste from a private garage to which paragraph 4 of Schedule 1 applies.

2. Waste from a laboratory.

3.—(1) Waste from a workshop or similar premises not being a factory within the meaning of section 175 of the Factories Act 1961 because the people working there are not employees or because the work there is not carried on by way of trade or for purposes of gain.

    (2) In this paragraph, "workshop" does not include premises at which the principal activities are computer operations or the copying of documents by photographic or lithographic means.

4. Waste from premises occupied by a scientific research association approved by the Secretary of State under section 508 of the Income and Corporation Taxes Act 1988.

5. Waste from dredging operations.

6. Waste arising from tunnelling or from any other excavation.

7. Sewage not falling within a description in regulation 7 which—

    (a) is treated, kept or disposed of in or on land, other than by means of a privy, cesspool or septic tank;

    (b) is treated, kept or disposed of by means of mobile plant; or

    (c) has been removed from a privy or cesspool.

8. Clinical waste other than—

    (a) clinical waste from a domestic property, caravan, residential home or from a moored vessel used wholly for the purposes of living accommodation;

    (b) waste collected under section 22(3) of the Control of Pollution Act 1974; or

    (c) waste collected under sections 89, 92(9) or 93.

Table 8-2 (continued) 329

9. Waste arising from any aircraft, vehicle or vessel which is not occupied for domestic purposes.
10. Waste which has previously formed part of any aircraft, vehicle or vessel and which is not household water.
11. Waste removed from land on which it has previously been deposited and any soil with which such waste has been in contact, other than—
    (a) waste collected under section 22(3) of the Control of Pollution Act 1974; or
    (b) waste collected under sections 89, 92(9) or 93.
12. Leachate from a deposit of waste.
13. Poisonous or noxious waste arising from any of the following processes undertaken on premises used for the purposes of a trade or business—
    (a) mixing or selling paints;
    (b) sign writing;
    (c) laundering or dry cleaning;
    (d) developing photographic film or making photographic prints;
    (e) selling petrol, diesel fuel, paraffin, kerosene, heating oil or similar substances; or
    (f) selling pesticides, herbicides or fungicides.
14. Waste from premises used for the purposes of breeding, boarding, stabling or exhibiting animals.
15.—(1) Waste oil, waste solvent or (subject to regulation 7(2)) scrap metal, other than—
    (a) waste from a domestic property, caravan or residential home;
    (b) waste falling within paragraphs 3 to 6 of Schedule 1.
    (2) In this paragraph—
    "waste oil" means mineral or synthetic oil which is contaminated, spoiled or otherwise unfit for its original purpose; and
    "waste solvent" means solvent which is contaminated, spoiled or otherwise unfit for its original purpose.
16. Waste arising from the discharge by the Secretary of State of his duty under section 89(2).
17. Waste imported into Great Britain.
18.—(1) Tank washings or garbage landed in Great Britain.
    (2) In this paragraph—
    "tank washings" has the same meaning as in regulation 2 of the Control of Pollution (Landed Ships' Waste) Regulations 1987; and
    "garbage" has the same meaning as in regulation 1(2) of the Merchant Shipping (Reception Facilities for Garbage) Regulations 1988.

Definition in section 75(7) EPA 1990

(7) Subject to subsection (8) below, "commercial waste" means waste from premises used wholly or mainly for the purposes of a trade or business or the purposes of sport, recreation or entertainment excluding—
    (a) household waste;
    (b) industrial waste;
    (c) waste from any mine or quarry and waste from premises used for agriculture within the meaning of the Agriculture Act 1947 or, in Scotland, the Agriculture (Scotland) Act 1948; and
    (d) waste of any other description prescribed by regulations made by the Secretary of State for the purpose of this paragraph.

Definition in Schedule 4, Controlled Waste Regulations 1992, SI 1992/588

SCHEDULE 4   Regulation 6

WASTE TO BE TREATED AS COMMERCIAL WASTE

1. Waste from an office or showroom.
2. Waste from a hotel within the meaning of—
    (a) in England and Wales, section 1(3) of the Hotel Proprietors Act 1956; and
    (b) in Scotland, section 139(1) of the Licensing (Scotland) Act 1976.
3. Waste from any part of a composite hereditament, or, in Scotland, of part residential subjects, which is used for the purposes of a trade or business.
4. Waste from a private garage which either has a floor area exceeding 25 square metres or is not used wholly or mainly for the accommodation of a private motor vehicle.
5. Waste from premises occupied by a club, society or any association of persons (whether incorporated or not) in which activities are conducted for the benefit of the members.
6. Waste from premises (not being premises from which waste is by virtue of the Act or of any other provision of these Regulations to be treated as household waste or industrial waste) occupied by—
    (a) a court;
    (b) a government department;
    (c) a local authority;
    (d) a body corporate or an individual appointed by or under any enactment to discharge any public functions; or
    (e) a body incorporated by a Royal Charter.
7. Waste from a tent pitched on land other than a camp site.
8. Waste from a market or fair.
9. Waste collected under section 22(3) of the Control of Pollution Act 1974.

**Table 8-4: Wastes Covered by Existing EU and UK   331
Legislation**

Waste Type	Legislation
Radioactive waste	Council Directive 80/836/Euratom Radioactive Substances Act 1993
Mineral and quarrying waste	Town and country planning legislation Mines and Quarries (Tips) Act 1969

Animal carcasses and agricultural
    waste
	Animal Waste Directive, 90/667/
	    EEC
	Animal By-Products Order 1992

Waste waters, except waste in
    liquid form
	Dangerous Substances Directive,
	    76/464/EEC
	Water Resources Act 1991

Decommissioned explosives	Explosives Act 1875
	Control of Explosives
	    Regulations 1991
	Road Traffic (Carriage of
	    Explosives) Regulations 1989
	Other Regulations under the Health
	    and Safety at Work Act 1974

- Annex I – EU Waste Framework Directive 91/156/EEC as amended by 91/692/EEC and 96/350/EC
- Part II, Schedule 4, Waste Management Licensing Regulations 1994, 1994/1056
- Schedule 2B, Environmental Protection Act 1990, as amended

SUBSTANCES OR OBJECTS WHICH ARE WASTE WHEN DISCARDED etc.

Q1. Production or consumption residues not otherwise specified in this Part of this Schedule.

Q2. Off-specification products.

Q3. Products whose date for appropriate use has expired.

Q4. Materials spilled, lost or having undergone other mishap, including any materials, equipment, etc. contaminated as a result of the mishap.

Q5. Materials contaminated or soiled as a result of planned actions (e.g. residues from cleaning operations, packing materials, containers, etc.).

Q6. Unusable parts (e.g. reject batteries, exhausted catalysts, etc.).

Q7. Substances which no longer perform satisfactorily (e.g. contaminated acids, contaminated solvents, exhausted tempering salts, etc.).

Q8. Residues of industrial processes (e.g. slags, still bottoms, etc.).

Q9. Residues from pollution abatement processes (e.g. scrubber sludges, baghouse dusts, spent filters, etc.).

Q10. Machining or finishing residues (e.g. lathe turnings, mill scales, etc.).

Q11. Residues from raw materials extraction and processing (e.g. mining residues, oil field slops, etc.).

Q12. Adulterated materials (e.g. oils contaminated with PCBs, etc.).

Q13. Any materials, substances or products whose use has been banned by law.

Q14. Products for which the holder has no further use (e.g. agricultural, household, office, commercial and shop discards, etc.).

Q15. Contaminated materials, substances or products resulting from remedial action with respect to land.

Q16. Any materials, substances or products which are not contained in the above categories.

Table 8-6: Waste Disposal Operations*   333

- Annex II, A – EU Waste Framework Directive 91/156/EEC as amended by 91/692/EEC and 96/350/EC

- Part III, Schedule 4, Waste Management Licensing Regulations 1994, 1994/1056

WASTE DISPOSAL OPERATIONS

D1. Deposit into or onto land (e.g. landfill, etc.).

D2. Land treatment of waste (e.g. biodegradation of liquid or sludgy discards in soils, etc.).

D3. Deep injection of waste (e.g. injection of pumpable discards into wells, salt domes or naturally occurring repositories, etc.).

D4. Surface impoundment of waste (e.g. placement of liquid or sludgy discards into pits, ponds or lagoons, etc.).

D5. Specially engineered landfill of waste (e.g. placement of waste into lined discrete cells which are capped and isolated from one another and the environment, etc.).

D6. Release of solid waste into a water body except seas or oceans.

D7. Release of waste into seas or oceans including seabed insertion.

D8. Biological treatment of waste not specified elsewhere in this Annex which results in final compounds or mixtures which are discarded by means of any of the operations numbered D1 to D12.

D9. Physico-chemical treatment of waste not listed elsewhere in this Annex which results in final compounds or mixtures which are discarded by means of any of the operations numbered D1 to D12 (e.g. evaporation, drying, calcination, etc.).

D10. Incineration of waste on land.

D11. Incineration of waste at sea.

D12. Permanent storage of waste (e.g. emplacement of containers in a mine, etc.).

D13. Blending or mixing of waste prior to the waste being submitted to any of the operations numbered D1 to D12.

D14. Repackaging of waste prior to the waste being submitted to any of the operations numbered D1 to D12.

D15. Storage of waste pending any of the operations numbered D1 to D12 (excluding temporary storage, pending collection, on the site where the waste is produced).

*Note: At the time of writing, the UK Regulations had not been modified to include the latest amendment to the Directive. Table 8-6 reflects these changes in 96/350/EC.

Table 8-7: Waste Recovery Operations*

- Annex II, B – EU Waste Framework Directive 91/156/EEC as amended by 91/692/EEC and 96/350/EC

- Part IV, Schedule 4, Waste Management Licensing Regulations 1994, 1994/1056

WASTE RECOVERY OPERATIONS

R1. Use of waste principally as a fuel or for other means of generating energy.

R2. Reclamation or regeneration of solvents.

R3. Recycling or reclamation of organic substances which are not used as solvents (including composting and other biological transformation processes).

R4. Recycling or reclamation of metals and metal compounds.

R5. Recycling or reclamation of other inorganic materials.

R6. Regeneration of acids or bases.

R7. Recovery of components used for pollution abatement.

R8. Recovery of components from catalysts.

R9. Oil re-refining or other reuses of oil.

R10. Land treatment resulting in benefit to agriculture or ecological improvement.

R11. Use of wastes obtained from any of the operations numbered R1 to R10.

R12. Exchange of wastes for submission to any of the operations numbered R1 to R11.

R13. Storage of wastes pending any of the operations numbered R1 to R12 (excluding temporary storage, pending collection, on the site where it is produced).

Note: At the time of writing, the UK Regulations had not been modified to include the latest amendment to the Directive. Table 8-7 reflects these changes in 96/350/EC.

	INDEX
01 00 00	Waste resulting from exploration, mining, dressing and further treatment of minerals and quarrying
02 00 00	Waste from agricultural, horticultural, hunting, fishing and aquaculture primary production, food preparation and processing
03 00 00	Wastes from wood processing and the production of paper, cardboard, pulp, panels and furniture
04 00 00	Wastes from the leather and textile industries
05 00 00	Wastes from petroleum refining, natural gas purification and pyrolytic treatment of coal
06 00 00	Wastes from inorganic chemical processes
07 00 00	Wastes from organic chemical processes
08 00 00	Wastes from the manufacture, formulation, supply and use (MFSU) of coatings (paints, varnishes and vitreous enamels), adhesive, sealants and printing inks
09 00 00	Wastes from the photographic industry
10 00 00	Inorganic wastes from thermal processes
11 00 00	Inorganic waste with metals from metal treatment and the coating of metals; non-ferrous hydrometallurgy
12 00 00	Wastes from shaping and surface treatment of metals and plastics
13 00 00	Oil wastes (except edible oils, 05 00 00 and 12 00 00)
14 00 00	Wastes from organic substances employed as solvents (except 07 00 00 and 08 00 00)
15 00 00	Packaging; absorbents, wiping cloths, filter materials and protective clothing not otherwise specified
16 00 00	Waste not otherwise specified in the catalogue
17 00 00	Construction and demolition waste (including road construction)
18 00 00	Wastes from human or animal health care and/or related research (excluding kitchen and restaurant wastes which do not arise from immediate health care)
19 00 00	Wastes from waste treatment facilities, off-site waste water treatment plants and the water industry
20 00 00	Municipal wastes and similar commercial, industrial and institutional wastes including separately collected fractions

08	**WASTES FROM THE MANUFACTURE, FORMULATION, SUPPLY AND USE (MFSU) OF COATINGS (PAINTS, VARNISHES AND VITREOUS ENAMELS), ADHESIVE, SEALANTS AND PRINTING INKS**
08 01	*wastes from MFSU of paint and varnish*
08 01 01	**waste paints and varnish containing halogenated solvents**
08 01 02	**waste paints and varnish free of halogenated solvents**
08 01 06	**sludges from paint or varnish removal containing halogenated solvents**
08 01 07	**sludges from paint or varnish removal free of halogenated solvents**
08 02	*wastes from MFSU of other coatings (including ceramic materials)*
08 03	*waste from MFSU of printing inks*
08 03 01	**waste ink containing halogenated solvents**
08 03 02	**waste ink free of halogenated solvents**
08 03 05	**ink sludges containing halogenated solvents**
08 03 06	**ink sludges free of halogenated solvents**
08 04	*wastes from MFSU of adhesives and sealants (including waterproofing products)*
08 04 01	**waste adhesives and sealants containing halogenated solvents**
08 04 02	**waste adhesives and sealants free of halogenated solvents**
08 04 05	**adhesives and sealant sludges containing halogenated solvents**
08 04 06	**adhesives and sealant sludges free of halogenated solvents**

Environmental Protection Act 1990 (as amended by section 88, Schedule 2 Environment Act 1995)

Section 75

(2) "Waste means any substance or object set out in Schedule 2B to this Act (section 95, Sch. 22, Environment Act 1995) which the *holder* discards or intends to discard or is required to discard."

[The exclusion of explosives under the Explosives Act 1875 is removed]

(3) The "presumption"/evidential provision is deleted under the 1995 Act.

(4) "Controlled waste" means household, industrial and commercial or any such waste.

Waste Management Licensing Regulations 1994, SI 1994/1056

Regulation 1

"Directive waste means any substance or object set out in Part II of Schedule 4 which the producer or the person in possession of it discards or intends or is required to discard, but with the exception of anything excluded from the scope of the Directive by Article 2 of the Directive."

Controlled Waste Regulations 1992, SI 1992/588, as amended by Regulation 24 of SI 1994/1056

Regulation 1(4)

Excludes:

— mine and quarry waste, and waste from premises used for agriculture within the meaning of the Agriculture Act 1947;

— sewage, including matter in or from a privy.

Regulation 7A

"For the purposes of Part II of the [EPA 1990] Act, waste which is not Directive Waste shall not be treated as household, industrial or commercial waste."

Chapter 9

"SPECIAL WASTE" AND ITS CONTROL

THE DEVELOPMENT OF CONTROLS FOR SPECIAL WASTE

Prior to the Hazardous Waste Directive

Within most waste management regimes, particular attention is directed towards those wastes which present the greatest risk to man and to the environment. In the UK, the first statutory controls on the management of wastes were restricted to "poisonous, noxious, or hazardous wastes" and while the Control of Pollution Act 1974 extended these to a much wider range of household, domestic and commercial wastes, it was nevertheless considered necessary to introduce specific provisions with respect to certain "dangerous or intractable waste". These "section 17" provisions gave rise to the Special Waste Regulations 1980, which remained in force, albeit amended in 1988, until the implementation of the Hazardous Waste Directive in 1996. The amended 1980 Regulations satisfied the requirements of the EU Directive on Toxic and Dangerous Waste, 78/319/EEC, but when this was replaced by the Hazardous Waste Directive, 91/689/EEC, as amended by 94/31/EC, it became necessary to modify these measures.

The formulation of an adequate definition of "hazardous waste" is in many ways more difficult than the task of deriving a satisfactory "general" definition, since it is the "hazardous" properties of the material that are the objectives of the controls, yet these are not always fully understood or able to be assessed. Particular problems arise as the result of the paucity of data for assessing certain areas of "harm", such as eco-toxicity, and the absence of common standards which are easily applicable to waste materials.

An important issue is whether to base the legislative controls on the potential for *harm*, using the material's properties as guidance, or on the *risk* such a material poses, taking into consideration the possible pathways and targets. Early UK legislation in this area was essentially risk-based, as are the current contaminated land provisions. However, following the implementation of the EU Hazardous Waste Directive, the assessment of materials as special waste is based upon their harmful properties.

Early attempts at a definition of "hazardous waste" were unsuccessful – the Deposit of Poisonous Waste Act 1972 approached this by means of a list of materials which were considered *not* to present a risk of harm, and the Directive on Toxic and Dangerous Waste, 78/319/EEC, provided a "hopelessly vague" definition of "toxic and dangerous waste",[1] which applied to waste containing one or more of 27 listed substances "of such a nature, in such quantities, or in such concentrations as to constitute a risk to health or the environment". In addition to a lack of specificity which caused local, practical problems in the determination of such wastes, this definition permitted Member States to adopt their own criteria, contrary to the objectives of the Waste Framework Directive, 75/442/EEC, of providing a common terminology and definition of waste.

Under the Special Waste Regulations 1980, SI 1980/1709, as amended by SI 1988/1790, "special waste" was defined as *any controlled waste* which:

— consists of, or contains any of the substances listed in Part I of Schedule I to the Regulations, *and* by the reason of such presence is dangerous to life, as defined in Part II of Schedule I, viz:

— a single dose of not more than 5 cubic centimetres would be likely to cause death, or serious damage to tissue, if ingested by a child of 20 kg body weight; or

— exposure to it for 15 minutes or less would be likely to cause serious damage to human tissue by inhalation, skin contact or eye contact;

or

— has flash point of 21 degrees Celsius, or less, as determined by British Standard BS 3900: Part A, 8: 1976 (EN 53);

or

— is a medicinal product, as defined by section 130 of the Medicines Act 1968, which is available only by prescription from an "appropriate practitioner" – a doctor, dentist, veterinary surgeon or veterinary practitioner.

With regard to mixed wastes, paragraph 4 of the Regulations provided that waste was to be regarded as "dangerous to life" if a sample of 5 cubic centimetres taken from any part of a consignment fell within the description of paragraph 1 of the Schedule. In addition, under paragraph 3, where waste was in such a form that:

— the ingestion of less than 5 cubic centimetres is not possible; or

---

[1]   "The Problematic EU Hazardous Waste List", R Hunter, [1995] *EELR* March, 83.

— there is no risk that a toxic constituent could be assimilated if the waste were to be ingested,

then it was not to be regarded as "dangerous to life" under the criteria in paragraph 1(a).

The determination of whether a waste was "special" or not was a technically complex process and extensive guidance was given in Waste Management Paper 23 (now out of print but being revised in line with the 1996 provisions). Table 9-1 (page 384) summarises the criteria to be satisfied, in the form of a decision tree. From the point of view of the concept of special waste, this classification was dependent upon:

— a primary classification as controlled waste; which *either*

— contained or consisted of one of a list of 31 substances, compounds or groups of compounds, which were hazardous as a result of their being "dangerous to life" or having a low flash point; *or*

— was defined as a medicinal product.

The EU Hazardous Waste Directive

The EU Hazardous Waste Directive, 91/689/EEC, as amended by 94/31/EC, replaced the Directive on Toxic and Dangerous Wastes, 78/319/EEC, and adopted an approach to the designation of hazardous wastes based upon hazard, not risk. In order to be classified as a hazardous waste, it is necessary for such a waste:

— to satisfy the criteria for a "general waste" within the amended Waste Framework Directive (Article 3); *and*

— to feature on the Hazardous Waste List (HWL) drawn up on the basis of Annexes I and II of the Hazardous Waste Directive; *and*

— to have one or more of the properties listed in Annex III of that Directive (Article 4).

In addition, the Directive states that Member States may classify any other wastes displaying the "hazardous" properties listed in Annex III, and any such cases must be notified to the Commission and will be examined with a view to amending the HWL in accordance with Article 18 of the Waste Framework Directive.

The only exclusion within the Directive applies to *all* domestic wastes (Article 1(5) which was inserted in anticipation of "special rules" which are to be introduced for these materials). However, since hazardous waste must also meet the criteria of "general" waste, consequently the exclusions within the Framework Directive are also applicable.

Article 2 of the Hazardous Waste Directive places great emphasis on the requirement that establishments and undertakings that dispose of, collect, or transport hazardous waste do not mix different categories of hazardous waste, or mix it with non-hazardous waste, unless in accordance with Article 4 of the Framework Directive (i.e. without risk to human health or the environment). Furthermore, where hazardous waste is already mixed with other waste, substances or materials "separation must be effected where technically or economically feasible".

The Hazardous Waste List (HWL)

The Hazardous Waste List is critical to the definition of "hazardous waste" and, unlike the European Waste Catalogue from which it was derived, it forms an obligatory part of the process of defining waste as hazardous. As a consequence of this crucial role, the implementation of the Hazardous Waste Directive had to be delayed by eighteen months, until difficulties with the formulation of the HWL were resolved.

The HWL consists of a list of ~250 generic waste types – e.g. flue gas dust (10 05 03), waste from treatment of salt slags and black drosses (10 03 10), other still bottoms and reaction residues (07 01 08), aqueous washing liquids and mother liquors (07 07 01) – which are considered to display one or more of the properties of Annex III of Directive 91/689/EEC (which render them harmful) and, with regard to properties H3 to H8, one or more of the following:

— a flash point $\leq 55°C$

— one or more substances classified as very toxic at a total concentration $\geq 0.1\%$

— one or more substances classified as toxic at a total concentration $\geq 3\%$

— one or more substances classified as harmful at a total concentration $\geq 25\%$

— one or more corrosive substances classified as R35 at a total concentration $\geq 1\%$

— one or more corrosive substances classified as R34 at a total concentration $\geq 5\%$

— one or more irritant substances classified as R41 at a total concentration $\geq 10\%$

— one or more irritant substances classified as R6, R37, R38 at a total concentration $\geq 20\%$

— one or more substances known to be carcinogenic (categories 1 or 2) at a total concentration $\geq 0.1\%$.

Hunter[1] notes that, while the 1991 Directive instructs that waste "must have" one or more of these properties, the English version of the HWL uses "are considered to display", while in German the verb *annehmen* – to presume or assume – is used.

In addition to this technical issue as to its legal validity, Hunter suggests that the list in its present form is fundamentally flawed, being vague and over-broad, with entries based upon the EWC which are cryptic and susceptible to multiple interpretation. Furthermore, the HWL encompasses wastes that are not hazardous, such as waste acid and alkaline solutions (entries 06 01 99 and 06 02 99) – terms which could include any liquid whose pH is not exactly 7.0 – and no solvent concentration thresholds are given. There is also no indication in the list, or elsewhere, as to which property has triggered the hazardous classification of a particular waste. This places the burden of proof on the holder to show that a waste on the list is *not* hazardous.

The EU proposals to bring municipal waste within the ambit of the hazardous waste regime, *infra*, will necessitate a change to the EWC and HWL, which currently deal with "separately collected fractions" of municipal waste under Codes 2001 and 20 respectively. In addition, there is a separate proposal to make a substantial number of changes or additions (i.e. in excess of 350) to the EWC and HWL, based upon recommendations by Member States to the European Commission.

Implementation of the Hazardous Waste Directive within the UK

The Directive was implemented by means of the Special Waste Regulations 1996, SI 1996/972, as amended by SI 1996/2019, and under Regulation 2 there are three groups of controlled waste, other than household waste, which may be classified as special waste, viz:

— wastes included in the Hazardous Waste List which display any of the properties specified in Annex III of the Hazardous Waste Directive;

---

[1] "The Problematic EU Hazardous Waste List", R Hunter, [1995] *EELR* March, 83.

— wastes not included in the HWL which nevertheless display any of a restricted range of properties; and

— prescribed medicinal products.

A more detailed consideration of the technical issues associated with the classification of special waste and its management is given later in this chapter. However, in terms of the concept of hazardous/special waste, it should be noted that:

— the provisions of Regulation 2(2)(a) and (b) were introduced by the UK in order to maintain control over wastes which had been classified as "special" under the earlier measures;

— the DoE guidance in Circulars 6/96 and 14/94 has only "interim" status and more detailed guidance will be issued in a revised version of Waste Management Paper 23;

— both the HWL and the Regulations refer to six-digit codes in their definition of hazardous waste. However, the list of wastes in Circular 9/96 is based upon the European Waste Catalogue in which both "hazardous" and "non-hazardous" wastes are assigned six-digit codes, although the HWL entries have been emboldened. This is a potential source of confusion and the explanation in paragraph 6 of Annex B is unhelpful;

— the inclusion of certain radioactive wastes which are not "controlled wastes" within these controls, yet retaining the exclusion of mining, quarrying and agricultural non-controlled wastes, further confuses an already muddled situation;

— with regard to "household waste", the Directive excludes *all* wastes in this category but within the UK the revised Regulations (SI 1996/2019) define this term as meaning waste which is household waste for the purposes of section 75(5) EPA 1990 or is treated as household waste under the Controlled Waste Regulations 1992, as amended, other than:

— asbestos;

— waste from a laboratory;

— waste from a hospital, other than waste from a self-contained part of a hospital which is used wholly for the purposes of living accommodation.

The European Commission has produced an informal draft of a proposed Directive targeted at hazardous household waste (HHW) which would bring hazardous *municipal* waste within the controls of the Hazardous

Waste Directive, 91/689/EEC. These controls would introduce a new Article 1(5) defining the scope of the wastes covered and create an obligation on Member States to ensure that such materials, identified in an amended Code 20 to the Hazardous Waste List, are collected, separated and handled by undertakings licensed to carry out recovery or disposal operations (Articles 2(2) and (3)). In addition, the European Waste Catalogue would be amended, replacing Code 2001 with a new Code 20 for municipal waste.

There are potentially substantial costs associated with the requirement that the producers of products likely to become hazardous municipal waste mark these products or their packaging with a logo to indicate that they must be collected separately. (Note the parallel example of producer responsibility in the proposed Directive on End-of-Life Vehicles, COM 97 (358), *infra.*) It has been suggested that this proposal would impose costs of the same order of magnitude as those incurred under the Packaging Waste Directive.

A comparison of the revised Regulations with the Controlled Waste Regulations 1992 reveals that waste oil and clinical waste from domestic premises are not now regarded as special wastes. The DoE rationale behind this change is a desire that the rules do not add to the cost of separate collections of these materials from homes.

THE CURRENT UK CONTROLS ON SPECIAL WASTE

The present controls on special wastes may be considered as comprising three parts:

— the designation of certain controlled wastes and some other non-controlled wastes as "special";

— the regulation of the management of these wastes; and

— the ancillary measures, such as those concerned with their storage, labelling and packing, and transport.

Unlike the relatively straightforward criteria of the 1980 Regulations, the categorisation of a waste as "special" is now a much more complex, technical procedure. It is therefore important that producers of *any* waste ensure that its components may be identified readily and that any mixing with unknown substances is prevented. Although DoE guidance notes "it is not intended that industry should normally have to undertake expensive tests to determine whether or not their wastes have hazardous properties", such a statement is dependent upon the adoption of good waste management practices. The need for a greater specificity in the description of special waste, both on consignment notes and in relation to their packaging and labelling, will place a much greater emphasis on maintaining the identity of the major components of a waste which give rise to its hazardous properties. It will be appreciated that this may be best achieved by retaining identity from its point of production, segregating individual waste streams wherever possible and avoiding unnecessary contamination during storage.

It is no longer acceptable to assign a vague, generic description to a special waste when transferring it to another holder, and the Special Waste Regulations and others related to labelling and packing require that information is given on its associated hazards. However, until the practical implications of such requirements are fully appreciated by industry, a substantial amount of chemical and other analysis of poorly managed wastes may need to be undertaken in order to identify their components and hence the related hazardous properties. Once these costs become apparent, there will be an incentive to introduce better control of waste management procedures.

Controls Imposed on Special Waste

"Special waste" is defined in section 75(9) of the Environmental Protection Act 1990, as amended, as meaning "controlled waste as respects which regulations are in force under section 62" and this latter section empowers the Secretary of State to make provision by Regulations for the treatment, keeping or disposal of any kind of controlled waste which he considers as requiring such additional controls.

Under section 62(2), the Regulations may include, *inter alia*, a number of provisions with regard to:

— giving directions to the regulatory agency regarding the management of these materials;

— the quantities of special waste which may be stored;

— the re-delivery of special waste in the event of non-compliance;

— requiring the occupier of premises in which the waste is situated to notify the appropriate agency;

— the keeping of records by the regulators and by those involved in importing, exporting, producing, keeping, treating and disposing of these wastes.

Contravention of the Regulations is an offence which, on summary conviction, carries a fine of up to £20,000 and, on indictment, imprisonment for up to two years, a fine, or both. The Regulations may also provide for supervision by the Environment Agency and SEPA of the designated activities and the persons undertaking those activities. Certain of the regulatory costs, including the treatment, keeping, disposal and re-delivery of the special waste, are recoverable.

Although there is an appeal to the Secretary of State regarding the decisions made by the regulatory agencies under section 62(3)(c) EPA 1990, under section 114 of the Environment Act 1995, the Secretary of State may delegate to any appointed person his appellate functions. Under such provisions, the appointed person has the same powers as the Secretary of State in such situations, although under section 40(5) of the 1995 Act he is bound by any direction given to the Environment Agency or SEPA when determining an appeal from a decision of that body.

The Designation of a Waste as Special

Under Regulation 2 of the Special Waste Regulations 1996, SI 1996/972, as amended by SI 1996/2019, any controlled waste, other than household waste, is classified as a special waste if it falls into one of three groups, viz:

— subject to the threshold criteria on properties H4 to H8, it is assigned a six-digit code in Part I of Schedule 2 to the Regulations (the Hazardous Waste List); *and*

— it displays any of the properties specified in Part II of Schedule 2 to the Regulations (Annex III of the Hazardous Waste Directive) (Regulation 2(1));

or

— where it does not appear in the HWL, it displays any of a restricted range of properties specified in Part II of the Schedule (H3A [first indent – flashpoint <21°C], H4, H5, H6, H7 to H8) (Regulation 2(2)(a));

or

— it is a medicinal product, as defined by section 130 of the Medicines Act 1968 (Regulation 2(2)(b)).

Interim guidance on the Special Waste Regulations is given in Department of the Environment Circulars 6/96 and 14/96, the latter explaining the last minute corrections and alterations introduced as a result of SI 1996/2019.

There is little ambiguity in relation to the third group of special wastes – medicinal products – which is unique within the context of these Regulations since it has a single, all-encompassing, generic description. Department of the Environment Circular 6/96 states that since prescription medicine generally arises as many different items and in small quantities, the assessment of individual items would impose "an unnecessary burden". Medicine is defined with reference to section 130 of the Medicines Act 1968 and relates solely to those medicinal products which are available only in accordance with a prescription given by an appropriate practitioner as defined by section 58(1) of the Act. Consequently, the term does not apply to products which are available "over the counter" and DoE guidance states that these substances should be "judged by the other criteria".

With regard to the other two criteria for special waste, it is necessary to identify the hazardous properties of the waste's components more precisely and the "decision chart" approach as illustrated in Figure 9-1 on page 348 has been adopted in the interim guidance of the DoE Circulars (i.e. until the re-issue of Waste Management Paper 23 with more definitive guidance). In addition to this, Circular 6/96 includes decision charts relating to the determination of ten of the fourteen potential hazardous properties of the waste. It is intended that the majority of waste will be capable of such "desk top" analysis and will not be required to undergo chemical or physical testing. With reference to Figure 9-1, it will be noted that, apart from certain radioactive materials, a waste cannot be considered as special unless it is also classified as a controlled waste – hence the anomalous position of PCBs discarded from agricultural operations, which are neither controlled nor special.

Since the new special waste criteria have been set at equivalent levels to the thresholds for the 1980 Regulations wherever possible, the majority of substances formerly classified as special will continue to be so defined. However, the converse is not true and many additional materials will now be classified as special. The DoE Compliance Cost Assessment estimated that ~400,000 tonnes of waste oil would become special waste for the first time and that the overall number of annual waste consignments will increase from 387,000 to 500,000. The overall annual cost to business of these changes to the Regulations was put at £7.5 million.

The inclusion of additional wastes within the ambit of special waste with the implementation of the Hazardous Waste Directive, has necessitated the introduction of transitional provisions and "grandfather rights" in relation to existing waste management licences, through the Special Waste (Amendment) Regulations 1997, SI 1997/251.

Figure 9-1: Special Waste Interim Guidance – The Decision Chart Approach

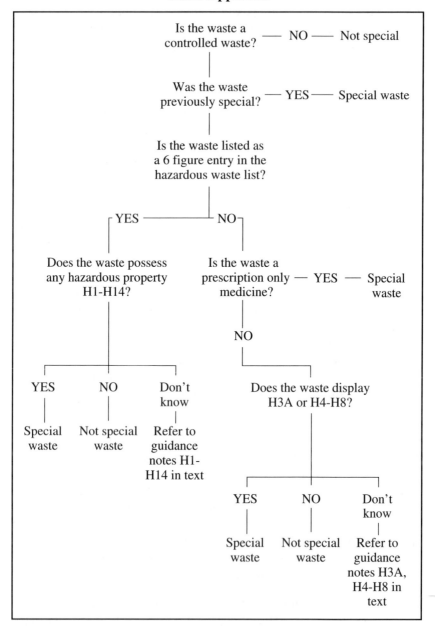

Even if a waste was formerly classified as special, it will nevertheless be necessary to undertake the "decision chart" type of analysis in order to determine which of its properties meet the hazardous criteria and how it is to be described in relevant documentation. Unless a special waste can be adequately described in terms of these hazardous properties, in effect it cannot be legally transported, processed or disposed of.

Despite the emphasis on special waste being a sub-group of controlled waste, the Special Waste Regulations 1996, SI 1996/972, as amended by SI 1996/2019, identify one group of non-controlled wastes – certain radioactive wastes – as being regarded as special.

THE HAZARDOUS WASTE LIST AND CHIP 96 REGULATIONS

Under Regulation 2(1)(b) of the Special Waste Regulations 1996, as amended, "special waste" includes any controlled waste which appears as a six-digit coded entry on the EU Hazardous Waste List (HWL) and this is reproduced as Part I of Schedule 2 to the Regulations. In some cases, the HWL is quite specific in describing a particular waste – e.g. fluorescent tubes (20 01 21), lead acid batteries (16 16 01) – but other entries are more generic and potentially may include many different types of waste, e.g. waste (acidic solutions) not otherwise specified (06 01 99). However, regardless of the apparent degree of specificity in the HWL entry, Regulation 2(1)(b) states that to be classified as special the waste must additionally exhibit one or more of the hazardous properties listed in Part II of the Schedule (Annex III of the Hazardous Waste Directive) and reproduced as Table 9-2 (page 385).

The Approved Supply List (ASL) – the 3rd edition of the document containing information approved by the Health and Safety Commission for the classification and labelling of substances and preparations for supply, for the purposes of the Chemicals (Hazard Information and Packaging for Supply) Regulations 1994, SI 1994/3274 as amended by SI 1996/1092 (the CHIP 96 Regulations) – uses the same hazardous properties as the 1996 Special Waste Regulations, Part IV of which provides for the use of the ASL and the associated guidance in the assessment of special wastes, for either the assessment (i.e. desk top investigation) or the testing of wastes, viz:

> "Any reference in Part III of Schedule 2 to a substance being classified as having a hazardous property, having assigned to it a particular risk phrase, or being placed within a particular category of a classification, is a reference to that substance being so classified, having that risk phrase so assigned to it, or being placed in that category –

— in the case of a substance listed in the approved supply list, on the basis of Part V of that list;

— in the case of any other substance, on the basis of the criteria laid down in the approved classification and labelling guide.

Except in the case of a substance listed in the approved supply list, the test methods to be used for the purposes of deciding which (if any) of the properties mentioned in Part II of the Schedule are to be assigned to a substance are those described in Annex V to Council Directive 67/548/EEC, as amended by Commission Directive 92/69/EEC."

The Directive on the Classification and Labelling of Dangerous Substances and Preparations (CPL), 67/548/EEC, and the associated UK legislation also employ the same hazard criteria but the use of CHIP 96 was adopted by the DoE since these regulations are more well-known within industry. The CHIP 96 Regulations are concerned with "substances" and "preparations", which have specific meanings, viz:

"Substances" are chemical elements and their compounds in the natural state or obtained by any production process, including any additive necessary to preserve the stability of the product and any impurity deriving from the process used, but excluding any solvent which may be separated without affecting the stability of the substance or changing its composition;

"preparations" are mixtures or solutions of two or more substances.

The 14 hazard criteria of the 1996 Special Waste Regulations are similar to the hazard criteria of CHIP 96 and, for labelling purposes, most hazards have an identifying symbol letter, viz:

Hazard		Symbol Letter
H1	Explosive	[E]
H2	Oxidising	[O]
H3A	Highly flammable (flash point <21°C)	[F]
H3B	Flammable (flash point ≥21°C and ≥55°C)	none
H4	Irritant	$[X_i]$
H5	Harmful	$[X_n]$
H6	Toxic and very toxic	[T] and [T+]
H7	Carcinogenic:Categories 1 and 2	[T]
	Category 3	$[X_n]$
H8	Corrosive	[C]
H9	Infectious	none
H10	Teratogenic: Categories 1 and 2	[T]
	Category 3	$[X_n]$
H11	Mutagenic: Categories 1 and 2	[T]
	Category 3	$[X_n]$
H12	Reaction to release toxic gases	none
H13	Formation of hazardous products after disposal	none
H14	Ecotoxic	[N]

Specific hazards arising from the properties of substances and the routes of exposure are described in terms of "R" numbers, or risk phrases, a complete list of which is given in Annex B6 to DoE Circulars 6/96 and 14/96. For each of these 64 risk phrases, there is an identified test procedure and defining limit value for that test, and combinations of these numbers may be used where appropriate.

Three documents have been issued by the Health and Safety Executive in support of the CHIP 96 Regulations and these are:

— the *Approved Guide to the Classification and Labelling of Substances and Preparations Dangerous for Supply* (3rd Edition), which identifies which risk phrases are appropriate to which hazards and defines, where available, the criteria upon which the risk phrases are based;

— the *Approved Supply List (ASL)* (3rd Edition), which contains detailed information on the dangerous properties of many substances and inclusion on which is indicative that the substance has dangerous properties; and

— the *Approved Code of Practice (Safety data sheets for substances and preparations for supply)*, which provides guidance on the preparation of safety data sheets.

In applying the CHIP 96 Regulations, it should be borne in mind that:

— waste is specifically excluded from the supply requirements of CHIP 96 and the use of such criteria for waste classification "is an extension of its role into a new field" (Annex B4, Circular 6/96);

— the CHIP 96 assessment is concerned with the physico-chemical, health and environmental properties of *substances*, but only the physico-chemical and health properties of *preparations*;

— many waste streams are heterogeneous in nature, and these should be considered as *preparations*, although assessments may be made on their components which may be *substances*;

— methods for testing waste against the 14 hazardous properties (but not the chemical analysis of waste to determine specific components) have so far been only partially identified in EU legislation; and consequently,

— the interim guidance in Circulars 6/96 and 14/96 deals only with the assessment of whether a waste displays any of the 14 properties, by reference to the known properties of the waste's components in the pure form or at reduced concentrations (paragraph 26);

— the CHIP 96 Regulations have no equivalent criteria for hazards H9 (infectious) and H13 (formation of hazardous products after disposal) since they were not intended for application to wastes or medicines (or cosmetics).

Wastes on the Hazardous Waste List

For those wastes falling within the Regulations – controlled wastes and certain radioactive wastes – the primary test for their categorisation is ascertaining whether they are listed as a six-digit code in the Hazardous Waste List, which forms Part I of Schedule 2 to the Regulations. (Note: Annex B8 of DoE Circular 6/96 reproduces the European Waste Catalogue (EWC), not the Hazardous Waste List, and in this format only the emboldened entries are on the HWL.)

The six-digit code of the HWL comprises three two-digit codes relating to:

— the industry type, process or waste type (first level);

— a specific group within the first level descriptor (second level); and

— a third level category, where appropriate.

These three levels of description may be used to identify particular wastes by selecting all the level 1 groups appropriate to the industry, etc., searching the second level for the descriptions appropriate to the activity in question, and then using the third level to look for the specific waste.

Groups 07 and 08 use the generic terms manufacture, formulation, supply and use (MFSU), which cover a wide range of different wastes:

— "manufacture and formulation" are industrial processes with the potential to produce waste by-products;

— "supply" relates to commercial activities such wholesaling and retailing, which generate wastes through damaged and redundant stock;

— "use" applies to a range of industrial, commercial and household situations, where wastes comprise process residues, cleaning wastes, partially used materials, contaminated and redundant products.

The categorisation "not otherwise specified" is used in relation to three third level descriptions of waste – 06 01 99, 06 02 99 and 13 06 01 – and group 16, comprising wastes not otherwise specified, contains four hazardous wastes – 16 02 01, 16 04 01, 16 04 02 and 16 04 03.

For wastes appearing on the HWL, it is necessary to determine whether they possess any of the hazardous properties H1 to H14 (cf. the test for waste *not* on the list, *infra*) and whether for properties H4 to H8 the concentration limits in Part III of Schedule 2 are exceeded.

Since this "first level" assessment is undertaken on the assumption of no cumulative effects from combinations of different components in the waste, it is necessary to account for such a possibility and this is particularly important in cases where analysis of the different components of the waste suggests that it is not special.

Wastes *Not* on the Hazardous Waste List

If a waste material does not appear on the Hazardous Waste List, it will be classified as hazardous only where:

— it is a prescription-only medicine; or

— it displays any of the hazardous properties H3A (first indent), or H4 to H8.

As noted earlier, prescription-only medicines may be described generically and the DoE guidance suggests that they should be classed as "H5: Harmful". For other wastes, a more detailed knowledge of the components is necessary and the concentration criteria in Part III of Schedule 2 apply.

ASSESSING THE HARMFUL PROPERTIES OF A SPECIAL WASTE

By their nature, special wastes present a number of potential risks to those involved in their management and, as a consequence, impose a number of legal obligations in addition to those associated with the special waste categorisation, viz:

— health and safety legislation, including the requirements of the Control of Substances Hazardous to Health Regulations 1994 (COSHH), SI 1994/3246, and that requiring the undertaking of risk assessments under the Management of Health and Safety Regulations 1992, SI 1992/2051;

— the Duty of Care provisions under section 34 EPA 1990, as amended;

— the requirement for certain components of the waste to be supplied with Safety Data Sheets (SDS), showing the hazard and risk phrases associated with the material.

Thus, in addition to a knowledge of the composition of a waste, there are a number of other potential sources of information relating to the hazards associated with some of its components. The guidance also notes at paragraph 51 that "the original Waste Management Paper 23 remains useful for assessing whether or not a waste is special by virtue of toxicity (H5 and H6) or a potential to cause tissue damage (H4 and H8)".

The Composition of the Waste

The importance of knowing the composition of a waste in order to undertake an assessment has been noted earlier. Since it is the hazardous properties of the waste which are being assessed, a knowledge of the compounds present is of more importance than that of the elements or ionic species present. A powdered waste known to contain aluminium would be classified as special under the flammability hazard, H3, if this were present in elemental form, but would present no problem if combined with oxygen to form aluminium oxide. Similarly, lead crystal glass should not be regarded as special, despite a high lead content, since the heavy metal is in the form of a complex silicate, with no hazardous properties.

A further factor to be considered is the homogeneity of the waste and the extent to which the known or assumed composition represents the bulk of the material. While certain substances are hazardous only at relatively high concentrations, others exist at relatively low values. This is illustrated in Table 9-3 (page 386) in relation to the limiting concentrations for a waste to be harmful or toxic by H5 or H6.

Simple, Homogeneous Waste Streams
Such wastes present relatively few problems in their assessment against the relevant hazardous properties, and may occur as:

— unused or spoiled material, similar in nature to the original product specification; and

— wastes consisting of manufactured goods, in which the hazardous substances or preparations are present in their component parts, e.g. PCBs in electrical insulation, mercury or sodium in fluorescent lighting units.

The DoE Circular suggests that the properties of these simple product wastes will be similar to, or can be inferred from, those of the original products or substances, and these may be obtained from the Safety Data Sheets (SDSs) or from other information supplied by the manufacturer. Schedule 5 of the CHIP 96 Regulations includes a list of 16 obligatory headings for which such information must be supplied in SDSs, including hazard identification, handling and storage, physical and chemical properties, stability and reactivity, toxicological information, ecological information and disposal considerations. However, information from this source is often general rather than specific.

Complex or Heterogeneous Waste Streams
There are a number of potential sources of heterogeneity within waste streams:

— the waste itself may be heterogeneous in form or phase, as a result of the lack of segregation in its collection (immediately post-production) and storage, or due to the nature of the method of its production. Such waste streams include liquids, solids, sludges and solids with discrete components;

— the presence of unused quantities of material within a container, such as discarded paint cans or oil drums left to fill with rainwater or other wastes;

— time-dependent factors such as oxidation, evaporation, or chemical or biological reactions during storage;

— partitioning of phases, components, suspended particles, during storage.

The assessment of process wastes is more complex, since these may contain unreacted feedstock and a range of reaction by-products, as well as the product itself. In view of the uncertainty in the composition of these materials, it may be necessary to undertake quantitative analysis and Circular 6/96 suggests that the physico-chemical properties of the waste – flammability, flashpoint and oxidation or explosive potential – may have to be determined where a hazard is indicated from a knowledge of the components.

Interpretation of the Analysis of a Waste

Heterogeneity, and the uncertainty in composition of process wastes, give rise to problems with regard to both the sampling and the categorisation of such wastes. This is one area in which the earlier risk-based approach gave a more useful assessment of theses issues than the present system based upon hazard alone. The DoE guidance suggests that, for mixed wastes, the species present should be quantified and where this is not possible one of the following options adopted:

— assuming the worst case, of the highest concentration of anionic and cationic species giving rise to a hazardous component; or

— considering the compounds most likely to be present, based upon the analytical results and a knowledge of the processes giving rise to the waste; or

— abandoning component analysis and testing against the hazardous properties in the Regulations.

Use of the Decision Charts

The decision chart shown in Figure 9-1 (page 348) forms the basic, interim, guidance for the determination of whether a substance is special waste or not. In many circumstances, this process will lead the waste holder to the conclusion that the material is or is not special waste but, where there is a degree of uncertainty, a "don't know" result will ensue and additional assessment procedures need to be undertaken. The ten "charts" forming figures B to K of Annex B of DoE Circular 6/96, amended in Circular 14/96, provide a means of employing existing data, to be found in CHIP 96 guidance, Safety Data Sheets, COSHH assessments and possibly Duty of Care information, to clarify the status of the waste. In cases where this is assumed to be special, such information may be used to identify the hazards associated with the waste. Two potential groups of users of these decision charts are:

— users of proprietary brand materials, or consumer products, who have limited facilities for determining the component parts of the resultant waste, who will rely upon information and guidance from suppliers, trade associations and regulators;

— suppliers who are currently required to classify their products for transport and supply purposes.

Any waste may exhibit a number of hazardous properties and, while any of these is sufficient to trigger the "special" status, it is necessary to determine *all* its primary hazardous properties in order to satisfy other provisions relating to waste and to health and safety. All properties for which precautions are required during the handling of a waste must be declared on the consignment note, even if they are not fully assessed.

An important difference between this part of the Circular and other DoE advice given in this format, such as that relating to the Waste Management Licensing Regulations in Circular 11/94, for example, is that while the status of each document is advisory, in Appendix B of Circulars 6/96 and 14/96 the information given is an interpretation of the technical issues of the legislation, rather than the legal ones. This will be an important issue where such matters are considered by a court and the advice of technical experts will probably be necessary.

Practical Issues
Details on the use of the decision charts are given in Appendix B of the amended Circular 6/96, to which reference should be made in making a decision on the hazards associated with a waste. However, the Circular forms only the framework within which an assessment might be made and the waste holder will need to consider other information such as that highlighted earlier and included in Appendix 1 on page 382.

In view of the technical complexity of such a decision, assistance should be sought where "in house" expertise is not available to the waste holder and in the longer term the possibility of drawing up a corporate waste list might also be considered. However, care must be exercised to ensure that a representative sample or analytical data of the waste is considered in any such analysis and unjustifiable extrapolation of the findings is resisted.

Inevitably, in view of the associated uncertainties in the categorisation process, there will be a degree of subjectivity on the part of those making the assessment and this will be coloured by the circumstances under which it is made: the waste holder will be anxious to avoid unnecessary costs and administrative effort, while consultants will wish to avoid any potential liabilities to their client and regulators will be aware of the broader issues involved in specific decisions.

The Decision Charts
A total of ten decision charts has been produced by the DoE for the assessment of the fourteen hazardous properties.

Some hazardous properties are subject to threshold concentrations and these cross refer to those in Part II of Schedule 2 to the 1996 Regulations. In some cases, the cumulative effects of the different components of a waste are considered in relation to a given hazardous property.

In order to assess fully the hazards associated with a specific waste, it is necessary to apply each of the decision charts to each of the components within that waste. This will be a lengthy task for multi-component wastes, particularly in view of the relatively low threshold concentrations for certain hazardous properties, e.g. <0.1% by weight for components assessed as very toxic, under risk phrases R26 to R28.

In addition, particular difficulties are likely to be encountered in the assessment of hazards H13 – the production of another hazardous substance after disposal, and H14 – ecotoxicity, where relevant (i.e. under the procedure of Part I of Schedule 2 to the 1996 Regulations, with respect to wastes included on the HWL). Hazard H13 includes the generation of methane or leachate in landfill sites and the production of dioxins as a combustion product after incineration. The guidance concedes that "almost any waste" could produce a substance which possesses any of the hazardous properties H1 to H12 and satisfies this criterion but argues that, since the function of the waste management licensing regime is to prevent pollution of the environment or harm to human health, the application of the H13 criterion should be restricted to conditions falling outwith these controls, such as the storage of limited quantities of waste at the site of production.

This logic seems quite strained, for one of the objectives of the Hazardous Waste Directive, and indeed of the Duty of Care, is to provide the holders of these licences with the hazard information, such as H13, in order to assist them in the prevention of pollution and harm. While certain *wastes* might be excluded from the ambit of the Waste Framework Directive, by virtue of existing legislation, it is a completely different matter to exclude a *single characteristic* from its classification and from the subsequent notification process.

This hazardous property has no decision chart to assist in the assessment process, although the Circular notes that work is in progress on the application of H13 in relation to its use under the Basel Convention on the Transfrontier Shipment of Waste, which also employs the same criteria.

The ecotoxicity criterion H14 relates to components which present, or may present, immediate or delayed risks for one or more sectors of the environment and, as with H13, virtually all wastes present some degree of risk to the environment. EU chemical legislation established criteria in this area – four concerned with the aquatic environment, four with toxicity to fauna, flora, bees and soil organisms, and others concerned with damage to the ozone layer and general, adverse long term effects.

Little advice is given on the application of these criteria and, apart from data relating to the aquatic environment, other information is limited. However, the Circular states that the testing of wastes for ecotoxicity "will rarely be necessary, since of the ~1500 dangerous substances classified by the EU to date, only ~100 are regarded as "dangerous to the environment" and of these all but 20 display the other hazards, H1 to 12. As with the guidance for hazard H13, this interpretation might not meet with EU approval.

OTHER CONTROLS ON SPECIAL WASTE

Since special wastes form a sub-group of controlled wastes, they are subject to all of the controls which are imposed on these as a result of the Environmental Protection Act 1990 and the relevant secondary legislation. They are also subject to a range of other controls associated with their management, including their transport and disposal, although the only measure introduced specifically for this group of materials is that for controlling their movement, by means of the consignment note procedure, contained in the Special Waste Regulations 1996, SI 1996/972, as amended by SI 1996/2019.

There is specific mention of special waste in some statutory controls, including:

— the Town and Country Planning (Assessment of Environmental Effects) Regulations 1988, SI 1988/1199, and the Environmental Assessment (Scotland) Regulations 1988, SI 1988/1221, as amended by SI 1994/

2012, relating to waste disposal installations for the incineration or chemical treatment of special waste;

— the Waste Management Licensing Regulations 1994, SI 1994/1056, as amended, which concern the scope of the licence exemptions and requirements for certificates of technical competence;

— charges for waste management licensing, made under section 41 EPA 1990, as amended.

However, the DoE guidance stresses that, in certain circumstances, the use of the term "special waste" is inappropriate, such as in waste management licences and authorisations, and states that only if there is an overriding legislative requirement which must be met, or a site is genuinely unsuitable in technical terms for *all* special wastes, should a comprehensive exclusion of special waste be considered.

With regard to the other legislative measures, there is a possibility that, with more substances coming within the ambit of special waste than under the 1980 definition, certain planning consents may be affected.

The Consignment Note Procedure

The consignment note procedure was introduced in the 1980 Special Waste Regulations as a means of informing holders of the waste – producers, carriers and disposers – of the associated risks and imposing on them the responsibility for transferring it to a competent person. Control was exercised through a six-part consignment note (also known as a "section 17" form) containing details of the type of waste, its producer, carrier and disposer.

An important part of the procedure was the pre-notification of the receiving WRA, who could object to the transfer or impose specific conditions as to how it was to be undertaken.

The Coding of Consignments

An important change to the 1980 Special Waste Regulations is the requirement for the Environment Agency or SEPA to issue a unique coding for each consignment of special waste which is made. Under Regulation 4(1), subject to paragraph (3) relating to the payment of fees for the issue of codes, the relevant Agency must supply forthwith to any person, on request, a code unique to the consignment or carrier's round.

The Environment Agency has established a central office which is responsible for the issue of all codes and the collection of fees. This office may be contacted by the Agency's special waste customers (where the starting point of the consignment is in England or Wales), by telephoning a dedicated local rate number, by post or by facsimile. SEPA is responsible for special waste movements originating in Scotland and different arrangements apply.

The format permissible for coding is laid down in Regulation 4(2) and a ten digit code has been adopted, e.g.

EA 12 34 56 78

The first digit denotes the issuing Agency:

E – Environment Agency

S – Scottish Environmental Protection Agency

an the second denotes the tariff rate:

A – £15

B – £10

C – £0.

This is followed by an eight digit sequential code unique to the consignment. The code may be issued in two formats – pre-printed on a consignment note or issued alone. This latter option provides for repetitive consignments (Regulation 7a) and carrier's rounds (Regulation 8).

Under Regulation 18(1), it is an offence, *inter alia*, to transport waste without a unique code having been assigned to that consignment. In the initial proposals for the new Regulations, the issue of a code was the trigger for payment to the Environment Agency or SEPA but current provisions permit payment to be made at any time up to two months after the issue of the code.

Although the Agencies may issue a code without pre-payment (Regulation 14(3)), they do have the power to withhold the issue until any fee required in respect of it under Regulation 14(1) has been paid. It is intended that this provision will only be used in the case of overdue fees for earlier consignment notes.

It is important to distinguish the request for a code and its associated payment from the pre-notification requirements in relation to a waste transfer and Table 9-4 (page 387) summarises the position for each of the options discussed below.

The Consignment Note

A consignment note is defined as "a note in a form corresponding to that set out in Schedule 1 to the Regulations, SI 1996/972" or "in a form substantially to the like effect" giving at any time the details required to be shown in respect of a succession of consignments (including, where part of a succession of consignments, any details required relating to these others). Although consignment notes will be produced and issued by the Environment Agency and SEPA, producers and carriers may generate their own forms, provided the same general content, layout and wording is followed.

The 1996 Regulations introduced a number of deregulatory measures with the purpose of streamlining the consignment note procedure and, in addition to abolishing the requirement for informing the consignor's WRA of the movement of the waste, established formal procedures for a number of the more commonly encountered situations, such as successive consignments and "carrier's rounds".

The terms "consignor" and "consignee" were introduced (c.f. "transferor" and "transferee" used in Duty of Care transfer notes) on the premise that special waste is not always consigned directly from producer to disposer and may pass to an intermediate stage such as storage, or to a recovery operation. The possibility of successive holders re-consigning the waste is reflected in the changed format of the consignment note.

The omission of the consignor's WRA as a recipient of a consignment note reduces the number of copies required from six to five, where pre-notification is necessary, and to four where it is not. In addition, the recommended order for the copies and their colours has changed and now becomes:

Copy	Colour	Description #
top	white	pre-notification copy for consignor to send to consignee's Agency Office
2nd	yellow	copy for consignee to send to own Agency Office
3rd	pink	consignee's own copy – keep for site lifetime
4th	orange	carrier's copy – keep for three years
5th	green	consignor's copy – keep for 3 years

 # retention period for documents may be different where the waste falls within landfill tax legislation.

This change should result in greater clarity on the document that accompanies the consignment when it changes hands and ensure that all of the original signatures are on the same copy. Circular 6/96 suggests that non-statutory guidance, such as that contained within its Annex C, is printed on the reverse side of the consignment note.

Apart from such administrative changes, the modification likely to present most problems is the information requirements for the description of the waste within section B, viz:

B2. Classification;

B6. The chemical/biological components that make the waste special, and their concentrations;

B7. The associated hazards.

The "classification" section, B2, requires that the recognised UK waste classification code, available from *Stage 3: development of a national waste classification scheme*, is given in addition to the SIC code, if known. (The SIC code is the Standard Industry Classification Code, to be found in the *SIC of economic activities*, produced by the Central Statistics Office, in 1992.) Such a classification bears no relation to the Hazardous Waste List and is not a requirement of the associated Directive. While it might be argued that the inclusion of such a classification will be of assistance in the description of the waste, in view of the other data included on the consignment note, this is likely to benefit the bean counters but confuse the waste holders.

With regard to sections B6 and B7, these are requirements of the Directive and the guidance states that "all of the most significant"(*sic*) components and hazardous properties of the waste should be shown. The codes H1 to H14 should be used in the completion of B6.

The consignment note procedure is described in Regulations 5 to 9 inclusive and the explanation below has been grouped into the following five sections, representing the most common situations which will be encountered in practice.

— the standard procedure;

— standard procedure for successive consignments;

— carrier's collection round procedure;

— extended carrier's collection round procedure;

— non-standard procedure.

The Standard Procedure

Pre-Notification

Before a consignment of special waste is removed from a site, five copies of the consignment note must be prepared, with Parts A and B completed and the code assigned by the Environment Agency or SEPA entered (Regulation 5). The relevant Agency must then be pre-notified of the consignment by sending one copy to the agency office of the consignee. This pre-notification must be received not less than 72 hours and not more than one month before the removal of the waste (Regulation 12). The minimum notification period may not apply where:

— the consignee does not accept the delivery and the consignment is to be delivered to other specified premises (Regulation 10(6)(c));

— the consignment cannot lawfully remain where it is for 72 hours.

Under these conditions, the requirements for the provision of the consignment note by "telephonic, electronic or other similar means of transmission" are treated as satisfied when the Environment Agency or SEPA is supplied with the requisite information within the time constraints and a copy is furnished to the relevant Agency before or, in accordance with paragraph (5), forthwith upon the removal of the consignment. This requires that a copy of the consignment note, or a written explanation of the reasons for refusing to accept delivery of any special waste, is sent to the Agency or SEPA – i.e. delivered to the Agency or posted by pre-paid first class post – within one day of the receipt, removal or refusal in question.

Carriage

Prior to the removal of waste from the site, Parts C and D on each of the four remaining copies must be completed by the consignor and the carrier. One copy is to be retained by the consignor and the remaining three are given to the carrier and must travel with the consignment and be given to the consignee on delivery.

Under Regulation 15(1), at each site from which any consignment of special waste is removed, a register is to be kept containing a copy of the consignment note and, in the case of carrier's rounds, a copy of that part of the carrier's schedule retained under Regulation 8(5).

Delivery

Except where a consignment is refused and the procedure in Regulation 10 followed, on receiving the consignment, the consignee must complete Part E of the three remaining copies and then give one to the carrier and furnish one to the enforcing agency for the place to which the consignment has been transported.

Each site receiving special waste is also required to keep a register containing a copy of the consignment note or carrier's schedule, as appropriate (Regulation 15(3)) and likewise each carrier is obliged to maintain a similar register.

Standard Procedure for Successive Consignments

The "season ticket" procedure of the earlier Regulations has been replaced by a new one for successive consignments, where:

— the special waste is of the same description;

— the consignor is the same person;

— the consignee is the same person;

— the collection premises is the same location;

— the receiving facility is the same location; and

— the successive consignments take place within one year.

Providing *all* of the above are satisfied, under Regulations 6(1)(a) and 6(2)(a) it is not necessary to pre-notify the Agency for each consignment and the following procedure may be used.

The "standard" procedure of Regulation 5 discussed above should be followed for the first consignment, but the consignor should indicate on Part A of the consignment note that there is to be a "succession" of consignments, with estimated quantities for the whole succession being shown in Part B.

When the first and each successive consignment is collected, the quantity and container details must be entered in Part C, since these will differ from the total quantity in the pre-notification. However, there is no need for pre-notification of the second and subsequent consignments, provided that these satisfy the requirements in Regulation 6(2)(a), above. For these consignments, only four copies of the consignment note need be prepared and distributed, according to Regulation 7(a). It should be noted that:

— details of the individual consignments should be included in Part C;

— each set of successive consignment notes must carry a unique code for that consignment, assigned under Regulation 4, in addition to a reference to the initial consignment note code; and

— the appropriate fee is payable for each consignment in the succession.

The advantage of this procedure is that, once the initial consignment has been undertaken, there is no requirement to approach the Agency for a direction or decision on subsequent movements, providing the conditions of the succession are met.

Carrier's Collection Rounds

The 1996 Regulations introduced a new procedure for the "Carrier's Round" which is defined in Regulation 1 as "a journey made by a carrier during which he collects more than one consignment of special waste and transports all consignments collected to the same consignee who is specified in the consignment note".

The controls imposed are contained in Regulation 8, and two forms of round are envisaged – the (standard) carrier's round, discussed in this section, and the extended carrier's round, which is outlined in the next. For the former, it is necessary for a number of conditions to be met:

— the journey made by the carrier must be to collect waste from more than one consignor;

— all consignments must go to the same consignee;

— the round must be completed within 24 hours of the collection of the first consignment; and

— a succession of carrier's collection rounds by the same carrier must start and finish within a 12 month period.

The First Round – Pre-Notification
Prior to the commencement of the first carrier round, Parts A and B of four copies of the consignment note must be completed, the code entered and one copy forwarded to the Agency within 72 hours of the proposed removal of waste (Regulation 8(1)(2)). This is similar to the standard procedure of Regulation 5, above, but the carrier must specify all of the consignors, together with their addresses and the total quantity of waste to be collected.

Changes in the names of the consignors or their addresses for collection are permitted, provided these are notified to the Agency in writing not less than 72 hours before the start of the round. This pre-notification is necessary only on the first carrier's round.

Procedure Following Pre-Notification: Prior to Collection
Apart from the pre-notification requirements, the procedure is essentially

the same for both the first and subsequent rounds. On each, the carrier must:

— prepare three copies of the consignment note, in addition to the pre-notification copy which is sent on the first round only;

— prepare an additional copy for each consignor from whom waste is to be collected on that round.

Parts A, B and C must be completed and the code relevant to that round inserted. For the second and subsequent rounds, the code for the first round is also required.

In addition to the consignment note, the carrier must complete three copies of the carrier's schedule, in the form set out in Part II of Schedule 1 to the Regulations or in a form substantially similar, for each site from which waste is collected during that round. The schedule and any continuation sheets must also carry the code assigned on the first round.

Procedure Following Pre-Notification: Waste Collection
At each site from which waste is collected, the carrier must certify the quantity of waste removed and the date of collection on all copies of the schedule. The consignor is also required to certify that the details in Parts A, B and C of the consignment note and in the carrier's schedule are correct. This certification by carrier and consignee is in lieu of Part D of the consignment note. On completion, the consignor retains one copy of both documents in respect of each site from which a collection was made.

As in the standard procedure, the documentation must travel with the waste to which it refers and be given to the consignee on delivery of the waste. It is necessary to include the time as well as the date of each collection, so that the regulators may ensure that the relevant time restrictions are being adhered to (Regulation 5(d) as amended).

Under Regulation 8(5A), before the removal of the last consignment of waste, the carrier must complete Part C of the three copies of the consignment note retained by him.

Procedure Following Pre-Notification: Receipt of Waste
On receiving the waste, the consignee must certify Part E on the three remaining copies of the consignment note, retaining one copy of the consignment note and carrier schedule, giving one copy of these documents to the carrier and "furnishing forthwith" the other copy of both documents to his (the consignee's) Agency office.

General Issues

Once the pre-notification has been completed, any number of rounds may be undertaken within twelve months of the first removal of waste, provided that the criteria of Regulation 8 are satisfied. Under this procedure, a carrier's round cannot extend over more than 24 hours, although not all of the sites specified in the pre-notification notice need be visited on each round. However, for each round:

— a unique code must be assigned by the Environment Agency or SEPA;

— a set of consignment notes and carrier schedules recording the addresses visited must be produced;

— a separate fee is payable.

The amended Regulations now permit more than one description of waste to be carried on a carrier's round and, under Regulation 8(5A), each type of waste collected from each consignor must be listed separately and quantified on the carrier's schedule.

Provided they are properly identified on the consignment note and meet other regulations on packaging and labelling, there is no limit to the number of different special wastes that may be carried in a single carrier's round.

Extended Carrier's Round

Regulation 14(2) permits a variation of the carrier's round procedure in which, subject to certain conditions, the second and subsequent rounds do not require the payment of a fee. This type of collection is sometimes referred to as an "extended carrier's round" and the following conditions must apply:

— the carrier and the consignee are the same person;

— no more than one consignment is collected from each consignor;

— the total weight in each round does not exceed 400 kg;

— the time between the first consignment on the first round in the succession and the delivery of the last consignment to the place to which it is to be transported is no more than a week.

The procedure followed is the same as for the standard carrier's round, except for the weight limitation and the time allowed for the succession.

The fee is payable on the first round only, although a separate code must be used on each round of the succession. Under Regulation 14(6)(b), this arrangement only applies to a succession of rounds undertaken with the same vehicle and a further fee will be payable for each additional vehicle which operates a succession of rounds.

Non-Standard Procedures

In addition to the repetitive movements of waste described above, the are a number of non-standard procedures which do not require pre-notification, including *inter alia*:

— intra-group consignments of waste; and

— the return of off-specification wastes to the manufacturer,

and these are covered in Regulations 6 and 7.

Intra-Group Consignments of Waste

Under certain circumstances, movement of waste within the same group of companies is excluded from the pre-notification procedure (Regulation 6(1)(c)). It is necessary for the consignor and the consignee to belong to the same group of companies as defined in Regulation 6(3), and the exemption is restricted to circumstances in which the waste is being removed for the purpose of storage, as in D15 of Part III and R13 of Part IV of the amended Waste Management Licensing Regulations 1994. Waste destined for recovery or final disposal still falls within the pre-notification control procedure. Exemption from pre-notification is the sole difference between this and the standard procedure and it is still necessary to have a code allocated by the Environment Agency or SEPA, complete the consignment note documentation, use a registered carrier and pay the requisite fee.

Off-Specification Products

When a person to whom a product or material has been supplied is satisfied that it fails to meet any specification which he expected it would meet, he may return a single consignment to the supplier or producer without pre-notifying the appropriate Agency. No payment is necessary under Regulation 14(2)(b) but the guidance states that, where these materials fall within the definition of waste and also of special waste, then all the provisions of the Regulations apply, including the requirement for a consignment note for the "return journey".

Prior to the introduction of these Regulations, it was the established custom and practice (though not established case law) for such materials to be regarded as non-waste. It would be possible to argue that the rejection of goods under these circumstances constituted "discarding", particularly in view of the emphasis placed in the Regulations on the part played by the person returning the waste. However, the existence of documentation indicating that the material was being returned for testing by the manufacturer might assist in determining intent.

However, since no costs and no pre-notification are involved, there can be few practical objections against completing the consignment note document-ation which accompanies such returns, and using a licensed carrier.

OTHER MOVEMENTS OF SPECIAL WASTE

Lead Acid Batteries

The movement of consignments consisting entirely of lead acid batteries from motor vehicles, though not from other industrial sources, is exempt from the pre-notification provisions (Regulation 6(1)(e)) and, following the amendments in Regulation 8(2)(a)(ii), this exemption applies to carrier's rounds as well as to single movements. The rationale behind the exemption is not given in the Circular, but it could be argued that the components of such a waste and the attendant hazards are well-known and are subject to little variation. Furthermore, established disposal or recovery processes are generally used.

Such movements of special waste attract a reduced payment to the appropriate Agency of £10 per consignment.

Removal of Ships' Waste to Reception Facilities

Regulation 9 is concerned with the particular case of special waste removed from a ship in a harbour area to either a reception facility within the harbour or by pipeline to any such facilities outwith the harbour area. In general, no waste carrier is involved and this is reflected in the modified procedure which requires that the relevant parts of the consignment note are completed by the ship's master and by the operator of the facilities.

No pre-notification procedure is involved, since this might conflict with the MARPOL Convention, which requires no undue delay to shipping, and practical problems could be encountered in obtaining consignment notes in advance of arrival at a port.

Although there is no fee to be paid, a code must be obtained from the Environment Agency or SEPA. Circular 14/96 emphasises that, following from the definition of "carrier" in Regulation 1(4), these provisions do not apply to movement of waste by pipeline in circumstances other than in relation to the unloading of a ship.

THE RECONSIGNMENT OF WASTE

This is not considered specifically within the Regulations, although the Circulars state that a new set of consignment notes will be required in a number of circumstances, viz:

— where special waste, once removed, is subsequently transported by more than one carrier before it reaches its final destination;

— where it is taken to a transfer station and re-consigned;

— where a new special waste is created by treatment of other waste (noting the restrictions on the mixing of special wastes, *infra*).

In these cases, the initial recipient of the waste – the first carrier or the transfer station – then becomes the consignor and the next recipient the consignee, and so on until it is finally disposed of.

REGISTERS AND SITE RECORDS

Regulations 15 and 16 require those involved in the management of special wastes to maintain registers relating to these activities, together with copies of the consignment notes and the consignment schedules, where relevant. These requirements are summarised below and are in addition to any imposed by the legislation associated with the landfill tax.

Person	Location of register	Period of retention
Consignor	Site from which consign-ment made	Not less than 3 years
Carrier	Not specified	Not less than 3 years
Consignee	Site at which consignment received	Until waste management licence surrendered or revoked
Agency	Agency Office	Any register from surrendered/revoked licence, not less than 3 years

The retention of registers by the appropriate Agency provides for situations in which the waste licence is surrendered or revoked and, by placing an obligation on the consignee to forward the documentation to the Agency local office, ensures that there is a mechanism for retaining such records.

Regulation 15(8) states that, insofar as is consistent with the remainder of the Regulation, the registers may be kept in any form, although the need for consignment notes and schedules to travel with the waste will impose certain practical limitations. With regard to the consignor's responsibility for keeping site registers, this may pose difficulties in cases in which brokers are employed or there is central management of waste for multi-site organisations.

In addition to these registers, Regulation 16 requires that any person who makes a deposit of special waste in or on any land shall retain a record of the location of each such deposit until his waste management licence is surrendered or revoked, and shall then send records to the Agency for the site. Site records may consist either of a site plan marked with a grid or a site plan with overlays on which deposits are shown in relation to contours of the site (Regulation 16(2)). For non-contained liquid wastes discharged into underground strata or disused workings, the documentation may be limited to a written statement of the quantity and composition of special waste discharged, and the date of its disposal (Regulation 16(4)).

In view of the case law pertaining to the meaning of "deposit" and the absence of a definition in the Regulations, it could be argued that such records should also be kept for intermediate storage of waste, prior to its final disposal, such as at Transfer Stations. The requirement of Regulation 16(3) is that deposits are described by reference to the register of consignment notes described above, although for waste disposed of by pipeline (from a ship) or within the curtilage of the premises on which it was produced (where no consignment note is required), deposits may be described by reference to a record of the quantity and composition of the waste and the date of its disposal.

THE MIXING OF SPECIAL WASTES

The Hazardous Waste Directive places restrictions on the mixing of hazardous wastes and Regulation 17 provides that an establishment which undertakes the disposal or recovery of special waste, or which collects or transports it, shall not:

— mix different categories of special waste; or

— mix special waste with non-special waste,

unless the activity is covered by a Waste Management Licence, a Part I authorisation or an exemption under the 1994 Regulations. Unfortunately, the Directive does not define the meaning of "category", although the guidance interprets this in terms of the possible effects on the environment and on human health of such mixing.

THE CARRIAGE, PACKAGING AND LABELLING REGULATIONS

In addition to the waste-specific legislation discussed above, there are a number of other controls associated with its transport. From the waste manager's point of view, the most relevant are those related to packaging and labelling and, apart from general measures such as those related to health and safety, e.g. the Control of Substances Hazardous to Health Regulations (COSHH), the majority of such specific controls are directed towards special wastes.

By virtue of their hazardous properties, special wastes came within the control of the Carriage of Dangerous Goods by Road and Rail (Classification, Packaging and Labelling) Regulations 1994, SI 1994/669 (CDG-CPL), which required an assessment of the hazardous components of the waste to be undertaken on the basis of which particular packaging and labelling was specified. This measure was superseded when a new tranche of regulations was introduced in 1996, to give effect to two EU Directives, 94/55/EC and 96/49/EC, incorporating into UK law the international agreements for the carriage of dangerous goods by road and rail – the "Accord Européen Relatif au Transport Internationale des Marchandises par Route (ADR)" and "Regulations concerning the International Carriage of Dangerous Goods by Rail (RID)", respectively. The new measures are:

— The Carriage of Dangerous Goods (Classification, Packaging and Labelling) and Use of Transportable Pressure Receptacles Regulations 1996, SI 1996/2092 (the "CDGCPL Regulations");

— The Carriage of Dangerous Goods by Road Regulations 1996, SI 1996/2095;

— The Carriage of Explosives by Road Regulations 1996, SI 1996/2093;

— The Carriage of Dangerous Goods by Road (Driver Training) Regulations 1996, SI 1996/2094;

— The Carriage of Dangerous Goods by Rail Regulations 1996, SI 1996/2089; and

— The Packaging, Labelling and Carriage of Radioactive Materials by Rail Regulations 1996, SI 1996/2090.

As with CHIP 96, these are supported by HSC approved documents and a Code of Practice. The majority of these new provisions replace existing regulations which are basically unchanged, although controls have been included on petrol vapour emissions, as appropriate, and SI 1996/2090 gives separate statutory effect to the requirements for carriage of radioactive materials by rail.

The Carriage of Dangerous Goods (Classification, Packaging and Labelling) and Use of Transportable Pressure Receptacles Regulations 1996, SI 1996/2092, are common to all of the above provisions. These are the Regulations which are of most relevance to waste managers, since they place a number of obligations on the consignor of hazardous waste, and they are discussed in greater detail below.

The other measures are specific to the form of transport considered within the relevant Regulations and follow a similar format including, *inter alia*, approved documents, loading and unloading, mode of carriage, safety/security/emergency provisions, and information requirements. While the majority of these requirements are placed upon the operator of the transport, as part of the Duty of Care the consignor (and consignee) should be aware of the sections which impinge on their activities and the carriage arrangements made by them. This will include issues such as:

— the prohibition on the carriage of dangerous goods in bulk in a container or vehicle, in a tank, or on a rail wagon/container, unless the letter "Y" appears in column 8 of the Approved Carriage List (Regulation 8(1), SI 1996/2095; and Regulation 5, SI 1996/2089);

— the compatibility of the carriage arrangements with the restrictions placed upon the supervision and parking of road vehicles (Regulation 21, SI 1996/2093; and Regulation 24, SI 1996/2095);

— the precautions to be taken against fire or explosion (Regulation 22, SI 1996/2089; and Regulation 23, SI 1996/2095);

— prohibitions on the carriage of certain mixed loads (Regulation 17, SI 1996/2089; Regulation 28, SI 1996/2090; and Regulation 18, SI 1996/2095);

— loading and unloading requirements (Regulation 18, SI 1996/2089; Regulation 29, SI 1996/2090; Regulation 19, SI 1996/2093; and Regulation 19, SI 1996/2095).

Classification

Waste managers must despair of the plethora of different schemes of classifications to be applied to the same consignment of special waste. In addition to the hazardous waste code, risk phrases and UK waste classification required for the consignment note, *supra*, the labelling regulations demand that the hazardous waste is placed into one of the nine classes listed in Table 9-5 on page 388, and assigned a four-digit code and description (referred to as the proper shipping name), in order that the appropriate combination of labels and packaging may be selected.

While most of the CDGCPL Regulations are concerned with the carriage of dangerous goods in packages and in "transportable pressure receptacles", Regulation 5 is more generally applicable and states that " a person shall not consign dangerous goods for carriage unless the classification for those goods and the particulars specified in the following paragraphs have been ascertained ...". The basis of the classification used in these Regulations is the HSC-approved documents:

— the *Approved Carriage List*;

— the *Approved Requirements and Test Methods for the Classification and Packaging of Dangerous Goods*; and

— the *Approved Requirements for Transportable Pressure Receptacles*.

The first two documents have a common basis with the "Approved Supply List" and the "Approved Classification and Labelling Guide" which is used, *inter alia*, for the categorisation of special waste and, although not identical, have sufficient areas of commonality to permit a degree of cross-referencing to be made in the associated classification processes.

The Scope of the Regulations

Not all dangerous goods for transport fall within these measures and Regulation 3(1) details 17 situations which are exempted. These include certain international transport operations which are subject to other controls, activities which are not connected with work, explosives, live animals and specific activities of the regulatory agencies in connection with their duties or in emergency situations.

In addition to these general exclusions, Schedule 3 lists the combinations of goods and classification/packing group/maximum quantity per receptacle, for which the packing and labelling requirements of Regulation 6(1)(e) do not apply.

Regulation 18 provides that, subject to the requirements imposed by EU obligations, the Health and Safety Executive may issue an exemption certificate, which exempts:

— any person or class of person;

— any dangerous goods or class of dangerous goods; or

— any type or class of package, or transportable pressure receptacle,

from all or any of the requirements of the regulations.

The System of Classification

Under the Regulations, there are a number of mandatory requirements to be satisfied prior to the consignment of dangerous goods for carriage, which include, *inter alia*:

— its classification into one of the nine categories in Table 9-5 (page 388);

— the identification of subsidiary hazards;

— the designation of one of the proper shipping names specified in the Approved Carriage List, together with additional information, as in the explanatory notes. Where the goods are not individually named in the Approved Carriage List, the proper shipping name and UN number "which most fully and accurately describe the goods" are to be used.

Having determined these, it is then necessary to assign:

— the UN number (the four-digit United Nations Serial Number for the identification of the hazardous goods);

— the packing group, meaning the group to which dangerous goods with relevant properties are allocated in accordance with Regulation 5; and

— the danger sign in Part I of Schedule 1, and any subsidiary hazard sign, if any, shown in column 2 of Schedule 2.

The procedure for determining the classification of the goods is contained in Regulation 5(2) for those named in the Approved Carriage List, and in Regulation 5(3) for all other goods. Regulation 5(3) details the packing and labelling requirements which are imposed on *all* goods.

The approved methods state that, if testing is not possible without disproportionate cost, as for some kinds of waste, then the goods shall be placed in the class of the component presenting the predominant danger. Where there is reasonable doubt as to precisely which classification is correct, then it is acceptable to over-classify, i.e. to classify the goods as if they are more hazardous than they actually are.

Packaging

The consignor must not consign dangerous goods for carriage in packages unless those packages are suitable for the purpose (Regulation 6) and all aspects relating to the packages and any packaging or pallets – their design, construction, maintenance, filling and closure – must be taken into account to ensure that the contents do not escape during the normal conditions encountered during handling and carriage.

It is important to note the Regulation's definitions of the terms used, viz:

— "package" means the package in which the dangerous goods are carried and which is liable to be individually handled during the course of carriage, and includes:

— the dangerous goods being carried; and

— any packaging (other than a tank or overpack) associated with the dangerous goods;

— "packaging" means the receptacle (whether or not a transportable pressure receptacle) and any component materials or wrappings associated with the receptacle for the purpose of enabling it to perform its containment function, but does not include a skip, pallet, a vehicle or other article of carriage equipment;

— "receptacle" means a vessel or the innermost layer of packagings which is in contact with any dangerous goods therein, and includes any closure or fastener;

— "overpack" means the unit formed when one or more packages are assembled on or in a device, including ropes or straps, which enable them to be handled as one unit, but does not include a container.

The Approved Carriage List contains special provisions for certain goods and these must be adhered to (Regulation 6(1)(d)). The packaging used must be of a design type which has been tested by an approved testing laboratory using approved tests and has received a test certificate to that effect (Regulation 6(1)(e)). It must have been allocated an ADR mark, a RID mark, a UN mark, or a joint ADR and RID mark by a competent authority and must bear that mark. (The definitions of these terms are given in Regulation 2(1).)

The packages, receptacles and packaging must be constructed of materials which are not adversely affected by the contents to create a risk to the health and safety of any person. Replaceable closures, where fitted, must be designed to be repeatedly re-closed without the contents escaping. There are also restrictions relating to the packaging and overpacking associated with the packages.

It is permissible to use reconditioned packaging, as defined in Regulation 6(4), which meets the above criteria and which has been allocated an appropriate marking.

There are a number of exemptions to the above within Regulation 6(3), which include:

— transportable pressure receptacles or aerosols, together with any associated packaging (*sic*);

and packages which:

— have a capacity exceeding 3 cubic metres;

— fall within the criteria laid down in Schedule 3, and the gross mass of any package containing any receptacles does not exceed 30 kilogrammes; or

— have a nominal capacity of 25 litres or less, are uncleaned, empty, and which are being consigned to "a suitable place" for no other purpose than cleaning or disposal,

or where the entry in the Approved Carriage List or the Approved Method so indicates.

It is not mandatory to use new, unused containers to transport hazardous goods but, where they are re-used, they must be inspected to ensure that they are clean and uncontaminated, undamaged and not adversely affected by earlier contents or carriage. Any faults identified must be corrected before use and replaceable closures should be checked to ensure their continuing effectiveness.

Labelling
The requirements for the marking and labelling of dangerous goods are contained in Regulations 7 to 11 and the basic requirement is that the outer layer of the packaging displays one or more of the standard hazard labels, in order to alert anyone handling the package to the presence of hazardous substances. (Note that there are other instruments which are specific to the mode of transport used and the other precautions which must be taken.)

Hazardous waste must carry the following labels:

— the hazard warning diamond relevant to the classification group, as shown in Part I of Schedule 1 to the Regulations;

— a second hazard warning diamond, indicating a subsidiary hazard, if appropriate, as shown in Part I of Schedule 2 to the Regulations (this symbol does not have the hazard classification number at the base);

— a carriage label, containing the proper shipping name, with the corresponding UN number prefixed by the letters "UN".

Regulation 11 is concerned with the methods of marking or labelling packages and lays down that the minimum side length of the danger and subsidiary hazard signs shall be 100 millimetres although, if the package is small or of an awkward shape, then the sign must be "as large as is practicable". The labelling must stand out from the background so as to be noticeable and must be displayed so that it can be read easily. It must either be clearly and indelibly marked on the package, or clearly and indelibly printed on a label which is securely fixed to the package, with its entire surface in contact with it.

Except where the goods are to be supplied to a recipient in another Member State, the labelling is to be in English.

Carriage
For the purposes of the Regulations, dangerous goods are deemed to be carried from the time when they are placed upon the vehicle carrying them by road or rail, until they are removed from the vehicle, or the receptacle containing the goods which is on the vehicle has been cleaned or purged so that there is no longer a significant risk to the health or safety of any person.

The Regulations make no distinction as to whether the vehicle is on a road or railway or not, and cover the carriage of "uncleaned, empty packages which have contained dangerous goods, where those packages still contain sufficient of those dangerous goods (or vapours therefrom) to create a significant risk to the health or safety of any person".

Offences

The CDGCPL Regulations were introduced by the Secretary of State, using his powers under sections 15 and 16 and Schedule 3 to the Health and Safety at Work etc. Act 1974 (HASAWA), and consequently, by section 3(c) of that Act, it is an offence for a person to contravene any of its requirements. As with "environmental" legislation, this extends to placing individual criminal liability on any director, manager, secretary or similar officer who, through his consent, connivance or neglect, is held responsible for an offence committed by the body corporate (section 37).

No additional offences are specified within the 1996 Regulations but Regulation 19 provides a defence for a person charged with an offence, where he can prove:

— the commission of the offence was due to the act or default of another person not being one of his employees (the other person); *and*

— he took all reasonable precautions and exercised all due diligence to avoid the commission of the offence.

In order to use this defence, the person charged must comply with the requirements of Regulations 19(2) and (3), giving notice of his intention to use this defence and serving on the prosecutor a notice in writing giving such information identifying or assisting in identifying the other person. However, for the purpose of enabling the other person to be charged and convicted by virtue of section 36 HASAWA 1974, the person establishing this defence shall nevertheless be treated for the purposes of that section as having committed the offence.

These Regulations are enforced by the Health and Safety Executive and the Vehicle Inspectorate, with the assistance of the police in roadside checks and inspections of vehicle depots.

FURTHER READING

(see also Appendix 1 overleaf)

CHIP 2 for Everyone, HSE

Croners Waste Management, Croner Publications (regularly updated)

Environmental Protection Act 1990: Part II – Special Waste Regulations, Department of the Environment Circulars 6/98 and 14/96, HMSO, 1996

"The Problematic EU Hazardous Waste List", R Hunter, [1995] *EELR* March, 83

Special Wastes – Waste Management Paper No. 23, Department of the Environment, HMSO, 1981 (out of print, currently under revision)

Appendix 1

SOURCE OF DATA FOR USE IN ASSESSMENT OF HAZARDOUS PROPERTIES OF A WASTE

1. *The Approved Supply List*, and associate guidance from the Health and Safety Commission produced in accordance with CHIP 2 (1994). Available from HSE Books. The ASL is supplied as a paper copy. Data is also provided on computer disks.

2. Royal Society of Chemistry – "Chemical Safety Data Sheets": Vol. 1, *Solvents* (1989) (ISBN 0 85186 903 3); Vol. 2, *Main Group Metals and Compounds* (1990) (ISBN 0 85186 913 0); Vol. 3, *Corrosives and Irritants* (1990) (ISBN 0 85186 923 8); Vol. 4A, *Toxic Chemicals (M-Z)* (1992) (ISBN 0 85186 321 3); Vol. 5, *Flammable Chemicals* (1992) (ISBN 0 85186 411 2), RSC (Cambridge).

3. Royal Society of Chemistry – *Agrochemicals Handbook* (3rd Edition) and updates (ISBN 0 85186 416 3), RSC (Cambridge).

4. L Bretherick – *Handbook of Reactive Chemical Hazards* (3rd Edition) (ISBN 0 408 013887 5), Butterworths (London).

5. BDH – *Hazard Data Sheets* (1990) + Addendum, BDH Product No. 57053 1S and 57053 2T, Merck Ltd., Broom Road, Poole, BH12 4NN.

6. R J Lewis Snr. (Ed.) – *Sax's Dangerous Properties of Industrial Materials* (8th Edition, 3 vols.) (1992) (ISBN 0-442-01132-6), Van Nostrand Rheinold, London.

7. *The Merck Index* (ISBN 911910 28 X), Merck and Co. Inc., Rahway, NJ, USA.

8. D R Lide (Ed.) – *Handbook of Chemistry and Physics* (74th Edition) (1993/4) (ISBN 0 8493 0474 1), CRC Press, London.

9. L H Keith & D B Walters – *Compendium of Safety Data Sheets for Research and Industrial Chemicals, Vols. I-III* (ISBN 0 89573 313 7), VCH Publishers Inc., Deerfield Beach, Florida, USA.

10. NFPA – *Fire Protection Guide to Hazardous Chemicals* (10th Edition) (1991) (ISBN 0 87765 366 6), National Fire Protection Association, 1 Batterymarch Park, PO Box 9101, Quincy, Maryland, USA.

11. NIOSH – *Register of Toxic Effects of Chemical Substances (RTECHS)*. Available as paper copy, microfiche, or on CD-ROM from Microinfo Ltd., PO Box 3, Omega Park, Hants. GU34 2PG.

12. *Environmental Hazard Assessment*: a series of papers prepared by the Building Research Establishment (BRE) and the Institute of Terrestrial Ecology for the DOE. They review the distribution, fate and effects of particular chemicals on the environment. Available from BRE Bookshop, BRE, Garston, Watford WD2 7JR. Telephone: (01923) 664444.

13. *Environmental Health Criteria Documents (EHCs)* and *Health and Safety Guides* prepared under the International Programme on Chemical Safety provide detailed information on a number of chemicals.

14. *Materials Safety Data Sheets* on substances and preparations are available from manufacturers and/or suppliers. Schedule 5 of CHIP 2 provides a list of 16 obligatory headings under which particulars are to be provided in Safety Data Sheets. These include hazards identification, handling and storage, physical and chemical properties, stability and reactivity, toxicological information, ecological information and disposal considerations.

15. The National Centre for Environmental Toxicology can provide information and advice on chemical contaminants in drinking water and the aquatic environment.

16. The Waste Management Information Bureau (WMIB), part of the National Environmental Technology Centre (NETCEN) can provide information on environmental hazards from its bibliographic database "WasteInfo". WMIB, AEA Technology, F6 Culham, Oxon., OX14 3DB. Telephone: (01235) 463162.

Table 9-1: Criteria for Special Waste, Prior to Implementation of the Hazardous Waste Directive

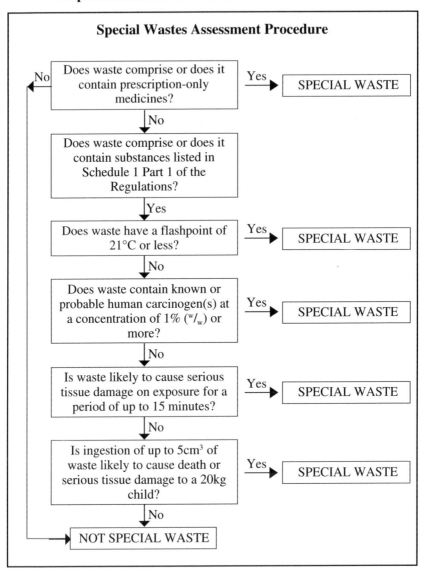

Special Wastes Assessment Procedure

H1	"Explosive": substances and preparations which may explode under the effect of flame or which are more sensitive to shocks or friction than dinitrobenzene.
H2	"Oxidising": substances and preparations which exhibit highly exothermic reactions when in contact with other substances, particularly flammable substances.
H3-A	"Highly flammable": — liquid substances and preparations having a flash point below 21°C (including extremely flammable liquids), or — substances and preparations which may become hot and finally catch fire in contact with air at ambient temperatures without any application of energy, or — solid substances and preparations which may readily catch fire after brief contact with a source of ignition and which continue to burn or to be consumed after removal of the source of ignition, or — gaseous substances and preparations which are flammable in air at normal pressure, or — substances and preparations which, in contact with water or damp air, evolve highly flammable gases in dangerous quantities.
H3-B	"Flammable": liquid substances and preparations having a flash point equal to or greater than 21°C and less than or equal to 55°C.
H4	"Irritant": non-corrosive substances and preparations which, through immediate, prolonged or repeated contact with the skin or mucous membrane, can cause inflammation.
H5	"Harmful": substances and preparations which, if they are inhaled or ingested or if they penetrate the skin, may involve limited health risks.
H6	"Toxic": substances and preparations (including very toxic substances and preparations) which, if they are inhaled or ingested or if they penetrate the skin, may involve serious, acute or chronic health risks and even death.
H7	"Carcinogenic": substances and preparations which, if they are inhaled or ingested or if they penetrate the skin, may induce cancer or increase its incidence.
H8	"Corrosive": substances and preparations which may destroy living tissue on contact.
H9	"Infectious": substances containing viable micro-organisms or their toxins which are known or reliably believed to cause disease in man or other living organisms.
H10	"Teratogenic": substances and preparations which, if they are inhaled or ingested of if they penetrate the skin, may induce non-hereditary congenital malformations or increase their incidence.
H11	"Mutagenic": substances and preparations which, if they are inhaled or ingested or if they penetrate the skin, may induce hereditary genetic defects or increase their incidence.
H12	Substances and preparations which release toxic or very toxic gases in contact with water, air or an acid.
H13	Substances and preparations capable by any means, after disposal, of yielding another substance, e.g. a leachate, which possesses any of the characteristics listed above.
H14	"Ecotoxic": substances and preparations which present or may present immediate or delayed risks for one or more sectors of the environment.

Table 9-3: Criteria for Assessing Waste as Harmful or Toxic – Hazards H5 and H6

Risk Phrase	Hazard	Minimum limiting total concentration to be special
R20 – Harmful by inhalation	Harmful, H5, X_n	$\geq 25\%$
R21 – Harmful by skin contact		
R22 – Harmful by ingestion		
R23 – Toxic by inhalation	Toxic H6, T	$\geq 3\%$
R24 – Toxic by skin contact		
R25 – Toxic by ingestion		
R26 – Very toxic by inhalation	Very Toxic, H6, T+	$\geq 0.1\%$
R27 – Very toxic by skin contact		
R28 – Very toxic by ingestion		

Table 9-4: Pre-Notification Requirements and Payment of Fees

Movement Type	Pre-notification	Fee
Single movement	✓	✓
First repetitive movement	✓	✓
Second and subsequent repetitive movements	✗	✓
First carrier's round	✓	✓
Second and any subsequent carrier's round	✗	✓
First extended carrier's collection round	✓	✓
Second and any subsequent extended carrier's round	✗	✗
Off-specification material	✗	✗
Intra-group movements	✗	✓

Class 2   – Gases, subdivided as:
— 2.1: flammable
— 2.2: non-flammable, non-toxic and non-corrosive
— 2.3: poisonous (including substances which are poisonous via their corrosive effect)

Class 3   – Flammable liquids: liquids with flashpoint under 61°C. Between 35°C and 61°C the substance must also be combustible in order to be classified as a flammable liquid under CDGCPL.

Class 4   – Flammable solids: readily combustible or self reactive substances; certain desensitised explosives; substances liable to spontaneous combustion and substances which on contact with water or damp air give off flammable gas in dangerous quantities.

Class 5   – Oxidising substances and organic peroxides.

Class 6.1 – Poisonous (toxic) substances that are liable to cause death or serious injury to human health if inhaled, ingested or absorbed through the skin.

Class 6.2 – Infectious substances.

Class 8   – Corrosive substances which by chemical action will cause severe damage to living tissue or will materially damage or destroy the mode of transport in case of leakage.

Class 9   – Other dangerous substances; miscellaneous substances which have been found to present a danger not covered by other Classes, e.g. asbestos.

Note

Class 1   – Explosives are subject to the Classification and Labelling of Explosives Regulations 1983, SI 1983/1140

Class 6.2 – See recommendations on Clinical Waste in Chapter 11

Class 7   – Radioactive materials come under the Radioactive Substances (Carriage by Road) Regulations 1974, SI 1974/ 1735, as amended

Class 9   – It is no longer permissible to give wastes a non-specific, generic description under Class 9

Chapter 10

WASTES SUBJECT TO OTHER LEGISLATIVE CONTROLS

The objective of Chapter 8 was to examine the "general" definition of waste as contained in the Waste Framework Directive and the following discussion considers the manner in which other legally defined wastes are identified and are compatible with the overall legislative scheme of control. The introduction of landfill tax through "financial" legislation is a case in point, for although this is imposed upon wastes disposed by landfill and subject to "environmental" legislation, it uses a different definition of waste and imposes additional constraints on the implementation of this legislation.

WASTE SUBJECT TO THE LANDFILL TAX

Whilst the *concept* of the landfill tax is environmental – i.e. the use of an economic instrument to encourage resource maximisation – in *execution* it has been introduced as a fiscal measure, and this has a number of implications on those "registerable persons" involved since there are a number of areas in which the requirements of the environmental and fiscal legislative measures differ, viz:

— the definition of waste and the relevant exemptions;

— the retention periods for the associated documentation;

— the information to be included on Waste Transfer Notes.

The first issue is of fundamental importance and relevant statutory provisions are:

— sections 39 to 71 and Schedule 5, Finance Act 1996, c8;

— the Landfill Tax Regulations 1996, SI 1996/1527, as amended by SI 1996/2100, dealing with the implementation of the tax, registration and accounting procedures;

— the Landfill Tax (Qualifying Material) Order 1996, SI 1996/1528, defining the categories of waste to which the lower rates of tax will apply;

— the Landfill Tax (Contaminated Land) Order 1996, SI 1996/1529, setting out provisions under which waste from historically contaminated land is exempt from tax; and

— the Landfill Tax (Amendment) Regulations 1996, SI 1996/2100, amending Part XII of the Regulations in relation to the rank of Customs Officer empowered to take action in cases of non-payment of tax.

In addition to these, H M Customs & Excise have issued guidance notes on various aspects of the tax, including *inter alia*: *Introduction to Landfill Tax* (1/96, revised); *Tax Liability* (3/96); *Calculating the Weight of Waste* (4/96); *Reviews and Appeals* (10/96) and *Contaminated Land* (1/97). Notes 1/96 to 10/96 inclusive have been amalgamated into a public notice entitled *A General Guide to Landfill Tax*, LFT 1.

Although it is the form of the definition of "waste" that is pertinent to the present discussion, it should be noted that the legislation is written in the form of "taxable waste", for which the Act's definition of "waste" is only one component. Section 40 states that a disposal is taxable if:

— it is a disposal of a material as waste;

— it is made by way of a landfill;

— it is made at a landfill site; and

— it is made on or after 1st October 1996.

Exemptions to Landfill Tax

The provisions of the Act currently permit four groups of material to be exempted from taxation on disposal:

— material removed from water ("dredged waste") (section 43);

— mine and quarry waste (section 44);

— pet cemeteries (section 45); and

— historically contaminated land (section 43A and section 43B, SI 1996/ 1529),

and section 46 confers the power to vary the scope of taxable disposals by means of an Order.

Tax-Free Zones

In addition to the above categories of exempted material, by virtue of Regulations 38 to 40 of SI 1996/1527, it is possible for waste managers to create tax-free zones where there is temporary storage of "material" pending re-use, recycling (including composting), incineration or sorting. (Such "material" *is* waste for the purposes of section 75(2) EPA 1990 but is *not* taxable waste under sections 64 and 65 of the Finance Act 1996, since although there is an intention to discard it, there is no intention to landfill it.) Written approval must first be obtained from the landfill tax officer, prior to operating a "tax-free zone" and, in general, waste may not be held in such an area for longer than 12 months.

Dredged Waste

The exemption in section 43 relates to the disposal of any material which has been removed from a river, canal, watercourse, dock or harbour, where it formed part of the bed or projected from it, prior to removal. Also included is material which is removed from the approaches to a harbour in the interests of navigation, and naturally-occurring materials removed during commercial operations to obtain substances, such as sand and gravel, from the sea bed.

Mine and Quarry Waste

Naturally-occurring material from commercial deep or open cast mining or from quarrying operations is also excluded, provided this results directly from the extraction operations and not from an intermediate process or one which permanently alters the material's composition. However, the process giving rise to the waste need not be undertaken at the mine or quarry.

Pet Cemeteries

The provision relating to pet cemeteries excludes from taxation the disposal of material consisting entirely of the remains of dead domestic pets, provided no landfill was made at the site during the relevant period and that such disposals were consisting entirely of remains of dead domestic pets. The prescriptive use of the term "entirely", if strictly applied, would not permit the coffins, collars or other memorabilia of the deceased animal included in the interment to be non-taxable.

Contaminated Land

The contaminated land provisions were a last-minute modification to the tax, hence their incorporation as modifications to the Act, as section 43A and 43B, by means of SI 1996/1529. This exemption is a contentious measure, since it encourages material which is proven to be contaminated to be re-deposited in a landfill site without pre-treatment. A review of this exemption is planned for October 1998.

In order to gain exemption, it is necessary to apply for an exemption certificate, which will be issued subject to the satisfactory examination of documentary evidence. Conditions for the issue of a certificate are that:

— the reclamation is, or is to be, carried out:

  — with the objective of facilitating development, the provision of a public park or other amenity, or the use of the land for agriculture or forestry; or

  — with the objective of reducing or removing the potential of pollutants to cause harm;

— the waste must result only from the reclamation of the contaminated land;

— the exemption will not apply unless the cause of pollution has ceased. Current polluters may not make use of this exemption but an owner may apply for a certificate where his land is being polluted by a third party;

— the land must not be subject to a Works Notice or a Remediation Notice. This applies where the owner is undertaking the work himself but not where it is being carried out by the regulatory agency, or on their behalf.

Calculation of the Tax Chargeable

Although the initial proposals for the landfill tax were based upon an *ad valorem* surcharge of 30-50% on the costs of disposal, in the face of strong opposition this was replaced by a two-tier, flat-rate scheme, whereby a sum of £7.00/tonne or £2.00/tonne was charged on taxable deposits (section 42). The reduced rate is, subject to section 63 of the Act, applicable to material consisting entirely of "qualifying material", a term defined in Regulations (SI 1996/1528) to denote material "of a kind commonly described as "inactive" or "inert". (This is somewhat of a misnomer as some of these qualifying materials, such as furnace slags, are potential sources of leachate and likewise certain of the materials exempted from taxation are potential sources of leachate or methane generation.)

The scheme is described in detail in the Schedule to the Regulations and is based upon nine groups of substances, as follows:

Col. 1 Group	Column 2 Description of Material	Column 3 Conditions
Group 1	Rocks and soils	Naturally-occurring
Group 2	Ceramic or concrete materials	
Group 3	Minerals, inc. foundry sand	Processed or prepared, not used
Group 4	Furnace Slags	
Group 5	Ash	
Group 6	Low activity inorganic compounds	
Group 7	Calcium sulphate	Disposed of either at site not licensed to take putrescible waste, or in containment cell which takes only calcium sulphate
Group 8	Calcium hydroxide and brine	Deposited in brine cavity
Group 9	Water	Containing other qualifying material in suspension

Qualifying material is material listed in column 2, subject to the exemptions and inclusions in the Notes attached to the Schedule and the qualifying conditions within column 3. There is a requirement that Transfer Notes relevant to such waste include a description of the material, according with its description in column 2 or any relevant Note in the Schedule, or "some other accurate description" (presumably not "muck away", the term commonly used for material removed from demolition/development sites). With regard to Group 9, the description must include "water" and the details of the material in suspension which in the absence of the aqueous component would comply with the other qualifying requirements.

"Mixed" loads of "qualifying material" and other ("active") wastes are subject to the higher rate of tax, unless the special provisions of section 63(2) of the Act apply, in cases where only small quantities of non-qualifying material are present. Although such "incidental" quantities are not statutorily defined, Guidance Note 3/96 on Tax Liability gives examples of what is acceptable (a piece of wood in a skip) and what is not (a *large* piece of wood in a skip or lorry!).

Since the tax is concerned with the quantities of waste that are taxable, the "definition" element is extended to include how the amount of waste is calculated when there is no weighbridge, and what allowances are made for the water content of certain wastes. With regard to the former, with the approval of the local landfill tax officer, it is permissible to discount the water content of the waste where this is not present naturally, in cases in which:

— it has been added to allow transportation for disposal; or

— it has been used for the extraction of minerals; or

— it has arisen or been added, or both, in the course of an industrial process.

However, the water must comprise at least 25% by weight of the waste. With regard to effluent or sewage sludge from waste water treatment works or sewage disposal works, the water content may be discounted, but:

— that which is present naturally cannot be discounted; and

— any water which has been extracted prior to disposal will be treated as added water in preference to water naturally in the material.

This is considered more fully in SI 1996/1527 and in the Guidance Note 4/96 *Calculating the Weight of Waste*, which also gives conversion factors for volumes of specific waste types to their equivalent mass in tonnes.

Tax Credits

Apart from errors in the completion of landfill tax returns, there are three circumstances under which tax credits may be claimed, viz:

— permanent removals of waste;

— bad debts; and

— contributions to environmental bodies.

Permanent Removals of Waste

This may arise as a result of the enforced removal of waste at the direction of the regulatory agency, in cases where the waste has been deposited in breach of the licensing conditions. Removal will necessarily be to another suitably licensed site, where the recipient operator will be paid the landfill tax. Credit may be given on the tax originally paid at the first site, providing the direction from the waste regulator is available as evidence.

Alternatively, where a disposal has been made with the intention of recycling, incinerating or using the waste (other than at a landfill), and Customs and Excise have been notified in advance of this intention, credit may be claimed in accordance with the intention, within 12 months of the date of disposal or, where water has been added to assist disposal, within five years.

Bad Debts
In cases in which the value of a landfill tax invoice has to be written off as a bad debt, then a tax credit may be claimed for the landfill tax included in the invoice, provided that details of the tax chargeable are contained in the invoice.

Environmental Bodies
In practice, the landfill tax will generally be incorporated into the disposal fees paid to site operators. However, up to 20% of these funds can be donated on a voluntary basis to "environmental bodies", the site operators claiming a tax credit amounting to 90% of these donations from Customs and Excise. These environmental bodies must be registered with, and approved by, the regulatory agency, who will issue them with a registration number.

ENTRUST has been formally approved by H M Customs and Excise as the regulator of the environmental bodies which will spend the landfill operators' contributions under the landfill tax credits system on "environmental good works". ENTRUST is a private-sector regulator and is independent of government, of the waste industry landfill operators and of the environmental bodies.

It is responsible for enrolling environmental bodies intending to attract funding from landfill operators, and for monitoring the operations of the environmental bodies, ensuring that the expenditure complies with the Landfill Tax Regulations. ENTRUST has the power to withdraw the enrolment of any body that fails to meet the conditions of the scheme and will report such cases to H M Customs and Excise, who may then seek repayment of tax credits.

The "environmental good works" which may qualify for such funding include, *inter alia*:

— reclamation of land to facilitate economic, social or environmental use;

— operations to prevent or minimise pollution on land previously polluted;

— research and development, education, or collection and dissemination of information about waste management practices;

— provision, maintenance or improvement of a public park or amenity within the vicinity of a landfill site, where it is for the protection of the environment;

— maintenance or repair of a building or structure which is a place of public worship or of historic or architectural interest, within the vicinity of a landfill site, where it is for the protection of the environment;

— provision of financial or administrative services for the approved body itself.

The operators may not themselves benefit from any of these supported activities and the tax credits may only be claimed *post facto*.

Conditions of Disposal

As noted, *supra*, the tax is triggered by a person undertaking taxable activities and, while this goes beyond the basic definition of "waste", in view of the dependence upon the intent and activities of the current holder (i.e. the disposer) and producer, further discussion is appropriate.

Material is regarded as being disposed of as waste if the person making the disposal does so with the intent of discarding it (section 64). (Note that the usage of "dispose" and "discard" has parallels with the German and French meanings of these words discussed earlier.) When the disposal is made on behalf of another person – i.e. at their request or in pursuance of a contract – the person on whose behalf the disposal is made is treated as making the disposal (section 64(3)) and as a consequence is regarded as undertaking a taxable activity. This is considered in section 69, which states that a person carries out a taxable activity if he makes a taxable disposal himself or permits any other person to make that disposal on which the first-mentioned person is liable to pay tax. There is a presumption under section 69(2) that the disposal is permitted by the person liable to pay the tax, whether this is undertaken with his knowledge or not.

THE TRANSBOUNDARY MOVEMENT OF WASTE

Although the transboundary movement of waste represents only a relatively small part of the waste management industry, it is nevertheless of central importance, for it is closely linked to the issues of sustainable development and the "proximity principle" (the treatment or disposal of waste as close to its source as possible), and is dependent for its success upon the derivation of an internationally-agreed definition of the meaning and scope of the term "waste".

European concern within this area was prompted by the Seveso incident, in which 2 kg of dioxin was released over a 20 minute period, contaminating an area of 4 km^2. The objective of the following Directive, 84/631/EEC, was to provide a rigorous system of control over the transboundary movement of hazardous waste within, into, and out of Community Member States. Although this measure was limited in its effectiveness due to the lack of specificity in the definitions of waste upon which it was based – i.e. in Directives 75/442/EEC and 78/319/EEC – it did lay down the principle of prior informed consent (PIC), which has been a key element in subsequent legislation in this area. This requires that two conditions are met:

— the "competent authorities" of the Member State concerned must be notified of any proposed shipment by the holder of the waste;

— the state of destination, or the state of transit (for extra-Community shipments), must acknowledge receipt of the notification before the waste can be shipped and, under Article 4, may refuse such shipment on environmental, safety, public policy or health protection considerations.

The Directive was modified in 1986 to reflect the concern regarding pollution caused by waste exported outside the Community, and made it a requirement that the holder of the waste obtains an agreement from such "third states" before initiating the notification procedure. However, this involved no participation on the part of the third state in the notification process and the Directive did not recognise its rights to object to the shipment. In addition, the simplified procedure within Article 17 relating to non-ferrous metal intended for re-use, regeneration or recycling provided a loophole by which the PIC procedure could be circumvented for these materials.

Outside the EU, there was increasing international concern about the transboundary movement of waste and the revised Community provisions – the Regulation on the Supervision and Control of the Shipment of Waste within, into, and out of the European Community, 259/93/EEC – incorporated three important agreements: the Basel Convention, the Lomé IV Convention and the OECD Decision. The resulting controls took account of three different factors:

— the hazards posed by the waste;

— the countries involved in its movement;

— the purpose of its movement, i.e. whether for recovery or disposal, and the Regulation details the controls in place for all combinations of these.

The Basel Convention on the Control of Transboundary Movements of Hazardous Waste and their Disposal, 1989

The Convention was adopted on 22nd March 1989 and was in effect a compromise between the requirements of industrialised countries and those of the developing countries. The latter group favoured a ban on transboundary waste movements but the Convention adopted a mechanism for control based upon OECD (Organisation for Economic Co-operation and Development) principles and Directive 84/631, as amended. The basis of the adopted procedure was the requirement for prior informed consent for any waste export and this was accompanied by a number of general principles: waste minimisation, the proximity principle, environmentally sound management as an essential export condition and the self-sufficiency principle.

The UK and the EU became signatories of the Basel Convention on 8th May 1994.

The Lomé IV Convention

This was the sixth in a series of co-operation and development agreements between the European Community and the African, Pacific and Caribbean (APC) countries and, under Article 39(2), pronounced a ban upon Community exports of both hazardous *and* radioactive wastes (unlike Basel) to APC countries, from the EU or any other country.

The Convention used the definitions of hazardous waste and radioactive waste in the Basel Convention and in IAEA (International Atomic Energy Agency) standards, respectively.

The OECD Decision

Both of the Basel and Lomé Conventions are concerned with the movement of waste in relation to its disposal and, to address the situation in which waste was transported for the purposes of recovery within the 24 OECD Member States, a supplementary agreement – the OECD Decision on the Control of Wastes Destined for Recovery Operations – was written into the Basel Convention as Article 11.

The objective of this Decision was to impose different degrees of control upon wastes destined for recovery, according to their hazardous nature, and this was achieved by placing such materials into one of three lists – "green", "amber" and "red" – in order of increasing hazard.

The Regulation on the Supervision and Control of the Shipment of Waste within, into, and out of the European Community, 259/93/EEC

Under Community law (Article 228(2) of the EC Treaty), treaties concluded and ratified by the Community within its sphere of competence are binding on Community institutions and on Member States and international agreements such as Basel and Lomé take precedence over secondary legislation. However, such measures require further legislative and administrative measures to be introduced by the contracting parties to become fully effective. Thus it was necessary for the EU to introduce the Regulation on the Supervision and Control of the Shipment of Waste within, into, and out of the European Community, 259/93/EEC, incorporating these obligations. Similarly, although this Regulation was directly effective in all Member States and needed no enabling legislation, certain local measures such as the Transfrontier Shipment of Waste Regulations 1994, SI 1994/1137, were necessary.

The Regulation contains a series of detailed controls relating to the movement of waste, which are arranged as follows:

Title	Chapter	Content	Article
I	–	Scope and Definitions	1-2
II	–	Shipments between Member States	
	A	— *for disposal*	3-5
	B	— *for recovery*	6-11
	C	— *for disposal and recovery between Member States, with transit via third state*	12
III	–	Shipments within Member States	13
IV	–	Export from EU	
	A	— *for disposal*	14-15
	B	— *for recovery*	16-17
	C	— *to ACP States*	18
V	–	Imports to EU	
	A	— *for disposal*	19-20
	B	— *for recovery*	21-22
VI	–	Transit from outside and through EU, for disposal and recovery outside EU	
	A	*Transit not covered by OECD Decision*	23
	B	*Transit covered by OECD Decision*	24
VII	–	Common Provisions	25-31
VIII	–	Other Provisions	32-44
	Annex I	List of International Transport Articles	
	Annex II	Green List of Waste	
	Annex III	Amber List of Waste	
	Annex IV	Red List of Waste	

From the above, it can be seen that the Regulations establish a number different regimes relating to the control of hazardous waste, depending upon the requirements of the relevant international agreement.

The Scope of the Regulation

The Regulation does not cover all transboundary movements of hazardous waste and Article 1 defines its scope and exclusions. The latter include:

— the off-loading of waste from ships and off-shore platforms, provided that the waste is subject to specific, binding international agreements;

— shipments of civil aviation waste;

— shipments of radioactive waste, which are covered by the Supervision and Control of Shipments of Radioactive Waste Between Member States, and into and out of the Community Directive, 92/3/Euratom;

— shipments of waste excluded from the control of the Waste Framework Directive, provided that other controls exist;

— shipments of waste into the EU in accordance with the Protocol on Environmental Protection to the Antarctic Treaty.

Shipments of "green list"(Annex II) wastes destined for recovery are also excluded from the majority of the provisions, under Article 1, paragraph 3, but such waste is subject to the controls imposed by the Waste Framework Directive. This exclusion does not apply:

— where they exhibit any of the hazardous characteristics of Annex III of the Hazardous Waste Directive, 91/689/EEC;

— in exceptional cases, for environmental and public health reasons, although the Commission must be notified by the Member State undertaking such action;

— where waste is shipped in contravention of the Regulation or of the Waste Framework Directive.

Terminology

All of the regimes within the Regulation have the same format, which is based upon the system of prior informed consent and adopts the following terminology:

"notifier": the person intending to ship the waste, e.g. the producer or broker;

"competent authority": the responsible authority designated by the Member State, on non-Member State;

"competent authority of dispatch": the competent authority for the area from which the shipment is dispatched;

"competent authority of destination": the competent authority for the area in which the shipment is received;

"competent authority of transit": the competent authority for the Member State through which the shipment is in transit.

The term "shipment" is not defined in the Regulation but DoE Circular 13/94 suggests that this may be taken to mean the movement by land, sea or air of waste from its place of original production (or where originating from several producers, the place where it is collected) to the place of its recovery or disposal.

The Definition of Waste

Although the EU Regulation uses the "standard" EU definitions of "waste", "hazardous waste", "disposal" and "recovery", as given in the Waste Framework Directive and the Hazardous Waste Directive, for countries to which the OECD decision applies, the classification of waste into the "green", "amber", and "red" categories must be used.

As this classification is currently under revision, a detailed description of the content of the "coloured lists" will not be given, although the current provisions are summarised below.

Red List
Wastes appearing on the red list are subject the greatest degree of control, and include:

— wastes containing or contaminated with polychlorinated biphenyls (PCBs), polychlorinated terphenyls (PCTs), polybrominated biphenyls (PBBs) and other polybrominated analogues, at a concentration of 50 mg/kg or higher;

— wastes that contain or consist of any congenor of dibenzo-dioxin or dibenzo-furan;

— asbestos dust and fibres, and similar ceramic-based fibres;

— lead anti-knock compound sludges;

— certain waste tarry residues; and

— peroxides, other than hydrogen peroxide.

This is quite a restricted list and it could be argued that certain of the amber list wastes, *infra*, present as great a risk as some of the red list entries.

Amber List
This contains 72 waste materials and these are generally subject to fewer controls than red list wastes. Typical of these wastes are: lead acid batteries; used oils; zinc slags containing up to 18% zinc; pickling liquors; phenols; nitro-cellulose; mercury waste and residues; waste containing organic cyanides; arsenic waste and residues; and halons.

Green List
The green list of waste is the largest of the three and includes those presenting the least hazard, although it does contain some toxic compounds such as antimony waste and scrap, and spent catalysts. In general, green list wastes are subject only to normal commercial controls, unless they are found to exhibit hazardous characteristics, there are exceptional environmental or public health reasons for applying extra controls, or a non-OECD country requests that certain categories are subject to further control.

These wastes are grouped into thirteen major headings:

A: metal and alloy wastes in metallic, non-dispersible form.

B: other metal-bearing wastes from melting, smelting and refining.

C: wastes from mining operations in non-dispersible form.

D: solid plastic wastes.

E: paper, paperboard and paper product wastes.

F: glass wastes in non-dispersible form.

G: ceramic waste in non-dispersible form.

H: textile wastes.

I: rubber wastes.

J: untreated cork and wood wastes.

K: wastes arising from agro-food industries.

L: wastes arising from tanning, fell-mongery and leather use.

M: other wastes,

and individual wastes are listed within these headings.

The term "non-dispersible" excludes those wastes which are in the form of powder, sludge or dust and solid items containing encased hazardous liquid wastes.

Guidance on the application of this Regulation has been produced by the OECD, although Member States tend to differ in their approach to its implementation in practice. Within the UK, an important interpretation in relation to the mixing of green list wastes was given in the judicial review hearing of *R v The Environment Agency ex parte Dockgrange Ltd, Mayer Parry Ltd, and The Robinson Group Ltd*. The applicants' business involved the importing of fragmentiser waste, which is not expressly listed as a green list waste, although its individual components are. Prior to April 1996, the Waste Regulation Authorities responsible were satisfied that this mixture should be treated as a green list waste, but their successor, the Environment Agency, ruled that since this waste was not listed individually within the Regulations it should be regarded as "unassigned" and treated as a red list waste.

Whilst Mr Justice Carnwath agreed with the Agency that the allocation of unassigned wastes was in general consistent with the precautionary principle, there was no justification in the present case, since all the facts were known and the quantities of the components of the mixture could be estimated to an accuracy of at least 95%.

In each of the three lists, codes have been allocated to individual wastes. However, not all wastes are coded and of the coded wastes some have a code relating to the harmonised customs code heading.

As noted above, a revised grouping of hazardous wastes is being produced in relation to the ban on export to non-OECD countries which will take effect from January 1998. This will take the form of two principal groupings:

— List A, which comprises waste categories and constituents which cannot be exported post-1998;

— List B, specifying wastes not covered by the Basel definition of hazardous and which are *ipso facto* excluded from its controls.

Within the EU, the ban on exports will be implemented by introducing a new Annex V to Regulation 259/93/EEC which lists the banned wastes.

Most of these will be amber or red list, although the proposed amendment to the Regulation states that full consideration must be given to wastes on the EU's hazardous waste list, and "any lists of waste characterised ... under the Basel Convention".

The allocation of wastes to List A or List B has been problematic (see *ENDS Report* 248, September 1995, page 41, and *ENDS Report* 267, April 1997, page 40), and the incidence of "mirror listing" – i.e. the occurrence of a named waste on both the A and B list – has caused confusion. Whilst the allocation of some wastes to these lists has been straightforward, for others there has been substantial scientific discussion and commercial lobbying from interested parties.

Procedure for the Transboundary Movement of Waste

A prerequisite for the transboundary movement of waste is the existence of a contract between the notifier and the person disposing of or recovering the waste. This must contain some or all of the information required on the consignment note, including *inter alia*:

— the source, composition and quantity of the waste;

— the producer's identity;

— a detailed inventory of the waste, if produced by various sources;

— the arrangements for routing and for insurance against damage to third parties;

— the measures to be taken by the carrier to ensure safe transport and compliance with Member States' requirements;

— the identity of the consignee, the location of the waste management facility to be used and the type and duration of its authorisation.

After agreeing a contract with the consignee, the notifier must inform the relevant "competent authority" of destination of the intention to make the shipment. Such notification must include any intermediate stage involved in the shipment.

This is effected by means of a consignment note, which in this context means a note which follows the requirements laid down in Commission Decision 94/774/EEC, giving the details indicated above. The consignment note and other documentation requested must be sent to the competent authority of destination, who must acknowledge this and forward copies within three days to the competent authorities of dispatch and of transit (if applicable).

Where required by Member State legislation, this procedure may be modified and the notification sent to the competent authority of dispatch, who itself will then send copies to the relevant parties.

All affected competent authorities then have a fixed period of time – 20 days in the case of movement of waste between EU Member States and 60 days in other cases – to raise and inform the notifier of any reasoned objections, lay down conditions or request additional information. The competent authority of destination then has a further 10 days in which to make a decision, which must be conveyed to the other parties involved. Approved consignment notes must carry the "stamp of authorisation" of the relevant competent authority.

Three days prior to the shipment, the notifier is required to send copies of the completed consignment note, which must state the date of shipment, to all the competent authorities involved. As with the transfer and consignment notes used in UK legislation, this consignment note must accompany the shipment and be signed by all the parties involved – notifier, carrier, and consignee – who must also retain a copy for a fixed period of time. In addition, Article 28 provides for the issue of "season tickets" to cover a number of identical shipments made within the period of a year.

The consignee is required to send a certificate of disposal or recovery as soon as possible and not greater than 180 days after receiving the waste.

Article 27 provides that all shipments of waste covered by the Regulation require a financial guarantee or other insurance in respect of the costs of shipment and, if necessary, re-shipment of the waste, and of disposal and recovery. These guarantees are returned when proof has been furnished, by means of:

— a certificate of disposal that the waste has reached its destination and has been disposed of/recovered in an environmentally sound manner;

— a control copy T5, drawn up pursuant to Commission Regulation 2823/87/EEC, where the waste has been in transit through the EU and has left the Community.

This Article also requires that national laws be drawn up and the Commission so informed.

The Return of Waste Shipments

There are two instances in which waste must be returned from the country of destination:

— where the shipment of waste cannot be completed in accordance with the terms of the consignment note or contract (Article 25);

— where the movement is deemed to be an illegal traffic in waste (Article 26).

In the former case, within 90 days of receiving the information, the competent authority of dispatch must ensure that the notifier returns the waste to its area of jurisdiction, or elsewhere within the state of dispatch, unless it is satisfied that the waste can be disposed of or recovered in an alternative and environmentally sound manner.

It is necessary to make a further notification of such returns but no Member State of dispatch or transit may oppose such a return of waste.

An "illegal traffic of waste" relates to any shipment of waste:

— without notification to all relevant competent authorities or without their consent; or

— without such consent, as a result of falsification, misrepresentation or fraud; or

— which is not specified in a material way in the consignment note; or

— which is contrary to Articles 14, 16, 19 or 21, or results in disposal or recovery in contravention to Community or international rules.

Where the illegal traffic is the responsibility of the notifier, the competent authority of dispatch must ensure that the waste is taken back by the notifier or, where necessary, by the competent authority itself, into the state of dispatch. If this is impracticable, the waste must be disposed of or recovered in an environmentally sound manner, within 30 days of the competent authority receiving the information on the illegal traffic. Again, a further notification is required, informing the relevant competent authority, although their consent is not required.

Where the illegal traffic is the responsibility of the consignee, the competent authority of destination must ensure that the consignee disposes of it in an environmentally sound manner or undertake this themselves.

If responsibility for the illegal traffic cannot be imputed to either notifier or consignee, then all of the competent authorities involved in the shipment are required to co-operate in the disposal or recovery of the waste, according to the procedure in the Waste Framework Directive. It is the responsibility of the Member States involved to take appropriate legal action to prohibit and punish illegal traffic.

The Application of the Regulation within Great Britain

Since the EU controls were introduced as Regulations, they are directly effective within Member States and need no secondary legislation at this level. The UK issued the Transfrontier Shipment of Waste Regulations 1994, SI 1994/1137, and these cover only those areas in which specific local provisions are necessary, e.g. the identification of "competent person". (To avoid confusion, the UK Regulations refer to the EU measures as "the principal Regulation".) The majority of the controls are contained within the principal Regulation and, consequently, the UK provisions must be read in conjunction with, rather than as an alternative to, the principal Regulation.

Prior to the establishment of the Environment Agency, the 1994 Regulations designated the Waste Regulation Authorities (in Great Britain) and the district councils (in Northern Ireland) as the competent authorities of destination and dispatch, and the Secretary of State as the competent authority of transit. Although the role of the WRAs has been subsumed by the Environment Agency and SEPA, the Environment Agency has been given the responsibility of the day to day administration of these Regulations. However, since the principle Regulation demands a single competent authority of transit, this function will remain with the Secretary of State.

Movement of Waste – Northern Ireland and Gibraltar

Under Title III of the EU Waste Shipment Regulations 259/93/EEC, imports and exports between Great Britain, and Northern Ireland and Gibraltar are regarded as shipments within a Member State and under Article 13 must be controlled by an appropriate system established by the Member State although, alternatively, the trans-Community procedure within the Regulations may be used.

Within the UK, the above movements fall within the control of the Special Waste Regulations 1996. These make specific provisions for such movements of waste and state that, for imports into Great Britain, the importer is regarded as the consignor and the waste is considered as if it was being removed from the point of entry into the country. Likewise, for exports from Great Britain, the exporter is regarded as the consignee and the waste is considered as being received at the point of departure.

For all other circumstances under which special waste is subject to transboundary movement, Regulation 13(4), the provisions of the Transfrontier Shipment of Waste Regulations 1994, SI 1994/1137, or the Transfrontier Shipment of Radioactive Waste Regulations 1993, SI 1993/ 3031, apply as appropriate.

Legal Issues Associated with Controls on the Transboundary Movement of Waste

The use of a number of different schemes for waste classification/ categorisation is clearly incompatible with effective control and it is possible that such international definitions of waste might ultimately shape those used internally within individual countries both within the EU and outside. In this respect it is interesting to note the extent to which the EU waste definitions or categories have been used or applied. In addition to the Basel Convention which used the EU Hazardous Waste Directive, 91/689/ EEC, in both its original and in its final form, the Directive itself is in force throughout the European Economic Area (EEA).

As noted earlier, restrictions on trade have international repercussions and it is necessary to consider waste legislation within this broader framework. This was demonstrated by a GATT (General Agreement on Tariffs and Trade) ruling in which it was held that the US could not instigate a unilateral ban in order to protect the environment outside its borders. A consequence of this is the possible incompatibility of the ban on the export of hazardous waste from OECD to non-OECD countries under the Basel Convention.

In addition, the Basel Convention itself poses potential problems in terms of existing trading agreements, once the 1994 ban on export to non-OECD countries becomes effective. This ban was inserted into the Convention as Article 4A, in apparent conflict with the existing Article 11 which permitted trade to continue under bilateral, multilateral or regional agreements, provided environmentally sound management of waste was ensured, using Article 4.5 as the minimum acceptable standard. However, on the basis of legal advice, the EU has stated that Article 11 only applies to Article 4.5 and not to Article 4.A which takes precedence.

For a more detailed consideration of the conflicts between multilateral environmental agreements and those made under the World Trade Organisation (WTO), the reader is directed towards papers by Lennard[1] and by Zedalis.[2]

The Transboundary Movement of Radioactive Waste

As noted above, the Transboundary Movement of Radioactive Waste is not subject to the EU Regulation and there are separate provisions within

---

[1] "The World Trade Organisation and Disputes Involving Multilateral Environmental Agreements", M Lennard, [1996] *EELR* 306.
[2] "Product v Non-Product Based Distinction in Article III Trade and Environment Jurisprudence – Recent Developments", R J Zedalis, [1997] *EELR* 108.

the EU Directive, 92/3/Euratom, the Supervision and Control of Shipments of Radioactive Waste Between Member States, and into and out of the Community. The Directive follows a pattern similar to that of the Regulation and establishes two regimes – one for shipments between Member States and one for shipments involving third (non-EU) countries.

For shipments between Member States, the waste holder must apply to the competent authority of the waste's origin for an authorisation. There is a two month period allowed for consultation and determining whether and under what conditions the waste may be transported. However, if no reply is given, the countries of transit and destination are deemed to have given their consent.

Copies of the documentation must accompany the shipment and acknowledgement of receipt be made within 15 days of its arrival, and provision must be made for the return to the original holder of shipments which cannot be completed.

With regard to exports to a third country, the procedure is similar to that for movement between Member States, except that export is not permitted:

— to any destination south of 60° south;

— to ACP countries that have signed the Lomé IV Convention;

— to any country which, in the opinion of the competent authority of dispatch, lacks the technical, legal or administrative procedures to manage the waste safely.

For imports from a third country into the EU, the person importing the waste must obtain authorisation from the competent authority of their State and, for shipments between third countries via the EU, the Member State which the waste enters first is deemed as the country of origin. It is the responsibility of the importer within that State to inform the relevant competent authority.

Since this measure was introduced in the form of a Directive, secondary legislation within the Member States is necessary and in the UK this was implemented by the Transfrontier Shipment of Radioactive Waste Regulations 1993, SI 1993/3031.

MEASURES RELATING TO SPECIFIC TYPES OF WASTE

In addition to general legislation relating to wastes and hazardous wastes, it has been necessary to introduce measures directed towards specific waste streams, in view of their potentially hazardous nature, such as PCBs and clinical waste, or to address a more general environmental problem, such as packaging waste. At EU level, following the Council Resolution of 7th May 1990, a number of priority waste streams were identified, with the objective of examining new instruments for implementing Community waste management policy (see Chapter 1). These priority waste streams include used tyres, halogenated hydrocarbons, healthcare wastes, electronic waste and end-of-life vehicles, and represent the issue-related problems of the Community rather than ones of waste definition. However, there have been a number of waste-specific Directives issued, including ones relating to waste oils, PCBs and PCTs, sewage sludge, packaging waste and batteries.

In some instances, these wastes were covered by existing UK legislation but for others specific instruments were introduced and a number of the relevant UK and EU measures are summarised below.

Packaging Wastes

Introduced as a harmonisation measure under Article 100a, the EU Directive on Packaging and Packaging Waste, 94/62/EC, establishes a free market framework for the circulation of packaging throughout the Community, provided it meets certain environmental objectives and other considerations. Article 6 places an obligation on Member States to implement the measures necessary in order to achieve recovery rates between a minimum of 50% and a maximum of 65%, and to attain a minimum recycling of 15% by weight for each material. In addition to the recycling requirements, the Directive also places limits on the concentrations of heavy metals – lead, cadmium, mercury and hexavalent chromium – which may be present in these materials. These concentrations limits are:

—   600ppm by weight by 30th June 1998;

—   250ppm by weight by 30th June 1999; and

—   100ppm by weight by 30th June 2001.

It is intended that these measures will be followed by a number of "daughter" Directives or Decisions on issues related to the format for the associated databases and systems for the identification of materials and their marking.

Many of the definitions in the Directive – "waste", "recovery", "disposal" – use those within the Waste Framework Directive as the frame of reference. However, it should be noted that, as with the proposed Directive on end-of-life vehicles, the recovery and recycling targets are based upon materials in anticipation that they will become waste, thus extending and blurring the boundaries of the concept of "waste". Recovery includes recycling, energy recovery from heat generated during incineration, and composting. Recycling refers to the re-processing of used packaging where the material can be re-used for its original or another purpose. This includes composting.

From 1st January 1997, subject to turnover and tonnage criteria, all businesses which manufacture, fill or sell packaging materials are subject to certain obligations on the recycling of these materials under the Producer Responsibility Obligations (Packaging Waste) Regulations 1996, SI 1996/648. These Regulations are accompanied by a "User's Guide" produced by the Department of the Environment and it is anticipated that sector specific guidance will be produced by a number of trade associations and endorsed by the Environment Agency and SEPA.

The objective of the UK Regulations is to:

— achieve a more sustainable approach to dealing with packaging waste;

— reduce the amount of packaging waste going to landfill;

— implement the recycling and recovery targets of the EU Directive;

— respond to industry's wish to have:

    — legislative underpinning for the recovery and recycling obligations, in order to deter "free riders";

    — business-led collective schemes to discharge businesses' obligations on their behalf; and

    — a sharing of these obligations between all parts of the packaging chain.

The activities which fall within the ambit of these controls include all four stages in the packaging chain, viz:

— manufacturing of packaging raw materials;

— converting materials into packaging;

— packing and filling;

— selling packaging to the final user.

With effect from 1st January 2000, the wholesaler obligation comes into force – "wholesaler being defined as a supplier of packing which they have not packed or filled, to small retailers below the thresholds, q.v."

An interesting situation arises in relation to the service industries, such as ferries and passenger airlines, who "supply" their customers with meals as part of their travel benefits. This was considered by the European Court of Justice in *Faaborg-Gelting Linien A/S v Finanzamt Flensburg*, where it was held that for Value Added Tax purposes, restaurant transactions, other than ones in "take-away" establishments, were to be regarded as supplies of services rather than goods and, with regard to ferries, were deemed to have been carried out at the place where the supplier has established his business.

Under the Regulations, a business is regarded as an "obligated business" if:

— it performs or has performed on its behalf any of the above activities in the packaging chain;

— it owns the packaging involved;

— it meets both of the threshold criteria, viz:

— the quantity of packaging involved is above 50 tonnes per annum; and

— the turnover is more than £5.0 million in the obligation years (i.e. the years in which the business is considered to be a producer) of 1997 to 1999 inclusive, or more than £1.0 million in the obligation year of 2000 and thereafter;

— it supplies to another stage in the packaging chain,

and it must register with the Environment Agency or SEPA or join a registered collective scheme such as Valpak.

Those businesses choosing the "individual route", in addition to registering with the appropriate Agency before 31st August 1997, must pay the appropriate registration fee and provide prescribed data on the quantities of packaging materials – paper/glass/metals/plastics/other – relevant to the business's part in the packaging chain. Once registered, the business must calculate its recovery and recycling obligations and determine the tonnage of packaging waste of each material that it must recycle during the year.

Alternatively, businesses joining a "compliance scheme" must check that the scheme itself is registered and pay any fees and fulfil other requirements of membership. Any such scheme must have been registered with the Environment Agency or SEPA before 31st August 1997 and must demonstrate that it has the technical and financial capacity to deliver the aggregate of what otherwise would be the obligation of its individual members. It must also provide data in aggregate for its members by 1st April 1998.

However, there are a number of hurdles to be cleared by a compliance scheme before it is approved by the Department of the Environment and registered with the Environment Agency or SEPA. Potential schemes must first submit their proposals to the Office of Fair Trading and also apply to the European Commission's Directorate General IV in relation to issues of competition.

Members of such a scheme have no individual legal liability to meet the recycling and recovery obligations, since the scheme assumes this on behalf of all of its members. However, packaging waste cannot be split between "individual" and "compliance" schemes and, although it may be possible to change at a later date, this may be complex and expensive.

Valpak was the first compliance scheme to be established and subsequently a number[1] of other schemes have been introduced either by waste management organisations – Wastepack (Wastelink Ltd) and Bifpack (Biffa Ltd) – or by organisations specific to certain industry sectors – Difpak (Dairy Industry Federation) and Glaspak (Glass Materials Organisation – Glasmo).

In order to calculate the tonnage of packaging waste an individual business is required to recover and recycle, it is necessary to know:

— *the obligated packaging handled:* the tonnages of packaging and packaging materials for the year. A critical factor in this calculation is the determination of what constitutes "packaging" within the context of the Regulations, and Table 10-1 (page 415) shows a decision chart produced by the Environment Agency and SEPA which determines this on the basis of eight tests. Fuller details of these are given in the accompanying document *Producer Responsibility Obligations – (Packaging Waste) Regulations 1997 – The Agencies' Interpretation of Packaging*;

— *the activity obligation:* the percentage obligation associated with each activity, viz:

— packaging raw material manufacturing: 6%

— converting: 11%

---

[1]   The schemes listed represent some of the compliance schemes available.

— packing/filling: 36%

— selling: 47%

— importing transit packaging: 100%

— *the UK targets* for recovery and recycling, which are:

Year	UK Recycling Target for each material (Min.)	UK Recovery Target	Recovery of UK Packaging Waste
1998-1999	7%	38%	32%
2000	11%	43%	40%
2001	16%	52% (of which minimum 26% by recycling)	50%

The calculations are then made as follows:

Recovery   = Obligated x Activity   x UK Recovery Target
Obligation   Packaging   obligation
                Handled

Recycling   = Obligated x Activity   x UK Recycling Target
Obligation   Packaging   obligation
(by material) Handled (by
                material)

The tonnage of packaging supplied includes all imports and imported transit packaging but excludes exports, process waste and that packaging which has been re-used at least three times. A certificate of compliance must be provided by individual companies to demonstrate that they have met the interim targets which have been set. Such certificates can be issued by a director or the company secretary of a business, although they should be supported by evidence, such as weighbridge tickets, from reprocessors.

The overall scheme will be phased in over a number of years and the initial obligation was to join a registered scheme or to register individually by the end of February 1997. Businesses must also provide an assessment of the packaging handled during 1996. At the beginning of each subsequent year, individual companies must re-register, pay the requisite fee and provide data for the previous year. Those companies which are in a compliance scheme must continue to be members and to meet its conditions.

Table 10-1: Decision Chart for Determining Meaning of "Packaging" within Regulation SI 1997/648*

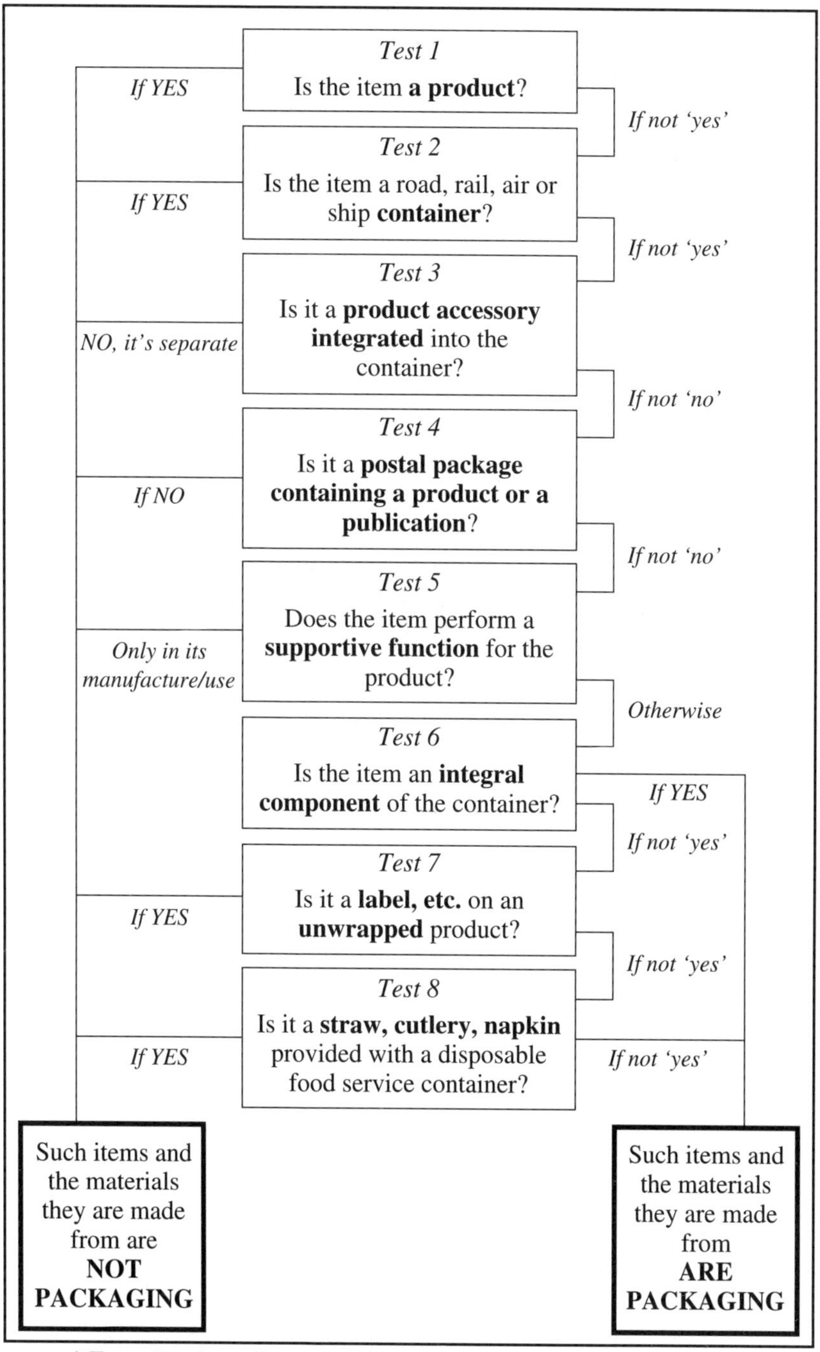
Test 1
Is the item **a product**?
If YES
If not 'yes'
Test 2
Is the item a road, rail, air or ship **container**?
If YES
If not 'yes'
Test 3
Is it a **product accessory integrated** into the container?
NO, it's separate
If not 'no'
Test 4
Is it a **postal package containing a product or a publication**?
If NO
If not 'no'
Test 5
Does the item perform a **supportive function** for the product?
Only in its manufacture/use
Otherwise
Test 6
Is the item an **integral component** of the container?
If YES
If not 'yes'
Test 7
Is it a **label, etc.** on an **unwrapped** product?
If YES
If not 'yes'
Test 8
Is it a **straw, cutlery, napkin** provided with a disposable food service container?
If YES
If not 'yes'
Such items and the materials they are made from are **NOT PACKAGING**
Such items and the materials they are made from **ARE PACKAGING**

* From *Producer Responsibility Obligations – (Packaging Waste) Regulations 1997 – The Agencies' Interpretation of Packaging*

By the end of 1998, individual companies must provide a certificate of compliance to demonstrate compliance with the interim targets and these are also required of schemes on behalf of their members. The full recovery and recycling targets become mandatory from the year 2001.

Compliance of the scheme is in the hands of the Environment Agency and SEPA, who are responsible for registering individual companies and collective schemes, monitoring whether businesses are registered or exempt and ensuring that the compliance conditions are satisfied. Where necessary, the Agencies may de-register schemes and also bring prosecutions against individual companies. The penalties imposed on conviction may be one-off fines or on-going daily penalties until the requirement has been satisfied.

Although introduced as an harmonisation measure, this particular Directive has been subject to more different interpretations within Member States than the definition of "waste", and an item which is considered to be within its ambit in one country will not necessarily be so in another. Within the EU, the so-called "Article 21 Committee" has been established to assist the Commission with the Directive and it is possible that, in view of the discrepancies which are arising, further guidance will be given.

Experience within the UK has been no less problematic and Mr Michael Meacher, when in opposition, was quoted as describing the UK Regulations as "a masterpiece of muddle, mismanagement and market excesses" which was "fundamentally flawed". When the new administration took office, a two-stage approach to the review and modification of the Regulations was announced. In the first phase, the apportionment of the obligation between the four parts of the packaging chain will be re-assessed and an equitable split determined. The second phase will consider the possibility of introducing separate recycling targets for household and industrial/commercial packaging waste. Under such a scheme, all obligated businesses would be required to contribute to the recovery of household packaging waste and the role of local authorities and voluntary bodies as partners in household recovery and recycling schemes would be strengthened. Guidance on the use and interpretation of the Regulations has become available from a number of sources – The Environment Agency and SEPA, the Department of the Environment and non-governmental bodies such as Incpen (the Industry Council for Packaging and the Environment) and trade associations (see "Further Reading"). In addition, a number of practical "toolkits" – ready-reckoners and statistical methods – have been generated by industry to assist in the implementation of these Regulations.

End of Life Vehicles (ELVs)

A vehicle which has reached the end of its "operational" life presents a number of problems in relation to its disposal or recycling. The proportion of non-recoverable residues in motor vehicles, particularly plastics and polymers, has risen significantly over the past few years in response *inter alia* to other environmental pressures such as vehicle weight and fuel economy. In addition, most scrapped cars contain a number of hazardous substances, including oils, lubricants and sulphuric acid, which pose a hazard to those involved in their handling, as well as to the environment. Nevertheless, even the *current* recycling rates of end-of-life vehicles, i.e. in excess of 75%, are substantially higher than those of many less technically complex goods – glass containers, 28%; plastic packaging, 5%; steel cans, 14%; paper and board packaging, 49%.[1]

ELVs were identified as one of the EU's "priority waste streams" and, subsequently, voluntary agreements were drawn up between industry and government in a number of Member States – Germany, France, Spain, Austria, the Netherlands and the UK. In addition, the Commission has been working on a Directive, an unofficial version of which appeared in July 1996, and a formal draft proposal was issued in July 1997.

Within the United Kingdom, the government's view is that statutory measures are not necessary since the industry has already committed itself to increasing the amount of recovery from ELVs. The Automotive Consortium on Recycling and Disposal (ACORD) was established in 1992 under the aegis of the Society of Motor Manufacturers and Traders (SMMT), with representatives from vehicle manufacturers, component suppliers, trade associations and government.

In July 1997, the ACORD agreement was signed by the majority of bodies involved in the recycling of end-of-life vehicles on behalf of their member companies – the Society of Motor Manufacturers and Traders (SMMT), Motor Vehicles Dismantlers Association (MVDA), British Metal Federation (BMF), British Rubber Manufacturers Association (BRMA), British Plastics Federation (BPF). In many respects, the ACORD agreement reflects the objectives and targets of the proposed Directive, *infra*, which are achieved without the additional enforcement and take-back costs associated with a mandatory regime.

The agreement set general targets on the maximum levels of material from ELVs which would be disposed of to landfill, viz. maxima of 15% of the initial vehicle weight from 1st January 2002 and 5% from 1st January

---

[1]   Data from *Making Waste Work*, Department of the Environment, HMSO, 1995.

2015, with intermediate targets being set as necessary. In addition, specific undertakings were agreed for each of the industrial sectors involved, including *inter alia* the development of dismantling techniques and information by 31st December 1999, ensuring that vehicles homologated from 1st January 2002 would be capable of reprocessing to yield a final waste of less than 10% of the initial weight, and reporting requirements.

Despite the existence of such voluntary agreements within most Member States, and the Commission's commitment to "environmental agreements" (see Chapter 2), the proposals for an ELV Directive, COM (97) 358, are based upon the imposition of mandatory controls, including *inter alia*:

— a target of 85% of a vehicle's weight to be re-used or recovered, and 80% re-used and/or recycled by the year 2005;

— a target of 95% re-use or recovery, and 85% re-use or recycle by the year 2015;

— these targets to be incorporated into the vehicle type-approval process after 2005, through an amendment to Directive 70/156/EEC;

— Member States to ensure that collection, treatment and re-use/recovery operations are undertaken by approved persons under regulated conditions;

— a scheme involving the issue of certificates of destruction is to be instituted;

— after 2003, car dealers, acting on behalf of the manufacturers or importers, must agree to take back a car at the end of its life at no cost, or pay the last owner the amount of "negative value" when the owner delivers the car to a dismantler.

The preamble to these proposals acknowledges that national initiatives such as negotiated agreements may co-exist with the proposed legislative measures, and clearly a substantial amount of negotiation on the details of both the voluntary and mandatory schemes will be necessary if a workable system is to be established by the target dates within the proposal.

In contrast to ELVs, rail vehicles, with their longer life cycle of up to 40 years, present a different set of disposal problems as a consequence of the presence of "older technology" materials – asbestos (insulation), PCBs (electric motor capacitors, fluorescent lighting "starters"), mercury (door switches and other electrical equipment), as well as sulphuric acid in lead-acid batteries. There is, however, no specific legislation directed at this waste stream.

Air Bags and Seat Belt Pre-Tensioners

Although Article 6.3(a) of the proposed ELV Directive specifies that air bags and other hazardous components must be stripped from end-of-life vehicles, the Annex makes no reference to their storage, deployment or disposal. Yet, when fitted, air bags and seat belt pre-tensioners are possibly the most hazardous components within a vehicle. The energy associated with a free-flying passenger air bag module after initiation is significantly greater than many types of bullet that are capable of inflicting fatal injury, e.g. the .357 magnum and .38 special ammunition. The propellants commonly used are sodium azide (NaN_3) and nitro-cellulose/nitro-glycerine, the former having a toxicity in the same order of magnitude as sodium cyanide.

As a consequence, there are a number of important health and safety and environmental considerations relating to these products, including, *inter alia*:

— the protection of workers from physical injury and burns when these devices are deployed;

— the protection of workers from the toxic components;

— the safe and secure storage and transport of air bags following their removal from vehicles;

— environment related issues, particularly noise.

The determination of whether air bags and pre-tensioners are a Class 1 explosive or not is the responsibility of the Health and Safety Executive, and such a decision made under the Classification and Labelling of Explosives Regulations 1983 is made prior to a device being put into service. This assessment determines whether the product is subject to the Explosives Act 1875 and its associated Regulations, or not.

An increasing number of vehicles are being produced with these components fitted as standard and in the short to medium term their disposal from ELVs will become a serious problem. The HSE has produced a document *Guidance on the Handling, Storage and Transport of Air Bags and Seat Belt Pre-Tensioners* to assist those involved in this area.

Waste Oils

The first Waste Oil Directive, 75/439/EEC, was introduced in response to the increasing quantities of oils and emulsions generated within Member States and the need to ensure that no unavoidable damage to the environment resulted from their collection and disposal. This pre-dated the Waste Framework Directive (by about one month) and made no reference to it. As with other contemporary Directives, much was left to the discretion of the Member States, although any establishment producing, collecting or disposing of 500 litres of waste oils (or less if specified by the Member State) was required to keep a record of the quality, quantity, origin and location of such oils and of their despatch and receipt.

The amendments to the Directive in 87/101/EEC sought *inter alia* to impose controls on the combustion of waste oils and to prevent Member States from banning such processes on their territory. The term "waste oils" was prescriptively defined as meaning:

> "Any mineral-based lubrication or industrial oils which have become unfit for the use for which they were originally intended, and in particular used combustion engine oils and gearbox oils, and also mineral lubricating oils, oils for turbines and hydraulic oils",

and although not part of the "waste" definition, "disposal" was defined as meaning:

> "The processing or destruction of waste oils as well as their storage and tipping above or under ground."

No specific legislation was necessary within the UK to implement this general duty imposed upon Member States, since this was covered by the Waste Management Licensing Regulations 1994, SI 1994/1056.

Polychlorinated Biphenyls (PCBs) and Polychlorinated Terphenyls (PCTs)

The hazards associated with PCBs and PCTs have long been known and, by the end of 1972, the sale of PCBs for use in "open" applications (other than hydraulic oils) was discontinued and, although production continued in other countries until the late 1980s, UK-manufactured material ceased to be available from 1977. The sale and use of PCBs for "closed" applications was banned by Directive 85/467/EEC, which was implemented through the Control of Pollution (Supply and Use of Injurious Substances) Regulations 1986, SI 1986/902.

A Directive on the disposal of PCBs and PCTs was introduced in 1976, 76/403/EEC, and this has been replaced by Directive 95/59/EC which introduces specific measures for the phasing-out of these materials within a fixed time scale. For this specific waste stream, the general requirements of the Waste Framework Directive, 75/442/EC, have been supplemented by this Directive and under Article 2(a) PCBs is taken to mean:

— polychlorinated biphenyls;

— polychlorinated terphenyls;

— monomethyl-tetrachlorodiphenyl methane, monomethyl-dichloro-diphenyl methane and monomethyl-dibromo-diphenyl methane; and

— any mixtures containing any of the above substances in a total of more than 0.005% by weight (50ppm).

An important feature of these provisions is that they relate both to substances which would currently be regarded as "waste" and those at present in service which are required to be disposed of within the time periods stated.

The term "used PCBs" is taken to mean any PCBs which are waste within the meaning of the Framework Directive, 75/442/EEC. Equipment likely to have been contaminated by PCBs falls within these regulations and, providing it is of a type which may contain PCBs, it is to be treated as if it contains PCBs unless "it is reasonable to assume the contrary". The term "holder" is extended to include the natural or legal person who is in possession of PCBs, used PCBs and/or equipment containing PCBs, and "disposal" is defined in terms of operations D8, D9, D10, D12 and D15 within Annex II, A of the Waste Framework Directive.

It is interesting to note that the provision in the proposed Directive which imposed strict liability for environmental damage on the holders of disposal licences and required them to take out appropriate insurance was removed from the final version.

Article 3 of the Directive places an obligation on Member States to ensure that used PCBs are disposed of, and PCB-containing or contaminated equipment is decontaminated or disposed of "as soon as possible". For equipment and the PCBs therein which are subject to the inventory requirements of Article 4, decontamination or disposal is to be effected by the end of 2010 at the latest. However, this provision is made "without prejudice to the international obligations of Member States" and the earlier date of 1999 will be applicable within the UK in view of its obligations under the North Sea Conference.

Member States are required to produce an inventory of all equipment containing PCB in volumes greater than 5 dm^3 (5,000 cm^3) and forward such information to the Commission within three years of the adoption of the Directive. The inventory must comprise:

— the names and addresses of the holders;

— the location and description of the equipment and the quantity of PCB contained;

— the dates and types of treatment or replacement carried out or envisaged; and

— the date of the declaration.

In addition, all such equipment and premises where it is located must be labelled. Until they are decontaminated, taken out of service or disposed of, the maintenance of transformers may only continue provided certain technical standards are adhered to.

The undertakings disposing of PCBs are to maintain registers of the quantity, origin, nature and PCB content of all such materials delivered to them. The "waste" requirements of the disposal will be covered by the special waste regulations and, where incineration is employed as the disposal route, the Council Directive on the Incineration of Hazardous Waste, 94/67/EC, will apply.

In March 1997, the Department of the Environment published its Action Plan for the phasing out and destruction of PCBs and dangerous PCB substitutes, of which there are estimated to be up to 8,000 tonnes within the UK, most of which are held in some 1,800 transformers and 450,000 capacitors.

A *de minimis* level of 5 dm^3 (i.e. 5 litres) has been set and this will exclude what the document refers to as the "very small quantities" of PCB found in older (pre-1986) white goods – domestic refrigerators, washing machines and some domestic light fittings.

The current ban on the supply by way of sale or use in new plant and equipment has been extended to cover all monochlorinated and dichlorinated biphenyls, all mixtures and wastes of >50ppm PCB equivalents, and any object such as a redundant transformer tank and internal windings that is so contaminated with PCB equivalents that physical or chemical interaction with another object will produce contamination of >50ppm.

Clinical Waste

Clinical waste is defined in the Controlled Waste Regulations 1992, SI 1992/588, and whilst the "waste" issues are dealt with under "environmental" legislation, it is also subject to a number of other pieces of legislation as a result of its "clinical" designation. The term "clinical waste" is often quite loosely applied and may be used to describe anything from a discarded plaster to human tissue and blood. A useful approach is to apply the categorisation used by the Health Services Advisory Committee in *Safe Disposal of Clinical Waste*, which uses the following five groupings:

Group A (a) soiled surgical dressings, swabs and other contaminated waste from treatment areas.
(b) waste materials, where the COSHH assessment indicates a risk to staff handling them, for example infectious disease cases.
(c) all human tissue, including blood (whether infected or not), animal carcasses and tissues from veterinary centres, hospitals or laboratories, and all related swabs and dressings.

Group B discarded syringes, needles, cartridges, broken glass and other contaminated disposable sharp instruments or items.

Group C microbiological cultures and potentially infected waste from pathology departments (laboratory and post mortem rooms) and other clinical research laboratories.

Group D certain pharmaceutical and chemical wastes.

Group E used disposable bedpan liners, urine containers, incontinence pads and stoma bags.

It should be noted that in the new proposal for a Landfill Directive, clinical waste is one of the materials which will not be acceptable for disposal through this route.

Animal Wastes

Controls on the disposal and processing of animal wastes were introduced at Community level through Directive 90/667/EC and Decision 92/562/EEC, the former defining animal waste as:

"Carcasses or parts of animals or fish, or products of animal origin not intended for direct human consumption, with exemption of animal excreta and catering waste."

It is fortunate that animal carcasses are excluded from the scope of the Waste Framework Directive, for it would be difficult to reconcile the criterion "not intended for direct human consumption" with other aspects of its definition of waste. Furthermore, within the UK these substances have traditionally been regarded as by-products rather than wastes, as witnessed by the title of the enabling legislation, the Animal By-Products Order 1992, SI 1992/3303.

The Directive distinguishes between high risk material "which is suspected of presenting serious health risks to animals or man" and low risk material "which does not present serious risks of communicable disease to animals or man". These categories are defined quite precisely and the treatment and disposal of such wastes is subject to rigorous control.

Sewage Sludge

The practice of spreading sewage sludge on agricultural land is widespread and, in view of the potential health-related hazards, EU Directive 86/278/EEC was introduced to impose controls in relation to the heavy metal concentration of the receiving soil, i.e. cadmium, copper, nickel, lead zinc, mercury and hexavalent chromium. The Directive lays down detailed requirements relating to the content of the sludge, the nature of the receiving soil, the precautions to be taken and the information requirements.

This was implemented thorough the Sludge (Use in Agriculture) Regulations 1989, SI 1989/1263, and the sludge deposited on agricultural land under these provisions is exempted from the definition of controlled waste and the associated controls. Similar exemptions are in place in relation to waste management licensing and these are discussed in Chapter 11.

Additional requirements relating to the treatment of sewage sludge are imposed by the Urban Waste Water Directive, 91/271/EEC, which was implemented by the Urban Waste Water Treatment (England and Wales) Regulations 1994, SI 1994/2481.

MEASURES RELATED TO THE CONTROL OF INDUSTRIAL PROCESSES

Some EU and UK legislation is introduced for the regulation of particular processes or industries and this may place obligations on operators and others regarding the disposal of the associated waste.

Asbestos

Directive 87/217/EEC is concerned with processes involving the manufacture and processing of asbestos-containing components and is notable since it is an early, pre-IPC instrument aimed at controlling emissions to all three environmental media. With regard to waste (Article 2(5)), it makes direct reference to the definition in the Waste Framework Directive.

Titanium Dioxide

The objective of the ill-fated Titanium Dioxide Directive, 78/176/EEC, was the "prevention and progressive reduction, with a view to its elimination, of pollution caused by the titanium dioxide industry". Despite post-dating the Waste Framework Directive, it makes no reference to it, although the definitions of "waste" and "discard" do reflect its general format, viz:

— "waste means:

  — any residue from the titanium dioxide manufacturing process of which the holder disposes or is obliged to dispose under current national legislation;

  — any residue from a treatment process of a residue referred to in the first indent."

— "discard means:

  — the collection, sorting, transport and treatment of waste as well as its storage and tipping above ground or underground and its injection into the ground;

  — the discharge thereof into surface water, ground water and the sea, and dumping in the sea;

  — the transformation operations necessary for its re-use, recovery or recycling."

Radioactive Waste

Radioactive waste is exempted from the Waste Framework Directive and within the UK is governed by the Radioactive Substances Act 1993. Under section 2 of the Act, radioactive waste means waste which consists wholly or partly of:

(a) a substance or article which, if it were not waste, would be radioactive material; or

(b) a substance or article which has been contaminated in the course of production, keeping or use of radioactive material, or by contact with or proximity to other wastes falling within paragraph (a) or this paragraph.

There are thus two principal characteristics defining such materials – their radioactivity and their status as waste. Waste is defined in section 47(1) of the Act as including:

"Any substance which constitutes scrap material or an effluent or other unwanted surplus substance arising from the application of any process, and also includes any substance or article which requires to be disposed of as broken, worn out, contaminated or otherwise spoilt."

"Disposal" is given a much broader meaning than in other contemporary measures, and includes:

"Removal, deposit, destruction, discharge (whether into water or into the air or into a sewer or drain or otherwise) or burial (whether underground or otherwise)",

and "dispose of" is to be construed accordingly. In addition, in section 47(4) there is a "presumptive" clause to the effect that:

"Any substance or article which, in the course of the carrying on of any undertaking, is discharged, discarded or otherwise dealt with as if it were waste, shall ... be presumed to be waste unless the contrary is proved."

It will be noted that the Act retains the format of the pre-Framework Directive definition of waste (since radioactive waste is not a controlled waste), an important corollary of which is that the pre-1994 case law remains applicable to this group of waste materials. However, there is a provision in Regulation 3 of the Special Waste Regulations 1996, SI 1996/ 972, that where the Secretary of State uses his powers under section 62 EPA 1990 in relation to radioactive waste, Regulations 2(1) and 2(2) apply to this waste "as if it were controlled waste", i.e. the Framework Directive's definition of waste applies (and the former case law is inapplicable) but the "presumptive" provisions of section 47(4) of the 1993 Act remain!

There are a number of features specific to radioactive wastes which either require a greater degree of control to be imposed, e.g. in relation to the accumulation of radioactive materials, or permit a more quantitative approach to be taken in the assessment of the hazard created by measuring its activity.

The Department of the Environment guide to the administration of the 1960 Radioactive Substances Act draws the necessary distinction between "storage" and "disposal": the former is regarded as the placement of radioactive substances in a facility with the intention of taking action at a later time, while disposal is seen as the dispersal of radioactive waste into one of the environmental media or its placement in a facility with the intention of no further action other than monitoring.

MEASURES RELATED TO THE MARKETING OR USE OF CERTAIN PRODUCTS

There are a number of circumstances in which "waste" products have a commercial value and, in addition to the issues concerned with whether such substances should be classified as wastes or not, it is necessary to consider the implications of these items being regarded as "products". This classification may involve the waste holder/vendor in a range of legislation associated with issues such as consumer protection, contractual obligations and hazardous materials. Much will depend upon individual circumstances but some relevant legislation is outlined below.

Supply and Use of Injurious Substances – PCBs, PCTs and Asbestos

Under the Control of Pollution (Supply and Use of Injurious Substances) Regulations 1986, SI 1986/902, as amended by SI 1992/31, measures were introduced restricting the supply, by way of sale for any purpose or the use in connection with any trade or business or manufacturing process, of any injurious substance. These apply to PCBs, PCTs, lead carbonate and lead sulphate in paint, mercury in heavy duty textiles and mercury, arsenic and organostannic compounds for the treatment of industrial waters. Additional restrictions have now been placed on PCBs through the Directive 96/59/EC, as discussed above.

Similar Regulations exists in relation to asbestos – the Asbestos (Prohibitions) Regulations 1992, SI 1992/3067 – and while the supply of an article containing these substances to a waste processor for treatment or disposal would not come within their control, the supply for use in its present form (albeit after repair) would not be permissible. Thus a railway carriage which contained both asbestos (as insulation) and PCBs (in capacitors) could not be disposed of to a "heritage" railway society for continued use, whether payment was made or not.

Conditions of Sale

A similar situation arises when an item is offered for sale "as seen", with the implication that it may continue to be used for its present purpose although there is also the possibility that it could be broken up for its component parts or used for its scrap value. Such terms of sale are often included with the objective of overcoming the liabilities associated with goods and their fitness for purpose but leave a degree of uncertainty regarding the classification of such goods as waste or not.

However, greater problems were created when the "presumptive" clause of section 75(3) EPA 1990 was extant, which resulted in a number of organisations taking this possibility into account in the wording of their "Conditions of Sale".

Batteries and Accumulators

A completely different issue is involved in relation to the two Directives on batteries and accumulators, 91/157/EEC and 93/86/EEC, which are aimed at reducing the environmental damage resulting from primary and secondary batteries which contain specified amounts of lead, mercury and cadmium. These were implemented within the UK by the Batteries and Accumulators (Containing Dangerous Substances) Regulations 1994, SI 1994/232, which *inter alia* ban the marketing of certain alkaline batteries containing mercury and require that manufacturers of battery-powered appliances ensure that spent batteries or accumulators can be easily removed.

Regulation 2(2) defines a number of terms used in the Statutory Instrument (and some that are not) and reference is made to Annexes II, A and B of the Waste Framework Directive in relation to disposal and recovery operations "provided they are applicable to batteries and accumulators". In this context, "spent" means a battery or an accumulator which is not re-usable and is intended for recovery or disposal.

An important feature in relation to the Duty of Care obligations of those discarding the batteries and subsequently treating or disposing of them is the requirement in Regulation 4 that they are printed with a separate collection mark and the relevant heavy metal content mark.

OTHER MEASURES RELATING TO WASTE

Not all of the legislative controls on the treatment and disposal of wastes are contained within waste management legislation and before disposing of any item it is prudent to review the constraints which may be imposed. This is clearly demonstrated in the legislation associated with horticulture and agriculture. While the examples described below may seem obscure, to those involved they impose legal obligations which must be satisfied.

In some circumstances, it is necessary to prevent the spread of plant disease by imposing controls on the associated waste, as in the Disposal of Waste (Control of Beet Rhizomania Disease) Order 1988, SI 1988/45. This provision was made under the Plant Health Act 1967 and prohibits the deposit of waste from commercial processing of prescribed root crops on land, other than on approved land. In addition, it lays down other conditions relating to the treatment of these wastes, including the transport of the waste in "leak-proof" containers.

Another more indirect example of waste control applies in the case of non-native plants such as Japanese Knotweed. Section 14(2) of the Wildlife and Countryside Act 1981 makes an offence of "planting or otherwise causing to grow in the wild any plant which is included in Part II of Schedule 9". The Schedule lists four species of plant, including Giant Hogweed (*Heracleum Mantegazzianum*) and Japanese Knotweed (*Polygonium Cuspidatum*). Section 14(2) distinguishes between "planting" and "otherwise causing to grow" and it may be assumed that the latter term was introduced to cover situations other than those in which intentional planting was carried out.

Since the term "cause to grow" is not defined within the Act, reference must be made to the relevant case law on causation.[1] Following *Alphacell v Woodward*, one possible interpretation is that, for existing plants, "cause to grow" means something more than maintaining the *status quo*, with the implication that there is no obligation to kill any existing growth. However, since the Japanese Knotweed is such a prolific plant, it could also be argued that by failing to curb the existing growth, new growth is being caused. This would follow the argument used in *Attorney-General's Reference (No 1 of 1994)* that a failure to prevent an occurrence (through not maintaining a sewer in this case) was "causing", provided the questions were phrased in the correct way. While this argument may not prove persuasive, it could more readily be applied if reasonable precautions were not taken in the disposal of any plants.

Knowing that a plant listed in Schedule 9 is present on its land, a company might be prosecuted if, as a result of its actions *or inaction*, there was new growth of this plant, although section 14(3) provides an "all reasonable steps and all due diligence" defence. This might require precautions to be taken such as those required under SI 1988/45, above. Thus, while there are no *formal* requirements for the control of the disposal of these plants through waste management legislation, there are *implied* controls as a result of the 1981 Act.

One practical problem in the application of this legislation is the degree of uncertainty surrounding the scientific name of plants referred to by the common name of Japanese Knotweed, and a number of books and publications name it as *Reynoutria Japonica*, *Fallopia Japonica* or *Fallopia Sachalinensis* and not *Polygonum Cuspidatum*. In *Nature Conservation Law*,[2] Reid notes that such uncertainties arise as a result of two factors –

---

[1]   This is considered further in the author's paper "Polygonium Cuspidatum – A Knotty Problem of Causation?", [1997] 11 *Environmental Law* 9.

[2]   *Nature Conservation Law*, C T Reid, W Green, Edinburgh, 1994, page 201.

the continual reassessment of plant classification by plant taxonomists, and the ease with which plants hybridise. While such discrepancies may seem to be of academic interest only, it should be noted that Schedule 9 of the 1981 Act states that, in the event of any dispute or proceedings, "the common name [i.e. Japanese Knotweed] shall *not* be taken into account"!

Within the above statutory provisions, there is no means whereby an aggrieved owner of adjacent land may himself initiate action; section 19 of the 1981 Act gives powers of enforcement to a constable who suspects with reasonable cause that any person is committing an offence or has committed an offence. There is, however, the possibility of action at common law. In *Giles v Walker*, an occupier was held to owe no duty of care to an adjoining occupier to cut naturally growing weeds (thistle seeds, in this case) on his land, so as to prevent them seeding on the adjoining land. However, in *Leakey v National Trust for Places of Historic Interest or Natural Beauty*, this general rule that a landowner cannot be liable for the spread of naturally occurring items from his land was overturned.

These issues of liability for wildlife are dealt with in more detail by Reid,[1] who notes that "although it cannot be wholly ruled out, it therefore seems unlikely that a landowner taking measures on his own land to further nature conservation will be liable to a neighbour who claims to have suffered damage as a result of wild plants or animals being encouraged."

The disposal of genetically modified organisms (GMOs) presents an interesting situation in view of the format of the controls imposed under Part VI of the Environmental Protection Act 1990. Under section 107(10), there are three possible states of control for GMOs, viz:

— containment under control;

— release; and

— escape,

and the offences in section 118 are weighted towards the infraction of consent conditions and the use of BATNEEC, rather than "pollution" type offences such as those found elsewhere in the Act and in other environmental legislation. Consequently, the concept of disposal is preceded by a requirement of the regulatory agency, such as through a prohibition notice or by the intent of the holder of the GMO to "cease keeping" the organism. A corollary of this formulation of the legislation is that any disposal

---

[1] *Nature Conservation Law*, C T Reid, W Green, Edinburgh, 1994, pages 305-308.

operation associated with GMOs in this context results in the classification of the material as "waste". However, there are additional liabilities imposed on the holders of GMOs.

Within the general duties relating to those involved with GMOs (section 109), there is a requirement that, where a person is required to cease keeping organisms, he shall dispose of them as safely and as quickly as practicable and that, until he has done so, he shall use BATNEEC for keeping the organism under his control and for preventing any damage to the environment. There is no definition of BATNEEC within this Part of the Act although, as Tromans[1] points out, it is likely that it will be interpreted in the same way as in Part I. Damage to the environment is defined in section 107(3) as "capable of causing harm to the living organisms supported by the environment" and in section 107(6) "harm" has an extended meaning, compared with other Parts of the Act, and means:

> "Harm to the health of humans or other living organisms or other interference with the ecological systems of which they form a part, and in the case of man, includes offence caused to any of his senses or harm to his property."

While the disposal of GMOs is covered by Part II of the Act, it is clear that the provisions within Part VI impose a much greater onus on the holder of the GMO.

---

[1] *The Environment Acts 1990-1995, 3rd Edition*, S Tromans, M Nash and M Poustie, Sweet & Maxwell, 1996, page 325.

FURTHER READING

"The Challenge of Environmentally Sound and Efficient Regulation – The Need for Enhanced International Understanding", J T Smith II, [1993] 5 *JEL* 91

Defining What Is Packaging, Industry Council for Packaging and the Environment, Incpen, July 1997

The Draft Producer Responsibility Obligations (Packaging Waste) Regulations – How would they affect you? Department of the Environment, July 1996

"The European Legal Background to Health Care Waste Management", J Salter, [1995] *IWM Proceedings*, July, 20

Guidance on the Handling, Storage and Transport of Airbags and Seat Belt Pre-Tensioners, HSE, 1997

"Heading for the Great Scrapyard in the Sky – or Not ?", R Fairley, [1996] *Environmental Law, UKELA Journal* Winter, 4

"Landfill Tax Information Notes"

    1/96 (Revised) *Introduction to Landfill Tax*

    2/96   *Registration*

    3/96   *Tax Liability*

    4/96   *Calculating the Weight of Waste*

    5/96   *Tax Points*

    6/96   *Records*

    7/96   *Accounting for Tax*

    8/96   *Environmental Bodies*

    9/96   *Penalties and interest*

    10/96   *Reviews and Appeals*

    1/97   *Contaminated Land*

issued by H M Customs and Excise, 1996. Information Notes 1/96 to 10/96 have been amalgamated into a notice entitled *A General Guide to Landfill Tax*, LFT 1. Information Note 1/97 has been reissued as a separate notice, *Contaminated Land*, LFT 2.

The Law of Nuclear Installations and Radioactive Sources, S Tromans and J Fitzgerald, Sweet & Maxwell, 1997

LWRA Guidelines for the Segregation, Handling, and Transport of Clinical Waste, London Waste Regulation Authority, 1995

Nature Conservation Law, C T Reid, W Green, Edinburgh, 1994

"The Packaging and Packaging Waste Directive", D A Reid, [1995] *EELR* August/September, 239

A packaging catalogue to support the Producer Responsibility Obligations (Packaging Waste) Regulations 1997 – Ready Reckoner, Department of the Environment, July 1997

"Polygonium Cuspidatum – A Knotty Problem of Causation?", D N Pocklington [1997] 11 *Environmental Law* 9

Producer Responsibility Obligations 1997, 1st Edition – Guidance on evidence of compliance and voluntary accreditation of reprocessors, The Environment Agency and SEPA, 1997

Producer Responsibilty Obligations (Packaging Waste) Regulations 1997 – the Agencies' Interpretation of Packaging, The Environment Agency and SEPA, 1997

Producer Responsibilty Obligations (Packaging Waste) Regulations 1997 – User's Guide, Department of the Environment, March 1997

"Producer Responsibility – Packaging Waste", Supplement to *Environment Business*, September 1996

"Product v Non-Product Based Distinction in Article III Trade and Environment Jurisprudence – Recent Developments", R J Zedalis, [1997] *EELR* 108

"Specialised Waste Streams" in *Croner's Waste Management*, Croner Publications (regularly updated)

"Transboundary Movements of Waste Under EC Law: The Emerging Regulatory Framework", A Schmidt, [1992] 4 *JEL* 57

"Vehicle Airbags – Research to Evaluate the Possible Hazards to Workers and Rescue Personnel", A E Jeffcock, in *Explo-96*, University of Leeds, September 1996, pages 19-29

Waste Management Papers, the Department of the Environment (see Chapter 11 for full list)

"The Weights and Measures aspects of the Landfill Tax", [1996] *Wastes Management* May, 53

"The World Trade Organisation and Disputes Involving Multilateral Environmental Agreements", M Lennard, [1996] *EELR* 306

Chapter 11

PRACTICAL ASPECTS OF WASTE MANAGEMENT

INTRODUCTION

The complexities of the legislation surrounding the designation of a substance or object as "waste" have been explored in earlier chapters and, while such considerations provide ample opportunity for lawyers and academics to exercise their minds, waste producers and waste holders have the additional problem of applying these measures in their day-to-day operations.

Once the criteria for the designation of "waste" have been satisfied, there are number of other issues to be determined in order to apply the relevant parts of the legislation. For each waste stream, it is necessary to examine every part of the route from production to the point at which the material ceases to be waste (through re-use, recycling or recovery) or is finally disposed of. The controls imposed will depend upon a number of factors, including *inter alia*:

— the composition of the "waste" and the presence of any components which might trigger specific controls;

— its location, the quantities of material involved and the time it will remain at that location;

— the person(s) legally responsible for the "waste".

The compositional aspects are of primary importance since these will determine the legislative framework for control, the liability for landfill tax, the acceptability for specific disposal or recovery operations and, as a consequence, the positive or negative commercial value to the current holder.

The second of the above factors will influence whether a waste management licence is required or if the process is subject to one of the many exemptions. This in turn will have a bearing on the economics of managing the waste.

While it is not possible to examine all possible combinations of these factors for all commonly occurring wastes, a number of examples will be discussed and relevant issues highlighted. However, it should be stressed that, in relation to the classification of a specific waste, there are important technical factors to be considered in the process of satisfying the legal ones, and this may require either a "desktop" study of its possible components or a full chemical and physical analysis. As a consequence, the general advice on the classes of waste discussed below should be regarded as a starting point, from which a more detailed consideration may be carried out. In this respect, some guidance may be obtained from publications such as *Croner's Waste Management*, which includes technical advice such as that reproduced in Table 11-1 on page 478.

THE DUTY OF CARE

The introduction of a statutory Duty of Care in section 34 of the Environmental Protection Act 1990 imposed a number of obligations on those involved in the management of waste. This concept has its origins in common law actions in negligence, after *Donoghue (McAlister) v Stevenson*, but it was the 11th Report of the Royal Commission on Environmental Pollution in 1985 which first proposed its application to waste. The Commission considered that the individual organisations controlling waste should bear the responsibility for ensuring that it is properly handled and disposed of, stating "the producer incurs a duty of care which is owed to society, and we would like to see this duty reflected in public attitude and enshrined in legislation and codes of practice".

The Duty of Care was incorporated into the 1990 Act in relation to controlled wastes and imposes a duty on anyone who imports, produces, carries, keeps, treats or disposes of these, to take all reasonable measures to:

— prevent any person dealing with the waste illegally, in contravention of section 33 (section 34(1)(a));

— prevent the escape of waste from his own or another person's control (section 34(1)(b));

— transfer waste only to an authorised person, or to a person for authorised transport purposes (section 34(1)(c)(i)); and

— supply a description of the waste on transfer which is adequate to enable others to comply with the duty of care (section 34(1)(c)(ii)).

Although a mandatory provision of the 1990 Act, the Code of Practice states that the Duty of Care is "designed to be an essentially self-regulating system which is based upon good business practice", and the Environment Agency and SEPA do not have a specific duty to enforce the Duty of Care. The duty does not apply to the occupier of a domestic property as respects household waste produced on that property (section 34(2)), although it still applies to waste from a workshop on that property, waste brought from other premises, septic tank sludge and building waste resulting from work undertaken on that property.

A similar, though not as far-reaching provision is included in Article 8 of the Waste Framework Directive and, while both of these measures are based upon the "polluter pays principle", neither imposes a complete "cradle to grave" responsibility on the waste producer, such as that envisaged in the draft Directive on Civil Liability for Damage Caused by Waste.

It is interesting to note that the proposed Directive on Hazardous Household Waste excludes householders from the periodic inspection and record keeping requirements applied to other waste holders.

In some respects, the scope of the Duty of Care is quite restricted, since the obligations placed upon the holder of the waste are determined by the capacity in which he has control of the waste and he is only required to take those measures which are "reasonable in the circumstances". Waste producers are solely responsible for the care of the waste while they hold it and have the primary duty of ensuring that the description of the waste on transfer is correct. After the waste leaves the holder's premises, he is still responsible for alerting the regulators to any suspicion he might have that the waste is not being dealt with lawfully.

The Code of Practice gives some guidance on the conduct expected of a "reasonable waste manager", although to date this has received no judicial consideration. It is possible, however, that this may include an element of "reasonable foreseeability", as in *Overseas Tankship (UK) Ltd v Miller Steamship Co Pty Ltd (The Wagon Mound) (No 2)*.

Prevention of a Contravention of Section 33 EPA

The first element of the duty concerns the prevention of a contravention of section 33 EPA 1990 and requires that the waste holder ensures that no person:

— deposits controlled waste on land otherwise than in accordance with a waste management licence (section 33(a));

— treats, keeps or disposes of controlled waste otherwise than in accordance with a waste management licence (section 33(b)); and

— treats, keeps or disposes of controlled waste in a manner likely to cause pollution of the environment or harm to human health (section 33(c)).

In order to satisfy his obligations, the holder will be obliged to check the "downstream" treatment of his waste, including its transport, and ensure that the relevant waste management licences are held or appropriate exemptions from licensing exist, and are currently valid. This will involve viewing an actual licence or its authorised copy and checking the details of any relevant exemptions, such as quantities and descriptions of the waste involved.

Although not part of the Duty of Care, it would be prudent to undertake or commission an audit of the activities of all third parties involved in the downstream treatment of the holder's waste. There are now some organisations who will undertake the auditing of disposal sites on behalf of a number of clients, in order to reduce costs and increase coverage of the sites audited. Ideally, however, the entire route taken by the waste should be verified, checking documentation specific to the holder.

Transfer of Waste

Waste must only be transfered to authorised persons or for authorised transport purposes. For the purposes of section 34(1)(c), authorised transport purposes are:

— the transport of controlled waste within the same premises, between different places in those premises (section 34(4)(a));

— the transport to a place in Great Britain of controlled waste which has been brought from a country outside Great Britain, not having been landed in Great Britain until it arrives at that place (section 34(4)(b));

— the transport by air or sea of controlled waste from a place in Great Britain to a place outside Great Britain (section 34(4)(c)),

where "transport" has the same meaning as in the Control of Pollution (Amendment) Act 1989.

Storage of Waste

The duty to prevent the escape of waste within the holder's control encompasses a wide range of circumstances including:

— corrosion or wear of waste containers;

— accidental spillage, leakage or inadvertent leaching from waste unprotected by rainfall, e.g. in an uncovered skip;

— accident or weather resulting in the breaking open of a container and allowing waste to escape;

— waste blowing away or falling while stored or transported;

— scavenging of waste by vandals, thieves, children, trespassers or animals.

Important factors in storage are the retention of the identity of the waste and the possibility of changes in its composition, reactions between components of the waste and the release of gases as a result of its degradation. In addition, equipment, procedures and training should be provided for the treatment of emergency situations such as leakages and spills.

Such liability extends from the storage of waste on site until its transfer to the waste carrier and includes a need to protect it for future handling requirements. The consignor of the waste has responsibility for its correct containment and labelling, although in practice many carriers assist in relation to these operations.

Transfer Operations

With regard to the transfer operation, the holder must transfer the waste to an "authorised person" as defined in section 34(3), which includes:

— any authority which is a waste collection authority for the purposes of Part II of the 1990 Act (section 33(3)(a));

— any person who is the holder of a waste management licence under section 35 of the 1990 Act, or a disposal licence under section 5 COPA 1974 (section 33(3)(b));

— any person to whom section 33(1) does not apply, by virtue of regulations under section 33(3) (section 33(3)(c));

— any person who is registered as a waste carrier under section 2 of the Control of Pollution (Amendment) Act 1989 (section 33(3)(d));

— any person exempt from registration as a carrier of controlled waste by virtue of regulations under section 1(3) of that Act (section 33(3)(e));

— a waste disposal authority in Scotland (section 33(3)(f)).

Persons exempted from licensing for the carriage of waste, include:

— charities and voluntary organisations;

— waste collection authorities who are collecting any waste themselves (an authority's *contractors* are not exempt), waste disposal authorities and the Agencies;

— certain railway undertakings when carrying waste by rail;

— ship operators where waste is to be disposed of under licence at sea;

— persons authorised under the Animal By-Products Order 1992 to hold or deal with animal waste, or the holder of a knacker's yard licence.

Waste Brokers

Annex E of the Code of Practice defines a waste broker as a person who arranges for the disposal or recovery of controlled waste on behalf of another. (No definition is given within the 1990 Act.) Since waste is defined in terms of the "holder", the actions or intentions of the waste broker cannot have any bearing on the classification of a substance as "waste", although he may be party to a section 33 offence and is specifically included in section 34 as one of those subject to the Duty of Care. Case law defines a "broker" as someone who contrives, makes and concludes bargains and contracts between merchants and tradesmen for reward (*Milford v Hughes*). The position of a broker is that he arranges the transfer of waste between two parties and, although he need not handle the waste himself nor have it in his possession, has actions are such that he controls what happens to the waste and takes responsibility for the legality of the arrangement.

The Code of Practice states that as he does not handle the waste, he cannot be held responsible for its packing, although he may be in a position to advise on this and on other issues such as its subsequent handling. However, he *is* under a duty to ensure that a correct and adequate description of the waste is transferred along with the necessary documentation, and that it is carried by a registered or exempt carrier. His duties regarding the checks to be made after transfer are the same as those for a waste holder.

The Description of the Waste and Transfer Note

The Transfer Note
The obligations of a waste holder relating to the transfer of waste and the associated documentation are contained in the Environmental Protection (Duty of Care) Regulations 1991, SI 1991/2839, and those who are also subject to the landfill tax must additionally meet the requirements of section 48 of the Finance Act 1996, Regulation 16 of the Landfill Tax Regulations 1996, SI 1996/1527, and Regulation 6 of the Landfill Tax (Qualifying Material) Order 1996, SI 1996/1528.

The Duty of Care Regulations are written in terms of the "transferor" and "transferee" which, in relation to the transfer of controlled waste by a person who is subject to the duty imposed by section 34(1) of the 1990 Act, mean the person who in compliance with that section transfers a written description of the waste and the person who receives that description, respectively. Regulation 2(1) states that the transferor and the transferee shall, at the same time as the written description of the waste is transferred, ensure that such a document as is described in paragraph (2) ("a transfer note") is completed and signed on their behalf. The implications of these provisions are:

— the terms "transferor" and "transferee" relate only to the transfer of information on the waste transfer (Regulation 1(2));

— a written description of the waste is an obligatory part of the transfer operation;

— it is envisaged that the description of the waste will normally be a separate document from the waste transfer note.

The Regulations do not specify what format the transfer note will take but its contents must:

— identify the waste to which it relates and state:

   — its quantity and whether on transfer it is loose or in a container;

   — if it is in a container, the kind of container; and

   — the time and place of the transfer;

— state whether or not the transferor is the producer or importer of the waste and, if so, which;

— give the name and address of the transferor and transferee and the capacity in which they are acting, according to the table in the Regulations;

— if the transfer is to a person for authorised transport purposes, specify which of those purposes.

The Code of Practice notes that these requirements may be satisfied using some existing types of documentation, such as:

— the system of books that scrap metal dealers are obliged to keep, under the Scrap Metal Dealers Act 1964 or the Civic Government (Scotland) Act 1982;

— the consignment note system required for special waste transfers; and

— the consignment note system for the transfrontier shipment of waste,

provided they are suitably modified or adapted to meet the information requirements of the Regulations. In the light of these considerations, it is clear that a transfer note is not a particular form to be used when waste changes hands but is any type of documentation which satisfies the above requirements.

Both parties to the transfer must keep the written description of the waste and the transfer note, or copies of these, for a minimum period of two years from the transfer. Different conditions apply in relation to special waste and the landfill tax and these are summarised in the table below.

Transfer Data Retention Requirements

Legislation		Persons under Duty	Minimum Time Period
Duty of Care	SI 1991/2839, Reg. 3	Transferor	2 years
		Transferee	2 years
Special Waste	SI 1996/972, Regs. 15(1)&(2)	Consignor	3 years
	SI 1996/972, Regs. 15(1)&(2)	Carrier	3 years
	SI 1996/972, Reg. 15(5)	Consignee *	Until licence expiry +
Landfill Tax	SI 1996/1527, Reg. 16	Persons liable for tax	Six complete tax years

* Additional requirements for site records   + Data to agency on expiry of licence

Under the Deregulation and Contracting Out Act 1994, a new subsection was added to the Duty of Care provisions (section 34(4A)) in relation to the transfer of the written description of the waste, whereby:

— the transfer of waste in stages is to be treated as if it is taking place when the first stage of the transfer takes place (section 34(4A)(a)); and

— a series of transfers between the same parties, of waste of the same description is to be treated as a single transfer taking place when the first of the transfers in the series takes place (section 34(4A)(b)).

No time limit is defined in relation to the series of transfers, although the Code of Practice states that this period should not exceed one year. However, since the holder must comply with the law, rather than with the

Code, it would be difficult to obtain a conviction on the strength of exceeding the one year suggested limit alone.

Tromans[1] notes the potential problems relating to the meaning of "the transfer of waste in stages" and how this differs from "a series of transfers", and suggests that the latter refers to the situation in which a number of journeys are necessary to remove a large amount of a given waste from the premises of the holder to those of a single third party.

The Description of the Waste

One of the objectives of supplying a description of the waste on transfer is "to provide enough information to enable subsequent holders to avoid mismanaging the waste" and the Code of Practice suggests that the description should include "some combination of the following":

— the type of premises from which the waste originates;

— the name of the substance(s);

— the process that produced the waste; and

— a chemical and physical analysis,

and should mention any special problems associated with the waste. With regard to the latter, these may include: the need for special containers; any restrictions on its mixing or handling (in addition to the legal restrictions); problems which might be encountered when using a specific disposal route; possible changes of physical state during storage or transport; and problems previously encountered with similar wastes.

One of the objectives of the National Waste Classification scheme is to provide this type of information and the scheme, described in Chapter 8, uses a six-field description of each waste, the fields supplying information on: the industry producing the waste; the process producing the waste; the waste category; the properties of the waste, mainly relating to its potential to pollute; the physical form of the waste; and a label for additional information.

Read in conjunction with the Code of Practice, this scheme has the potential for overcoming most of the problems associated with providing the correct description of a waste. However, the value of such a scheme will be lost unless it is used by all those involved in the transfer of waste. For

---

[1] *The Environment Acts 1990-1995, 3rd Edition*, S Tromans, M Nash and M Poustie, Sweet & Maxwell, 1996, page 117.

this to happen, the scheme will need either to be made a mandatory requirement or, if voluntary, to be perceived by waste holders as giving "added value" to their activities.

In addition to the above requirements, where the lower rate of landfill tax is to be claimed, Regulation 6 of the Landfill Tax (Qualifying Material) Order 1996, SI 1996/1528, states that for each type of material disposed of, the document used as a transfer note must include:

— a description of the material:

  — which accords with its description in column 2 of the Schedule to the Order, or

  — where a note contained in that Schedule lists the material (other than by way of exclusion), which accords with that description, or

  — which is some other accurate description, or

  where the material is water within group 9 of the Schedule:

  — the description "water", and

  — a description of the material held in suspension which, if that material had been disposed of separately, would comply with the requirements of the paragraph above.

The Duty of Care Code of Practice

Under section 34(7) and (8) of the Environmental Protection Act 1990, the Secretary of State may prepare Code(s) of Practice for the purpose of providing practical guidance on how to the discharge the Duty of Care, and may modify, amend or revoke such Codes as appropriate. Although different Codes of Practice may be prepared and issued for different areas (section 34(11)), to date only a one Code has been issued, initially in 1991 (the A5 "Green Book") and an updated version in 1996 (the A4 "Blue Book") which revokes the earlier document.

The major changes introduced in the 1996 Code of Practice were the incorporation of the Framework Definition of "waste" and the extension of the Duty of Care to the handlers of waste metal. As will be discussed below, guidance on who is regarded as the producer of construction and demolition waste was removed completely from Annex B, and in addition the new Code acknowledges that it is *not* an offence to accept waste from an unregistered carrier (paragraph 4.3). In addition, the Code states that, when the National Waste Classification Scheme is finalised, the description of the waste on the transfer note should refer to the appropriate scheme entry wherever possible (paragraph 1.8). A number of other minor modifications were also made.

The legal obligation of waste holders is to comply with the Duty of Care itself rather than with the Code of Practice, and the measures and procedures recommended within the Code should perhaps be regarded as the minimum requirements expected of waste producers and waste holders. Nevertheless, Codes of Practice issued under these provisions are admissible as *prima facie* evidence of compliance or non-compliance with the Duty of Care and in addition may be used in civil actions in negligence in relation to the handling of waste or in proceedings under section 33 of the 1990 Act.

COMPANY WASTE DIRECTORIES

In the majority of organisations, the range of waste materials produced is virtually constant and "new" wastes are only infrequently encountered. Consequently, a company might find it useful to draw up a directory of all the wastes currently disposed of, which may include, *inter alia*, details of their classification, composition, the description to be used in relevant documentation, the method of storage on site and the approved route(s) for disposal.

In addition to providing a source of reference for those involved in these materials, such a list has a number of other possible applications:

— sub-sets of the list can be located on or adjacent to waste containers/ storage areas to indicate the permissible contents of skips, drums, etc.;

— copies can be given to waste carriers/disposers to indicate the range a materials being placed within a given container;

— the list can be made available to inspectors of the regulatory agencies, to indicate the waste management practices at a particular site;

— it may provide documentary evidence to demonstrate the company's compliance with the Duty of Care relating to this part of their waste management operations.

Although there are undoubted benefits to be gained from such lists, their effectiveness is dependent upon the extent to which they represent current day-to-day waste management practices and the degree to which employees have regard to their content. If the procedures are not followed, the existence of such a document may be used against a company, since it demonstrates that its management is aware of the obligations placed on the company but has not extended its control to this area.

All companies dealing with waste should consider whether any of their waste products should be treated as "special" or not and, in view of the complexity of this task, it would be prudent to record formally the basis upon which such decisions are made. In these circumstances, a classification that waste is *not* "special" is equally important, since it identifies the data used should any future problems arise regarding the validity of the classification. This will also assist future assessments of similar materials and will facilitate any re-classification which becomes necessary in the light of new data or information, or changes in legislation.

In drawing up a corporate waste directory, it is important not to underestimate the potential stupidity or bloody-mindedness of employees, who for a variety of reasons may place their own interpretation on its content. Ambiguity in the description of waste types and disposal routes must be avoided and particular attention paid to advice on the treatment of "empty" containers, contaminated materials and any unqualified numerical data, such as the number of fluorescent tubes which may be placed in a container – such quantification is of value only where a single person is involved in their disposal or a record of such numbers is kept. Nevertheless, a company waste directory is, on balance, a useful practical means of assisting a company to meet its Duty of Care obligations. However, in view of the potential for changes in legislation and technical knowledge, it should be reviewed regularly and updated on a regular basis and ideally be made subject to controlled issue distribution.

ENVIRONMENTAL MANAGEMENT SYSTEMS

It will be appreciated that the production of a company waste directory and associated procedures for the storage and disposal of waste has much in common with a number of aspects of the formal environmental management systems which are available – EMAS and ISO-14,000. Some of the liability issues posed by such systems have been examined in an earlier chapter and, in relation to the control of waste management operations and satisfying the Duty of Care requirements, there are clear benefits to be gained from the introduction of a rigorous system of control.

The complexities and uncertainties associated with waste management and its legislation are such that it is essential that some form of formal management control is imposed but, from the management point of view, there is no particular merit in introducing a system which also considers the "badgers and bunnies" issues, when the major problem is, for example, to ensure that the right waste goes into the right skip. There is also the danger that a formalised system will emphasise efficiency rather than effectiveness

– in Drucker's words "doing the right things, but *not* doing things right".[1]

However, there are other factors which will influence a company in deciding to implement an environmental management system, such as stakeholder perception and, providing the scope of environmental factors considered does not detract from the major issues and the company is committed to its effective operation (rather than gaining another certificate for the wall of the MD's office), then it may assist both in achieving and maintaining compliance with the legislation.

GENERAL ISSUES OF WASTE MANAGEMENT

Unknown Substances

Implicit in the Duty of Care's obligations is the holder's knowledge of the substances he is transferring to a third party. Normally the holder will be aware of the type and origin of his waste but there may be occasions on which he is faced with disposing of unknown material, produced either on his own undertaking or resulting from the actions of unknown third parties, such as litter, refuse and fly-tipped materials.

In the latter circumstances, providing the actions of the holder in disposing of these substances are "reasonable in the circumstances", then the duty will be satisfied. With regard to fly-tipped material, while the disposer would not be expected to provide a detailed description of the waste concerned, he should investigate any items which give him cause for suspicion, such as gas canisters and drums containing liquids.

There is no excuse for unknown waste substances occurring within a waste holder's own premises and ultimately poor management control is responsible. Unknown wastes arise as a result of a number of causes:

— loss of identity of the waste through the use of unmarked or wrongly marked containers for waste;

— empty or part-empty drums left open to allow the ingress of rainwater;

— poor security resulting in employees/third parties using the company's waste containers for a variety of materials.

When faced with such materials for disposal, the holder must ensure that they are adequately identified and should consider the possibility of their classification as special wastes. From a knowledge of the operations

---

[1]   *Management*, P F Drucker, Pan Books, 1977

undertaken at the site and the consumables purchased, it may be possible to narrow down the potential components of the waste by a process of elimination but in cases of doubt a full chemical analysis may be required. Such an analysis will be costly but will prove a useful exercise for concentrating the mind of the manager responsible and provide an incentive for the introduction of a more effective system of waste management. It may also be less costly than the fine and associated legal costs involved in a prosecution.

"Empty" and "Part-Empty" Containers

The correct disposal of "empty" containers presents waste managers with a major problem in relation to their classification.[1] In addition to the identity of any residual material contained within, *supra*, is the criterion by which the container is judged as being "empty". This was considered in *Durham County Council v Thomas Swan & Co Ltd* in relation to a waste transfer station licensed to dispose of 60 tonnes of empty drums per week. An inspection found that the drums contained a slurry of phenol and water, and an action was brought based, *inter alia,* on the deposition of controlled waste on land that was not licensed. The court, dismissing an appeal against the magistrates' finding for the defendant, held that the concept of "empty" was dependent upon the context in which it was to be considered, and on the facts of the case the only realistic standard to be applied was the practice of the trade. On the evidence of an expert witness, this was taken to be less than 1% of the original volume *under these particular circumstances.*

There is a danger that the <1% figure will be taken as the norm for "empty" and the major points of the case will be adumbrated, viz:

— the practice in the trade is the standard to be applied;

— the context was the interpretation of a particular part of a waste management licence in relation to the operation of a waste transfer station, not an interpretation of the meaning of waste in such circumstances.

(The issue under consideration was the part of the licence imposed by a local WRA which stated that any barrels/drums containing more than *de minimis* quantities were to be returned immediately to the sender.)

With regard to the first point, a source of reference used by the waste industry – *Croner's Waste Management* – gives details of the retention of liquid to be expected within the "heel" of an open-ended drum. A

---

[1] This is considered further in the author's paper "Provisions within UK Law relating to the Treatment of 'Empty' and 'Part-Empty' Containers", [1997] 9 *ELM*, 179.

conventional 45 gallon (217 litre) drum when emptied by up-ending will retain 1200 ml liquid (0.55% by volume), whereas an "optimally-drainable" design of drum will leave only 50 ml (0.02% by volume). (Note that in *Swan*, 100 grammes (0.05% by mass) of *solid* phenol was retained in the 200 kg drum.)

In practice, much will depend upon the viscosity of the material in question, itself a function of the temperature, and of the time allowed for draining the drum. It is a useful exercise to translate these "percentages of retention" into volumes of liquid and their equivalent depths in a drum, in order to gain an impression of how they would appear in practice, e.g. the "1%" value in *Swan* equates to 2 kg of waste.

For cases in which there is a deposit of "general" waste within the "empty" container, the major impacts of an incorrect description are on the holder's duty of care in relation to the subsequent treatment of the waste. Special wastes present additional problems in view of their hazardous nature and the potentially greater risk of harm to those handling the containers and to the environment on disposal.

The criteria by which a waste is designated as "special" are important in this respect for, while there is no general *de minimis* provision in the definition, such considerations do apply where the classification is on the basis of certain of its characteristics. The former Special Waste Regulations, SI 1980/1709, stated in Schedule 1 that, for "mixed wastes", a waste was considered as "dangerous to life" if a sample of 5 cubic centimetres (5 mls) taken from any part of the consignment falls within either of the descriptions in paragraph 1 of the Schedule. There were, however, no *de minimis* provisions in respect of the other criteria – flash-point and medicinal product.

Similar provisions are now included in the current Regulations, SI 1996/ 972, whereby under Regulation 2(5) waste displaying any of the properties H4 to H8 which has concentrations below the applicable threshold in Part III of Schedule 2 (Article 1 of Decision 94/904/EC) is not regarded as special waste. However, in this case, the thresholds are defined in terms of percentages and there are two possible approaches to their use:

— to apply them to the container *plus* its contents, treating it as a single item of waste; or

— to apply them *only* to the contents of the container.

The latter is the approach of the 1980 Regulations and more closely satisfies the objectives of the Hazardous Waste Directive. However, in most cases the container is not solely for the transport of the waste but is discarded along with it and then, according to the definition of waste in the

Waste Framework Directive, the drum itself should be considered as waste. Although some of the proposed changes to the EWC and HWL relate to part-empty containers or contaminated materials, *supra*, these are inconsistent and contradictory, and a co-ordinated approach must be developed before the measure is adopted.

As in *Swan*, in relation to the definition of "empty" within the terms of a waste management licence, it is the responsibility of the Environment Agency or SEPA to specify what criteria it wishes to impose within the conditions of a licence. Some commentators have suggested the use of the term "clinically clean" in order to avoid confusion but this is clearly ambiguous since such a term implies the absence of substances with the potential to cause infection, rather than referring to the quantity of residual contents in a container. Similarly, the term "trace" has a certain meaning in the context of chemical analysis. The most logical solution to end such woolly thinking would be to specify permissible quantities of specific components which may be left in containers.

Whether or not a container is deemed to be empty for the purposes of the waste legislation, it will be subject to the controls imposed by the Carriage of Dangerous Goods (Classification, Packaging and Labelling) and Use of Transportable Pressure Receptacles Regulations 1996, SI 1996/2092. Under Regulation 3(2)(b)(ii), the requirements for classification, labelling and packaging are extended to the carriage of "uncleaned, empty packages which have contained dangerous goods where those packages still contain sufficient of those dangerous goods (or vapours therefrom) to create a significant risk to the health or safety of any person".

These provisions were brought in as a health and safety measure, and as such there is no reference to the environmental consequences and they are risk-based, not hazard-based (as the new special waste Regulations).

Contaminated Substances

There are many examples of materials which are discarded as the result of intentional or unintentional contamination. Swabs, cloths and rags are often discarded instead of being cleaned and re-used, and the question of their classification is an important issue. In the case of swabs, etc. from medical use, these will fall within the broad definition of clinical waste and more specifically within Group A(a) of the Health Services Advisory Committee, and should be treated accordingly. Unlike the other examples below, it is their overall potential for infection, rather than the percentage of a given component, which is of importance.

As with "empty" containers, other soiled rags and swabs present the greatest problems when contaminated with special rather than general waste, and for the latter a description of "swabs contaminated by 'x' " should be sufficient to satisfy duty of care requirements. However, greater attention must be given where the contaminant is a special waste and, while it is acceptable to dispose of everything as if it were special waste (necessitating an accurate description of the hazardous components), this may involve a company in significant additional costs and such circumstances may justify a more detailed analysis to be undertaken. It is relatively straightforward to carry out a gravimetric assessment of the amount of contaminant, preferably on a "worst case" basis, and from this and from a knowledge of the contaminant to determine whether the waste should be classified as special.

With regard to other contaminated products, such as materials used to soak up spillages and leaks, these probably have a greater degree of homogeneity, permitting a more straightforward determination.

SPECIFIC WASTE STREAMS

In earlier chapters the general definition of waste and other legally-defined wastes were considered. The legal controls relating to these materials will now be discussed in more detail and some of the practical issues associated with their management examined.

Radioactive Waste

As noted in Chapter 10 in relation to its definition, the accumulation of radioactive waste must be strictly controlled and an authorisation is required under the Radioactive Substances Act 1993 for both the accumulation and disposal of radioactive wastes which arise either from premises or from mobile radioactive apparatus.

Unless an authorisation has been granted by the Environment Agency or SEPA, it is an offence for a person to dispose of radioactive waste on or from any premises which are used for the purpose of any undertaking carried on by him, or to cause or permit any radioactive waste to be so disposed of, if he knows or has reasonable grounds for believing it to be radioactive waste (section 13(1)). This also applies to mobile plant (section 13(2)) and to the receipt of any such waste for the purpose of its disposal, unless an authorisation is held (section 13(3)).

Similarly, it is an offence for a person to accumulate radioactive waste with a view to its subsequent disposal, or to cause or permit it to be accumulated, on any premises which are used for the purpose of his undertaking (section 14(1)). In addition, under section 14(4), when radioactive material is produced, kept or used on any premises and, as a result, any material arising from these activities is accumulated and retained there for longer than three months, then unless the contrary is proven, it is presumed that:

— the material is radioactive waste; and

— it has been accumulated on the premises with a view to its subsequent disposal.

The 1993 Act provides that certain radioactive wastes are exempt from the requirements of sections 13 and 14, such as that arising from watches and clocks (section 15(1)), although this does not apply to the premises at which watches and clocks are manufactured or repaired. In addition, the Secretary of State may by order exclude particular descriptions of radioactive waste, either absolutely or subject to limitations and specific conditions, and there are a number of Statutory Instruments which give exemptions. Examples of these are the Radioactive Substances (Waste Closed Source) Exemption Order 1963, SI 1963/1831, and the Radioactive Substances (Hospitals) Order 1990, SI 1990/2512. The former excludes the disposal of sealed (closed) sources of radioactivity, provided that:

— the waste is disposed of using a person authorised under the Act;

— records are kept showing the disposal date, the name and the number of millicuries of each radionuclide in the source, and the name and address of the person to whom the waste was sent or by whom it was removed.

The accumulation of these wastes is also excluded, provided that:

— no such waste source is retained on the premises for more than 12 weeks;

— no material forming part of the waste source is removed from that source; and

— reasonable measures are taken in its storage and security.

The Radioactive Substances (Hospitals) Order 1990 gives an exemption for the disposal of waste arising on hospital premises where it contains no alpha emitters and no strontium-90. Schedule 2 of the Order details the permissible disposal routes, which include, *inter alia*:

— the disposal of solid radioactive waste by a waste collection authority (WCA) with a view to disposing of it elsewhere.

    At the time of the removal from the hospital premises, the sum total activity in any 0.1 m^3 of waste must not exceed 400 kBq and the sum total activity of any individual article in the waste must not exceed 40 kBq.

— the incineration of solid or flammable radioactive waste in an incinerator designed for clinical waste, either on or remote from the hospital premises, provided it meets certain design criteria and the total activity of the radionuclides in the waste burned on the premises in any month does not exceed:

— 25 MBq of carbon 14 and tritium, taken together; and

— 5 MBq of all other radionuclides.

— the disposal of aqueous liquid radioactive waste from hospital premises by discharge to the foul water drainage system, where the total sum activity of the radionuclides in human excreta in the aqueous discharge in any month does not exceed:

— 1.0 GBq of technium 99m; and

— 500 MBq of all other radionuclides; and

the total sum activity of the radionuclides other than in human excreta in any month does not exceed 50 MBq.

As with other environmental legislation, there is a requirement for the retention of records (section 20) and for public access to such information. Authorisations made under sections 13 and 14 are subject to these provisions and the appropriate Agency may impose requirements in relation to site or disposal records:

— to retain copies of the records for a specified period after the holder of an authorisation ceases to carry on the activities so regulated, or

— to furnish the Agency with copies of the records in the event of ... the authorisation being revoked, or in the event of ceasing to carry on the activities so regulated.

Oils and Greases

Segregation and Storage
There are a number of reasons for targeting the segregation and storage of oils and greases within a waste management programme:

— there are substantial savings to be made in the recycling and re-use of oils, although it is important that they not contaminated with other wastes such as solvents;

— spillages, leaks and the overfilling of fuel tanks on delivery are responsible for over 25% of water-related prosecutions;

— only a small quantity of oil is required to cause significant pollution (one gallon of oil can cover an area of water the size of two football pitches) and this is reflected in the quantity of oils permitted in discharge consents;

— the presence of oil in water is easily detected, even at low concentrations.

While certain statutory restrictions are imposed on the storage of oil for agricultural use – the Control of Pollution (Silage, Slurry, and Agricultural Fuel Oil) Regulations 1991, SI 1991/324, as amended by SI 1996/2044 – there are at present no such controls applying to industry, although these are currently under discussion. It would be possible to introduce controls through the designation of water protection zones under section 93 of the Water Resources Act 1991 but these would be primarily applicable to areas rather than substances.

For industrial applications, the Environment Agency has produced a number of Pollution Prevention Guidelines, such as *The Safe Storage and Disposal of Used Oils*, PPG8, and the video *Pollution Prevention Pays*. Such guidance, however, is not mandatory.

Classification
Apart from oils containing PCBs and those with a flash point less than 21°C, under the 1980 Regulations waste oils were not classified as special waste. However, all oils are now included in the Hazardous Waste List (Part I of Schedule 2 to the 1996 Regulations) and as such are subject to assessment for any of the properties H1 to H14.

Some oils may be harmful to the skin with repeated contact, due the presence of contaminants, while others may be classified as special under the changed flash point criterion of 55°C.

Department of the Environment guidance suggests that unless there is specific evidence to the contrary, waste oils (and presumably greases) should be classified as special waste.

Clinical Waste

Classification
Within the Hazardous Waste List, the entry relevant to clinical wastes is under the general heading relating to natal care, diagnosis, treatment or

prevention of disease in humans and refers to "other wastes whose collection and disposal is subject to special requirements in view of the prevention of infection (18 01 03)". However, as noted earlier, within the UK prescription medicines are also classified as special waste.

The DoE guidance in Circular 6/96 interprets the term "special requirements" as the special packaging requirements applied to clinical wastes in Category A, under the Carriage of Dangerous Goods by Road and Rail (Classification, Packing and Labelling) Regulations 1994, SI 1994/669 (CDG(CPL)), as opposed to Category B. Category A comprises:

— infectious substances affecting humans or animals, which are considered to include micro-organisms that can cause severe human or animal disease, which may present a high risk of spreading and for which there is usually no effective prophylaxis or treatment available;

— infectious substances affecting humans or animals, which are considered to include micro-organisms that can cause severe human or animal disease, which may present a high risk of spreading but for which there is usually effective prophylaxis or treatment available.

Such wastes are to be regarded as special, unless adequately sterilised. The guidance states that the distinction drawn by the CDG(CPL) regime can also be useful in interpreting hazard risk phrase H9 – "infectious", viz. substances and preparations containing viable micro-organisms or their toxins which are known or reliably believed to cause disease in man or other living organisms.

There are other categories of clinical/healthcare waste which are not contained on the Hazardous Waste List and these need to be assessed against hazardous properties H3A (first indent) and H4 to H8. Although initial guidance stated that waste sharps from human and healthcare were to be regarded as "harmful" under H8 and should be classified as special, the revision (Circular 14/96), following hard on the heels of the original document, reversed this advice and commented "waste sharps are not on the Hazardous Waste List and will not normally be special waste".

Healthcare waste was identified as one of the Community's "priority waste streams" and a group was established to consider the associated issues and the formulation of a common European definition. Within the UK, Waste Management Paper 25, *Clinical Waste*, is under review and when re-issued will give additional, more detailed advice.

It should also be borne in mind that clinical waste is one of the wastes which may not be treated as "household waste" under section 33(2) EPA 1990.

Storage and Transport

In view of their potential for harm, clinical wastes are subject to a number of regulations in relation to the health and safety of those who might be affected by their storage, transport and subsequent disposal. In addition to the general provisions made under the Health and Safety at Work Act 1974 and the Control of Substances Hazardous to Health Regulations 1988, SI 1988/1657, other more specific controls apply, such as the CDG(CPL) Regulations mentioned above and the Road Traffic (Carriage of Dangerous Substances in Packages, etc.) Regulations 1992, SI 1992/742, which require vehicles to carry Tremcards and hazard warning panels and specify that training on the safe handling of the waste is given to drivers.

The Public Health (Control of Diseases) Act 1984 prohibits the placing of matter exposed to infection from a notifiable disease (such as cholera, plague, relapsing fever, smallpox and typhus) in a dustbin or ashpit, unless it has been disinfected.

Waste Management Licensing

The incineration of clinical waste is a prescribed process under Part I of the 1990 Act and larger units having a combustion chamber capacity of one tonne per hour, or greater, come under central control as a Part A process, with smaller units falling within Part B. The relevant Guidance Note is S2 5.01, *Waste Incineration Processes*.

Under the Waste Management Licensing (Amendment, etc.) Regulations 1995, SI 1995/288, the scope of "mobile plant" was extended to include, *inter alia*, plant for the microwave treatment of clinical waste and, as a consequence, a licence is now required for the operation of such plant.

Exemptions from Waste Management Licensing

Paragraph 39 of Schedule 3 to the 1994 Regulations contains two exemptions from licensing in relation to the storage of clinical waste. A pharmacy may store returned waste medicines, including those classified as special waste, which have been returned by households or individuals, provided that the amount stored does not exceed five cubic metres and the maximum period of storage is six months. In this context, "returned" does not necessarily require that the medicines are returned to the pharmacy from which they were obtained.

A medical, nursing or veterinary practice may store up to five cubic metres of the waste produced as a result of carrying on the practice, for a maximum of three months. This may also include special waste and "the carrying on of the practice" appears to include all waste generated by the practitioners when making professional visits away from the premises at which they are based.

Animal Wastes

Although many of the hazards imposed by animal "wastes" are similar to those associated with clinical wastes, the control of these materials is more complex since it is necessary to segregate those by-products which are destined for human consumption from those which have other commercial applications, and from those which are disposed of to landfill and incineration. The problems associated with Bovine Spongiform Encephalopathy (BSE) have served to emphasise the importance of the identification, segregation and destruction of infected material.

Certain animal wastes – carcasses, faecal matter and other natural, non-dangerous substances used in farming – are excluded from the scope of the Waste Framework Directive through Article 2(1)(iii), provided they are covered by other legislation. The disposal and recovery of animal carcasses is covered by the Animal Waste Directive, 90/667/EEC, supplemented by Commission Decision 92/562/EEC, which were implemented within the UK through the Animal By-Products Order 1992, SI 1992/3303. In addition to these materials, all wastes from premises used for agriculture, as defined by the Agriculture Act 1947 or the Agriculture (Scotland) Act 1948, fall outside the definition of controlled waste.

Waste Management Licensing

Department of the Environment Circular 11/94 notes that the Animal By-Products Order meets many of the same objectives as the Waste Management Licensing Regulations and "for the avoidance of doubt, a number of exceptions have been incorporated into the Regulations for persons dealing with the materials covered by, and in accordance with that Order", viz:

— the Controlled Waste Regulations 1992 are amended so that animal waste, collected and transported in accordance with Schedule 2 to the 1992 Order, is not considered as industrial or commercial waste for the purposes of the Duty of Care provisions of the 1990 Act (Regulation 24(7));

— the Controlled Waste (Registration of Carriers and Seizure of Vehicles) Regulations 1991 are amended to exempt from registration certain carriers of animal waste (Regulation 23(3)); and

— a waste management licence is not required for keeping or treating animal by-products in accordance with the Animal By-Products Order (paragraph 23, Schedule 3). This exemption, however, does not apply to the final deposit of such waste.

Exemptions from Waste Management Licensing

There are instances in which material from the processing of animal by-products is stored, used, or disposed of alongside other waste materials and such operations are subject to specific exemptions from the Waste Management Licensing Regulations 1994, SI 1994/1056, as amended. These exemptions are:

— the spreading of blood and gut contents from abattoirs onto land used for agriculture (paragraph 7, Schedule 3);

— the carrying on, in accordance with the conditions of a licence granted under paragraphs 7 and 8 of the Diseases of Animals (Waste Food) Order 1973, SI 1973/1936, of any activity authorised by the licence (paragraph 16, Schedule 3);

— the keeping or treatment of animal by-products in accordance with the Animal By-Products Order 1992, SI 1992/3303 (paragraph 23, Schedule 3).

The BSE provisions relating to the incineration of carcasses have resulted in the modification, through SI 1996/1279, of paragraph 17 of Schedule 3 to the Regulations – storage of waste in a secure place. Waste mammalian protein and tallow are added to the list of exempted wastes, where "mammalian protein" is defined as proteinaceous material and "mammalian tallow" means fat. In each case, the material is to be derived from the whole or part of any dead animal by a process of crushing, cooking or grinding. The maximum total quantities which may be stored under the exemption are 60,000 tonnes and 40,000 tonnes respectively.

Classification

The Animal By-Products Order 1992, SI 1992/3303, defines "animals" in relation to section 87(1) of the Animal Health Act 1981, as:

— any kind of mammal, except man;

— any kind of four-footed beast, which is not a mammal; and

— fish.

Poultry is included in this definition, for which the definition in section 87(4) of the 1981 Act has been extended to include quails.

The "high-risk" and "low-risk" categories of the Directive are included in Parts I and II of Schedule 1 to the Regulations and are reproduced in Table 11-2 on page 479. A mixture of high- and low-risk material is considered as high-risk.

These provisions do not apply to waste food as defined in, and required to be processed under, the Disease of Animals (Waste Food) Order 1973, nor to a number of defined animal products – hides, skins, hooves, feathers, wool, horns, hair, blood, and similar products from animals slaughtered "in the normal way", which are not used in the manufacture of feedingstuffs.

The controls do apply where such products originating from animals show signs of any disease, communicable through that product to man or animals, during a veterinary inspection at the time of slaughter.

Controls on Animal Wastes

Movement of Animal By-Products
An important primary control is imposed under Article 7 of the Animal By-Products Order 1992, which prohibits a person from "moving" or "causing or permitting to be moved" any animal by-product from any animal, except in accordance with Schedule 2. This places conditions on the collection, storage and transport, record keeping and the labelling of these materials. Although outside the controls of Part II EPA 1990, these provisions follow a similar pattern to the requirements of the Duty of Care.

Additional obligations are imposed by the Meat (Sterilisation and Staining) Regulations 1982, SI 1982/1018, which specify that certain by-products – knacker meat, meat from animals which have died/been slaughtered outside an abattoir or knacker's yard, and meat not handled/kept hygienically in a slaughterhouse – are presumed to be unfit for human consumption and must be sterilised or stained to indicate unfitness and sent for disposal in accordance with the Animal By-Products Order 1992.

Disposal and Processing of Animal By-Products
The controls imposed by the 1992 Order define the processes which may be employed for the disposal and processing of both high- and low-risk animal by-products, and both these and the exempted applications require that the associated premises are approved or registered, as appropriate.

High- and low-risk material may be disposed of by:

— rendering, i.e. subjecting the material, at a rendering, fishmeal or other plant, to any of the systems of treatment stated in Schedule 4;

— incineration;

— burial, i.e. interment at a depth beyond the reach of carnivorous animals.

High-risk material need not be subject to such disposal where the use of the by-product is for scientific (i.e. diagnostic, educational or research) purposes or where by-products in paragraphs (a), (b), or (e) of Part I of Schedule 1 are used at a knacker's yard or at premises used for feeding zoo, circus or fur animals, recognised packs of hounds, or for feeding to maggots farmed for fishing bait (Article 5).

Schedule 4 to the Order sets out the requirements to be met by plants used for rendering high- and low-risk materials – Parts I and II respectively – and specifies three areas for control:

— the design and operational aspects of the premises and facilities (section A);

— the hygiene requirements relating to the plant operations (section B);

— the microbiological standards for the finished products (section C).

Under Article 6, low-risk material may additionally be collected or used for the preparation of petfood, or of technical or pharmaceutical products (i.e. products intended for purposes other than human food and animal foodstuffs), provided the premises are registered under Article 9.

In addition, the Minister is empowered to issue notices in relation to the conditions for the disposal of high- and low-risk material. Article 8 requires that written approval of the Minister is obtained for any premises involved in the commercial rendering of animal by-products. Furthermore, registration is necessary for any premises, other than those on which animal by-products originate, for the collection of by-products where there is an intention of the preparation of petfood, the production of petfood (other than at knacker's yards) or technical or pharmaceutical products. Similarly, registration is required for the feeding of animal by-products to zoo, circus or fur animals, recognised packs of hounds or maggots farmed for fishing bait.

Disposal of Diseased Carcasses
Under certain circumstances, it is necessary to impose measures to prevent the spreading of disease, and the Animal Health Act 1981 permits the seizure and disposal of animal carcasses. Under the Act, carcasses of animals slaughtered under Ministerial instructions belong to, and are required to be disposed of as directed by, the Minister.

It is an offence to put, or to cause to put, the carcasses of an animal that has died of a disease or been slaughtered as diseased, or suspected to be so, into any inland waters or into the sea within 4.8 km of the shore. The Act also prohibits the digging up of a carcass that has been buried under the direction of the Minister or a local authority. In addition to these provisions, specific measures may be introduced in relation to a specific disease, for example the Swine Fever Order 1963, SI 1963/286. This prescribes the action to be taken where the disease exists or is suspected to exist, and requires the disposal of carcasses by:

— burial at a minimum depth, with quicklime or disinfectant;

— incineration or destruction at high temperature;

— destruction by chemical agents; or

— removal under veterinary control for disposal elsewhere.

BSE Provisions

A number of UK and Community measures have been introduced to prevent the spread of BSE, which is a notifiable disease. The Bovine Offal (Prohibition) Regulations 1989, SI 1989/2016 as amended, seek to ensure the removal of BSE agent from the human food chain by imposing controls on the method of removal and disposal of specified offals.

The Bovine Spongiform Encephalopathy Order 1991, SI 1991/2246, defines "specified bovine offals" which are prohibited from being used in feeding any animals or poultry, including petfood uses.

Commission Regulation 716/96/EEC relates to the measures to support the beef market in the UK and permits the UK government to purchase animals over 30 months old which show no signs of BSE. The carcasses must be permanently stained and transported in sealed containers "to specially authorised incarceration or rendering plants, where they shall be processed and destroyed".

The mismatch between the number of cattle to be culled and the capacity of the incineration plants available necessitated the changes to the waste management licensing regulations relating to the quantity of carcasses that may be stored prior to incineration, *supra*.

Waste Food

The use of unprocessed "waste food" – i.e. any part of an animal or poultry carcass, including blood and any other waste food which has been in contact with such material – intended for use as animal feedingstuffs, is controlled by the Diseases in Animals (Waste Food) Order 1973, SI 1973/1936. These provisions act in a manner similar to the Animal By-Products Order 1992 and prohibit any unauthorised possession of unprocessed waste food. The movement of unprocessed waste food must be under a licence, unless it is to be made into meal, and there must be no contact between waste food and animal food.

Wastes Containing Mercury

Environmentally, all mercury-containing waste is problematic, since on incineration mercury will tend to be released into the atmosphere, assisted by its high vapour pressure, while other disposal processes generating aqueous waste or leachate will be restricted by "Red List" criteria. The table below shows the results of a survey conducted for the Department of the Environment in 1996, on the annual amounts of waste mercury generated.

Mercury Sources, tonnes/annum (tpa)				
	Products	**Industry**	**Waste**	**Total**
Atmosphere	0.38	41.3	9.42	51.2
Landfill	4.48	37.1	46.3	87.7
Soils	9.19	0.08	2.06	11.3
Surface waters	0	0.54	5.93	6.47
Recycling	10.5	2.70	0	13.2
Total	24.52	81.7	63.71	170

Fluorescent Tubes
These account for 4.0 tonnes per year of the annual total of 87.7 tonnes of mercury which are landfilled, the majority coming from industrial sources such as the chlor-alkali process and non-ferrous metal smelting. The Department of the Environment considers landfill as a low-risk disposal route, with little potential for human exposure. Its guidance on the Special Waste Regulations concludes that fluorescent tubes containing up to 0.01% (10 mg) mercury are not to be classified as special waste.

Mercury is toxic by inhalation (R23) but the mercury content of a tube is a factor of 300 below the limiting concentration. For the other relevant hazard criteria, since neither mercury nor any of its compounds is classified as a class "N" substance, it does not meet the criteria to be classified as H14. Similarly, the data suggest that mercury is not hazardous in relation to the other relevant criterion (H13).

The main options presently available for the disposal of fluorescent tubes are:

— disposal at one of the landfill sites at which this is permissible;

— using purpose-built equipment crushing the tubes and collecting the debris in absorbent material;

— recycling the tubes for the recovery of the mercury.

The first option is most commonly adopted and, providing the DoE's view regarding their classification does not change and there are landfill sites licensed to accept this material, then this situation is likely to continue. However, the recovery and re-use of mercury must be, in the long term, the favoured environmental option although at present cost considerations make this option prohibitive.

As with end of life vehicles, an industry group has been established, including both manufacturers and disposers, with a view to investigating the short-term options for the disposal of the current materials and developing a longer-term strategy in relation to this form of lighting.

Elemental Mercury
A number of electrical devices employ elemental mercury and waste from these is generated following their failure or replacement. There are also a number of laboratory applications in which elemental mercury is used. The limiting concentration for toxicity by inhalation is 3% and, consequently, elemental mercury at 100% will be classified as a special waste.

In this form it would seem to be ideal for treatment and re-use, but a major problem is that the quantities arising at a single location are generally seldom sufficiently large to warrant the costs involved in its separate collection.

Dental Amalgams
The DoE report indicated that 81% of the mercury in sewage effluent comes from dental amalgam and this contributes the majority of the mercury discharged to surface waters. Although the discharge to surface waters is only a fraction of the total discharges to all environmental media, it represents a significant risk as a result of human exposure through eating fish.

The report suggests that ~80% of dental amalgam can be removed from the effluent by means of simple, inexpensive sediment traps, and up to 95% by more sophisticated systems. These would generate a mercury waste for disposal, to which the same criteria as for fluorescent tubes would need to be applied. However, in this case the percentage of mercury in the waste is likely to be much higher and typically the mercury content of encapsulated dental amalgam, as supplied to dentists, is between 40% and 50%, although the content of *in situ* fillings is less.

Since the characteristic properties of dental amalgam are determined by the mercury/silver/tin phase diagram, it is not possible to reduce the mercury content and the long term solution would seem to be to change to another material for filling teeth. Not only would this reduce the risks to dental practitioners and their patients but would overcome the problems of mercury emissions at crematoria. Based upon an average of four fillings per person, it has been estimated that a typical-sized crematorium releases about 12 kg of mercury into the atmosphere per year.

Mercury-Containing Batteries

Under the Batteries and Accumulators (Containing Dangerous Substances) Regulations 1994, SI 1994/232, the relevant heavy metal content must be marked on the batteries themselves. The only batteries which now contain significant amounts of mercury are mercury oxide button cells, and these contribute 4.4 tpa of mercury to landfill. DoE guidance suggests that the same criteria for inorganic mercury compounds are applied as for fluorescent tubes.

Construction and Demolition (C&D) Waste

Waste from these operations, while containing a high proportion of materials which present little risk of harm to man and to the environment, may also include some with hazardous components. There are a number of statutory provisions dealing with "C&D" wastes and it is important to note the context of the definition used and the scope of materials covered by the term.

The Producer of C&D Waste

In view of conflicting views on the identity of the waste producer of C&D waste and the associated Duty of Care obligations, Annex B of the 1991 Code of Practice gave detailed guidelines on this issue. It stated that "the person undertaking the works which give rise to that waste, not the person who issues or lets contracts which give rise to that waste is regarded as the producer." Where several contractors or sub-contractors are on site, the producer of the waste is the particular contractor who takes an action which creates waste or begins to treat something as of it were waste.

The implementation of the Framework Directive changed the position regarding the producer of C&D waste, as discussed in Chapter 8. However, the 1996 revision of the Code of Practice makes no reference to the designation of the producer of C&D waste. Although the absence of such guidance will not influence the legal position, which will be determined by the courts on the facts of the cases in question, the Environment Agency and SEPA will be faced with the dilemma of how to approach such situations and, until this has been judicially considered, it will remain an area of uncertainty.

Carriage of Waste
In relation to waste carrier registration:

— "building or demolition waste" means waste arising from works of construction or demolition, including waste arising from preparatory work thereto (Regulation 2, The Controlled Waste (Registration of Carriers and Seizure of Vehicles) Regulations 1991, SI 1991/1624);

— "construction" includes improvement, repair or alteration (Regulation 1(1), The Controlled Waste Regulations 1992, SI 1992/588),

and this is the only case in which an unlicensed producer of waste cannot transport his own waste materials.

Activities Subject to Licensing
The operation of concrete crushers comes within section 3.4(c) of Schedule 1 to SI 1991/472, as amended, and since this is a " Part B" process within Part I of the 1990 Act, it requires an authorisation from the local authority (or SEPA, in Scotland). Guidance is available in the Secretary of State's Guidance Note PG3/8(91) *Quarry Processes, Including Roadstone Plants and the Size Reduction of Bricks, Tiles and Concrete.*

Exemptions from Waste Management Licensing
Activities associated with the storage and processing of C&D waste are exempt from waste management licensing and in this context "construction work" includes repair, alteration or improvement of existing works (Regulation 1(3), The Waste Management Licensing Regulations 1994, SI 1994/1056).

Within Schedule 3 to the Regulations, the storage exemptions are in paragraph 19 and the treatment exemptions are in paragraphs 13 and 24.

Storage
Under paragraph 19, the storage of materials consisting of ash, slag, clinker, rock, wood or gypsum arising from demolition, construction and tunnelling or other excavations (undefined) is exempted from licensing

where the waste in question is suitable for relevant work which will be carried on at the site. Waste not produced on the site is also exempt, provided that it is not stored at the site for more than three months prior to the start of "relevant work".

"Relevant work" is defined as construction work, including the deposit of waste on land, in connection with the provision of recreational facilities or the construction, maintenance or improvement of a building, highway, railway, airport, dock or other transport facility, but not in relation to any other deposit or reclamation of land.

In the case of road planings which are stored pending relevant work elsewhere, limits of 50,000 tonnes and three months are applied.

Waste Treatment
The processes exempted through paragraph 13 relate to the manufacture from waste of:

— construction materials such as timber products, straw board, plasterboard, bricks, blockstone, roadstone and aggregate;

— soil or soil substitutes, at the place where the waste is produced or where the product is to be applied to the land, provided this does not exceed 500 tonnes per day;

and

— the treatment of waste soil or rock up to 100 tonnes per day which, when treated, is to be spread on land, in accordance with paragraphs 7 or 9.

The storage for these activities is also exempt, provided the waste is stored at the place where the activity is to be carried on, and the maximum quantity is 50,000 tonnes of waste in the case of the manufacture of roadstone from road planings and 20,000 tonnes in other cases.

Burning
Paragraph 30 permits the burning in the open of waste wood, bark and other plant matter which *inter alia* is produced on land as a result of demolition work, provided it is burned on the land where it is produced and provided that the total quantity burned in any 24 hour period does not exceed 10 tonnes. The associated storage of these materials is also exempt.

Landfill Tax
The definitions in the landfill tax provisions relate to "qualifying materials" which are subject to the lower rate of tax, and these include:

— "rocks and solids" in Group 1 including (naturally-occurring) clay, sand, gravel, sandstone, limestone, crushed stone, china clay, construction stone, stone from the demolition of buildings and structures, slate, topsoil, peat, silt and dredgings;

and

— "ceramics and other materials" in Group 2 comprising only the following – glass, ceramics, concrete.

(Schedule, The Landfill Tax (Qualifying Material) Order 1996, SI 1996/1528.)

Inert Waste

When applied to waste, the use of the term "inert" is intended to convey that a particular material is benign with regard to its effects on man and the environment. Historically, its usage was derived from the perceived inactivity of certain substances when subject to landfill conditions, and the term was widely employed in landfill site licences, where it was used to describe the waste materials which were acceptable at a given site.

The majority of wastes undergo some physical or chemical changes under appropriate ambient conditions and, as understanding of the reactions which take place within a landfill has grown, it has become clear that, for the majority of materials, "inert" is an inappropriate description.

Waste Management Paper 4 notes that, although many landfill sites were licensed under the Control of Pollution Act 1974 to accept "inert" waste, a very high proportion contained slowly degrading materials, such as wood from demolition wastes, that subsequently gave rise to the production of landfill gas and leachate. The Paper recommends that licence conditions should avoid using the term "inert", except where categorising the licence. However, while such advice is pertinent to the setting of conditions for new sites, unless there is a complete rationalisation of all existing licences there will still be a significant number of sites which are licensed to accept "inert" waste.

While the introduction of the landfill tax will not affect site licences *per se*, it will have a significant effect on the use of the term "inert" to describe the waste accepted at *all* landfill sites. The term "qualifying material" relates to wastes of a kind commonly described as "inactive" or "inert", which attract the lower rate of tax. As a consequence, the definition of "qualifying material" in SI 1996/1528 effectively determines the scope of materials which may be classified as "inert waste" and, in view of the financial implications of this definition, such materials are certain to receive the close attention of H M Customs and Excise. Although in practice some of the substances falling within the definition of "qualifying material" (and also materials which are exempt from the tax) are clearly *not* inert in their characteristics, the merit of this measure is that there is now a single, relatively unambiguous definition which is applicable to the whole of the UK and which will attract much greater scrutiny than the compliance with site conditions did in the past.

Waste from Contaminated Land

On-Site Operations

In the past, a number of different methods of assessing the acceptability of waste for landfill were developed by the former WRAs. This resulted in discrepancies in the classification of most wastes and this was most apparent in relation to those presenting a significant hazard to man or the environment. Further complications were caused by the need to involve the WRAs of both the consignor and consignee, with the consequence that, where more than one disposal site was being used, the waste manager was sometimes faced with satisfying three or more different set of criteria for determining how to classify his waste.

Some attempts were made to overcome these problems at a regional level, for example the development of the SEWRAC system (South East Waste Regulation Authorities Classification), although in practice discrepancies still arose in relation to the criteria applied to "difficult", "special" and "prohibited" wastes.

However, the changes introduced by the Special Waste Regulations and the establishment of overall control by the Environment Agency and SEPA should assist in resolving these difficulties and it is also possible that the landfill tax requirements will exert a unifying influence.

When contaminated spoil is to be removed from a site, the developer or his contractor must consider how to determine its composition, both *in situ* and post-excavation, and the optimum means of storage prior to removal from site. Much will depend upon local circumstances, but the main issues to be addressed are:

— obtaining samples which are representative of the bulk of the material;

— the retention of the identity of the material when it has been excavated and is stockpiled elsewhere on site prior to despatch;

— the prevention of contamination of groundwater or other waste by any spoil which has been identified as containing contaminants.

The heterogeneous nature of contaminated sites introduces a degree of uncertainty into the assessment of the levels of contamination and, even with a grid of 20 m x 20 m across a large site, it is still possible to miss "hot spots" of contamination. Furthermore, management control is difficult on a site whose physical nature is changing as a result of the operations and the movement of spoil about a site is undertaken by the dumper truck driver of the sub-subcontractor, whose major concern is not normally the client's duty of care.

Removal of Waste Off-Site
A major problem is the acceptance criteria of the receiving landfill site and, as noted earlier, this may be based upon "Kelly's Tables" (a system originally designed for the classification of contaminated soils in relation to the associated health and safety risks), the guidelines drawn up by the ICRCL (Interdepartmental Committee for the Redevelopment of Contaminated Land and intended for the classification of land for redevelopment of brown field sites, not the material from them for landfill), or some variant of either of these.

The ability of a landfill site to receive wastes is a function of its design and location, and these factors will determine the types and compositions of waste and the quantities which may be deposited over a given time period. While these will vary from site to site, the methodology for determining such acceptance criteria should be the same. This is an area in need of urgent attention and rationalisation by the Environment Agency and SEPA.

Landfill of Spoil
In some circumstances, contaminated spoil may be exempt from the landfill tax and full details of the conditions are contained in the Landfill Tax (Contaminated Land) Order 1996, SI 1996/1529. In order to gain exemption, it is necessary for the person carrying out, or intending to carry out, the land reclamation to apply in writing for an exemption certificate 30 days before the certificate is to take effect. It is not possible to apply for a certificate after the intended construction work has commenced (section 43A(3), Finance Act 1996). In addition, a certificate cannot be issued when the pollutants have been cleared to the extent that they either no longer prevent the objective of the work (as defined in section 43B(7)(a)) from being fulfilled, or the harmful components have been removed or reduced to such a level that they no longer constitute potential harm (section 43B(7)(b)).

An exemption cannot be granted where the remediation work is being carried out under a mandatory procedure, such as a remediation notice under section 78E EPA 1990 or a works notice under section 161A WRA

1991. However, this limitation does not apply where the work is being undertaken by the regulators themselves, or on their behalf (section 43A(5), Finance Act 1996).

The application for exemption must be accompanied by such general or specific information as is required and, by standardising such information, H M Customs and Excise could indirectly influence the parameters used to assess the extent of the contamination. In order for a certificate to be issued, the purpose of removing the pollutants from the site must be to enable the site to be developed, conserved, made into a public park or another amenity, or used for agriculture or forestry, or to reduce or remove the potential of the pollutants to cause harm. The waste must result only from the reclamation of the contaminated land, although it is not necessary that all of the pollutants are removed (section 43B(9)). In addition, it is not necessary for the entire site to be cleared and it is permissible to clear contaminants from one part of the site and to dispose of them on a different part of the same site. Current polluters may not make use of this exemption which does not apply unless the cause of pollution has ceased, but an owner may apply for a certificate where his land is being polluted by a third party.

In the first year of operation of the landfill tax, a dispute arose as to whether the removal of contaminated material from building "footings" and service trenches was considered as "facilitating development" of the contaminated land and as a consequence the material was exempt from taxation under section 43B(7(c)), or not. As a result of lobbying by the trade association, Customs and Excise changed their view and the Guidance Note on contaminated land, 11/96, was re-issued as notice LFT 2 to reflect the new interpretation.

Perhaps the most important aspect of this change is that it resulted from a modification to the non-statutory guidance made by the regulatory agency, rather than from alterations to the primary or secondary legislation, or as the result of judicial consideration.

Scrap Metal

In many respects, scrap metal presents fewer legal difficulties than other waste materials. By its very nature "scrap" tends to be synonymous with substances which have been, or about are to be, discarded, i.e. they fulfill the criteria in the definition of "waste", and the term "scrap metal" provides a well-understood "first level" description of the material. In addition, most scrap metal has a finite value and as such the holder has an incentive to ensure its security, although this does not necessarily extend to some of the other materials associated with the scrap. This distinction is acknowledged in the amended Waste Management Licensing Regulations which refer to these materials as "scrap metal" and "non-scrap waste" respectively (paragraph 45(5), Schedule 3).

As a consequence, the major issues associated with these materials are the registration of operations processing and handling scrap, and the application of the Duty of Care, rather than those of its definition. The industry demonstrated significant resistance to the classification of scrap metal as "waste" and its associated controls, and this resulted in a number of delays to the application of waste management legislation to this area. However, this was finally achieved in the Waste Management (Amendment, etc.) Regulations 1995, SI 1995/288, which amended the Controlled Waste Regulations 1992, SI 1992/588, to include scrap metal in the definition of "controlled waste" and imposed a number of controls on the licensing of these activities.

Duty of Care

As a controlled waste, scrap metal comes within the ambit of the Duty of Care, although DoE Circular 6/95 and the Code of Practice give the impression that the expectations in this area will not be high. The Circular states that the Environment Agency and SEPA "should have regard to the source of benefit to the environment and sustainable development of scrap metal recovery and waste motor vehicle dismantling" and "a balance should be struck between advice/encouragement and regulation/ enforcement" and that they should "distinguish between and act proportionately in relation to technical breaches of the Regulations ...".

Documentation

Operators who are subject to the Scrap Metal Dealers Act 1964 or the Civic Government (Scotland) Act 1982 are required to keep a book at each place occupied by them as a scrap metal store, containing specific information concerning all scrap metal received there and all scrap metal processed or despatched from there.

In addition to the particulars to be recorded under section 2(2) and (3) of the 1964 Act, the only other information which is required by the 1991 Duty of Care Regulations is:

— the means of containment of the material in transit;

— whether the transferor is the producer or importer of the material;

— to which category of authorised person the transferor and transferee belong; and

— the place of transfer.

Itinerant Metal Traders

"Itinerant collectors" ("itinerant metal dealers" in Scotland) are also subject to the Duty of Care and must ensure that transfer notes are completed and retained for the requisite period. However, such documents are not required for the collection of a householder's own waste from his home.

Waste Management Licensing

Scrap metal recovery sites are referred to as "metal recycling sites (MRS)" and are classified as recovery operations for the purposes of waste management licensing. Guidance on the licensing of sites is given in Waste Management Paper No. 4A, which draws attention to their distinctive features, viz:

— the operator is likely to have "a sound knowledge" of the materials he receives;

— a significant proportion of the scrap metal received will have a positive value both to the transferor and the transferee;

— the operator of a MRS "is likely to have a direct interest in taking measures to prevent the escape of waste from his control".

While the exemptions to waste management licensing below include a wide range of activities, those that do not satisfy the conditions will need to gain either a waste management licence under Part II of the 1990 Act, or an authorisation under Part I if they are a prescribed process within Chapter 5 (Waste Disposal and Recycling) of Schedule 1 of the Environmental Protection (Prescribed Processes and Substances) Regulations 1991, SI 1991/472, as amended. Aspects of the control of these waste management processes are discussed in more detail in Chapter 13.

Exemptions from Waste Management Licensing

The 1995 amendments to the Waste Management Licensing Regulations added two categories of processes associated with the scrap metal trade to the 43 other processes within Schedule 3 which are exempt from waste management licensing. The new processes are:

— de-greasing or de-oiling ferrous or non-ferrous metal in a furnace(s) of an aggregated net rated thermal input of less than 0.2 Megawatts, but excluding cable-burning (paragraph 44); and

— the dismantling of waste motor vehicles and the recovery of scrap metals (paragraph 45).

Although these measures fall within Schedule 3 to the Regulations – "Activities Exempt from Waste Management Licensing" – the format of these particular exemptions, unlike others within the Schedule, places a number of demands on those subject to their provisions which have many features much more akin to licence conditions, although licences and authorisations are subject to greater controls and sanctions. These conditions of exemption include, *inter alia*:

— the payment of a registration fee and an annual fee;

— the imposition of a number of detailed requirements on both the construction of the infrastructure (drainage, bunding, etc.) and its operation (quantities of materials, height of stacks of waste);

— details of the amount of scrap metal and "non-scrap waste" which may be stored, with both total and short-term (7 day) limits;

— the requirement of a monthly audit to confirm compliance with the terms and conditions of the exemption (paragraph 46(3)(a)(ii)).

With regard to the latter point, it is interesting to speculate whether section 111(4) of the Environment Act 1995, relating to the admissibility in evidence of the absence of an entry in a record, applies both to licences and licensing exemptions.

It is an offence under Regulation 18 of SI 1994/1056 to carry on an exempted activity unless it has been registered with the appropriate registration authority. While for most exempted activities this merely entails supplying:

— the name and address of the establishment or undertaking;

— the activity which constitutes the exempt activity; and

— the place where the activity is carried on,

it is significant that more detailed information is required in relation to scrap metal activities falling within paragraph 45, including a plan of the site showing:

— the boundaries of the site;

— the location within the site at which the exempted activity is carried on;

— the locations and specifications of any impermeable pavements or drainage systems or hardstandings, as required by the Regulations; and

— the location of any secure containers, as required by the Regulations.

With regard to the carrying on of exempted activities "at any *secure* place designed or adapted for the recovery of scrap metal or the dismantling of waste motor vehicles", Table 4A of the Regulations specifies the kinds of waste involved, the activities associated with these scrap metals and the seven day limit applied to the storage of these materials. The maximum total quantities of different forms of scrap metal are detailed in Table 4B. Other conditions of the exemption are given in paragraph 45, including the establishment of administrative arrangements to ensure the compliance with these conditions (paragraph 45(3)) and the limits placed upon the acceptance and storage of "non-scrap" waste at the site.

In addition to the operations covered in paragraphs 44 and 45, there are other scrap-related processes which are exempted from waste management licensing, viz:

— *paragraph 2*, which refers to scrap metal furnaces of less than 25 tonnes capacity which are subject to "Part I EPA control" and the associated storage facilities, unless these are also used for scrap metal trading.

— *paragraph 14*, which permits *inter alia* the storage of up to 15,000 tonnes of waste metal for "the manufacture of finished goods", provided that this is stored at the place of manufacture;

— *paragraph 17*, which permits the storage in a secure place of up to 500 tonnes of waste steel cans, aluminium cans or aluminium foil, for re-use or for subsequent baling (as under paragraph 11), provided the period of storage is not greater than 12 months;

— *paragraph 40(2)*, which relates to the temporary storage of scrap rails on the operational land of a railway, provided that the total quantity "in any one place" (whatever that means in these circumstances) does not exceed 10 tonnes and that the storage is incidental to the collection or transport of the rails.

Sewage Sludge

Classification
The exclusion of sewage sludge from the definition of controlled waste is limited to situations under which it is treated, kept or disposed of within the curtilage of a sewage treatment works. For other conditions such as when it is being transported or is being spread on land, it falls within the controlled waste regime and its associated licensing requirements. DoE Circular 6/96 notes that, although sewage sludges are not generally regarded as special waste and do not constitute an entry in the Hazardous

Waste List, it is possible that "exceptional sludges" from industrial areas could have properties such as H5 (harmful) when all the components are considered together.

With regard to the landfill tax, the water content of effluent or sewage sludge from waste water treatment works or sewage disposal works may be discounted, but:

— that which is present naturally cannot be discounted; and

— any water which has been extracted prior to disposal will be regarded as added water in preference to water naturally in the material.

Details of these requirements are contained in the Landfill Tax Regulations 1996, SI 1996/1527, and in Guidance Note 4/96 *Calculating the Weight of Waste*.

Exemptions from Waste Management Licensing: Spreading of Waste on Land
Activities involving the spreading on agricultural land of the wastes listed in Table 2 of Schedule 3 to the 1994 Regulations are exempted from licensing under paragraph 7. The wastes include, *inter alia*, septic tank sludge and sludge from biological treatment plants, and the activities are subject to the limitations that no more than 250 tonnes of this waste is spread on the land in any 12 months and the activity results in benefit to agriculture or ecological improvement.

It is necessary to provide the Environment Agency or SEPA with advance notice of such spreading activities, including details of the waste, its source, the estimated quantity to be applied and the location and time when this is to be carried out. Details of the storage arrangements must also be supplied. Furthermore, the rate of application of sewage sludge to land is controlled by the Sludge (Use in Agriculture) Regulations 1989, SI 1989/1263, and where the land falls within a nitrate sensitive area made under section 94 of the Water Resources Act 1991, further limitations on its application may be imposed. A Code of Practice has been produced by the DoE on the Agricultural Use of Sewage Sludge, and the second edition includes:

— a reduction in the recommended maximum concentration of zinc; and

— a reduction in the recommended maximum concentration of cadmium, when sewage sludge is applied to grass managed in rotation or grown for conservation.

It should be noted that the Control of Pollution (Silage, Slurry, and

Agricultural Fuel Oil) Regulations 1991, SI 1991/324, as amended, impose controls on the storage of slurry from livestock only.

Exemptions from Waste Management Licensing: Storage of Waste for Use in Agriculture
In addition to the above, paragraph 8 of the Waste Management Licensing Regulations 1994, SI 1994/1056, provides an exemption for the storage, in a secure container or lagoon (or in the case of de-watered sludge, in a secure place) on land used for agriculture, of sludge which is to be used in accordance with the Sludge (Use in Agriculture) Regulations 1989, SI 1989/1263, as amended by SI 1990/880.

If the land is not agricultural land under the 1989 Regulations, the exemption still applies if the spreading results in ecological improvement and it does not cause the concentration in the soil of any of the elements listed in column 1 of the soil table in Schedule 2 to the Regulations to exceed the limit specified in column 2.

Exemptions from Waste Management Licensing: Treatment Within a Sewage Works
Any recovery operation carried on within the curtilage of a sewage works in relation to sludge or septic tank sludge brought from another sewage works is exempt provided the annual quantity does not exceed 10,000 cubic metres (paragraph 10).

Exemptions from Waste Management Licensing: Railway Operations
Paragraph 31 permits the discharge of waste onto the track of a railway from a sanitary convenience or sink forming part of a vehicle used for the carriage of passengers on the railway, if the discharge in question does not exceed 25 litres.

This practice is not always approved of, and one local authority considered a challenge to this exemption on the grounds that it was contrary to the requirements of the Waste Framework Directive, on health grounds. This raised the prospect of British Rail, as it then was, preventing such discharges as trains travelled within the county borders. Although the challenge was not followed through, it does emphasise the fact that the 45 exemptions are not absolute and must be compatible with the controlling legislation.

Exemptions from Waste Management Licensing: Other Sources of Sewage Sludge
Paragraph 32 of the Regulations provides for the burial on the premises of waste arising from the use on those premises of a sanitary convenience

equipped with a removable receptacle, if the total amount buried in any period of 12 months does not exceed five cubic metres.

Another source of sewage sludge is the use of temporary chemical toilets supplied by hire firms for use at open air events. Such facilities are supplied as a result of the absence of suitable sewerage arrangements and the disposal of the resulting sludge raises a number of waste management issues. Since it will be necessary to remove the waste from site, a waste carrier licence must be held and the disposal of the waste must be supported by the appropriate Duty of Care documentation.

Thereafter, much will depend upon the means of disposal but, if any physical transfer of waste occurs prior to the final disposal, then a transfer station licence may be required. The options available are:

— direct disposal to a sewage treatment works;

— direct discharge into the foul sewer; and

— disposal to a landfill site.

The operator of a sewage treatment works is permitted to accept a certain amount of sewage under the exemption within paragraph 10, although he is not obliged to accept such material. Some sewerage undertakers require that the discharging company holds a "sewage discharge licence" and a charge is made per litre of material accepted.

For discharge to the foul sewer, again there is no obligation to accept the discharge but, if a commercial agreement is set up, the discharging company will require a discharge consent under the Water Industry Act 1991 and this may require a certain amount of rudimentary pre-treatment, such as coarse screening, prior to discharge.

FURTHER READING

Clinical Waste – A guidance to local authority client officers on the disposal of clinical waste, Institute of Wastes Management and National Association of Waste Disposal Officers, April 1995

LWRA Guidelines for the Segregation, Handling, and Transport of Clinical Waste, London Waste Regulation Authority, 1995

"Provisions within UK Law relating to the Treatment of 'Empty' and 'Part-Empty' Containers", D N Pocklington, [1997] 9 *ELM*, 179

"Specialised Waste Streams" in *Croner's Waste Management*, Croner Publications (regularly updated)

"Waste Charts" in *Croner's Waste Management*, Croner Publications (regularly updated)

"Waste Management Papers", Department of the Environment

WMP 6   *Polychlorinated Biphenyls* (1995)
WMP 7   *Mineral Oil Waste* (1976)[#]
WMP 8   *Heat Treatment of Cyanide Waste (2nd Edition)* (1986)[#]
WMP 9   *Halogenated Hydrocarbon Solvent Wastes from the Cleaning Processes* (1976)[#]
WMP 11 *Metal Finishing Wastes* (1974)[#] – to be revised
WMP 12 *Mercury Bearing Wastes* (1977)[#]
WMP 13 *Tarry and Distillation Wastes and Other Chemical Based Wastes* (1977)[#]
WMP 14 *Solvent Wastes (excluding Halogenated Hydrocarbons)* (1977)[#]
WMP 15 *Halogenated Organic Wastes* (1978)[#]
WMP 16 *Wood Preserving Wastes* (1980)[#]
WMP 17 *Wastes from Tanning, Leather Dressing and Fellmongering* (1978)[#]
WMP 18 *Asbestos Waste* (1979)
WMP 19 *Wastes from the Manufacture of Pharmaceuticals, Toiletries and Cosmetics* (1978)[#]
WMP 20 *Arsenic Bearing Wastes* (1980)[#]
WMP 21 *Pesticide Wastes* (1980)[#]
WMP 23 *Special Wastes* (1981)[#] – to be revised
WMP 24 *Cadmium Bearing Wastes* (1984)[#]
WMP 25 *Clinical Wastes* (1983)[#] – to be revised
WMP 26 *Landfilling Wastes* (1986)[#] – to be revised

[#] out of print

Table 11-1: Example of Technical Information Contained in the "Waste Charts" of *Croner's Waste Management*

Infectious waste including viable pathogenic micro-organisms (see page 2-675)

HAZARDS

Physical/chemical	Medical	Environmental
	Risk of infection and possibility of toxic or allergenic hazards.	Some organisms may be infectious for plants and animals.

HANDLING PRECAUTIONS	LABELLING
Avoid all skin contact, exposure to contaminated sharps and routes of inhalation/ingestion. Standard PPE. Boots, waterproof apron, face protection and/or HSE approved respiratory protection as necessary. Ensure adherence to containment procedures. Observe strict personal hygiene.	**Infectious substance** UN 2814 (infectious to humans) UN 2900 (infectious to animals) UN 3291 (clinical waste)

STORAGE
Keep clinical wastes in colour coded bags, segregated from other wastes.
General infectious waste: obtain information from local medical officer for environmental health. Category "A" pathogen waste: obtain information from HSE.
Awaiting autoclaving: seal securely in autoclave bags, place in solid bottomed containers.
Awaiting disposal after autoclaving: keep in secure sealed colour coded containers.
DO NOT mix human tissue with other clinical wastes.

TREATMENT AND DISPOSAL
Autoclaving: the centre of the waste load must reach 121°C for at least 15 minutes. Higher temperatures required for transmissible spongiform encephalopathy agents. Some waste can then be landfilled, but incineration is normally the best practicable environmental option, and is always required for soiled surgical dressings, swabs, contaminated waste from treatment areas, infected laboratory carcasses. Supervised incineration is required for human tissue, limbs, placentae.
BAG COLOURS FOR CLINICAL WASTE:
Yellow — all waste destined for incineration
Yellow with black band — preferably incinerate, but may be landfilled if suitable arrangements are made (eg home nursing waste)
Light blue — waste for autoclaving before ultimate disposal.

RECYCLING/RE-USE

STATUTORY
Health and Safety (Dangerous Pathogens) Regulations 1981
Public Health (Control of Disease) Act 1984

REFERENCES
SP 48, 49; WMP 25; ACDP Notes as appropriate. IPC: IPR 5/2
London Waste Regulation Authority 1989 "Guidelines for the segregation, handling and transport of clinical waste"
British Medical Association 1990 "Code of practice for the safe use and disposal of sharps". Health Services Advisory Committee 1992 "The safe disposal of clinical waste"

Table 11-2: High Risk and Low Risk Wastes, as Defined 479
in Schedule I of the Animal By-Products Order 1992,
SI 1992/3303

SCHEDULE 1

PART I

(a) All bovine animals, pigs, goats, sheep, solipeds, poultry and all other animals kept for agricultural production, which have died or been killed on the farm but were not slaughtered for human consumption, including stillborn and unborn animals;

(b) dead animals not referred to in paragraph (a) but which are designated by the Minister by notice in writing to the person in charge of the dead animals or by such other means as the Minister thinks fit;

(c) animals other than those slaughtered for human consumption, which are killed in the context of disease control measures either on the farm or in any other place designated by the Minister;

(d) animal by-products including blood originating from animals which show, during the veterinary inspection carried out at the time of slaughtering, signs of diseases communicable to man or other animals;

(e) with the exception of hides, skins, hooves, feathers, wool, horns, hair, blood and similar products, all those parts of animals slaughtered in the normal way which are not presented for post mortem inspection;

(f) all meat, poultrymeat, fish, game and foodstuffs of animal origin which are spoiled in such a way as to present a risk to human and animal health;

(g) animals, fresh meat, poultrymeat, fish, game and meat and milk products, imported from any country other than a member State which fail to comply with the veterinary requirements for their importation into the Community, unless they are re-exported or their import is accepted under restriction laid down in Community provisions;

(h) farm animals which have died in transit other than those slaughtered for reasons of welfare;

(i) animal by-products containing residues of substances which may pose a danger to human or animal health; milk, meat or products of animal origin rendered unfit for human consumption by the presence of such residues;

(j) fish which show clinical signs of diseases communicable to man or to fish.

PART II

(a) Animal by-products other than those covered in Part I of this Schedule;

(b) products excepted from Schedule 1 Part I paragraph (e) (namely hides, skins, hooves, feathers, wool, horns, hair, blood and similar products) when used in the manufacture of feedingstuffs;

(c) fish caught in the open sea for the purposes of fishmeal production;

(d) fresh fish offal from plants manufacturing fish products for human consumption.

Chapter 12

THE REGULATION OF WASTE MANAGEMENT OPERATIONS – PART II ENVIRONMENTAL PROTECTION ACT 1990

INTRODUCTION

Since measures directed towards the control of waste disposal operations were first introduced under COPA 1974, there has been a significant expansion to the scope of waste management operations subject to some form of control and now a number of different regimes are in force. The 1994 Waste Management Licensing Regulations and their subsequent amendments form the basis for the regulation of controlled wastes. Under Regulation 17, certain operations are *exempted* from these licensing requirements, though registration of the exemption with the Environment Agency or SEPA is needed.

Other activities are *excluded* from licensing, under Regulation 16, such as those processes subject to control through Integrated Pollution Control (IPC) or Local Air Pollution Control (LAPC) under Part I of the Act. A further regulatory regime is that for the registration of the carriers of waste, which falls within the Control of Pollution (Amendment) Act 1989 and exhibits a number of similarities to that relating to the registration of brokers within the 1994 Regulations.

Whilst its objective was not the regulation of waste management operations *per se*, section 47 of the Finance Act 1996 also has required the registration of persons involved in taxable activities in relation to the landfill tax. Although this measure is concerned with the disposal of material as waste by means of landfill (section 40), unlike the other provisions described above, it is not restricted to controlled waste.

THE EU WASTE FRAMEWORK DIRECTIVE

The Framework Directive is the primary source of waste legislation within EU Member States and is addressed in the following instruments:

EU Instrument	Content/Purpose of Modification	Reference
75/442/EEC	the initial Framework Directive	OJ[1975]L194/39
91/156/EEC	a major amendment of 75/442/EEC	OJ [1991] L78/32
91/692/EEC	standardisation and rationalisation of the reporting of certain Directives	OJ[1991]L377/48
96/350/EC	Commission Decision adapting Annexes II, A and II, B of 75/442/EC	OJ[1996]L135/32

The amended Directive includes a number of requirements relating to the licensing of waste management operations and their supervision by the relevant authorities. The reference point for the granting of licences (referred to as "permits" in the Directive) is the processes listed in Annex II, A (disposal operations) and Annex II, B (recovery operations), and Member States must ensure that all waste falling within the ambit of the Directive is handled by a public or private waste collector or by an undertaking which carries out the operations in these Annexes. Where the waste holder recovers or disposes of the waste himself, this must be in accordance with the provisions of the Directive (Article 8).

Any of the disposal operations in Annex II, A must by authorised by a fixed-term permit issued by the competent authority and, under Article 9, this must cover:

— the types and quantity of waste;

— the technical requirements;

— the security precautions to be taken;

— the disposal site; and

— the treatment method.

Under Article 10, any recovery operation within Annex II, B must be covered by a permit, although no specific requirements are given with respect to the content of such permits. Any undertaking covered by Articles 9 and 10 is required to maintain a record of the quantity, nature, origin and, where relevant, the destination, frequency of collection and mode of transport of the wastes referred to in Annex I, and to make such information available to the competent authorities. The IPPC Directive, 96/61/EC, will necessitate further modification of Annexes II, A and II, B when some of the disposal and recovery operations come under its control.

Establishments which collect or transport waste on a professional basis or which arrange for the disposal or recovery of waste on behalf of others (i.e. dealers and brokers) and are not subject to authorisation, must be registered by the competent authorities.

A comprehensive system of waste regulation is envisaged by the Directive and, whilst some components were operational within the UK under pre-1994 Regulations, it was necessary to modify the legislation to include all these requirements.

WASTE MANAGEMENT LICENSING REGULATION WITHIN THE UK

The licensing of waste management operations is addressed in sections 35 to 44 of the Environmental Protection Act 1990, and the 1994 Waste Management Licensing Regulations provide the framework for control. These Regulations were issued by the Secretary of State, under a range of powers included in the European Communities Act 1972, Control of Pollution Act 1974, Control of Pollution (Amendment) Act 1989 and the Environmental Protection Act 1990, and have since then been subject to a number of modifications:

Statutory Instrument	Title	Purpose of Modification
SI 1994/1056	Waste Management Licensing Regulations 1994	Initial Regulations
SI 1995/288	Waste Management Licensing (Amendment etc.) Regulations 1995	Introduction of provisions for scrap metal
SI 1995/1950	Waste Management Licensing (Amendment No. 2) Regulations 1995	Extends transitional exemption for effluent treatment plants
SI 1996/634	Waste Management Regulations 1996	Further modifications re: scrap metal and effluent plants
SI 1996/1279	Waste Management Licensing (Amendment) Regulations 1996	Exemption provisions for storage of meat (re: BSE)

Through Regulation 19 and Schedule 4, these Regulations bring into effect "certain provisions" of the Waste Framework Directive.

THE SCOPE OF THE REGULATIONS

Processes Included Within the Regulations

There are a number of references within Part II of the 1990 Act which relate to the requirement for a licence for the treatment, keeping or disposal of controlled waste and, through paragraph 9 of Schedule 4 to the 1994 Regulations, such references are taken to include a reference to any operation listed in Part III or IV of the Schedule (i.e. Annexes II, A and II, B of the Framework Directive). Consequently, although these lists are non exclusive, the processes included form the basis of those for which there is a requirement for a waste management licence.

Processes Excluded From the Regulations

Regulation 16 excludes from licensing those activities which fall within the control of other legislative regimes, including:

— the recovery or disposal of waste under an authorisation under Part I of the 1990 Act, where the activity is or forms part of a process designated for central control under section 2(4);

— the disposal of waste under an authorisation granted under Part I of the 1990 Act, where the activity is or forms part of a process within paragraph (a) of Part B of section 5.1 (incineration) of Schedule 1 to the 1991 Regulations, SI 1991/472 as amended, insofar as the activity results in releases of substances to the air;

— the disposal of liquid waste under a consent in accordance with Chapter II of Part III of the Water Resources Act 1991 or under Part II of the Control of Pollution Act 1974;

— the recovery or disposal of waste where the activity is or forms part of an operation which is for the time being either:

— the subject of a licence under Part II of the Food and Environmental Protection Act 1985 (FEPA); or

— carried on in circumstances where such a licence would be required but for an order under section 7 of that Act.

The first two provisions above are inapplicable where the activity involves the final disposal of waste by deposit in or on land. This position will change, however, with the introduction of the IPPC Directive. The term "is or forms part of" is not defined and it is uncertain whether this includes the situation in which waste material is treated or stored on the site of an incinerator which uses waste oil as a fuel.

With regard to the disposal of *liquid waste*, this follows from the Framework Directive, which excludes this category of waste from its controls but not *waste in liquid form*.

Although FEPA 1985 is primarily concerned with the deposit of waste in the sea, it should be noted that the term "land" in section 29(8) of this Act includes land covered by water above the low water mark and the Act is not restricted in its application to the tidal parts of rivers and estuaries, e.g. the Thames up to Teddington. With regard to the exemptions to its provisions under section 7, these are currently detailed in the Deposits in the Sea (Exemption) Order 1985.

PROCESSES EXEMPTED FROM THE REGULATIONS

Whilst *excluded* processes are subject to controls outwith Part II of the Act, those which are *exempted* are subject to a limited degree of control under Regulation 18 of the 1994 Regulations. These excluded processes are described in more detail in the following section.

The Role of the Exemptions

In order to fulfil the requirements of Articles 9 and 10 of the Waste Framework Directive, it is necessary for the competent authorities of the Member States to establish systems for the issue of permits for the processes included in Annexes II, A and II, B. There is no threshold below which these requirements cease to apply and the system of exemptions is a means by which thresholds may be applied, whilst seeking to meet the aims of the Directive. This is evident from paragraph 6.25 in Annex 6 of DoE Circular 11/94, which states that, in applying the "exemption provisions", authorities and operators "should have regard to the aim of both the Directive and of waste management licensing", i.e. the prevention and minimisation of pollution and harm.

The guidance continues by stating that, when an activity is carried on properly within the scope of an exemption and within all other requirements of the Directive and the licensing Regulations, then "this aim will be achieved". Whilst such weasel words are based on flawed logic (i.e. suggesting that, by subjecting certain processes to no formal controls, the requirements of Articles 9 and 10 of the Directive are met where these uncontrolled processes comply with the other parts of the Directive) and may not meet detailed scrutiny by the ECJ, they represent a pragmatic, practical solution to the problem.

The Scope of the Exemptions

The processes exempt from licensing are described in Schedule 3 to the 1994 Regulations, which is reproduced in Table 12-1 on pages 520-521. These processes fall into one of the following headings:

— recovery or re-use of waste: paragraphs 1 to 23;

— operations leading to recovery/re-use or disposal: paragraphs 24 to 28;

— disposal of own waste at the place of production: paragraphs 29 to 35;

— other deposits of waste: paragraphs 36 to 41;

— transitional exemptions: paragraphs 42 and 43;

— scrap metal: paragraphs 44 and 45.

These exemptions are not absolute and are subject to the condition that the type and quantity of waste and the methods used for disposal or recovery are consistent with the objectives of the Waste Framework Directive, re-stated in paragraph 4(1)(a) of Schedule 4. In addition, the exemptions relating to the activities in paragraphs 4, 7, 9, 11, 13, 14, 15, 17, 18, 19, 25, 37, 40 and 41 only apply where they are carried on by, or with the consent of, the occupier of the land, or the person carrying on the exempted activity is otherwise entitled to do so on that land.

Details of the Exempted Processes

Whilst some of the descriptions of the activities in Schedule 3 are quite specific, others are less clear in their application. A number of the relevant definitions such as "construction work", "scrap metal" and "waste oil" are included in Regulation 1(3) of SI 1994/1056, and others are defined in the paragraph relating to the exemption. Further guidance on the interpretation of the exemptions is contained in Annex 5 of Department of the Environment Circular 11/94 and, although its advice is less confusing than that in Annex 2 (on the definition of waste), in many cases it does little more than reiterate the section within the Schedule.

The reader is directed to the Regulations and the Circular for details of specific exemptions. There are, however, a number of features which are either common to more than one exemption or where specific clarification has been given, and these are discussed below.

General Issues
It should be noted that the exemptions relate to the activity specified and not to the waste, which is still subject to waste-related legislation provided it comes within the definition of controlled waste. This issue is highlighted by paragraph 7 which relates to materials spread on land for agriculture. The Circular warns that the inclusion of a material on this list does not imply that it is waste and that materials originating from agricultural operations are not controlled wastes within the scope of the Regulations.

In general, special wastes are not covered by the exemptions in Schedule 3 unless specific provision is made. Certain exemptions – 1 to 3 and 24 – apply only in cases where a Part B authorisation under Part I of the 1990 Act is held.

Secure Storage of Waste
The majority of exemptions include provisions relating to the storage of waste associated with the exempted activity and in addition there are eight paragraphs which are exclusively concerned with the storage of waste prior to its disposal, recovery or re-use. These are:

— *paragraph 17*: storage of certain specified wastes including some special wastes in a secure place and some wastes in quantities exceeding those allowed in the more general exemption in paragraph 40, provided they are destined for recovery;

— *paragraph 18*: storage of specified wastes in secure containers at sites for the reception of waste recovery;

— *paragraph 19*: storage of waste used in construction;

— *paragraph 36*: temporary storage of garbage and tank washings incidental to their collection and transport, whether for disposal or recovery;

— *paragraph 38*: the deposit and storage of samples of waste for testing or analysis;

— *paragraph 39*: storage, prior to disposal, of medical, nursing and veterinary waste;

— *paragraph 40*: a general exemption for the storage of non-liquid waste incidental to its collection and transport, for recovery or disposal, but subject to a quantity limit;

— *paragraph 41*: a general exemption for the temporary storage of waste on the site where the waste is produced, pending its collection for disposal or recovery.

Regulation 17(5) states that, for the purposes of Schedule 3, a container, lagoon or place is considered as secure if all reasonable precautions are taken to ensure that the waste cannot escape from it and members of the public are unable to gain access to the waste. Likewise, secure storage is taken to mean storage in a secure container, lagoon or place.

Paragraphs 1-28: Exemptions relating to recovery or re-use
Where the exemption is specific to recovery, this is limited to the recovery operations listed in Part IV of Schedule 4 (Annex II, B of the Directive) by the definition in Regulation 1(3). However, for those exemptions relating to "recovery or re-use", there are fewer restrictions on the intended destination of the waste, provided it is not for disposal.

Paragraph 4(1): The cleaning, washing, spraying or coating of waste consisting of packaging or containers for re-use
This exemption relates to the return and re-use after recovery of whole containers and packaging, and not the recycling of the materials from which these are made. In addition, the potential problems of defining when a container is "empty" should be noted (see Chapter 12).

Paragraph 6: Burning waste oil as fuel in an engine, and its associated storage
This exemption is necessary since this application of fuel oil does not come within the ambit of Part B of section 1.3 of the "prescribed processes ands substances" Regulations, SI 1991/472 as amended, and as such is not covered by the exemption within paragraph 3(a)(ii) of Schedule 3.

Paragraph 10(1): Treatment of sewage by treatment works, brought from other such works
When treated as an integral part of the operations within the curtilage of a sewage treatment work (and not by means of mobile plant), sewage, sludge and septic tank waste are *not* defined as controlled wastes under the Controlled Waste Regulations 1992, SI 1992/588 as amended. However, in other situations such as when moved from place to place, even when these places are sewage treatment works, such waste is considered as controlled waste and as such would fall within the licensing regime were it not for this exemption.

Paragraph 30: Burning waste in the open
The guidance notes stress that, whilst the prescribed activities are exempt,

they are nevertheless subject to control under the statutory nuisance provisions in Part III of the 1990 Act or, in Scotland, by the Clean Air Act 1993. It should be noted that such controls through statutory nuisance provisions are not limited to those referred to in this paragraph.

Paragraph 31: Discharge of waste onto a railway track
This provision permits discharge onto the track of a railway from a sanitary convenience or sink forming part of a vehicle used for the carriage of passengers on the railway, if the discharge does not exceed 25 litres. This exemption is necessary since sewage from a railway vehicle *is* regarded as a controlled waste under Regulation 5(1) and Schedule 3, paragraph 7(a) of the Controlled Waste Regulations 1992, SI 1992/588.

Paragraph 36: The temporary storage of ships' garbage or tank washings
The reasons behind this particular exemption are complex and result from a number of legislative provisions. The International Convention for the Prevention of Pollution from Ships 1973 (Cm 5748) and the associated protocol of 1978 known as "MARPOL" require the provision of facilities in harbours for three categories of landed ships' wastes. These are controlled by a number of UK instruments, including: the Prevention of Pollution (Reception Facilities) Order 1984, SI 1984/862; the Merchant Shipping (Prevention of Pollution) Regulations 1983, SI 1983/1398; the Merchant Shipping (Control of Pollution by Noxious Liquid Substances in Bulk) Regulations 1987, SI 1987/551; the Merchant Shipping (Prevention of Pollution by Garbage) Regulations 1988, SI 1988/2292; and the Merchant Shipping (Reception Facilities for Garbage) Regulations 1988, SI 1988/2293.

Tank washings and garbage are defined as industrial and therefore controlled waste by the 1992 Regulations and, although the storage of such waste at reception facilities does not come within the definition of recovery or disposal, Circular 11/94 states that unless exempted their use would come within the offence of depositing (section 33(1)(a)).

In view of the specialist nature of this exemption, there are a number of definitions specific to these operations and the interested reader is directed to the Circular for a fuller description.

Paragraph 38: The storage of samples for analysis
This is a wide ranging exemption for the storage of samples of waste, including special waste, which are being or are to be subjected to testing and analysis. It should be noted that the exemption applies only before the

required examination is performed and such samples are regarded as waste after analysis or testing. This raises two interesting situations.

Certain samples, such as those from asbestos-containing substances, are often retained for a fixed but extended period after the analysis has been performed, for quality assurance reasons, *inter alia*.

Secondly, the wording "taken by or on behalf of the owner or occupier of the land from which the samples are taken" suggests that samples taken by "common interest groups" without the owner's knowledge would not qualify for the exemption and consequently their "deposit" at a laboratory would be contrary to section 33(1)(a) of the Act.

Paragraph 40: Storage of non-liquid waste at premises other than where it was produced
In *North Yorkshire County Council v Boyne*, some clarification was given to paragraph 40(1)(d) in relation to storage of waste on premises where the storage is "incidental" to the business. The business in this case was involved in the hire of skips and for the operation in question the respondent was found on a number of occasions to have a backlog of filled skips on his site – a combination of using a distant, but economic, disposal site and only having the use of a single vehicle.

The Divisional Court held that the justices were entitled to find that storage was incidental to the primary business of collection of waste, since the evidence showed that the respondent could not achieve an immediate disposal to landfill and some storage on his site was necessary. This decision does not seem to be consistent with the objective of the exemption which relates to the storage of waste which is incidental to the collection or transport of waste. This was not so in the present case, since this was the primary business of the respondent.

The presence of filled skips on unlicensed sites is a widespread problem and it is possible that these findings could have similar repercussions to the *Leigh* decision, since the Environment Agency and SEPA have little other means of recourse. Although such businesses require a waste carrier licence, objections against its renewal can only be made if, and only if, there has been a contravention of any of the requirements of the regulation relating to the renewal. Where appropriate, action might be taken by means of the "general" pollution offence of section 33(1)(c), or the Duty of Care provisions, provided there was evidence of an infraction. However, such remedies as these are essentially "one-off" courses of action which cannot impose the same degree of control as an appropriate waste management licence.

Registration of Exempt Activities

Registration
The establishment and maintenance of public registers by the appropriate authorities provides the major control mechanism for exempted activities. Under Regulation 18(1) it is an offence for an establishment or undertaking to carry on an exempted activity involving the recovery or disposal of waste without it being registered, although, as a result of Regulation 3(11) of SI 1995/288, the associated fines have been reduced from a maximum of £500 to the nominal level of £10, except for the processes described in paragraph 45 (i.e. those relating to scrap metal). In addition, an appropriate authority cannot refuse to register an exemption and once registered it continues to be so indefinitely.

Regulation 18(4) states that the appropriate registration authority is to enter the relevant particulars in the register if it receives notice of them in writing or otherwise becomes aware of those particulars. In addition, the relevant authorities defined in Regulation 10 are deemed to be aware of "the relevant particulars" of the exempted activities under their control (Regulation 10(5)).

Processes to be Registered
Since the registers relate only to recovery and disposal operations, they do not include all of the processes listed in Schedule 3 and most importantly exclude the general exemptions relating to storage in paragraphs 40 and 41. In cases for which registration is required, Regulation 18(3) states that the register must contain the name of each establishment or undertaking claiming the exemption, the exempted activity and the place at which this activity is carried out.

Where the relevant paragraph in Schedule 3 is conditional on the type of waste, its quantity or specific containment requirements, then the means by which the conditions are satisfied should be included. Where a given undertaking carries on an exempted process at several of its premises, such as the use of compactors at sub-surface stations within London Underground, then a single exemption can be claimed provided the addresses of all the relevant locations are included in the registration.

Relevant Authorities
For the purposes of registration, the exempted processes fall within one of the four groups detailed in Regulation 18(10), for which the relevant authorities are as follows:

— *The local enforcing authority.* Within England and Wales, this is the local authorities and, in Scotland, SEPA. These bodies are responsible for three groups of processes which:

— are within paragraphs 1 (glass manufacture and production), 2 (scrap metal furnaces), 3 (burning waste as fuel) and 8 (crushing, grinding or other size reduction of bricks, tiles and concrete). To qualify for such exemption, the process must also be a process or part of a process subject to Local Air Pollution Control;

— relate to packing or containers in paragraph 4, if the activity involves the coating or spraying of metal containers and is subject to an authorisation under Part I of the Act or involves storage related to the authorised process;

— involve composting under paragraph 12, providing:

— the activity involves the composting of biodegradable waste;

— it is undertaken as a process or a part of a process within paragraph (a) of Part B of Section 6.9 of Schedule 1 to the Regulations, SI 1991/472 as amended; or

— the compost is to be used for cultivating mushrooms and either is subject to an authorisation under Part I of the Act or involves storage related to the authorised process.

— *The Minister of Agriculture Fisheries and Food (in England) or the Secretary of State (in Wales and Scotland).* The group of exempted activities is contained within paragraph 16 which relates to the carrying on of these operations, in accordance with the conditions and requirements of a licence granted under section 7 or section 8 of the Diseases of Animals (Waste Food) Order 1973, SI 1973/1936.

— *The Minister, the appropriate Minister (as defined) or the local authority.* For processes relating to animal by-products within paragraph 23, the relevant authority is determined by the Regulations imposed by the Animal By-Products Order 1992, SI 1992/3303, and the Slaughter-houses Act 1974 or the Slaughter of Animals (Scotland) Act 1980.

— *The Environment Agency or SEPA.* The Agencies are the relevant authority for all other exempted processes.

Enforcement

The penalties associated with exemption licensing offences are low and do not constitute a "relevant offence" for the purposes of other waste management licensing provisions. Furthermore, the guidance given in

Annex 6 to the DoE Circular suggests a "light touch" approach to enforcement, to the point of it being virtually non-existent. It is suggested that enforcement action should not be taken where the failure to register is the only breach of the Regulations and there is no threat of pollution or other harm. The Circular also acknowledges that, in view of the very wide scope of the exempted activities and the fact that formerly many of these would not have been subject to any controls in this area, there may be a substantial number of persons carrying on exempted processes which should be registered who remain for some time unaware or inadequately informed of the requirements.

It is suggested that the licensing of exemptions is given a significantly lower priority that the licensing and regulation of licensable activities, and should be undertaken as and when the Agencies become aware of such categories of process. On such occasions, provided the Agencies become aware of the information requirements of Regulation 18(3), then *ipso facto* Regulation 18(4) comes into effect and any contravention of Regulation 18(1) ceases!

The Inter-Relationship between Licensing Exemptions and Licence Conditions

The relationship between offences under section 33(6) of the Environmental Protection Act 1990 and the scope of the exemptions to waste management licensing under the 1994 Regulations was explored in the unreported case of *London WRA v Drinkwater Sabey Ltd*. The defendant operated a waste management site under a licence which stipulated *inter alia* the maximum tonnage of waste which could be deposited each day. The WRA brought the case on the basis that this tonnage had been exceeded, but the defence argued that much of the material concerned was dredgings from canals and as such was exempted from licensing under Regulation 17 and Schedule 3 to the Waste Management Licensing Regulations 1994, SI 1994/1056.

Under Regulation 17(1), sections 33(1)(a) and (b) of the 1990 Act do not apply to the carrying on of an exempted activity within Schedule 3 to the Regulations, but this does not dis-apply section 33(6) of the Act which relates to the contravention of any condition of a waste management licence. However, the respondents persuaded the court that when section 33(1)(a) and (b) is dis-applied in respect to exempt activities, there can be no breach of licence conditions created by section 33(6). Thus, once an activity is exempt, it falls outwith the scope of the licensing regime even if undertaken by a licence holder, although the general pollution offence in section 33(1)(c) is not dis-applied.

This case highlights the issues which must be taken into consideration by the regulatory authorities before granting permission for such operations to take place, viz:

— the planning authority should address the level of site activity in terms of the number of vehicles entering and leaving the site, and other amenity issues;

— the Environment Agency or SEPA should consider the means available within the licensing regime for restricting unlimited amounts of uncontrolled deposits at a licensed site.

With regard to the latter, although *Drinkwater Sabey* restricts the use of licence conditions in this context, Regulation 17 provides that the exemption to licensing is dependent upon:

— the person carrying on the certain exempted activities being "otherwise entitled to do so on the land in question" (Regulation 17(2)(b)); and

— the activity being consistent with the objectives of the Framework Directive (Regulation 17(4)).

A more satisfactory solution would be for the Secretary of State to use his powers in section 35(6) of the 1990 Act and remove this lacuna.

WASTE MANAGEMENT LICENSING

In addition to the increased scope of activities requiring a waste management licence, *supra*, the 1990 Act changed the emphasis of the licence itself by introducing criteria related to the holder of the licence, as well as site-specific factors. As with the forthcoming IPPC Regulations, controls are imposed upon all aspects of the operation of the licensed activity, from its inception to post-closure operations.

A waste management licence is defined in section 35 of the 1990 Act as a licence granted by the waste regulation authority which authorises the treatment, keeping or disposal of any specified description of controlled waste in or on any specific land, or by means of specific mobile plant. The scope of the term "mobile plant" is given in section 29(9) and includes plant which is designed to move or be moved, whether on roads or on other land. As a result of the provisions in section 29(10), a more wide-ranging description has been prescribed by Regulation 12 of the amended 1994 Regulations, which includes:

— incinerators which are exempt under section 5.1 of Schedule 1 to the 1991 Regulations, SI 1991/472 as amended; and

— plant for:

- — the recovery by filtration or heat treatment of waste oil from electrical equipment;

- — the destruction, by de-chlorination, of waste polychlorinated biphenyls (PCBs) or polychlorinated terphenyls (PCTs);

- — the vitrification of waste;

- — the treatment of clinical waste (as defined by SI 1992/588) by the use of microwaves.

Such plant must be designed to move or be moved by any means from place to place with a view to being used at each such place or, if not so designed, be readily capable of so moving or being so moved. No other description of plant falls within this exemption. With regard to the term "designed", in *Wilson v West Sussex County Council* it was held that this could mean either "intended" or "designed in structural or engineering terms".

LICENCE CONDITIONS

General Conditions

Licences are granted to the person who is in occupation of the land used for the relevant licensable activity, or the owner of the mobile plant, and the Agencies have a wide discretion regarding the activities which the licence authorises and the associated precautions to be taken or the work to be carried out. This may include work relating to both the preparation for the licensable activity and following the termination of these operations. However, following *Attorney General's Reference (No 2 of 1988)*, such discretion is limited to achieving the objectives of the legislation in question. This is emphasised by Regulation 13, whereby no condition may be imposed within a licence for the purpose of securing the health of persons at work within the meaning of Part I of the Health and Safety at Work Act 1974. However, the Health and Safety Executive is a statutory consultee in relation to licence applications (section 36(4)(a)), by which process they would be made aware of the scope of activities covered by a proposed licence.

Conversely, where a particular situation relates to waste management issues, then waste management legislation must be used to achieve the desired objective. This was demonstrated in *Cheshire County Council v Secretary of State for the Environment*, in which the County Council unsuccessfully attempted to use an enforcement notice under its planning powers, although more relevant enforcement remediation powers were available under the existing waste management legislation (i.e. COPA 1974).

The Environmental Protection Act 1990 imposes fewer restrictions on licensing conditions than the equivalent provisions under COPA 1974 and, under section 36(3), a licence may be rejected only where the Environment Agency or SEPA considers that the potential holder is not a "fit and proper person" or that its rejection is necessary for the purpose of preventing:

— pollution of the environment;

— harm to human health; or

— serious detriment to the amenities of the locality (unless planning permission is in force for the relevant activity).

In addition to licence applications, these objectives form the basis for *all* activities associated with waste management licensing – variation, suspension and revocation.

It is important to distinguish between the two different functions of a waste management licence – the authorisation of certain activities to be carried on, i.e. the keeping, treating and disposal of waste, and the imposition of certain conditions on the holder in connection with these activities. The latter are the means by which potentially deleterious consequences of the licensed activity are avoided or minimised, and it is an offence under section 33(6) to fail to comply with any condition of a licence.

This dichotomy is of particular relevance to enforcement action where, in addition to a total revocation of the licence, the Environment Agency or SEPA has the option of revoking the authorisation for some or all of the activities undertaken, while *inter alia* continuing the other conditions of the licence relating to the management of the site and the other preventative measures.

Specific Conditions

As a result of certain EU Directives there is a requirement for a number of specific conditions to be included in waste management licences and these are discussed below.

Waste Oils

This is a requirement of the Waste Framework Directive and relates to waste oil as defined in Regulation 1(3) of SI 1994/1056. Under Regulation 14, licences relating to the regeneration of these wastes must include conditions to ensure that the resulting "base oil" does not constitute a "toxic and dangerous waste" (as defined in Directive 78/319/EEC) and does not contain PCBs or PCTs "at all, or does not contain them in concentrations beyond a specified maximum limit which in no case is to exceed 50 ppm" (*sic*). (This clumsy draughting could have been avoided by reference to the definition of PCBs and PCTs in the relevant Directive, 75/439/EEC as amended by 87/101/EEC, which specifies concentrations above which the waste is to be regarded as a PCB or PCT – currently 50 ppm.)

Where such a licence includes the keeping of waste oil, there must be a provision to prevent it from being mixed with toxic and dangerous waste PCBs or PCTs.

Protection of Groundwater
A more generally applicable condition of licensing is imposed by Regulation 15, which implements some of the requirements of the Groundwater Directive, 80/68/EEC, in relation to:

— *preventing* substances in List I from entering groundwater: and

— *limiting* the introduction of List II substances into groundwater, so as to avoid pollution.

List I and List II substances are described in Table 12-2 (page 522). The Directive uses a narrower definition of "groundwater" than in UK legislation (Part III Water Resources Act 1991 (in England and Wales) and Part II COPA 1974 (in Scotland)) and divides discharges into "indirect" and "direct" depending upon whether they percolate through the ground or subsoil, or not.

With regard to waste disposal, Article 2(b) of the Directive states that its provisions do not apply to discharges containing List I or List II substances in quantities or concentrations which are so small as to obviate any present or future deterioration in the quality of the receiving groundwater. In *Commission v Germany*, case c-131/88, this provision was interpreted quite restrictively and it was held that such effects must be evident *prima facie*.

When the Environment Agency or SEPA receives an application for a waste management licence which might result in direct or indirect discharges of List I or List II substances to groundwater, under Regulation 15(1) and (2) they must ensure that the proposal is subjected to prior investigation. This must include, *inter alia*, an examination of the hydrogeology, the possible attenuation effects of the soil and subsoil, and the potential alteration of the quality of the groundwater. In addition, a licence may not be issued without the relevant Agency having made provision for the monitoring of the quality of the groundwater and guidance on the minimum acceptable level of surveillance is given in Appendix C of Waste Management Paper 4 (Table 12-3, page 523).

Regulations 15(4) to 15(7) make specific provisions for disposal activities which may lead to the direct or indirect discharge of List I or II substances, and other terms and conditions of licences required by the Directive. The importance of these considerations was highlighted in *R v Vale of Glamorgan ex parte James*, in which an albeit unsuccessful challenge was made regarding the granting of a licence, partly on the basis of a failure to consider properly Regulations 15(2) and 15(4). An important part of the judgment was the willingness of the court to accept the regulator's view (the NRA in this case) "unless it can be shown that their views are wholly irrational".

A further requirement of the groundwater Directive is that authorisations granted under licence should be limited in time (Regulation 15(8)) and Regulation 15(9) states that they must also be reviewed every four years.

In addition to the above, any discharges from a waste management site will require the appropriate discharge consent and will be subject to the water-related legislation.

Sampling and Record Keeping

In line with the provisions on the admissibility of sampling information introduced in section 111 of the Environment Act 1995, q.v., three new subsections have been introduced into Part II of the 1990 Act – section 35(7A), (7B) and (7C) – which state that, in any case in which an entry is required in any record as to the observance of any condition of a licence and that entry has not been made, then this fact is admissible as evidence that that condition has not been observed.

Furthermore, an offence is created for intentionally making a false entry in such a record. It is also an offence to forge or use a licence with intent to deceive, or make or have in possession a document so closely resembling a licence as to be likely to deceive.

Additional Conditions

The Secretary of State has power to make Regulations relating to general licence conditions (section 35(6)) and to issue directions to the Agencies with regard to the terms and conditions of any licence (section 35(7)). The Agencies are also under a duty to have regard to any guidance issued by the

Secretary of State with respect to licensing (section 35(8)) and a number of Waste Management Papers (WMPs) relevant to the landfill disposal of wastes have been issued by the Department of the Environment, viz:

WMP 4   : *Licensing of Waste Management Facilities* (1994)

WMP 4A   : *Licensing of Metal Recycling Sites* (1995)

WMP 26A : *Landfill Completion* (1994)

WMP 26B : *Landfill Design, Construction and Operational Practice* (1995)

WMP 26F : *Landfill Co-Disposal* (draft)

WMP 27   : *Landfill Gas* (second edition) 1991

As with other areas of waste management law, the licensing of these activities is becoming increasingly complex and is based upon "command and control", "black letter law" which is complemented by detailed technical requirements. Although the Waste Management Papers are issued under statutory powers, they do not themselves carry the same authority as primary or secondary legislative instruments. However, the Agencies are under a duty to have regard to these technical documents and, when specific criteria contained within them are incorporated into waste management licences, they have effect in law, since it is an offence to undertake the activities prescribed in section 33(1)(a) and (b) except "in accordance with" the relevant waste management licence.

Licensing Conditions and Third Parties

In view of the increased technical and engineering requirements placed upon the construction and operation of waste management facilities, it is sometimes necessary to impose licence conditions which require the holder to carry out works or to do things which he is not entitled to undertake on the land of third parties. This may occur either in fulfilment of the initial licensing conditions, section 35(4) of the 1990 Act, or as the result of a suspension of the licence under section 38(9A).

In either case, any person whose consent is required for such works must grant, or join with others in granting, such rights to the holder of the licence in order to enable him to comply with the requisite conditions. Where such rights are granted, section 35A provides for compensation to be paid to the third parties involved and the Secretary of State may by Regulations set out the conditions under which such payments are made.

GRANTING OF LICENCES

The 1990 Act established two forms of waste management licence – site licences relating to the treatment, keeping or disposal of waste on land, and plant licences covering such activities carried out with mobile plant (section 35(12)). The Environment Agency and SEPA are responsible for the issue of both, and an application must be made to the office with local responsibility for the site or the operator's principal place of business (section 36(1)). An application must be made on an application form and be accompanied by such information as the Agencies reasonably require together with the appropriate fee.

The minimum requirements for the information to be supplied are detailed in section 2.9 of WMP 4, and include:

— the location of the facility and existing developments within 250 metres of its site boundaries. "Existing developments" will include underground services where these are likely to be affected by mechanical disturbances, spillages, etc.;

— the location and identification of site boundaries;

— the planning permission, certificate of lawful use, appeal decision letter, planning application letter, or a statement showing why none of these is required;

— proof that the applicant is a "fit and proper person" (see below);

— an assessment of the physical environment of the site, its topography, geology, meteorology and hydrogeology; also the quality of the air, surface water, groundwater and soil, as appropriate;

— the working plan (see below).

Where the applicant fails to provide any of the required information, the Agency may refuse to proceed with the application or may await the supply of such information before proceeding further.

Provided that:

— planning permission or an established use certificate is in force, where appropriate (section 36(2)); and

— the applicant is a "fit and proper person" (section 36(3)),

the relevant Agency may not reject an application which has been duly made unless it is satisfied that its rejection is necessary for the purpose of preventing:

— pollution of the environment;

— harm to human health; or

— serious detriment to the amenities of the locality (unless planning permission is in force for the relevant activity).

Waste Management Paper 4 points out that well operated waste management facilities, particularly those for recovery, "are a potential source of sustainable development and positive benefit to the environment" and regulators should respond to proposals in a manner which is:

— proportionate to the risks and costs;

— reflects the underlying regulatory objectives; and

— does not place unwarranted burdens on those regulated.

The licence conditions should reflect the need for an operation which is prepared, developed, operated, restored and completed to appropriately high standards, and this may be achieved by setting conditions which are necessary, enforceable, unambiguous and comprehensive.

The Working Plan

Whereas the licence conditions are determined by the relevant Agency and set the performance standards to which the site must be operated, the working plan is prepared by the operator and defines, *inter alia*, how these standards are to be met. Since the working plan must be submitted to the Agency in relation to a licence application, its development must inevitably be an iterative process. Amongst the items covered by the plan should be descriptions of:

— the infrastructure relating to site operation, including the construction and location of all storage facilities;

— the waste management processes to be undertaken at the site;

— pollution control measures and the monitoring arrangements; and

— the operator's plans for the management of landfill gas, leachate run-off and capping for restoration, for landfill sites.

Guidance on these requirements is given in the Waste Management Papers listed above.

"Fit and Proper Persons"

The term "fit and proper person" is defined in section 74 of the Act and, in addition to licence applications (section 36(3)), is also a consideration in the revocation or suspension of a licence (section 38(1), (2) and (6)) and in the transfer of a licence (section 40(4)). The relevant Agency must have regard to any guidance issued by the Secretary of State with reference to the making of such determinations and currently this is contained within Waste Management Paper No. 4.

There are three limbs to such a determination and the Agency must ascertain whether:

— the applicant/licence holder or another relevant person has been convicted of a "relevant offence";

— the management of the licensed activity will be in the hands of a "technically competent person"; and

— the applicant/licence holder is in a position to make an adequate financial provision to discharge the obligations of the licence.

Relevant Offences

"Relevant offences" relating to Part II of the 1990 Act are defined in Regulation 3 of the Waste Management Licensing Regulations 1994, as amended by the Waste Management (Miscellaneous Provisions) Regulations 1997, SI 1997/351, and are reproduced in Table 12-4 on page 524. Subject to guidance issued by the Secretary of State and depending upon the facts of each case, the Agency has discretion under section 74(3) to determine how these affect its treatment of a person as a "fit and proper person".

Section 74(2) makes it clear that the context of a "fit and proper person" is the carrying on of the activities authorised by the licence and the fulfilment of its conditions. However, the "relevant offences" cover a wide range of environmentally-related provisions and need not have been committed in relation to the site to which the licence relates.

The term "another relevant person" is defined in section 74(7) and relates to a natural or legal person whose convictions are "relevant" to the extent that their convictions are imputed to the applicant or licence holder.

Waste Management Paper 4 suggests that, when assessing relevant offences, three factors should be taken into account:

Factor I: Whether it was the applicant/licence holder or another relevant person who has been convicted of a relevant offence or offences. It is necessary to consider whether the offence was committed by the applicant (or holder), who may be an individual, a partnership or a body corporate, or by another relevant person, and these factors are summarised in Table 12-5 on page 525.

When considering the actions of corporate bodies in this context, the term "manager" is given a narrow interpretation as in *R v Boal*, discussed in Chapter 6.

Under the Rehabilitation of Offenders Act 1974, the convictions of individuals are deemed to be spent after a prescribed time period which is dependent upon the gravity of the offence. This does not apply to corporate bodies and all such offences must be declared regardless of when they were committed. However, Waste Management Paper 4 suggests that the Agency should have regard to whether such convictions would have become spent if they had been committed by an individual. In addition, the implications of *Shanks & McEwan (Midlands) Ltd v Wrexham Borough Council*, discussed in Chapter 3, should be noted with regard to offences committed by companies with a different legal identity within a large group. It is evident from Table 12-5 that, in such cases, offences committed by companies with separate legal identities will not be "relevant" unless a natural person who is a director, manager, secretary or similar officer, or who is a partner of the applicant company, was involved in the committing of that offence.

Factor II: The number of relevant offences. The Agency must consider whether the applicant/licence holder or any relevant person has been convicted of more than one relevant offence. While an isolated conviction with mitigating circumstances should not result in a refusal, the repetition of offences would be viewed more seriously. With regard to "other relevant persons", consideration needs to be given to the position held by that person, particularly when more than one relevant person is involved.

Factor III: The nature of the offence. Although "relevant offences" encompass a wide rage of environmental measures, in view of the context of the determination of "fit and proper" (section 74(2)), particular attention is to be paid to those offences relating to the unlawful deposit, treatment, keeping, disposal or transport of controlled waste, and infractions of the Duty of Care provisions. In addition, the gravity of the offence is taken into consideration with regard to:

— the involvement of special waste in the offence;

— the seriousness of the pollution caused, if any; and

— the penalty imposed.

Whilst the penalty may not always be a reliable indicator, it does form an approximate benchmark of seriousness, ranging from absolute or conditional discharge (admonishment in Scotland), through fines or Community Service Orders, to custodial sentences. Each case will be considered on its merits but a custodial sentence incurred by an applicant or licence holder will be of particular significance.

Technically Competent Persons
The management of licensed sites must be "in the hands of" a technically competent manager (TCM) and, unlike the definition of "manager" used above in relation to relevant offences, in this context the person must be in a position of day-to-day control of the activities authorised by the licence. According to the Interpretation Act 1978, unless otherwise specified, singular includes plural and hence technically competent management need not rest with a single individual. Consequently, on a large, complex site several specialists may provide this function, whereas in companies in which such day-to day management is not delegated to site level, more than one site could be under the control of the same individual or group of individuals. However, where more than one individual is involved, each person will be required to demonstrate his technical competence to the Agency. The guidance suggests that the Agency should be notified of changes and absences of TCMs, although prior written approval ought not to be required.

In the absence of existing requirements, the establishment of a criterion of technical competence necessitated a number of transitional arrangements to ensure the continuity of operation of existing facilities and to enable an infrastructure of certification and monitoring to be established.

Under Regulation 4 of SI 1994/1056, as amended, a person is considered as technically competent for the purposes of section 74(3)(b) of the Act if, and only if, he is the holder of a certificate awarded by the Waste Management Industry Training and Advisory Board (WAMITAB), which is appropriate to the type of licensed facility (Table 12-6, page 526).

This definition of technical competence does not apply to facilities which are used exclusively for dismantling motor vehicles or carrying on a business as a scrap metal dealer (or metal dealer, in Scotland). Likewise, some small waste management sites do not come within the ambit of the WAMITAB scheme. However, it should be noted that the criterion of a technically competent person is a requirement of section 74 of the Act and the provisions of Regulation 4 are one means of satisfying this criterion. Where no formal scheme exists, the Agency must make individual assessments of technical competence on a case by case basis and guidance is given in WMP 4.

Regulation 5 provides transitional arrangements by giving "grandfather rights" to appropriately experienced persons aged 55 or over and other existing experienced operators who have applied for a WAMITAB certificate of technical competence (COTC). In view of the practicalities of establishing the WAMITAB scheme, the time periods within these transitional arrangements were extended by Regulation 4 of SI 1995/288 and again by Regulation 3 of SI 1995/1950 and, in relation to certain waste treatment plant, by Regulation 2 of SI 1996/634.

Financial Requirements
This aspect of the "fit and proper person" assessment requires that the applicant or licence holder has made, has the intention of making or is in a position to make "financial provisions adequate to discharging the operations arising from the licence". Such financial provisions will depend upon the potential risks of pollution and harm of the activity in question but, unlike the criteria of relevant offences and technical competence, this is not an area which the Agency needs to keep under review as something upon which a later revocation or suspension of a licence might be based. However, where specific financial provisions are considered necessary to meet certain obligations of a licence, these should form part of the licence conditions.

Whereas the requirements for a technically competent person were made by means of Regulations brought under section 74(6), there are currently no such measures in relation to financial provisions, although this situation might be influenced by measures such as the proposed Landfill Directive, or the Commission's Green Paper on Civil Liability for Remedying Environmental Damage.

Non-statutory guidance is given in WMP 4, which suggests that the financial provisions should be dependent upon the potential of a given site for pollution and harm, but should not be used to attempt to provide unlimited cover for unspecified future liabilities or deal with matters of compensation where "normal mechanisms" would apply.

Local authorities in Scotland who operate their own waste management sites are deemed capable of meeting the criteria for financial provisions, since their financial operations are supported by taxation.

Three factors must be assessed in relation to financial requirements:

— the financial standing of the licence holder in relation to the proposed licence. This must be considered in all applications;

— any particular conditions of the proposed licence which might entail significant expenditure on corrective or remedial action, in the event of some specified occurrence; and

— post-closure activities. These should be considered for all landfill licence applications.

Whilst this last criterion is specifically directed at landfill sites, it should not adumbrate the potential of other waste management operations for contaminating land or polluting watercourses. At the time of writing, only new or extended sites have been subject to these financial considerations, but the Environment Agency is now proposing to include pre-1994 sites, licensed under COPA 1974.

Financial Standing of the Licence Holder

The applicant should demonstrate to the Agency that it has a business plan for the development and operation of the facility, which makes adequate provisions for financing the requirements of the licence. Although the potential profitability of the operation is not an issue for consideration, the cash flow must be sufficient to meet the obligations of the licence. The plan must include all of the stages of operation:

— prior to the commencement of operations in relation to the required standards for all site equipment, the installation specifications and also contingencies;

— during the operational phase, to ensure that all equipment is maintained to the required standards to meet the conditions relating to site control, and for the phased installation of equipment for drainage and landfill gas control.

It is anticipated that these general principles may also be applied to waste handling and waste treatment operations, as well as to landfill.

Specific Conditions for Corrective or Remedial Action

As with other measures of this type, an important consideration is the scope of such conditions, viz:

— what event(s) would trigger payment;

— what specific works or other measures would be provided for; and

— the amount of cover.

The guidance discusses the options of satisfying these financial requirements through insurance, self-insurance or having an overdraft facility. In addition to self-insurance, internal provisions may include setting aside a sum to provide for such expenditure, through making a provision within the accounts or establishing a sinking fund.

Some form of cover should be provided for gradual as well as sudden and accidental damage.

Post-Closure Stages of Landfilling Operations

Licence holder liability for the post-closure stage presents a number of problems since at this point the site will be generating no income. However, under section 39(6), if the Agency considers that pollution of the environment or harm to human health are likely to result from the condition of the site, it must refuse the surrender of the licence. Furthermore, the period of post-closure monitoring required to determine the potential for future pollution may be in excess of 30 years and, during this period, licensing conditions are likely to cover:

— the installation of pollution control and monitoring systems;

— supervision of the site, with periodic sampling and analysis;

— maintenance and planned replacement of the equipment used.

Methods of long-term funding include the use of a bond to secure the preliminary restoration of the site after the cessation of landfilling, the use of an escrow account – an independently held account into which the licence holder pays, at a rate and up to a limit determined by the Agency, as income is earned from the operation of the site – and in-house or independently-held trust funds.

Any scheme would need to be clear and binding in order to ensure the accumulation of adequate resources.

OTHER ISSUES OF LICENSING

Consultation

When the relevant Agency has satisfied itself of the above criteria and intends to issue a licence, it must then approach a number of statutory consultees and consider any representations made by them during the allowed period – twenty eight days commencing from the receipt of the proposal by the Agency or longer by agreement in writing with the consultee in question (section 36(10)). These bodies include:

— the appropriate planning authority, as defined in section 36(11), and the Health and Safety Executive (HSE) (section 36(4));

— the Nature Conservancy Council for England, Scottish Natural Heritage or the Countryside Commission for Wales, as appropriate, in cases where, under section 43(2), any part of land to be used is land which has been notified under section 28(1) of the Wildlife and Countryside Act 1981 (protection of certain areas).

The Agency is deemed to have rejected the application for a licence if it has neither granted the application nor given notice of its rejection to the applicant within four months of its receipt of the application, or longer by agreement in writing with the applicant (section 36(9)). This provides a means by which an applicant may appeal to the Secretary of State in the absence of a determination by the Agency. However, this provision does not apply where the Agency refuses outright to proceed with an application under section 36(1A), although it does apply where such a refusal is accompanied by a condition under which the four month period is substituted by a period of four months commencing with the date upon which the Agency receives the information (section 36(9A)).

Transfer of Licences

Waste management licences are specific to the holder rather than the site and changes in the former must be accompanied by a transfer of the licence, according to the procedure in Regulation 2(5) and Schedule 2 of the 1994 Waste Management Licensing Regulations. Transfers may be made regardless of the "status" of the licence, i.e. whether it is in force, partly revoked or suspended (section 40(1)). The current and the proposed holder ("the proposed transferee") must make a joint application to the Agency using the appropriate form, which must be accompanied by information showing that the proposed transferee is a "fit and proper person", the prescribed fee and the licence itself.

If the Agency considers that the proposed transferee is a fit and proper person, it must effect the transfer by endorsing the licence with the name of the new holder and other relevant information. A transfer is deemed to have been rejected if the Agency does not give notice to the applicants within two months of the receipt of the application, or a longer time period if agreed in writing with the applicants. As with the granting of licences, this deemed rejection enables the applicants to appeal to the Secretary of State, under section 43.

Variation of Licences

Licences which are in force may be subject to variation at the instigation of the Environment Agency or SEPA, or on application from the licence holder (section 37(1)). A licence holder may wish to change the conditions of his licence to reflect an increase or decrease in the scope of his licensed activity, whilst changes required by the Agency may be necessary where in its opinion these are desirable, and it is unlikely to require unreasonable expense on the part of the licence holder. Except where the licence is revoked entirely, the Agency has a duty to modify licence conditions when it considers that this is necessary to secure the objectives of licensing (i.e. prevention of pollution, etc.) (section 37(2)(a)) or as a result of Regulations made by the Secretary of State under section 35(6) (section 37(2)(b)).

Prior to a modification under section 37(1) and (2)(a), the Agency must approach the statutory consultees in the application process (section 36(4), (7) and (10)), although this consultation may be postponed in the case of an emergency and is not necessary at all if the Agency considers that the changes will not affect the consultee. Third parties who might be affected by the modification must also be consulted under section 37A, which mirrors the conditions for licence applications in section 36A, *supra*.

The Secretary of State has powers to give directions to the Agency as to the modification of the conditions of any licence (section 37(3)) and the Agency is then required to serve a notice regarding the modification on the holder, stating when the change is to take effect. No consultation is required in this case.

For applications made by the licence holder, there is a period of two months from the date of receipt of the application (or longer period by written agreement), after which it is deemed to have been rejected.

Surrender of Licences

Procedure for Surrender
A waste management licence may be surrendered to the authority which granted it and, in the case of site licences, the authority must accept the surrender. The surrender of all waste management licences is covered in section 39(1) of the 1990 Act and Regulation 2(1) of the 1994 Waste Management Licensing Regulations. The surrender of site licences as defined in section 35(12) is subject to the additional requirements of section 39(2) to (6) and Regulation 2(2) to (4) and Schedule 1.

Consequently, the holder of a mobile plant licence need only make application to the relevant part of the Agency, who must then accept the surrender of the licence. However, when the holder of a site licence desires to surrender it, he must complete the appropriate form and submit this to the Agency together with the fee and such information as is required. This information is detailed in Schedule 1 and includes a record of the waste management activities which have been undertaken on the site, with the types and quantities of waste treated, sampling and monitoring data and details of the contaminants likely to be present on the site. Landfill sites and lagoons are subject to additional information requirements relating to details of the engineering works undertaken, geological, hydrological and hydrogeological data, and information on the flows of groundwater. Leachate and landfill gas are of particular concern, as is the deposit of special waste.

It is possible that some of this information may have been supplied already to the Agency or its predecessor and, under Regulation 2(3), there is no requirement to forward such information again. The information given need only cover the period following the applicant's first involvement with the site. Prior to this date, it is only necessary to supply such information so far as it is known to the person, partnership or corporate body making the application (Regulation 2(4)).

Duties of the Agency
When the Agency receives an application for the surrender of a site licence, it has a duty to inspect the land to which the licence relates and it may require the holder to furnish additional information (section 39(4)). The Agency has the responsibility of determining whether it is likely or unlikely that the condition of the land "so far as that condition is the result of the use of the land for the treatment, keeping, or disposal of waste (*whether or not in pursuance of the licence*)" will cause pollution of the environment or harm to human health (section 39(5)). Consequently, any historical pollution or contamination resulting from these activities is of relevance, although under this wording, contamination resulting from an adjacent site would be excluded, even if that land was used for waste-related activities. Furthermore, where the licensed activity is carried out on historically contaminated land, it will be necessary to prove that the contamination was the result of waste-related activities. For example, in the *Cambridge Water* case, the contamination resulted from the spillage of non-waste materials and thus would not have been subject to these provisions. It has been suggested that such spillages as occurred in *Cambridge* would qualify as waste under Q4 of Annex I to the Framework Directive *but* this would require the other limb of the definition of waste to be satisfied.

Details of the information to be supplied to the Agency and the criteria for assessment are given in Waste Management Paper 26A *Landfill Completion*, which was issued according to the powers in section 38(5). This document contains a number of definitions and, although they do not have statutory authority *per se*, they may have legal effect when forming part of the licence conditions. In addition, they provide a framework for the assessment of the state of a closed landfill.

Completion is defined as that point at which the landfill has stabilised physically, chemically and biologically to such a degree that the undisturbed contents of the site are unlikely to cause pollution or harm to human health (the completion condition). At completion, post-closure pollution controls, leachate management and gas removal systems are no longer required.

The stabilisation of the site in physical, chemical and biological terms is defined by reference to quantifiable criteria based upon the current knowledge of the landfilling process, viz:

— the quality and quantity of leachate present;

— the flow and concentration of gas;

— the future potential for leachate or gas generation;

— the potential for leachate or gas to reach sensitive targets;

— the possibility of physical instability of the waste or the retaining structures;

— the presence of wastes presenting particular problems which could present a hazard in the future.

Data on these factors should be built up during the life of the site but, where these are unavailable or inadequate, a system of completion monitoring will be required. The assessment of completion considers three broad categories of site:

— *Inert sites*. This category includes sites taking only "truly inert" wastes (*sic*). In such sites it is assumed that significant quantities of leachate or gas will never be generated and the emphasis is on demonstrating that no degradable wastes have ever entered the site "in significant quantities".

— *Low risk sites*. Although these sites will have taken non-inert wastes, in view of their remote situation or the geological conditions, there is a low probability that any pollutants could reach sensitive targets.

However, WMP 26A notes that modern containment sites, engineered to high standards "will rarely fall into this category".

For this category, the Agency will need to examine geological and hydrogeological surveys and assess the potential for the migration of leachate and landfill gas.

— *Non-isolated sites accepting non-inert wastes*. All other sites taking non-inert waste fall into this category and the Agency will need to be satisfied with all of the factors listed above in relation to the stabilisation of the site.

It is unfortunate that the term "inert waste", which is acknowledged in paragraph 5.17 of WMP 4 as being a misnomer, is perpetuated in WMP 26A. Further confusion will arise as a result of its use in relation to the landfill tax, particularly since a number of the wastes so categorised are clearly not inert.

Provided that monitoring has taken place throughout the life of the site, there should be sufficient data to indicate that the completion condition has been met. Where insufficient data are available with which to characterise the site, additional completion monitoring will be required and WMP 26A provides guidance on the number of sampling points to be used, the period over which monitoring is to take place, the frequency of sampling and the determinands to be assessed. Where no significant monitoring has been undertaken, a period of five years is recommended, although where the site is already reasonably well characterised two years may be adequate. The time factor, in combination with the costs of regular sampling and analysis for up to 20 sampling points, will add significantly to closure costs.

ENFORCEMENT

Supervision

By giving the Environment Agency and SEPA an overall supervisory duty, backed with specific powers of enforcement, section 42 of the Environmental Protection Act 1990 provides the basis for the enforcement of waste management licences. Whilst a licence is in force, the Agency is under a duty to take the steps needed to ensure that the environment is not polluted and there is no harm to human health or serious detriment to the amenities of the locality. In addition, it must ensure that the conditions of the licence are complied with.

When it needs to take action, the Agency has two main powers with which to undertake remediation or seek compliance. In an emergency, any officer who is authorised in writing by the Agency may carry out work on land or in relation to plant or equipment on land which is subject to waste management licensing conditions (section 42(3)). This includes operations involving mobile plant and under section 43(4) the Agency may recover the amount of the expenditure (i.e. costs rather than expenses) from the holder of the licence at the relevant time. These powers are initiated when it appears to the officer that there is an emergency requiring work to be carried out. However, no payments need be made if the holder of the licence proves that there was no such emergency and his liability may be limited to such expenditure that the Agency can prove was necessary.

Where it appears to the Agency that a licence condition is not being complied with, or it is likely not to be complied with, then, without prejudice to any action resulting from a prosecution under section 33(6), it may serve the holder of the licence with a notice informing him of the Agency's view on the non-compliance or anticipated non-compliance, specifying the steps to be taken and the time allowed for undertaking these steps (section 42(5)). If it appears to the Agency that the holder has not, or will not, comply with these requirements, then the additional powers of section 42(6) are triggered, under which a number of options may be taken:

— the licence may be revoked in relation to the carrying on of some or all of the activities specified in it;

— the licence may be revoked entirely; or

— the licence may be suspended in relation to the carrying on of some or all of the activities specified in it.

Should it appear that these measures will provide an ineffectual remedy, under section 42(6A) there is the further possibility of recourse to the High Court or, in Scotland, an appropriate court. There is also an overall power of the Secretary of State to give directions to the Agency regarding what action to take on a particular licence.

Revocation and Suspension of Licences

Revocation
The revocation of a licence may take one of two forms – a revocation of the entire licence (i.e. the authorisation and all of the licence conditions) or a selective revocation of the authorisation of some or all of the processes covered by the licence. The Agency is given power to revoke a licence, where in its opinion:

— the holder of the licence has ceased to be a fit and proper person, by reason of being convicted of a relevant offence (section 38(1)(a)); *or*

— the continuation of the activities authorised by the licence would cause pollution of the environment, harm to human health or would be seriously detrimental to the amenities of the locality (section 38(1)(b)); *and*

— that the pollution, harm or detriment cannot be avoided by modifying the conditions of the licence (section 38(1)(c)).

Note that the first two criteria are alternatives which are dependent upon the third being satisfied. There are also grounds for revocation where, in the opinion of the Agency, the holder of the licence has ceased to be a fit and proper person, by reason of the management of the activities of the licence having ceased to be in the hands of a technically competent person (section 38(2)).

Under these circumstances, the Agency may revoke the authority to carry on some or all of the licensed activities under section 38(3) and 38(5). While this option is available for the other three criteria above, the Agency may alternatively revoke the licence entirely (section 38(4)). However, there are advantages in adopting the former approach, for although this will deprive the holder of the necessary authority to undertake some or all of the activities on the site in question, he will still be legally bound by the other conditions of the licence.

Such an approach was the subject of an appeal to the Minister in relation to the decision by Merseyside WRA to issue notices of partial revocation under section 42 with respect to waste transfer stations in Southport (reference T/APP/WM/95/50 and 51, reported in [1997] JPL 283). The letter informing the unsuccessful appellant of the Minister's decision stated:

> "I have hesitation in accepting that the effective closing down of waste transfer facilities is accurately described as partial revocation of these licences. However, I recognise that there is a significant potential of pollution from these sites, and that it is therefore important to retain powers over these sites provided by the conditions of the licence."

As a consequence, section 42(7) may by means of section 38(5) permit the specification of requirements which continue to bind the licence holder.

Suspension

The suspension of a licence relates to the suspension of the authorisation for the carrying on of specified activities, and grounds for suspension are where it appears to the Agency that:

— the holder has ceased to be a fit and proper person, by reason of the management of the activities of the licence having ceased to be in the hands of a technically competent person (section 38(6)(a)); *or*

— serious pollution of the environment or harm to human health has resulted from, or is about to be caused by, the activities to which the licence relates or the happening or threatened happening of an event affecting those activities (section 38(6)(b)); *and*

— that the continuing to carry on those activities (*sic*), or any one of those activities, in the circumstances will continue, or as the case may be, cause serious pollution of the environment or serious harm to human health (section 38(6)(c)).

In addition to suspending the licence, the Agency may require the holder to take such measures to deal with or avert the pollution as it deems necessary (section 38(9)). Where this involves the land of third parties, consent must be given by these parties and this is subject to consultation and compensation provisions, as in sections 35A and 36A.

It is an offence to fail to comply with any requirement imposed under section 39(9) without reasonable excuse, and this carries the penalty of a fine up to the statutory maximum on summary conviction and, on conviction on indictment, of an unlimited fine, imprisonment for up to two years, or both (section 38(10)). Where special wastes are involved, a summary conviction may additionally carry a period of imprisonment for up to six months, or both imprisonment and fine, and the custodial sentence on conviction on indictment is increased to up to five years.

Where the Agency considers that proceedings under section 38(10) or (11) would afford an ineffectual remedy, it has the option of taking proceedings in the High Court or, in Scotland, in an appropriate court.

General

If he thinks fit, the Secretary of State may give directions to the Agency as to whether, and in what manner, the Agency exercises any of the powers discussed above, and it is the duty of the Agency to give effect to such directions (section 38(7)).

Any revocation or suspension of a licence or a requirement imposed during a suspension must be effected by a notice served on the holder, stating the conditions required by the Agency (section 38(12)).

APPEALS WITH RESPECT TO LICENCES

In view of the complexity of the conditions surrounding the holding of a waste management licence and the terms contained therein, it is inevitable that disputes will arise as a result of decisions made by the Agency and, under section 43(1), an appeal may be made to the Secretary of State in relation to:

— the rejection of a licence application or modification;

— the granting of a licence subject to conditions;

— the modification of a licence;

— the suspension of a licence;

— a revocation under section 38 or section 42;

— the rejection of an application to surrender a licence;

— the rejection of an application to transfer a licence.

Appeals relating to the transfer of licences are made by the proposed transferee and in the other cases above by the applicant, holder or former holder. However, an appeal cannot be made against a direction given by the Secretary of State.

Details of the appeals procedure are given in Regulations 6 to 9 of the Waste Management Licensing Regulations 1994. Notice of appeal must be given in writing within six months of the date of the relevant decision or deemed rejection, although this period may be extended where the Secretary of State allows. In the case of a request for commercial confidentiality under section 66(5), the appeal must be made within 21 days of the notification of the decision to the person concerned. This period cannot be extended.

Appeals are to be made in writing unless under section 43(2) either party requests a hearing, which may be in public or, at the discretion of the inspector, in private.

Under the modifications introduced through section 114 of the Environment Act 1995, the Secretary of State may appoint any person to undertake these appellate functions and he will have the same powers in relation to the appeal as the Secretary of State. The Agency is bound to implement the decision of the Secretary of State or his delegatee (section 43(3)).

On 1st April 1996, waste management licensing appeals were transferred to the Planing Inspectorate, along with those for waste carrier registration.

All decisions will be taken by the inspectors unless there are cases of "major importance or difficulty", when the Secretary of State for the Environment will be involved.

In cases relating to the modification or revocation of licences, the proposed changes are ineffective until the appeal is dismissed or withdrawn (section 43(4)). However, bringing an appeal has no effect on the suspension of a licence (section 43(5)) and the suspension remains in force until the appeal is heard.

If the Agency considers that a modification or a revocation should have immediate effect, then it may insert a clause to that effect into the relevant notice. However, this can result in a claim against the Agency should the Secretary of State or inspector find that it has acted unreasonably.

FALSE AND MISLEADING STATEMENTS

Section 44 creates two offences relating to false and misleading statements which apply to all of Part II of the Act, and under these provisions it is an offence:

— to knowingly and recklessly make a materially false statement:

    — in purported compliance with a requirement to furnish any information imposed by or under any provision within Part II (section 44(1)(a)); or

    — for the purposes of obtaining for himself or another any grant of a licence, modification of conditions, acceptance of surrender, or transfer of a licence (section 44(1)(b));

— to intentionally make a false entry in any record required by licence conditions (section 44(2)).

On summary conviction, these offences carry a fine up to the statutory maximum and, on conviction on indictment, an unlimited fine, imprisonment for up to two years, or both.

REGISTERS

As with most of the recent environmental legislation, the setting up and maintenance of registers which are accessible to the public is an important feature of waste management legislation. A particular feature of the provisions in Part II of the 1990 Act is the greater detail now required in relation to waste management licences, which includes not only administrative information relating to the issue of licences but also financial information, engineering data relating to the construction of the site and operational information.

Under section 64(1), the Environment Agency and SEPA are under a duty to maintain details of all current and "recently current" waste management licences. The term "recently current" relates to the period of 12 months after they have been in force or, in the case of applications, 12 months after the rejection or deemed rejection. The documents to be included on these registers are listed in section 64(1) and this information is expanded and detailed in Regulation 10 of the 1994 Waste Management Licensing Regulations. In addition to current and recently current licences, the registers must contain full particulars of applications and the associated supporting information, statutory notices, notices of appeal, relevant convictions, report and monitoring information, special waste consignment notes and other documents and information required by other provisions of the Act.

Sections 65 and 66 provide the usual exemptions relating to confidential information and national security, the former lapsing after four years unless a request for a further period of four years is made by the same person who made the initial request.

The Secretary of State may give directions to the Agency as to specified information, or descriptions of information, to be included in public registers on the grounds of public interest, regardless of its commercial confidentiality.

THE EU LANDFILL DIRECTIVE

Originally proposed in 1991 and amended in 1993, the EU Council reached a common position on the Landfill Directive in October 1995. However, in May 1996, this was soundly defeated by the European Parliament by 445 votes to 18. Critical to this decision was the apparent lack of support from the Commission for two amendments proposed by the Parliament, viz:

— the removal of the derogation for "small islands and sparsely populated regions", which would exempt about 50% of the EU including most of Scotland, Ireland, France and Spain from the Directive; and

— advancing the phase-out of the co-disposal of toxic and non-toxic waste by five years.

Following this decision, the Council invited the Commission to present a new proposal which would contain stricter conditions in line with the Parliament's requirements. The new proposal was drafted rapidly and adopted by the Commission in March 1997. This revision contains a number of provisions which, if contained in the final Directive, would affect significantly the method of landfilling currently practised in the UK.

It proposes that the co-disposal of waste would be eliminated within five to ten years of the Directive coming into force and Member States would need to introduce provisions which required the pre-treatment of waste prior to landfill. In addition, a number of materials would not be acceptable for landfilling, including:

— wastes with a total organic carbon content not greater than a limit to be determined, possibly 10%-20% (effective within 5 years);

— liquid waste (effective within 2 years);

— infectious hospital or other clinical waste (immediate effect);

— whole used tyres (immediate effect);

— shredded used tyres (effective within 5 years).

The emphasis on pre-treatment as a means of reducing waste volume and methane generation runs counter to UK philosophy on bioreactor landfill design, for which technologies are being developed in which wastes are encouraged to degrade as fast as possible. This as yet unproven technology is dependent upon the presence of organic matter within the landfill.

Under the proposed Directive, existing landfill sites would be required to present the competent authority (i.e. the Environment Agency/SEPA) with a conditioning plan relating to the finance and technical operation of the site and the means whereby compliance with the Directive would be achieved within a five year period. If such a conditioning plan did not satisfy the enforcing authority, it would have the power to close the site as soon as possible.

It is anticipated that the new proposals will become law by mid to late 1998 and Member States will have until 30th June 2000 to implement the provisions.

FURTHER READING

"The Difficulties of Enforcing Waste Disposal Licence Conditions", S Tromans, [1991] 3 *JEL* 281

Landfill Costs and Prices: Correcting Possible Market Distortions, Coopers and Lybrand, HMSO, 1993

Making Wastes Work: Strategy for Sustainable Waste Management in England and Wales, Department of the Environment, Cmnd 3040, HMSO, 1995

"Waste Management Papers", Department of the Environment
- WMP 1   *A Review of Options* (1992)
- WMP 4   *Licensing of Waste Management Facilities* (1994)
- WMP 4A   *Licensing of Metal Recycling Sites* (1995)
- WMP 26A *Landfill Completion* (1994)
- WMP 26B *Landfill Design, Construction and Operational Practice* (1995)
- WMP 26F *Landfill Co-disposal* (draft)
- WMP 27   *Landfill Gas (2nd Edition)* (1991)

"Waste Regulation and Recycling: Present Legal Requirements and Future Prospects for Resource Recovery", D Cuckson, [1991] 3 *LMELR* 6

Table 12-1: Activities Exempted from Waste Management Licensing – Schedule 3 and Regulation 17, SI 1994/1056

Exempted Process	Applies to Special Waste ↓	Requires Owner/ Occupier Consent ↓	Register with # ↓
RECOVERY OR RE-USE OF WASTE			
1. Glass manufacture and production	no	no	other
2. Scrap metal furnace	no	no	other
3. Burning waste as fuel	no	no	other
4. Packaging or containers	no	yes	other/Agency
5. Burning waste as a fuel in small appliances	no	no	Agency
6. Burning waste as a fuel in an engine	no	no	Agency
7. Waste for the benefit of land	no	no	Agency
8. Sludge and septic tank sludge on land	no	no	Agency
9. Land reclamation	no	yes	Agency
10. Sewage and water treatment works	no	no	Agency
11. Preparatory treatment of certain wastes	no	yes	Agency
12. Composting waste	no	no	other/Agency
13. Construction and soil materials	no	yes	Agency
14. Manufacture of finished goods	no	yes	Agency
15. Use of waste	no	yes	Agency
16. Disease of Animals (Waste Food) Order	no	no	other
17. Storage of waste in a secure place	yes	yes	Agency
18. Waste in secure containers	no	yes	Agency
19. Waste for construction	no	yes	Agency
20. Recovery of textiles	no	no	Agency
21. Preparatory treatment of waste plant matter	no	no	Agency
22. Recovery of silver	no	no	Agency
23. Animal by-products	no	no	other
OPERATIONS LEADING TO RECOVERY/RE-USE OR DISPOSAL			
24. Crushing, grinding or size reduction of bricks, tiles or concrete	no	no	other
25. Waterway dredging	no	yes	Agency
26. Recovery or disposal as part of the production process	no	no	Agency
27. Baling, compacting or pulverising	no	no	Agency
28. Storing returned goods	no	no	Agency

Table 12-1 (continued)   521

	Exempted Process	Applies to Special Waste	Requires Owner/ Occupier Consent	Register with #
DISPOSAL OF OWN WASTE AT THE PLACE OF PRODUCTION				
29.	Disposal by incineration at the place of production	no	no	Agency
30.	Burning waste in the open	no	no	Agency
31.	Waste from railway sanitary conveniences or sinks	no	no	Agency
32	Waste from sanitary convenience with removable receptacle	no	no	Agency
33.	Peatworking	no	no	Agency
34.	Railway ballast	no	no	Agency
35.	Waste from prospecting	no	no	Agency
OTHER DEPOSITS OF WASTE				
36.	Temporary storage of ships' garbage or tank washings	yes	no	N/A
37.	Pet burials	no	yes	N/A
38.	Samples of waste	yes	no	Agency
39.	Storage of medical, nursing or veterinary waste	yes	no	Agency
40.	Storage of waste *not* at place of production	yes	no	N/A
41.	Storage of waste at place of production	yes	no	N/A
TRANSITIONAL EXEMPTIONS				
42.	Scrap metal and motor vehicles	yes	no	N/A
43.	Activities previously not licensable	yes	no	N/A
SCRAP METAL				
44.	Heating ferrous and non-ferrous metal in a furnace of less than 0.2 Megawatt	no	no	Agency
45.	Recovery of scap metal and dismantling of waste motor vehicles	no	no	Agency

\# *Full details of the appropriate registration authority are given in Regulation 18(10) of the Waste Management Licensing Regulations 1994.*

"Agency" refers to the Environment Agency or SEPA, as appropriate.

Table 12-2: List I and II Substances within the Groundwater Directive, 80/68/EEC

ANNEX FROM GROUNDWATER DIRECTIVE 80/68/EEC

List I of Families and Groups of Substances

List I contains the individual substances which belong to the families and groups of substances enumerated below, with the exception of those which are considered inappropriate to List I on the basis of a low risk of toxicity, persistence and bioaccumulation.

Such substances which with regard to toxicity, persistence and bioaccumulation are appropriate to List II are to be classed in List II.

1. Organohalogen compounds and substances which may form such compounds in the aquatic environment.
2. Organophosphorus compounds.
3. Organotin compounds.
4. Substances which possess carcinogenic, mutagenic or teratogenic properties in or via the aquatic environment.*
5. Mercury and its compounds.
6. Cadmium and its compounds.
7. Mineral oils and hydrocarbons.
8. Cyanides.

List II of Families and Groups of Substances

List II contains the individual substances and the categories of substances belonging to the families and groups of substances listed below which could have a harmful effect on groundwater.

1. The following metalloids and metals and their compounds:–

1. Zinc	8. Antimony	15. Uranium
2. Copper	9. Molybdenum	16. Vanadium
3. Nickel	10. Titanium	17. Cobalt
4. Chrome	11. Tin	18. Thallium
5. Lead	12. Barium	19. Tellurium
6. Selenium	13. Beryllium	20. Silver
7. Arsenic	14. Boron	

2. Biocides and their derivatives not appearing in List I.

3. Substances which have a deleterious effect on the taste and/or odour of groundwater, and compounds liable to cause the formation of such substances in such water and to render it unfit for human consumption.

4. Toxic or persistent organic compounds of silicon, and substances which may cause the formation of such compounds in water, excluding those which are biologically harmless or are rapidly converted in water into harmless substances.

5. Inorganic compounds of phosphorous and elemental phosphorous.

6. Fluorides.

7. Ammonia and nitrites.

Where certain substances in List II are carcinogenic, mutagenic or teratogenic they are included in category 4 of List I.

Table 12-3: Monitoring of Groundwater from Landfill Sites – Guidance in Waste Management Paper 4

TABLE C.3
Determinands and Monitoring Frequencies for Surface Waters, Groundwaters, Leachates and Landfill Gas at Site Operation Phase

Surface Water if necessary.	**Monthly** will depend on water body and flow rate.	pH, Temp, EC, DO, NH_4-N, Cl, COD.
Groundwater where necessary.	**Monthly**	water level, pH, EC, Temp, DO, NH_4-N, Cl.
	Quarterly (may be reduced to 6 monthly if there is evidence of stable conditions).	as monthly plus: SO_4, Alk, TON, TOC, Na, K, Ca, Mg, Fe, Mn, Cd, Cr, Cu, Ni, Pb, Zn.
Leachate at Discharge Points	**Weekly**	discharge volume, pH, Temp, EC.
	Monthly (reduce to quarterly if stable conditions prevail).	as weekly plus: NH_4-N, Cl, biochemical oxygen demand (BOD), COD.
	Quarterly	as monthly plus: SO_4, Alk, TON, TOC, Na, K, Ca, Mg.
	Six monthly (reduce to annually if stable conditions prevail).	as quarterly plus: Fe, Mn, Cd, Cr, Cu, Ni, Pb, Zn.
Leachate at monitoring points[1]	**Monthly**	leachate level, pH, Temp, EC.
	Quarterly (may be reduced to annually if there is evidence of stable conditions).	as monthly plus: Cl, NH_4-N, SO_4, Alk, COD, BOD, TON, TOC, Na, K, Ca, Mg.
	Annually	as quarterly plus: Fe, Mn, Cd, Cr, Cu, Ni, Pb, Zn.
Landfill Gas	As WMP 27 (1991)[2]	CH_4, CO_2, O_2, AP, OMD, Temp.
Other parameters	**Annually**	void utilisation, settlement.

[1] Sump from which leachate is removed from the cell/site.   [2] Generally weekly to six-monthly depending on site-specific factors.

Note: In cases where wastes are known to contain specific elements or compounds, particularly list I and II substances, then those substances should be added to the appropriate list of determinands.

Table 12-4: Relevant Offences – Regulation 3, Waste Management Licensing Regulations 1994, SI 1994/1056, as amended by the Waste Management (Miscellaneous Provisions) Regulations 1997, SI 1997/351

An offence is relevant for the purposes of section 74(3)(a) of the 1990 Act if it is an offence under any of the following enactments—

(a) section 22 of the Public Health (Scotland) Act 1897;

(b) section 95(1) of the Public Health Act 1936;

(c) section 3, 5(6), 16(4), 18(2), 31(1), 32(1), 34(5), 78, 92(6) or 93(3) of the Control of Pollution Act 1974;

(d) section 2 of the Refuse Disposal (Amenity) Act 1978;

(e) the Control of Pollution (Special Waste) Regulations 1980;

(f) section 9(1) of the Food and Environment Protection Act 1985;

(g) the Transfrontier Shipment of Hazardous Waste Regulations 1988;

(h) the Merchant Shipping (Prevention of Pollution by Garbage) Regulations 1988;

(i) section 1, 5, 6(9) or 7(3) of the Control of Pollution (Amendment) Act 1989;

(j) section 107, 118(4) or 175(1) of the Water Act 1989;

(k) section 23(1), 33, 34(6), 44, 47(6), 57(5), 59(5), 63(2), 69(9), 70(4), 71(3) or 80(4) of the 1990 Act;

(l) section 85, 202 or 206 of the Water Resources Act 1991;

(m) section 33 of the Clean Air Act 1993;

(n) paragraph 15(1), (3), (4) or (5) of Schedule 5 to the Finance Act 1996.

Table 12-5: Person Convicted of Relevant Offences   525
(Factor I)

Factor I Whether it is the applicant (or licence holder) or another relevant person who has been convicted of a relevant offence or offences

There are three types of person who may apply for or hold licences. These are **(a)** an individual, **(b)** a partnership and **(c)** a body corporate. The questions which the WRA needs to consider are

In the case of an individual

Was the offence committed by the individual applying for or holding the licence, or by another relevant person? If the latter, was the offence committed

> by him in the course of his employment by the applicant or licence holder, or

> by him in the course of the carrying on of any business by a partnership one of the members of which was the applicant or licence holder, or

> by a body corporate at a time when the applicant or licence holder was a director, manager, secretary or other similar officer of that body corporate?

In the case of a partnership

Was the offence committed by one of the partners applying for or holding the licence, or by another relevant person? If the latter, was the offence committed

> by him in the course of his employment by one of the partners applying for or holding the licence, or

> by him in the course of the carrying on of any business by a partnership of which one of the partners applying for or holding the licence was a member, or

> by a body corporate at a time when one of the partners applying for or holding the licence was a director, manager, secretary or other similar officer of that body corporate?

In the case of a body corporate

Was the offence committed by the body corporate, or by another relevant person? If the latter, was the offence committed

> by him in the course of his employment by the applicant or licence holder, or

> by a person who is a director, manager, secretary or other similar officer of the applicant or licence holder, or

> by another body corporate and, at the time when the offence was committed, a director, manager, secretary or other similar officer of the applicant or licence holder held such an office in the body corporate which committed the offence?

Table 12-6: Relevant Certificates of Technical Competence

Type of facility	Relevant certificate	Type of facility	Relevant certificate
A landfill site which receives special waste.	Managing landfill operations: special waste (level 4).	A waste treatment plant where waste, none of which is biodegradable, clinical or special waste, is subjected to a chemical or physical process.	1. Treatment operations: inert waste (level 3); or 2. Managing treatment operations: biodegradable waste (level 4); or 3. Managing treatment operations: clinical or special waste (level 4).
A landfill site which receives biodegradable waste or which for some other reason requires substantial engineering works to protect the environment but which in either case does not receive special waste.	1. Managing landfill operations: biodegradable waste (level 4); or 2. Managing landfill operations: special waste (level 4).	A transfer station where— (a) clinical or special waste is dealt with; and (b) the total quantity of the waste at the station at any time exceeds 5 cubic metres.	Managing transfer operations: clinical or special waste (level 4).
Any other type of landfill site with a total capacity exceeding 50,000 cubic metres.	1. Landfill operations: inert waste (level 3); or 2. Managing landfill operations: biodegradable waste (level 4); or 3. Managing landfill operations: special waste (level 4).	A transfer station where— (a) biodegradable waste, but no clinical or special waste, is dealt with; and (b) the total quantity of waste at the station at any time exceeds 5 cubic metres.	1. Managing transfer operations: biodegradable waste (level 4); or 2. Managing transfer operations: clinical or special waste (level 4).
A site on which waste is burned in an incinerator designed to incinerate waste at a rate of more than 50 kilograms per hour but less than 1 tonne per hour.	Managing incinerator operations: special waste (level 4).	Any other type of waste transfer station where the total quantity of waste at the station at any time exceeds 50 cubic metres.	1. Transfer operations: inert waste (level 3); or 2. Managing transfer operations: biodegradable waste (level 4); or 3. Managing transfer operations: clinical or special waste (level 4).
A waste treatment plant where clinical or special waste is subjected to a chemical or physical process.	Managing treatment operations: clinical or special waste (level 4).	A civic amenity site.	1. Civic amenity site operations (level 3); or 2. Managing transfer operations: biodegradable waste (level 4); or 3. Managing transfer operations: clinical or special waste (level 4).
A waste treatment plant where biodegradable waste, but no clinical or special waste, is subjected to a chemical or physical process.	1. Managing treatment operations: biodegradable waste (level 4); or 2. Managing treatment operations: clinical or special waste (level 4).		

Chapter 13

THE REGULATION OF WASTE MANAGEMENT OPERATIONS – OTHER PROVISIONS

INTRODUCTION

Although the majority of waste management activities fall within Part II of the Environmental Protection Act 1990, some treatment operations such as incineration and certain recovery processes come under Part I of the Act. Within this Part, there are two regimes of control and those processes in which the predominant environmental effect is emissions to the atmosphere are subject to Local Air Pollution Control (LAPC) and are often referred to as "Part B" processes. These are administered by the local authorities within England and Wales, but in Scotland they fall within the remit of SEPA. (In view of SEPA's involvement, it is no longer correct to refer to Local Authority Air Pollution Control (LAAPC) in relation to Part B processes.) However, through section 4(4) and (6), the Secretary of State has powers to make a general or specific direction which brings Part B processes in England and Wales within the control of the Environment Agency, although such a direction may not extend the scope of the control beyond releases to the air (section 4(5)). Prior to the introduction of Part I of the Act, a preliminary estimate indicated that approximately 27,000 installations, comprising 12,000 industrial processes and 15,000 small waste-burning appliances, would fall within LAPC but, in practice, at 1st April 1995 there was a total of only ~12,000 authorised Part B processes within England and Wales.

Processes discharging to more than one environmental medium come within the Integrated Pollution Control (IPC) regime, which is administered by the Environment Agency and SEPA. It was initially estimated that there would be about 5,000 "Part A" installations covering 105 different processes but, after the final tranche of the phased implementation of IPC, it was revealed that there were only 2,090 Part A authorisations in total (*ENDS Report* 254, March 1996).

With its origins in the Fifth Report of the Royal Commission on Environmental Pollution, Integrated Pollution Control was developed over a number of years as a result of extensive consultation with industry, trade associations, regulatory bodies and environmental groups. The

527

concept of a single regime for the control of emissions to all three environmental media which directs pollution releases to the medium where least environmental damage would be done was a new approach and as such it is not surprising that, following its introduction, there were a number of issues to be resolved.

Although developed within the UK, this approach has parallels in an earlier EU Directive controlling the emissions of asbestos, 87/217/EEC, and subsequently a similar system of Integrated Pollution Protection and Control has been proposed for adoption by the EU. The UK system of IPC is not independent of external influences, having close links with the EU Directive on Limiting of Emissions of Certain Pollutants from Large Combustion Plants, 88/609/EEC, a number of Directives relating to incineration processes, and international agreements such as the UNECE Protocol to the 1976 Convention on Long-Range Transboundary Air Pollution.

Whilst many of the enforcement provisions within Part I of the Act follow the same general pattern as those within the waste management licensing regime, there are a number of apparent inconsistencies between the two systems, e.g.:

— despite the greater complexity of IPC processes, there are no *formal* legislative requirements equivalent to those of "fit and proper person" and "technically competent person" within Part II of the Act, although such considerations are an *implicit* component of BATNEEC;

— only activities subject to the waste management provisions of Part II EPA 1990 need satisfy the enforcement authority regarding start-up and post-closure conditions;

— landfilling operations are the only processes for which financial provisions must be made for environmental damage.

This mismatch appears to be contrary to government policy that regulation in the area of waste management should be proportionate to the risks involved and the benefits obtained (DoE Circular 11/94, para. 10). However, the implementation of the Integrated Pollution Prevention and Control Directive (IPPC), 96/61/EC, will necessitate a number of important changes to both regimes, viz:

— some processes currently coming within the waste management licensing regime will become subject to IPPC;

— all current IPC processes will be subject to additional requirements, including arrangements for the disposal of the waste produced, and this might provide the appropriate opportunity with which to secure a greater degree of consistency between Part I and Part II of the 1990 Act.

The registration of waste carriers is another area not covered by Part II of the Act, being regulated by means of the Control of Pollution (Amendment) Act 1989. However, this came into force at the same time as much of Part II of the 1990 Act, and the registration of waste brokers introduced in the 1994 Regulations follows a similar pattern to that for waste carriers.

PART I OF THE ENVIRONMENTAL PROTECTION ACT 1990

An authorisation is required for all Part A and Part B processes coming within Part I of the Act and, under section 2(1) and (2), the Secretary of State may prescribe by Regulations any description of such processes for control. These are referred to as "prescribed processes" and this description may be made by reference to:

— any characteristics of the process;

— the area or other circumstances in which the process is carried on; or

— the description of persons carrying it on.

The Regulations may also determine which processes are subject to central control by the Environment Agency or SEPA and those under LAPC (section 2(4)).

In addition, any description of substance whose release into the environment is subject to control under sections 6 and 7 of the Act may be prescribed by the Regulations, which may:

— prescribe for each environmental medium, the substances whose release is subject to control;

— prescribe for such substances in relation to any environmental medium, the amount of release over a given period, its concentration, or any other conditions under which a release may be made,

and for substances released into the air:

— specify whether they are for central or local authority control.

"Substance" is defined in section 1(13) and includes heat and electricity but excludes noise (appeal decision of Secretary of State, 8th April 1994, on appeal by Yeoman Bulk Cargoes against Yarmouth Borough Council's refusal to vary an authorisation), although there has been no clarification on whether "electricity" includes electromagnetic radiation. It is interesting to note that, in the drafting of the IPPC Directive, *infra*, consideration was given to the inclusion of not only light and vibrations but also "non-ionising radiation or similar influences" in the context of process emissions (COM(95)88 final – SYN 526).

A "prescribed substance" is a substance of a description prescribed by section 2(5), which, under section 2(6)(b), may be defined in terms of its threshold concentration in the environmental medium. Details of prescribed processes and prescribed substances are contained in the Environmental Protection (Prescribed Processes and Substances) Regulations 1991, SI 1991/472, which have been amended on a number of occasions (see Tromans[1] for details of these changes). The Regulations include a number of schedules:

Schedule 1 – Descriptions of processes.

Schedule 2 – Rules for the interpretation of Schedule 1.

Schedule 3 – Dates from which authorisations are required.

Schedule 4 – Releases into the air: prescribed substances.

Schedule 5 – Releases into water: prescribed substances.

Schedule 6 – Releases into land: prescribed substances.

EMISSION LIMITS AND QUALITY OBJECTIVES

Whilst the framework of prescribed processes and prescribed substances established under section 2 of the Environmental Protection Act 1990 provides for the source-based regulation of industrial processes, it is also necessary to have a mechanism for imposing more general controls relating specific industrial sectors, environmental quality objectives and the total emissions of a given substance on a national or a regional basis.

Section 3 of the 1990 Act enables such non source-based controls to be implemented and, for any substance released from a prescribed process into any environmental medium, Regulations may be made which prescribe standards for limiting the concentration, or the total or time-related quantity of the substance that may be released. These may also relate to any other characteristic of the substance for any circumstances in which it is released. Standards may be set for the measurement or analysis of the

---

[1] *The Environment Acts 1990-1995, 3rd Edition*, S Tromans, M Nash and M Poustie, Sweet & Maxwell, 1996, page 787.

substances under these controls, and the processes themselves may be subject to the imposition of standards or other requirements (section 3(2)(c)). Regulations made under section 3(2) may apply selectively and different provisions may be established for different processes, descriptions of person, localities or other circumstances. General or specific environmental objectives or quality standards may also be set for any environmental medium, relating to the release into that or any other medium of substances from any process (section 3(4)).

In addition, the Secretary of State has the power under section 3(5) to establish strategies in a number of areas, viz:

— setting total or time-related limits on any substance which may be released into the environment in, or within, any area within the United Kingdom;

— allocating, to persons carrying on processes, quotas for the release of substances subject to such limits;

— establishing limits on emissions in order to reduce progressively the pollution of the environment; and

— progressive improvements in the quality plans and quality objectives.

Whilst to date these measures have been restricted to the implementation of externally-determined measures, i.e. the Large Combustion Plant Directive, 88/609/EEC as amended by 94/66/EC, they provide the legal basis for the introduction of a system of control using economic instruments and the allocation of quotas.

In addition to obliging Member States to set limits on both the total amount and the concentration of emissions, the Large Combustion Plant Directive requires progressive reductions in these criteria to be achieved. This is being implemented by the establishment of the UK Programme and National Plan for Reducing Emissions of SO_2 and NO_X, which now sets annual targets for these emissions from three industry sectors – power stations, refineries and "other industries". However, such limits do not always correspond to those within Part A authorisations, in situations in which the regulator permits a given plant to be operated at emission levels in excess of the levels in the National Plan, providing this is offset by lower emissions from other plants operated by the same person (i.e. a form of "netting" of emissions – see Chapter 1).

Another link between source-based controls and ambient air quality is provided by section 4(4A), under which local authorities in England and

Wales, when exercising their LAPC and other functions under Part I, must have regard to the National Air Quality Strategy, section 80 of the Environment Act 1995. This enables them to exercise their "Part I powers" to secure relevant objectives within the Strategy, and establish their own action plans.

WASTE PROCESSES SUBJECT TO INTEGRATED POLLUTION CONTROL AND LAPC

Chapter 5 of Schedule 1 to the Environmental Protection (Prescribed Processes and Substances) Regulations 1991, SI 1991/472 as amended, lists the waste disposal and recycling processes prescribed for control under Part I and these are further sub-divided into incineration, recovery processes and the production of fuel from waste (Table 13-1, pages 571-572). In addition, there are other waste-related processes which are contained within Chapter 6 on "Other Industries" (Table 13-2, pages 573-574). Of the total of 2,090 processes subject to IPC, only 136 are waste-related and comprise 86 incineration processes, 45 chemical recovery operations, 4 waste-derived fuel units and a single authorisation in the "Other Industries" category relating to animal/vegetable matter.

The inclusion of a process within Schedule 1 to SI 1991/472 does not *ipso facto* categorise it for "Part I control". Under Regulation 4(1), where the process cannot result in the release of any prescribed substance:

— to the air, where the quantity of any such releases is "so trivial that it cannot result in any harm"; *and*

— into water, in concentrations not in excess of the background concentration (as defined in Regulation 4(7)); *and*

— into land,

it is not to be treated as a Part A process.

Similarly, Part B status does not apply unless the process will, or there is a likelihood that it will, result in the release into the air of one or more prescribed substances (Regulation 4(2)). However, the exceptions conferred by Regulation 4(1) and (2) do not apply if the process gives rise to an offensive smell outside the premises where it is carried on.

A number of other exemptions are detailed in Regulation 4(3) to (6) but these are unlikely to be of relevance to commercial waste management operations.

GRANTING OF AUTHORISATIONS

Part A and Part B processes may not be carried on without an authorisation granted by the appropriate authority and, in *Lewis v Graham*, it was held that for a person to be considered to be "carrying on" a process, he must have control and direction of it. Although there is no case law specific to "carrying on a process", in relation to a business this has been considered to require "a repetition or series of acts" (*Smith v Anderson*).

The application for an authorisation must be made to the appropriate authority (i.e. the Environment Agency or SEPA for Part A processes and the local authorities (in England and Wales) or SEPA (in Scotland) for Part B processes) and this is to be accompanied by either the appropriate charge, as required by section 41 of the Environment Act (for Part A processes), or the fee prescribed under section 8(2)(c) of the amended 1990 Act (in the case of LAPC).

Where an application has been "duly made" – i.e. the applicant has forwarded the fee or charge, fulfilled all of the legislative requirements and supplied the enforcing authority with all of the information it needs to assess the application – the appropriate enforcing agency must grant the authorisation, subject to the conditions of section 7 of the Act, or refuse the application. The Secretary of State has powers under which he may give directions to the enforcing authority as to whether it should or should not grant any particular authorisation (section 6(5)).

Although there are no formal criteria against which the potential holders of authorisations may be assessed, under section 6(4) the enforcing authority may not grant an authorisation unless it considers that the applicant has the ability to carry on the process in compliance with the conditions. Some early reports of the Secretary of State's findings in relation to authorisation appeals have suggested that it is the ability of the applicant to comply rather than the likelihood of him doing so which is taken into consideration. However, in *R v Secretary of State for the Environment and N C Compton t/a R J Compton ex parte West Wiltshire District Council*, the learned judge implicitly distinguished between the *possibility* of complying and the *ability* to comply and held that, in the instant case, to rely solely on the latter criterion would result in a wholly unsatisfactory situation. Thus, the previous activities of the applicant appear to be a relevant consideration and an enforcing authority may take into consideration what might happen in practice, rather than whether the applicant is theoretically able to comply with the conditions of an authorisation.

The application procedure for an authorisation is included in section 6 and

Schedule 1 to the 1990 Act and in the Environmental Protection (Applications, Appeals and Registers) Regulations 1991, SI 1991/507 as amended by SI 1991/836, SI 1994/1271, SI 1996/667 and 1996/979. The Regulations detail the information to be supplied with the application, and for IPC authorisation this must include:

— details of the applicant and the location of the process;

— a description of the prescribed process;

— a list of the prescribed substances and other substances, which will be used in connection with, or will result from, the carrying on of that process, and might cause harm if released into any environmental medium;

— a description of the techniques to be used for preventing the release of such substances or reducing the release of such substances to a minimum, and for rendering harmless any such releases;

— details of any proposed release of such substances into any environmental medium, an assessment of the environmental consequences and proposals for the monitoring of these;

— the matters upon which the applicant wishes to rely to satisfy the criteria of BATNEEC, BPEO and the other relevant objectives of section 7(2) and (7) of the Act;

— any additional material which the applicant wishes to be taken into account in considering the application.

For LAPC processes, such information need only relate to releases of prescribed substances into the air (Regulation 2(2)). There are specific requirements in Regulation 2(3) for authorisations relating to the burning of waste oil in any prescribed process with a net rated input of less than 0.4 megawatts, viz:

— information on the net rated thermal input of the appliance and whether or not it is constructed to conform with Part 2 of the British Standard BS 4256:1972;

— details of the fuel type and its source;

— details of the height and location of the chimney and certain specific information on the efflux waste gases;

— details of the location of the fuel storage tanks for the appliance.

However, under Regulation 6, a number of the requirements of Schedule 1 to the 1990 Act relating to the determination and variation of authorisations – paragraphs 1(2), 2, 6 and 7 – do not apply in relation to waste oil applications.

Consultation and Notification of Applications

A copy of the application must be forwarded to the statutory consultees listed in Regulation 4 and any persons specified by the Secretary of State in a direction. The statutory consultees include:

— the Health and Safety Executive, in all cases;

— the Ministry of Agriculture, Fisheries and Food, for all IPC processes carried on in England, or the appropriate Secretary of State for those in Scotland or Wales;

— the sewerage undertaker or, in Scotland, the regional or islands council, for IPC processes with releases to a foul sewer;

— the Nature Conservancy Council for England, the Nature Conservancy Council for Scotland or the Countryside Council for Wales, in respect of any prescribed process that may affect a site of special scientific interest (SSSI) within its area; and

— the harbour authority for all IPC processes which may result in releases into a harbour under its control.

Generally, these bodies will have 28 days within which to make representations in writing to the enforcing authority, although this period may be varied by the Secretary of State. All such representations must be considered by the enforcing authority within the time period allowed, as must any representations by any other persons. These might result from the advertisement of applications, which is also a statutory requirement. Advertisements must be made by both the enforcing authority, under paragraph 1(2) of Schedule 1 to the 1990 Act, and by the applicant or existing holder, under Regulation 5 of the amended 1991 Regulations. They must be placed within a specified time period in "one or more newspapers circulating in the locality in which the prescribed process will be carried on".

Transfer of Authorisations

This procedure differs appreciably from that within the waste management licensing regime, since it is the person to whom the authorisation is transferred who must notify the enforcing authority (section 9). This notification must be in writing and be undertaken within the 21 days after the date of the transfer. Tromans[1] notes that the wording of the section suggests that the transfer may only be made in advance of such a change and not once control of the process itself has been transferred.

There is no obligation to inform the enforcing authority of an intended transfer and, whilst it has no powers to object (unlike the situation in waste management licensing), the authority may take other enforcement action where appropriate. The authorisation is effective on and after the date of transfer and applies as if it had been granted to the transferee under the same conditions.

Variation of Authorisations

The enforcing authorities have a duty under section 6(6) to undertake a review of the conditions of each authorisation at least every four years, and it is possible that such a review might indicate that a variation is necessary. Alternatively, the need to change the conditions of an authorisation might result from information gained by inspectors on a routine visit or from other sources. In addition, the holder himself may wish to modify aspects of the process as a result of changes to the operational plant or the throughput of materials.

In the context of Part I of the Act, a variation is taken to include adding to, varying or rescinding any of the conditions or other provisions of the subsisting authorisation (section 10(8)).

Variation by the Enforcing Authority

Variations by the regulating authority are subject to section 10, and paragraph 6 of Part II of Schedule 1 to the 1990 Act. Subject to certain conditions, the enforcing authority may at any time vary an authorisation and is required to do so if it appears that the extant authorisation does not reflect the current operating conditions.

The holder must be notified and a variation notice served upon him, specifying the variations which the enforcing authority has decided to make and the date(s) from which these are to take effect (section 10(2) and (3)). As with the initial application procedure, the proposed change must be advertised and the statutory consultees and others given an opportunity to comment on the variation.

---

[1] *The Environment Acts 1990-1995, 3rd Edition*, S Tromans, M Nash and M Poustie, Sweet & Maxwell, 1996, page 61.

A variation notice remains valid until it is withdrawn or is modified under section 10(3A). In addition to specifying the changes to be made, the notice must also require the holder to inform the authority of what action he intends to take to comply with its stipulations, and to pay any such fee as is required. Where it is considered that the action proposed by the holder would constitute "a substantial change", the authority must then inform the holder of its opinion.

"Substantial Change"
The term "substantial change" is described (though not defined) in section 10(7) and may relate to the substances released from the process, or the amount and any other characteristic of any substance so released. Although there is some case law relating to the meaning of "substantial" (see *Palser v Grinling*; *Property Holding v Mischeff*; and *Atkinson v Bettison*), this gives insufficient guidance where quantifiable control parameters are involved. There are, however, a number of other measures in which this concept is applied.

Department of Environment Circular 7/89 suggests an increase in capacity of 20% or more should be regarded as "substantial" in relation to the limit values and quality objectives regarding the aquatic environment in Directive 86/280/EEC, and some of the Chief Inspector's Process Guidance Notes indicate a value of 5% increase in terms of the plant's design capacity/ authorised limit or changes in operating parameters/process equipment.

This 5% figure is in line with the earlier proposals for an IPPC Directive although, in the version which was adopted, Article 2(10)(b) defines "substantial change" as meaning "a change in operation which, in the opinion of the competent authority, may have a significant negative effect on human beings or the environment".

Variation by the Holder
The holder of an authorisation may request a change in its conditions, the procedures for which are covered by section 11 and paragraph 7 of Part II of Schedule 1 to the 1990 Act, and Regulation 3 of SI 1991/507 as amended. In addition to requesting a variation of the *conditions* of an authorisation, under section 11(10) the change may also relate to other *limitations* or *provisions* within the authorisation. As a consequence, section 11 distinguishes between "substantial changes", as described above, and "relevant changes" which term is defined in section 11(11) and provides the holder with a degree of flexibility in selecting a procedure appropriate to the change envisaged. A "relevant change" is defined as "a change in the manner of carrying on the process, which is capable of altering the substances released from the process or of affecting the amount

of any substance so released". However, regardless of the procedure chosen, where the proposed change is considered by the enforcing authority as being "substantial", then the formal procedure of application, notification and advertisement must be followed, as for section 10.

The holder of an authorisation who considers making a relevant change may approach the enforcing authority and request it to make a determination on the nature of the change and whether a variation is necessary (section 11(1)(b) and (2)). The authority must then determine whether this involves a substantial change in the carrying on of the process and if it would constitute a breach of the existing conditions. It must also determine what changes, if any, should be approved and notify the holder accordingly. The holder may then apply for a variation on this basis, using the conditions relating to a substantial change (section 11(3)) or a change which is not substantial (section 11(4)), as appropriate.

Where the holder himself considers that a variation of the conditions is required, he may make an application for a variation through section 11(6), without requesting the enforcement agency for a prior determination under section 11(1) and (2), *supra*. In both of the above cases, if the enforcing agency considers that there is a substantial change which requires a variation in the conditions, the appropriate application and consultation procedure must be followed.

There may be circumstances in which the proposed change does not involve a relevant change, and then a variation may be sought through section 11(5) which is not subject to the advertising and consultation requirements.

Surrender of Authorisations

Unlike waste management licences, authorisations may be surrendered unconditionally, and indeed the Act appears to encourage the enforcing authority to terminate authorisations in respect of non-operational processes. Section 12(2) of the Environmental Protection Act 1990 provides specific powers for the revocation of an authorisation where the enforcing authority has reason to believe that a prescribed process to which it relates has not been carried on for a period of 12 months. In this case, "not carried on" would tend to suggest the complete cessation of operations but such an interpretation is at odds with that in *Lewis v Graham*, above.

The appellate function in relation to all Part I activities, including authorisations, is with the Secretary of State or his appointee, and this is discussed further in the section relating to enforcement.

CONDITIONS OF THE AUTHORISATION

In view of the technical complexity of the processes subject to control, the application for an authorisation is an iterative process and the information supplied by the applicant under Regulation 2(1)(i) of SI 1991/507 must include, *inter alia*, evidence of how the applicant intends to satisfy the criteria of BATNEEC, BPEO and the other relevant objectives of section 7(2) and (7) of the Act. Such information will be reviewed by the enforcing authority, according to the requirements of section 7, which specifies the general and specific conditions to be included within an authorisation. Implicit within every authorisation is a general condition that the person carrying on the process in question must use the Best Available Techniques Not Entailing Excessive Cost (BATNEEC) for:

— preventing the release of prescribed substances into the environment or, where that is not possible, reducing their release to a minimum and rendering harmless any released substances (section 7(4)(a)); and

— rendering harmless any other substances (i.e. non-prescribed substances) which might cause harm if released into any environmental medium (section 7(4)(b)).

Section 7(10) states that, in addition to technical means and technology, references to BATNEEC in relation to a process (i.e. as distinct from such references to BATNEEC elsewhere in the Act) refer to the number, qualifications, training and supervision of persons employed in the process, and in the design, construction, lay-out and maintenance of the buildings in which it is carried on. These implicit conditions form one of the objectives of the Part I authorisations listed in section 7(2), which in addition include:

— compliance with any direction of the Secretary of State in connection with the implementation of EU or international law relating to environmental protection;

— compliance with any limits or requirements, and achievement of any quality standards or objectives prescribed by the Secretary of State under any relevant enactments (as defined in section 7(12));

— compliance with any requirements applicable to the grant of authorisations specified by, or under a plan made by, the Secretary of State.

An authorisation must also include, where appropriate, specific conditions which the enforcing authority considers appropriate to secure the achievement of the general conditions in section 7(4) and the objectives in section 7(2). In addition, any such conditions specified in directions given by the Secretary of State, and those considered appropriate by the authority, must also be included.

Where a process involves releases into more than one environmental medium and is subject to central control, the objectives must also include that of ensuring that BATNEEC will be used for minimising the pollution which may be caused by the releases to the environment as a whole, having regard to the best practicable environmental option (BPEO) as respects the substances that may be released.

THE RELATIVE ROLES OF BATNEEC AND BPEO

Although the concept of Best Practicable Environmental Option (BPEO) was considered in detail in the 12th Report of the Royal Commission on Environmental Pollution (RCEP) in 1988, it only became a component of process authorisation relatively recently when section 7(7) of the Environmental Protection Act 1990 came into force in April 1991.

While the identification of Best Available Technique Not Entailing Excessive Cost (BATNEEC) requires a potential operator to furnish relatively straightforward information relating to the techno-economic operation of the proposed process, the assessment of the effects of the process on the environment as a whole, as required for BPEO, is more problematic. These requirements of the 1990 Act have posed several fundamental and difficult questions to process operators, such as the manner in which the choice of a BPEO can be demonstrated and the environmental information required for the assessment of potential harm.

Best Practicable Means (BPM)

Although superseded by BATNEEC and BPEO for Part I processes under EPA 1990, the defence of Best Practicable Means remains for some categories of statutory nuisance under section 80(7) and (9) of the Act, and it is useful to consider this approach in the development of the mechanisms for the control of industrial pollution.

The term Best Practicable Means has been in use for the control of air pollution since the Alkali Act of 1874 but it has never been statutorily defined. However, guidance on its application to different processes was given in BPM Notes which were issued by HMIP and their predecessors. These Notes were drawn up in consultation with representatives of the relevant industry and other interested parties, and as a result they had the flexibility to cater for local and individual circumstances. However, these controls were essentially process-based and, although cost was a relevant factor, it was not the major consideration in determining practicability. In the Clean Air Act 1956, practicable is interpreted as "reasonably practicable, having regard amongst other things to local conditions and circumstances, to financial implications and to the current state of technical knowledge". It was HMIP's practice to regard the term practicable as being interpreted in this way, if no risk to public health existed.

The 12th Report of RCEP omitted the phrase "local conditions and circumstances" from its definition of practicable because "it would seem to open the way to local derogations being admitted to a BPEO for social or political reasons, in addition to local environmental factors".

Best Available Techniques Not Entailing Excessive Cost (BATNEEC)

The concept of BATNEEC is broader than that of BPM since, in addition to the technical means and technology of pollution abatement, it includes aspects of process design, plant layout and maintenance, and manning levels and competence. An explanation of the meaning of BATNEEC is given in the DoE document *Integrated Pollution Control: A Practical Guide*, which considers the individual components of the term:

"best": this is to be taken to mean most effective in preventing, minimising or rendering harmless the polluting releases from a process. It is not an absolute term and there may be a number of techniques which are so regarded.

"available": refers to being procurable by the holder of the process authorisation. The technique need not be one which is in general use but should be accessible to the operator. This would include:

— techniques developed or proven at the pilot plant scale, provided this permits commercial implementation;

— techniques available from outside the UK;

— techniques from a monopoly supplier, provided these are procurable by the operator.

"techniques": this is defined in section 7(10), *supra*.

"not entailing excessive cost": the document suggests that this must be considered with regard to the context of the process, i.e. whether it is a new or an existing process.

For new processes BAT and BATNEEC may be synonymous, although it is suggested that the following principles are applied:

— the cost must be weighed against the environmental damage from the process – the greater the damage, the greater the expenditure on BAT before it is regarded as excessive;

— the objective is to prevent damaging releases, or reduce such releases, so far as this does not impose excessive cost. However, if after applying BATNEEC serious harm could still result, then the application can be refused;

— the cost element should be considered as objectively as possible and without reference to the profitability of the operation.

With existing processes, the objective is to establish a time scale over which these will be upgraded to new standards, or as near to these as possible, or ultimately closed down. It is suggested that this may be achieved by adopting an approach similar to that in the Air Framework Directive, 84/360/EEC. Under Article 13 of the Directive, the factors to be taken into account regarding the application of best available technology to existing plants are, *inter alia*:

— the plant's technical characteristics;

— its rate of utilisation and length of remaining life;

— the nature and volume of polluting emissions; and

— the desirability of NEEC for the plant concerned, having particular regard to the economic situation of undertakings within the category in question.

Processes subject to central control which are likely to involve the release of substances into more than one environmental medium must also consider BPEO. Tromans[1] states that, from the wording of section 7(7) of the Act, the critical concept is BATNEEC, and BPEO is a secondary consideration, suggesting that the process envisaged by this subsection appears to be:

— identification of the substances that may be released;

— deciding the BPEO in relation to these substances (or possibly a combination of substances);

---

[1]   *The Environment Acts 1990-1995, 3rd Edition*, S Tromans, M Nash and M Poustie, Sweet & Maxwell, 1996, page 58.

— "having regard" to the BPEO so identified, determine the BATNEEC which will minimise the pollution to the environment as a whole, focusing on the carrying on of the process, rather than simply on the substances.

Initially, HMIP applied the Chief Inspector's Guidance Notes on a "universal" basis with no derogations to take account of local variations. However, Guidance Notes for the metals industry introduced the concept of "achievable release levels" for new and existing processes for which "the best combination of techniques to limit the impact in the context of the process" are applied. These stated that inspectors would not be expected to treat these levels as uniform emission standards and when considering BATNEEC/BPEO they should take account of the local effects of releases and other site-specific issues, including the financial position of the operator. In addition to jeopardising the "level playing field" approach to IPC, such changes significantly alter the overall level of control achievable through IPC.

Best Practicable Environmental Option (BPEO)

Since the publication of the 11th RCEP Report, the term Best Practicable Environmental Option has been applied to a number of different situations but there has been no uniformity in the interpretation given to the concept. The 12th RCEP Report notes that "the indiscriminate use of the term to describe almost any course of action which takes account of environmental factors can only undermine the underlying principles upon which BPEO is based". From the latter Report's description of the BPEO procedure and its use in the abatement and prevention of industrial pollution (Table 13-3, page 575), it is clear that in this case "the BPEO procedure" relates to the criteria for establishing a *process* option. However, the interpretation of section 7(7) EPA 1990, *supra*, indicates that, as far as the Act is concerned, BPEO relates to the examination of the options available for reducing the emissions of critical *substances* emitted from a given process, prior to the selection of BATNEEC for the process. This interpretation is used in the HMIP proposals for BPEO discussed later but the reader of some of the Chief Inspector's Guidance Notes could be excused for not fully realising the substance-based context of BPEO.

The Guidance Notes for steelmaking processes detail the techniques which are available for "release minimisation" and the achievable release levels for new and existing processes. Applicants are advised that a combination of several abatement techniques and good process control are required to deal with the releases, and that they should "review all the options that are available and demonstrate that the combination of primary processes and selected abatement equipment represents BATNEEC, and that the concept of BPEO is satisfied". Other than tabulating the possible releases of both prescribed and other substances for each stage of the process route, no practical advice on satisfying BPEO is given. This lack of guidance was reflected in the quality of the early IPC applications received by HMIP.

Proposals on Assessment Principles for IPC

Acknowledging industry's problems of addressing BPEO and the poor quality of many IPC applications, in July 1993 HMIP outlined proposals for a "BPEO Index" to assist firms to evaluate the environmental impact of different process options. While this attempted to provide an integrated, objective method of assessment, it omitted energy efficiency, waste heat and solid waste, and it was felt by industry that the strictly numerical basis of the formulae used failed to acknowledge gaps and uncertainties in the science of environmental impact assessment. In April 1994, a revised proposal was issued which was less rigorous than the earlier document and suggested that the assessment "should not be used in a mechanistic way" and that the final justification for the process choice "should weigh all the relevant factors based on expert judgment".

The objective of the document was to produce a structured, transparent and consistent method of determining BATNEEC to be followed for all IPC applications, the content of which would be available for public scrutiny. Much of the 137 page document was concerned with the scientific methods employed to assess harm but the proposed assessment itself was based upon a three-stage process for determining the BPEO/BATNEEC of the process, viz:

Stage I: Preliminary Assessment of the Base Case and Generation of Alternative Process and Abatement Options
Pollutants identified as being from the "base case" option are compared with releases from the "best practice" in the Guidance Notes and compliance with Environmental Quality Standards (EQSs) or HMIP's Environmental Assessment Levels (EALs) is determined. In setting the criteria for assessing environmental harm, HMIP deliberately avoided the use of parameters used in other countries, since these invariably are specific to that system of pollution control and cannot be meaningfully translated to another system.

From this, the requirements of primary or secondary abatement techniques are established and a range of practicable options for BPEO assessment is generated.

Stage II: Environmental Assessment of Generated Process Control and Abatement Options
The wider environmental consequences of the Stage I process options are considered in terms of:

— long-term, site-specific effects to all media assessments/calculation of an Integrated Environmental Index (IEI);

— calculated short-term, site-specific effects;

— global warming potential/ozone generating potential assessed;

— waste arisings/other site-specific environmental factors considered.

Stage III: Determination of Site-Specific BPEO Option
The process options are ranked and the Best Environmental Option (BEO) identified. If this is not adopted, cost options to give annual and incremental costs are required to justify the choice of the site-specific BPEO. Only at this stage is the IPC application made and assessed by HMIP for BATNEEC/BPEO.

From the above, it is clear that in this case BPEO is determined on a substance basis and is integral to the selection of the BATNEEC. However, HMIP notes that, because of site-specific circumstances, the methodology "should not be seen as prescriptive".

Whilst the setting of emission levels for the control of pollution is relatively straightforward, whenever environmental harm is considered it is necessary:

— to predict the levels of pollution within the medium/media;

— to assess the short and long term environmental effects of these levels.

A major criticism of these proposals is the attempt to characterise all the emissions from a process in terms of a single Integrated Environmental Index (IEI), on the assumption that the individual effects of substances in each of the media are additive. While the individual values of harm produced as a result of the exercise are, in most cases, a meaningful reflection of their potential effect, the single quasi-scientific value of IEI is thought to be meaningless and misleading.

This document forms the basis of the Environment Agency's two-volume Technical Guidance Note, E1, which is currently being assessed.

Statutory and Non-Statutory Guidance

The draft guidance issued on the assessment of BPEO is but one part of a broad range of documents which are available to assist in the interpretation of the control regime within Part I of the Act. Much of this was produced during the implementation phase of IPC and as such its preparation was subject to strict time constraints, although now that the system is fully operational, a number of these documents are being revisited and revised. In reading and applying this guidance, it is important to acknowledge to whom such guidance is addressed and whether it has statutory authority or not.

IPC Processes

At the present time, the majority of the guidance notes for IPC processes are those prepared by the Chief Inspector of HMIP for use by his inspectors in England and Wales. These notes do not constitute statutory guidance under the provisions of section 7(11) of the 1990 Act, although they provide a useful source of information on prescribed processes.

In addition to industry sector guides, a series of process-specific guidance notes (initially issued as the IPR/** series) and technical guidance notes (TGNs) have been produced. The format of the IPR series has been to include a section on release levels ("achievable release levels" in more recent notes), followed by more specific information on releases to each of the environmental media. Guidance is also given on what is considered as "substantial change" and a series of annexes is attached, covering processes included by the note, prescribed substances, required techniques for pollution abatement, compliance monitoring and any additional requirements.

The IPR notes have been revised for the fuel and power sector (and re-numbered as "series 2" (S2) notes) and, for the waste disposal industry, the following new guidance has been issued:

S2 5.01: *Waste incineration processes*. This guidance replaces a series of existing notes (IPR 5/1 to 5/5) on the incineration of chemical, clinical and municipal waste, as well as sewage sludge, animal carcasses and drum residues.

S2 5.02: *Making solid fuel from waste* – replaces IPR 5/6.

S2 5.03: *Cleaning and regeneration of carbon* – replaces IPR 5/7.

S2 5.04: *Recovery of organic solvents by distillation* – replaces IPR 5/8.

The following guidance in the IPR series has not yet been updated:

IPR 5/9: *Regeneration of ion exchange resins*

IPR 5/10: *Recovery of oil by distillation*

IPR 5/11: *Sewage sludge incineration*

and, in relation to "other industries":

IPR 6/7: *Processing of animal hides and skins*

IPR 6/9: *Paper making and related processes, including mechanical pulping, recycled fibres and de-inking.*

In these notes, HMIP (and now the Environment Agency) has for the first time set out its thinking on key environmental issues, alternative technologies and financial implications. Although the encouragement of incineration over landfill is beyond the present scope of IPC, the guidance suggests that HMIP's successor – the Environment Agency – will take a broader view under the national waste strategy.

The recovery of waste heat is a recommended feature for all new municipal waste incinerators, large plants burning clinical waste and a number of chemical waste incinerators. In addition, it is suggested that combined heat and power installations should be encouraged over those for simple electricity generation.

BATNEEC continues to be regarded as a site-specific issue and the guidance given to inspectors is non-prescriptive. Information is given on "benchmark" release levels for new processes, which may be subject to derogations to reflect site specific considerations. There appears to have been some relaxation in these levels from those mooted in the draft proposals. In addition, there is a move away from establishing timetables for the upgrading of existing plant.

This approach contrasts with that adopted by the Department of the Environment in their advice on LAPC processes, *infra*. The note considers the cost implications of BATNEEC and, whilst this should not take into account the profitability of individual concerns, the assessment should reflect:

— the resources typically available for capital expenditure within the industry sector; and

— the extent to which costs may be passed on to customers, back to suppliers or absorbed by lower returns within the industry.

With regard to alternative techniques, the issues of recycling and waste minimisation are beyond the remit of IPC, although the note suggests that in-process recycling should be explored fully by means of front-end materials reclamation or separation of solid components after combustion.

Apart from large combustion plants falling within Directive 88/609/EEC, incineration processes are the only other IPC processes which are subject to external, process-related controls, in this case the EU Directives on municipal waste incineration, 89/369/EEC and 89/429/EEC, and on hazardous waste incineration, 94/67/EEC. As a consequence, the "achievable release levels" are made with reference to these and there is little scope for site-specific factors to be included.

In addition to the above guidance, HMIP has issued a booklet seeking views on the Operator Pollution Risk Appraisal (OPRA) system, which has the objective of introducing a formal system of risk assessment for processes under IPC. The system is made up of two elements – operator risk appraisal (ORA) and pollution hazard appraisal (PHA), each of which will be determined by inspectors on the basis of an assessment of seven indicators which are scored between 1 (worst) and 5 (best). These scores are weighted and an overall score is obtained for the ORA and PHA.

It is intended that such information will give the regulatory agency a view of the risk posed by individual processes and may be used as a tool to assist:

— in the prevention of pollution, by focusing on the areas requiring attention;

— in the Environment Agency's work planning with a view to optimising the frequency of site visits;

— in the provision of strategic information on the performance of regulated processes;

— as a component of a revised charging scheme;

— as motivation to the holders of authorisations to adopt "sound environmental practice".

The system is to be reviewed after 12 months of operation and, subject to such a review, similar systems may be developed for processes regulated under the Water Industry Act 1991 and the Radioactive Substances Act 1993.

LAPC Processes

The guidance on "Part B" processes issued by the Secretary of State falls into the four groups below and, in addition, the Department of the Environment produces updated briefing notes on LAPC which are available on the Internet at http://www.open.gov.ik/doe/doehome.html.

Process Guidance (PG) Notes

These provide *statutory* guidance to local authorities in England and Wales, and to SEPA in Scotland on processes subjected to LAPC. They are issued for the purposes of section 7(11) of the 1990 Act and, as with the IPR series, contain process-specific information. Tromans[1] notes that these guidance notes are less complex than those relating to IPC and a common feature is the requirement for emissions to be free from persistent mist, fumes, droplets and visible black smoke during normal operations, and from offensive odours outside the process boundary, as determined by the relevant inspector or officer. There are also requirements on materials handling, chimney height and efflux velocity. As stated above, the guidance given is intended to be "universally" applicable, with no derogations in respect of local conditions.

General Guidance (GG) Notes

These offer general guidance and in most cases do not constitute statutory guidance.

Upgrading Guidance (UG) Notes

The purpose of the UG series is to revise and update the advice given in earlier guidance notes. To date only one UG note has been produced relating to revisions and additions to existing process and general guidance notes.

Additional Guidance (AG) Notes

A large number of these notes have now been issued, none of which has statutory authority. They tend to be less detailed than other notes relating to LAPC and are concerned with issues which have arisen as a result of implementing processes subject to LAPC.

A wide range of essentially miscellaneous issues is covered and particularly important inclusions are those indicating which processes within a given area are subject to the "triviality" criterion of Regulation 4(1) of SI 1991/ 472, *supra*.

---

[1] *The Environment Acts 1990-1995, 3rd Edition*, S Tromans, M Nash and M Poustie, Sweet & Maxwell, 1996, page 28.

AUTHORISATIONS AND ENFORCEMENT

Whilst the determination of authorisations by the enforcement agencies is an important component of the IPC and LAPC regimes, these bodies cannot exercise effective control without their complementary enforcement powers within Part I of the 1990 Act and Part V of the Environment Act 1995. Of particular importance in this respect are the powers of entry, examination and investigation within section 108 of the 1995 Act, and the authority to require information under section 19 of the 1990 Act.

In addition to the variation of conditions discussed earlier, the system of authorisations permits other forms of enforcement action, including the issue of enforcement notices and prohibition notices and the revocation of the authorisations. Other powers exist for situations in which action is required to remedy harm and, in addition to a number of offences related to the carrying on of prescribed processes, the authorities have recourse to action in the High Court or, in Scotland, the appropriate sheriff court or the Court of Session.

Revocation of Authorisations

The power to revoke an authorisation provides the enforcement authorities with an ultimate sanction which can be imposed upon a holder in relation to the operation of his prescribed process. The provisions within section 12 of the 1990 Act allow for the revocation of an authorisation at any time, provided that at least 28 days' notice is given in writing to the holder. During this period, the enforcement authority may withdraw the notice or vary the date specified within it. As noted earlier, a revocation notice may also be served where the enforcement authority believes that the relevant prescribed process has not been carried on for a period of 12 months.

Enforcement Notices

Enforcement notices provide a means whereby a regulatory agency may formally bring to the attention of the holder of an authorisation its opinion that there is an actual or potential breach of any condition of the authorisation. Under section 13(2), the notice must contain:

— a statement of the authority's opinion regarding the breach or anticipated breach, specifying the matters constituting this condition;

— details of the steps to be taken and the time period during which these must be carried out.

A practical test of whether such conditions are satisfied was given in

Miller-Mead v Minister of Housing and Local Government in the context of planning conditions, where it was held that the notice must inform the recipient "fairly what he has done wrong, and what he must do to remedy it".

The 1995 Environment Act modified section 13 by inserting a provision whereby the enforcing authority may withdraw an enforcement notice (section 13(4)).

Prohibition Notices

The prohibition notice procedure gives the enforcing authority wide-ranging powers with which to regulate prescribed processes operating under an authorisation. Where the enforcing agency is of the opinion that "the continuing to carry it on, or the continuing to carry it on in a particular manner involves an imminent risk of pollution to the environment", it must issue a prohibition notice on the person carrying on the process (section 14(1)). An important feature of the prohibition notice is that it may be served whether or not any condition of the authorisation has been breached and it may also extend to any aspect of the process regardless of whether it is regulated by the authorisation.

As with enforcement notices, the content of prohibition notices includes mandatory components relating to the authority's opinion, the risks involved in the process, the steps to be taken and the time period allowed for remedying the situation (section 14(3)(a) to (c)). In addition, the notice must direct that, until it is withdrawn, the authorisation shall wholly, or to the extent specified in the notice, cease to have effect. As a consequence, there is a mandatory obligation on the enforcing agency to withdraw such a notice when it is satisfied that the required steps have been taken (section 14(5)) (c.f. the discretionary position with enforcement notices).

Appeals with respect to Authorisations

The appeals procedure with respect to authorisations is contained in section 15 of the 1990 Act, as amended, and in the Environmental Protection (Applications, Appeals and Registers) Regulations 1991, SI 1991/507, as amended. Guidance relating to processes subject to LAPC has been issued by the Secretary of State in document GG5/91.

Appeals are made to the Secretary of State for the groups of circumstances listed in subsections (1) and (2) of section 15, for which different conditions apply, *infra*. Following the modifications in section 114 of the 1995 Act, these appellate functions may be delegated to any person to act on his behalf. In each section of the Act relating to enforcement – i.e. sections 12,

13 and 14 – the Secretary of State has an overall power under which he can give directions to the enforcing authority as to what action it must take, and there is no appeal under these circumstances.

Section 15(1) applies to a person:

— refused the grant of an authorisation under section 6;

— aggrieved by the conditions attached to his authorisation under any provisions of Part I of the 1990 Act;

— refused a variation of an authorisation under section 11;

— whose authorisation has been revoked under section 12,

who may appeal against the decision of the enforcing authority.

Section 15(2) applies to:

— variation notices issued under sections 10 and 11;

— enforcement notices issued under section 13; and

— prohibition notices issued under section 14.

The notice of appeal must be in writing and be accompanied by the following documents:

— a statement of the grounds of the appeal;

— a copy of any relevant application;

— a copy of any relevant authorisation;

— a copy of any relevant correspondence between the appellant and the enforcing authority;

— a copy of any decision or notice related to the appeal; and

— a statement as to the form in which the appellant wishes the appeal to be heard.

With regard to the last item, the appeal may be a written presentation or take the form of a hearing, which may be in private, or a local enquiry. There is a time limit for bringing appeals, dependent upon the decision which is being appealed against. Whilst an appeal against the revocation of an authorisation has the effect of suspending the authorisation until the final determination or withdrawal of the appeal, appeals against a variation, a prohibition or an enforcement notice do not affect the enforcement of that notice.

Under Regulation 14, the Secretary of State must notify the appellant in writing of the outcome of his determination and send him a copy of any report produced by a person appointed to conduct a hearing.

Full details of the appeal procedure are given in Regulations 9 to 14 of SI 1991/507, as amended.

OFFENCES

A wide range of offences is created by the provisions relating to the IPC and LAPC regimes, and these are contained within section 23 of the 1990 Act and section 110 of the 1995 Act. The latter Act made a number of modifications to the existing offences and in some cases the penalties were increased. The principal offence is carrying on a prescribed process without an authorisation (section 23(1)(a)), which on summary conviction carries a maximum fine of £20,000, up to 3 months' imprisonment, or both. Conviction on indictment is subject to an unlimited fine, up to two years in prison, or both (section 23(2)). These penalties also apply to the following offences:

— failing to comply with or contravening any requirement or prohibition imposed by an enforcement notice or a prohibition notice (section 23(1)(c));

— failing to comply with an order made by a court under section 26 for the cause of the offence to be remedied (section 23(1)(l)).

The offence in section 23(1)(a) is one of strict liability, which is not subject to the "reasonable excuse" defence that exists for some other offences within this section. Other offences within the 1990 Act include:

— failing to give the notice required by section 9(2) on the transfer of an authorisation (section 23(1)(b));

— failing, without reasonable excuse, to comply with any requirement of a notice, served by the enforcing authority under section 19(2), requiring information which it reasonably considers that it needs (section 23(1)(g));

— making a statement which a person knows to be false or misleading in a material particular, or recklessly making a statement which is false or misleading in a material particular, where the statement is made:

— in purported compliance with a requirement to furnish any information imposed by or under any provisions of Part I; or

— for the purpose of obtaining the grant of an authorisation to himself or any other person or the variation of the authorisation (section 23(1)(h));

— intentionally to make a false entry in any record required to be kept under section 7 of the Act (section 23(1)(i)); and

— to forge or use, with intent to deceive, any document issued or authorised in relation to section 7 of the Act. It is also an offence to make or have in one's possession a document so closely resembling any such document as to be likely to deceive (section 23(1)(j)).

These lesser offences carry a fine not exceeding the statutory maximum on summary conviction and on conviction on indictment an unlimited fine, imprisonment for up to two years, or both.

The offences concerned with the obstruction of the officers of the enforcement authorities in the performance of their duty – section 23(d) to (f) and (k) in the 1990 Act – have now been transferred to section 110 of the Environment Act 1995, which is concerned with the revised powers of authorised persons following the establishment of the Environment Agency and SEPA. These offences become:

— failing to comply with a requirement imposed by section 108, relating to the powers of authorised persons (section 110(2)(a));

— preventing any other person from appearing before an authorised person or answering questions to which that person may require an answer (section 110(2)(c));

— intentionally obstructing an authorised person in the exercise or performance of his powers or duties (section 110(1)); and

— falsely pretending to be an authorised person (section 110(3)).

The penalty provisions associated with these offences are now contained within section 110(4) and (5).

Under section 26, where a person is convicted of an offence under section 23(1)(a) or (c), the court may, in addition to or instead of imposing the relevant penalty, order him to take steps to remedy the cause of the offence within the time period determined by the court. Such an order may only be imposed where the person convicted has it in his power to undertake the required remedial action. Failure to comply with such an order is an offence (section 23(1)(l)) and, where the order is made by the High Court, it may also be contempt. However, no offence is committed until the expiry of the time period determined by the court (section 26(3)) and this may be extended or further extended if an application is made to the court before the expiry date (section 26(2)).

As with Part II of the 1990 Act, the enforcing authority has recourse to the High Court, or in Scotland any court of competent jurisdiction, although this provision is restricted to offences under section 23(1)(c) relating to compliance with enforcement or prohibition notices.

In addition, where the commission of an offence under section 23(1)(a) or (c) causes any harm which it is possible to remedy, the Environment Agency and SEPA (but not English and Welsh local authorities) may arrange for reasonable steps to be taken towards remedying the harm and recover the costs incurred from any person convicted of the offence (section 27). It is not necessary to await conviction before undertaking such action but written approval must first be sought from the Secretary of State and permission obtained from any person (other than the holder of the authorisation) whose land might be affected by the remedial action. This power does not extend to "contaminated land" as defined in Part IIA of the Act.

PUBLIC REGISTERS

The provisions relating to public registers for Part I processes are made in sections 20 to 22 and, in common with Part II and elsewhere within the Act, require the enforcing authorities to establish, maintain and make such registers available to the public. Details of the procedures to be followed, the form and content of the registers and the associated time limits involved are contained in the Environmental Protection (Applications, Appeals and Registers) Regulations 1991, SI 1991/507, as amended.

Registers must contain all of the formal communications, required by Part I of the Act and the associated Regulations, between the holder or prospective holder and the enforcing authority. These include all issues relating to the granting, holding and variation of authorisations, and to the exercising of the authority's statutory powers of enforcement, prohibition and revocation.

In addition to the registers maintained by the Environment Agency, SEPA, local authorities in England and Wales and port health authorities for the prescribed processes they themselves are responsible for, it is also necessary for English and Welsh local authorities to keep registers of the processes under IPC within their area (section 20(2)).

The Secretary of State has powers to give directions to enforcing authorities requiring the removal from any register of any specified information not prescribed for inclusion under section 20(1) and (2), or which ought to have been excluded from the register on the grounds of national security (section 21) or commercial confidentiality (section 22). In addition, he may stipulate the location of these public registers.

In view of the technical and financial information which may be required by the enforcing authorities, the issue of commercial confidentiality is of significant importance. In addition to that supplied as part of the applications process, paragraph 1(3) of Schedule 1 to the Regulations provides for the inclusion of any information furnished in response to a notice from the authority. Monitoring information obtained by the authority as a result of its own monitoring, or furnished to the authority in writing by virtue of a condition of the authorisation or section 19(2), must also be included. This will assume a greater importance as the potential for applying section 111 of the 1995 Act to self-monitoring within an authorisation is extended by the authorities.

It is also possible that an enforcing authority may be furnished with information on prescribed processes in circumstances other than those indicated above and, where it appears that this might be confidential, it has a duty under section 22(4) to inform the relevant persons or business, giving them an opportunity to apply for it to be withheld from the register on grounds of commercial confidentiality.

INTEGRATED POLLUTION PREVENTION AND CONTROL

As noted above, the incorporation of Integrated Pollution Prevention and Control (IPPC) within UK legislation will require a number of changes to be made to Parts I and II of the 1990 Act. The categories of industrial activity which come under IPPC, Article 1, are listed in Annex I of the Directive, and include a number of waste management operations. These are listed below, with the DETR's indicative figures of the number of processes within each category:

5. Waste Management

Without prejudice of Article 11 of Directive 75/442/EEC or Article 3 of Directive 91/689/EEC

5.1 Installations for the disposal or recovery of hazardous waste as defined in the list in Article 1(4) of Directive 91/689/EEC, as defined in Annexes II, A and II, B (operations R1, R5, R6, R8 and R8) to 75/442/EEC and in Directive 75/439/EEC on the disposal of waste oils, with a capacity exceeding 10 tonnes per day.
Likely number of processes – 600.

5.2 Installations for the incineration of municipal waste as defined in Directives 89/369/EEC and 89/429/EEC on the prevention of air pollution from new and existing municipal waste incineration plants, respectively, with a capacity exceeding 3 tonnes per day.
Likely number of processes – 8.

5.3 Installations for the disposal of non-hazardous waste as defined in Annex II, A to Directive 75/442/EEC under headings D8 and D9, with a capacity exceeding 50 tonnes per day.
Likely number of processes – 130.

5.4 Landfills receiving more than 10 tonnes per day or with a total capacity exceeding 25,000 tonnes, excluding landfills of inert waste.
Likely number of processes – 3,000.

In addition, there are other activities in which wastes are treated as falling within IPPC, such as:

6. Other Activities

6.3 Plant for the tanning of hides and skins, where the treatment capacity exceeds 12 tonnes of finished products per day.
Likely number of processes – 2.

6.4(a) Slaughterhouses with a carcass production capacity greater than 50 tonnes per day.
Likely number of processes – 95.

6.5 Installations for the disposal or recycling of animal carcasses and animal waste with a treatment capacity exceeding 10 tonnes per day.
Likely number of processes – 30.

It has been estimated that about half of the installations regulated under Part II of the Environmental Protection Act 1990 will fall within the scope of IPPC.

Changes may also be required where the IPPC regime contains components in addition to those within IPC, including, *inter alia*:

— the wider definition of "pollution" relating to the direct and indirect effects of human activity, and including noise and vibrations, damage to material property, and impairment or interference with amenities and other legitimate uses of the environment (Article 2(2));

— the wider definition of "emission" including diffuse as well as point sources (Article 2(5));

— measures relating to the management and disposal of waste (Article 3(c));

— the measures necessary to prevent accidents and limit their consequences (Article 3(e));

— the measures necessary to prevent pollution upon definitive cessation of activities to avoid any pollution risk and return the site of operation to a satisfactory state (Article 3(f));

— inclusion in the authorisation (permit) of measures to prevent pollution where other than normal operating conditions pertain, viz. start-up, leaks, malfunctions, momentary stoppages and definitive cessation of operations.

The IPPC Directive is concerned with the control of *installations* rather than *processes* and, in addition to the consequent exclusion of mobile plant, this will extend the scope of control from the present authorised processes to some of the of other activities carried out on the same site. Within the UK, it has been suggested that the ambit of IPPC control will be determined on the basis of a test as to whether or not these other activities are directly associated with, have a technical connection with, and could have an effect on emissions and pollution from, the relevant installation. However, it should be noted that the current "triviality" derogation within IPC will not be continued under IPPC.

Whereas the IPC regime is for controlling emissions of polluting substances, IPPC is aimed at regulating the environmental impact of the operation of an installation. This raises questions regarding the interrelationship of the Environmental Impact Assessment Directive, 85/337/EEC as amended by 97/11/EC, with the IPPC regime, where relevant, and the treatment within IPPC of issues such as contaminated land and energy efficiency.

The Directive allows for the possibility of more than one regulator to be involved centrally in the operation of IPPC for any given installation, and it is possible for IPPC to operate under a system of multiple, co-ordinated permits. The DoE (now called the Department of the Environment, Transport and the Regions (DETR)) is examining the merits of co-ordinated pollution control (CPC) under such a system.

A preliminary consultation paper on the UK implementation of the Directive in July 1997 has been issued by DETR, and the EU Commission has initiated the production of a series of "BAT reference documents" for the various types of installations covered in an attempt to reduce definitional and other uncertainties in the implementation of the Directive. In addition, the Commission has established a forum involving Member States, industry and non-governmental organisations.

IPPC and Small and Medium Sized Enterprises (SMEs)

Whilst the IPPC regime is directed towards larger installations which tend to generate high levels of pollution, a substantial volume of business within the EU and the attendant environmental impacts is associated with SMEs. A survey by the consultants KPMG (see *ENDS Report* 267, [1997] April, page 37) indicated that these firms account for 99.8% of all business, 65% of employment and 65% of turnover within the Community. In Holland, SMEs contribute 50% of the national industrial emissions of ozone-depleting substances and wastes, and about 25% of acid gas emissions and hazardous substances, including volatile organic compounds (VOCs).

Using the KPMG report as a basis, in 1997 the European Commission issued a working paper which proposed a Framework Directive Concerning Pollution from Smaller Installations – the so-called "mini-IPPC Directive". This was aimed at those industries which now fall outwith the IPPC system of controls, and are currently subject to Council Directive 84/360/EEC on air pollution from industrial plants and Council Directive 76/464/EEC on pollution caused by certain dangerous substances discharged into the aquatic environment. These provisions are subject to different permitting and monitoring requirements and, in the case of 76/464/EEC, there has been a significant number of infraction proceedings relating to its implementation in Member States.

The mini-IPPC Directive proposals seek to overcome these problems by:

— addressing emissions arising from SMEs and diffuse sources of pollution;

— co-ordinating permitting procedures;

— simplifying the authorisation procedure, through a "one-stop-shop" approach.

Certain of the principles such as Best Available Techniques (BAT) and the definitions within the existing IPPC scheme would be used, providing a degree of commonality to pollution control of industrial processes.

The initial reaction of most Member States to these proposals has been extremely negative and, whilst there is pressure on the Commission to produce an alternative control regime to replace Directive 76/464/EEC, substantially more work and consultation is required before a formal proposal for a mini-IPPC Directive can be adopted.

IPPC and Other Regimes of Industrial Control

Included within the wide range of industrial processes encompassed by IPPC and listed in Annex I of the Directive are a number of processes which are already subject to some form of pollution control as a result of earlier EU measures (Annex II). Following the period of transition to IPPC control detailed in Article 20, it is intended that the Directives relating to the control of specific industrial operations, i.e. those listed in Annex II, will be modified rather than repealed. However, Directive 84/360/EEC (air pollution from industrial plant) which is effectively replaced by the IPPC measure will be repealed and part of the dangerous substances Directive, 76/464/EEC, will be dis-applied to installations covered by IPPC.

Effectively, these changes give "framework" status to the IPPC Directive, with its emphasis on BAT, permitting, environmental quality standards and basic obligations to the operator, and place the more focused provisions in Annex II in the role of "daughter" Directives. This is clear from Article 18(2) which states that, in the absence of Community emission limit values defined pursuant to the IPPC Directive, the relevant emission limit values in the measures in Annex II will be applied as minimum emission limit values in relation to those processes listed in Annex I.

Within the sphere of waste management, specific Directives have been introduced in relation to new and existing incineration plant for municipal waste (89/369/EEC and 89/429/EEC respectively) and the incineration of hazardous waste (94/67/EC). It is intended that the first two of these measures will be replaced by a single Directive on the Incineration of Waste and a working paper on this proposal was issued mid-1997.

Hazardous Waste Incineration Directive (HWID) 94/67/EC

Adopted on 12th December 1994, this Directive establishes a permitting regime for hazardous wastes and imposes certain controls on the releases of air pollutants, waste water and residues from prescribed incineration processes. Whilst the HWID takes its definition of hazardous waste from Article 1(4) of the Hazardous Waste Directive, 91/869/EEC, a number of these wastes so defined are excluded from its controls, viz:

— combustible liquid wastes including oils as defined by Article 1 of Directive 75/439/EEC, providing that:

— the mass content of PCB equivalent is less than that set in current EU legislation;

— these wastes are not classified as hazardous by virtue of the presence of components listed in Annex II of Directive 91/689/EEC in quantities or concentrations which are inconsistent with Article 4 of Directive 75/442/EEC; and

— the net calorific value amounts to a minimum of 30 MJ per kilogramme;

— any combustible liquid wastes, which cannot cause, in the flue gas directly resulting from its combustion, emissions other than those defined in Article 1(1) of Directive 75/716/EEC, or a higher concentration of emissions than those resulting from the combustion of gas oil so defined;

— hazardous waste resulting from the exploration for, and the exploitation of, gas and oil resources from off-shore installations and incineration on board;

— municipal waste covered by Directives 89/369/EEC and 89/429/EEC;

— sewage sludge from the treatment of municipal waste waters which are not rendered hazardous by virtue of containing constituents listed in Annex II of Directive 91/689/EEC, present in quantities or concentrations which are inconsistent with Article 4 of Directive 75/442/EEC.

In addition to these restrictions, Article 2 further limits the application of the Directive by excluding:

— incinerators for animal carcasses or remains;

— incinerators for infectious clinical waste, provided it is not rendered hazardous by the presence of other constituents within Annex II to Directive 91/689/EEC; and

— municipal waste incinerators also burning clinical waste, provided it is not rendered hazardous by the presence of other constituents within Annex II to Directive 91/689/EEC.

Subject to certain derogations, new plant must comply with HWID from 31st December 1996, and existing plant from 30th June 2000. In its consultation paper on the implementation, the Department of the Environment noted that most, if not all, of the incineration plant covered by the Directive is currently subject to Integrated Pollution Control and as such will already be regulated by either the Environment Agency or SEPA. As a consequence, the most appropriate and straightforward mechanism for the implementation of the HWID would be via the IPC scheme.

Waste Incineration Directive

An initial draft proposal for a Directive to replace the existing legislation on municipal incinerators was produced in 1994, and this was re-drafted and re-issued in 1997. Whilst it is too early in the law-making process to comment in detail on its content, it is instructive to note its similarity in format to the HWID, viz:

— the exclusion of certain wastes from its controls;

— the restriction to stationary incineration plant;

— the imposition of controls over the entire *site* where the installation is situated (as in the IPPC Directive); and

— the prescription in detail of the allowable emissions to the three environmental media and the analytical techniques to be employed for their detection.

THE REGISTRATION OF WASTE CARRIERS AND BROKERS

In an earlier chapter reference was made to the duties of the Waste Collection Authorities in relation to the administrative arrangements for the collection and carriage of waste. However, the licensing and regulation of the waste-related part of these activities falls to the Environment Agency and SEPA and, unlike the majority of the waste management licensing regime, the basis for the registration of waste carriers is the Control of Pollution (Amendment) Act 1989, a measure which was introduced to overcome one of the deficiencies of the Control of Pollution Act 1974, viz. limitation of its controls to the *deposit* of waste and the exclusion of other areas of waste management.

However, these provisions were not enacted until 1st April 1992, the date upon which a number of important provisions within Part II of EPA 1990 came into force, including section 34(3)(d) which identifies persons who are registered under the 1989 Act as carriers of controlled waste as "authorised persons" for the purposes of the Duty of Care provisions of section 34 of the 1990 Act.

Registration

The general provisions for the registration of carriers are contained in sections 2 to 4 of the 1989 Act and more specific controls are imposed by the Controlled Waste (Registration of Carriers and Seizure of Vehicles) Regulations 1991, SI 1991/1624. There are strong similarities in both the procedures and the criteria for the registration of carriers under SI 1991/ 1624 and those for the registration of waste brokers in Schedule 5 to the 1994 Waste Management Licensing Regulations, *supra*. This is implicitly acknowledged in paragraphs 7(2) and (3) of the 1994 Regulations, which permit the initial registration of a waste broker to expire at the same time as that for an existing waste carrier licence held by the same person, and *vice versa*, in order to enable subsequent renewals to be made at the same time for both licences.

Applications for registration are to be made to the office of the Environment Agency or SEPA which is situated in the area in which the applicant has his principal place of business. They cannot be made while a previous application is pending or while there is an existing registration in place unless the application is made within the six months preceding the expiry date.

The details required when applying for registration are contained in the proforma in Part I of Schedule 2 to SI 1991/1624 for waste carrier licences, and in Part II of Schedule 5 to SI 1994/1056 for waste broker licences. Renewal of these licences is made on the forms in Parts II and III of the above two documents respectively, and all such applications must be accompanied by the requisite fee.

Although the procedure does not require the same detailed information as that for "fit and proper persons" in relation to waste management licences, it is necessary for the applicant to list any relevant convictions, as defined in Schedule 1 to the Regulations. As noted in Chapter 12, the convictions of individuals are subject to the Rehabilitation of Offenders Act 1974 but this does not apply to corporate bodies.

In common with other forms of licensing, under Regulation 10 the Agencies have powers under to revoke a registration if, and only if, the person or another relevant person is convicted of a prescribed offence *and* in the opinion of the agency it is undesirable for the carrier to continue to be authorised to transport controlled waste. In these circumstances, the registration remains in force until the expiry of the period for appeal, unless the carrier indicates that he does not intend to make or continue with an appeal (Regulation 11(6)). Where the offence was committed by a person other than the applicant, under section 3(6) of the 1989 Act the Agency must consider the extent to which the applicant "has been a party to the carrying on of a business in a manner involving the commission of prescribed offences". An appeal may be made against such a refusal under section 4(1) of the 1989 Act and the Agency must, as soon as reasonably practicable, make appropriate entries in their register indicating when the appeal was made and the result of the appeal.

As with waste management licence appeals, waste carrier registration appeals were transferred to the Planning Inspectorate, with effect from 1st April 1996, as part of the government's deregulation initiative. All decisions will be taken by the Inspectors unless there are cases of "major importance or difficulty", when the Secretary of State for the Environment will be involved.

Unless the carrier requests that his name is removed from the register prior to the expiry of the registration (Regulation 11(1)), the period of registration is three years. It is the duty of the Agency to inform the carrier, no later than six months before the expiry date, that renewal is required. When an application for renewal is made within the six months prior to the expiry, the registration remains in force until the application is withdrawn or accepted. If the regulation authority refuses an application, or the relevant period for application has expired without the applicant having been registered, then the existing registration continues until the date on which the applicant indicates that he does not intend to make or continue with an appeal.

Exemptions from Registration

Not all waste carriage is subject to registration and section 2(1) lists the persons who are not required to be registered as carriers of controlled waste. These include:

(a) waste collection authorities, waste disposal authorities and waste regulation authorities (i.e. the Environment Agency and SEPA);

(b) producers of controlled waste, except where it is building or demolition waste (i.e. waste arising from works of construction or demolition, including the associated preparatory work (section 2(2)). Note: following Regulation 10 of SI 1992/588, "construction" includes improvement, repair or alteration);

(c) British Railways Board, in relation to carriage by rail;

(d) ferry operators;

(e) operators of vessels, aircraft, hovercraft, floating containers or vehicles in relation to their use, after they have been loaded with waste in relation to the Food and Environmental Protection Act 1985;

(f) and (g) charities and voluntary organisations.

Modifications were made in paragraph 12 of Schedule 4 to the 1994 Waste Management Licensing Regulations, which require that persons in categories (a), (c), (f) and (g) above undertaking the collection or transport of waste "on a professional basis" be registered. Likewise, Regulation 20(4) requires that charities, voluntary organisations and waste collection authorities/waste disposal authorities/waste regulation authorities acting as waste brokers should be registered.

It should be noted that, in addition to the requirements for the carriage of waste, there are other legislative instruments which distinguish vehicles employed for "a general service performed in the public interest". In *Swain v McCaul and Another*, it was held that a lorry equipped with a tachograph, which was used in the course of commercial business solely for the delivery and collection of builders' skips, was not a vehicle "used in connection with ... refuse collection and disposal" within Article 4(6) of Regulation 3820/85/EEC and was not therefore exempt from the requirements under Regulation 3821/85/EEC on recording equipment in road transport.

Offences

It is an offence under section 1 of the Control of Pollution (Amendment) Act 1989 for any person, in the course of any business of his or otherwise *for profit*, to transport controlled waste to or from any place in Great Britain unless he is a registered carrier. Except in the case of one-man businesses, it is unlikely that the owner of the business will be directly involved in the transport of waste but section 33(5) EPA 1990, through its presumptive wording, places the implication of knowledge and therefore responsibility on the person who owns or controls the vehicle.

It should be noted that registration relates to legal or natural persons, not to specific vehicles, as demonstrated in *R v Cosmick Transport Services Ltd*, and therefore it is open for a registered person to hire or borrow vehicles, if necessary with a driver.

Section 1(2) of the 1989 Act states that it is not an offence for an unregistered person to transport controlled waste:

— between different places within the same premises;

— when importing controlled waste, up to the point at which that waste is landed in Great Britain;

— by air or sea from a place within Great Britain to a place outside.

The offence is actionable summarily and on conviction carries a fine. Perhaps more important is the fact that such a conviction is considered as a "relevant offence" to be taken into account in relation to the continued holding of a licence.

Section 1(4) provides that it is a defence for a person to show that:

— the waste was transported in an emergency of which notice was given, as soon as practicable after it occurred, to the disposal authority in whose area the emergency occurred;

— he neither knew nor had reasonable grounds for suspecting that what was being transported was controlled waste, and took all such steps as it was reasonable to take for ascertaining that it was waste; or

— he acted under instructions from his employer.

The term "emergency" in this context is defined in section 1(6) as meaning any circumstances in which, in order to avoid, remove, or reduce any serious danger to the public or serious risk of damage to the environment, it was necessary for the waste to be transported from one place to another without the use of a registered carrier. As noted above with regard to *Waste Incineration Services Ltd v Dudley MBC*, the emergency situation will be considered taking all the circumstances into consideration, not solely from the point of view of the waste carrier.

Enforcement

The general powers available to the Environment Agency and SEPA and persons authorised by them through section 108 of the Environment Act 1995 may also be exercised by them in relation to the 1989 Act, by virtue of section 7 of the latter. Section 5 provides more specific powers under which any duly authorised officer of the Agency or a constable has the power to stop anyone whom he reasonably considers to be, or have been, transporting controlled waste and require him to produce his or his employer's authority for undertaking that activity. However, the authority to stop a vehicle on a road is restricted to a uniformed police constable (section 5(2)). Bates[1] notes the potential difficulties in a police officer demonstrating that he has reasonable grounds for stopping a vehicle and suggests that these may arise as a result of prior information (*Baxter v Oxford*), the conduct of the vehicle or operator (*Monaghan v Corbett*) or other reasons, as a result of which the police officer can discover reasonable grounds for requiring the production of the authority (*Steel v Goacher*).

---

[1] *Waste Management Legislation in the UK*, J H Bates, Sweet & Maxwell, 1997, Chapter 9.

In addition, authorised persons may search any vehicle that appears to be being used, or to have been used, for transporting waste, carry out tests on anything found in the vehicle and take away for testing samples of anything so found. The taking of samples is governed by the provisions of section 111 of the Environment Act 1995, *supra*.

A person who is required to produce his authority (i.e. licence) must either produce the authority or a certified copy at the time of the request, or produce it at or send it to the principal office of the Agency within the area in which he was stopped, no later than seven days after the day on which he was required to produce it.

It is an offence intentionally to obstruct any authorised officer or a constable in the exercise of the powers in section 5(1), or to fail without reasonable excuse to comply with a requirement imposed in the exercise of that power (section 5(4)). On summary conviction, anyone found guilty of these offences will be subject to a fine. However, a person cannot be guilty of an offence unless it is shown that:

— the waste in question was controlled waste; and

— the person did transport it to or from a place in Great Britain.

In addition to these measures, under paragraph 10 of Schedule 15 to the 1990 Act, fly-tipping and other illegal waste-related activities may result in the loss of the goods vehicle operator's licence, under section 69 of the Transport Act 1968.

It will be appreciated that such Agency powers are quite extensive and it is not uncommon for the environmental agencies to work in conjunction with the police and H M Customs and Excise in the checking of vehicles.

Seizure of Vehicles

The measures relating to the seizure of vehicles were introduced to assist the authorities in the prevention of fly-tipping. Where, after taking prescribed steps, the authority has failed to ascertain the name and address of any person who is able to provide it with the prescribed information regarding the person using the vehicle at the time of the offence, it has certain powers, under section 6 of the Control of Pollution (Amendment) Act 1989, to seize vehicles and their contents under a warrant issued by a justice of the peace.

The steps which the authority must take prior to such action are prescribed in Regulation 20 of the 1991 Regulations and include obtaining information on the keeper of the vehicle from the relevant bodies and serving a notice on any person whom it considers able to provide it with the identity of the person using the vehicle at the time in question, under section 71(2) EPA 1990.

In addition, the Agency must have reasonable grounds for believing that:

— an offence under section 33(1) has been committed; and

— the vehicle was used in the commission of that offence,

and, furthermore, proceedings must not yet have been brought against any person. A vehicle seized under section 6 of the 1989 Act may be removed in accordance with Regulation 21, which also permits the separate removal of its contents where this is necessary to facilitate the removal of the vehicle, there are good reasons for storing them at different places, or their condition requires that they are disposed of without delay.

Unless the property has been disposed of under Regulation 23, it may be returned to a person who:

— produces satisfactory evidence of his entitlement and his identity; or

— is acting as the agent of a third party and produces evidence of that person's identity and of his authority to act for that person; or

— produces the registration book of the vehicle in question.

The powers for the sale, destruction or deposit at any place of property seized under section 6 of the Act may be exercised after the regulation authority has placed an advertisement in a local paper and served a copy of the notice on:

— the person served under section 71(2) of the 1990 Act;

— the chief constable for the area;

— the Secretary of State for Transport; and

— Hire Purchase Information plc.

In addition, 28 days must have elapsed after the publication of the notice, during which time there was no request for the return of the property under Regulation 22. However, where the condition of the property so requires, it may be disposed of without delay.

Following the disposal of the vehicle, a further notice must be served upon all but the first-named recipients of the earlier notice in the list above. The proceeds of any such disposal are to be used in the first instance to reimburse the authority of its *expenses* (i.e. not its *costs*)[1] in respect of undertaking its duties under section 6, and any remainder is to be made available for a potential claimant who satisfies the criteria in Regulation 22, *supra*.

Registers

The 1991 Regulations place a duty upon the waste regulation authorities to establish and maintain registers of the carriers of controlled waste which are open to inspection by members of the public and from which it is possible to obtain copies of the entries, on payment of "reasonable" charges. There are two aspects to the controls imposed by the registration of carriers of controlled waste, one limb being based upon the authority given to registered carriers of waste and the other, relating to the registers themselves, being directed at the users of the services of waste carriers.

The registers of carriers required by Regulation 3 are one means of assisting waste holders to fulfil their statutory duty of care under section 34(c)(i) EPA 1990 and in this respect their function differs from other "environmental" registers. In view of this, the maintenance of such registers assumes a new importance. It is clearly in the interests of both the regulators and the regulated that an indication of the most recent updating is given in the register and that a copy of any entry is accompanied by a record of when that copy was made.

---

[1] While some legislation allows for the recovery of *costs*, others of *expenses*, Doolittle points out (*LMELR* [1991] 3 (2) 38) that expenses cover not only "out of pocket" expenses but can also include a reasonable amount for overheads.

FURTHER READING

Air Pollution Control: An Integrated Approach, 5th Report of the Royal Commission on Environmental Pollution, Cmnd 6371, HMSO, 1976

"ALARP and BATNEEC – the synergy of legal regulation and system engineering", Peter Riley, *Engineering Management Journal*, October 1996, 237

"The Application of Integrated Pollution Control to Steelmaking Operations", D N Pocklington, [1995] 22 (2) *Ironmaking and Steelmaking* 105-109

Best Practicable Environmental Option, 12th Report of the Royal Commission on Environmental Pollution, Cmnd 310, HMSO, 1988

Best Practicable Environmental Option Assessments for Integrated Pollution Control, Volume I: Principles and Methodology and *Volume II: Technical Data (for consultation)*, The Environment Agency, The Stationery Office, 1997

Best Practicable Environmental Option for IPC – A Summary, The Environment Agency, 1996

The Environment Acts 1990-1995, 3rd Edition, S Tromans, M Nash and M Poustie, Sweet & Maxwell, 1996

A Guide to Risk Assessment and Risk Management for Environmental Protection, Department of the Environment, HMSO, 1995

Integrated Pollution Control: A Practical Guide, HMSO, 1993

"Integrated Pollution Control – EC Proposals and UK Practice", I Doolittle and T Secker, [1994] *ELM* 168

"Integrated Pollution Prevention and Control: UK and EC Approaches and Possible Next Steps", N Emmott and N Haigh, [1996] 8 (2) *JEL* 301

"IPPC: An Environmental Perspective", M G Faure and J G J Lefevre, [1996] *EELR* April, 112

"IPPC: Re-Regulation or De-Regulation", M Pallemaerts, [1996] *EELR* June, 174

"Legal Aspects of IPC", A Waite, [1992] *LMELR* 2

Local Air Pollution Control in England and Wales: Five Year Report 1991-1996, Department of the Environment, 1996

Operator and Pollution Risk Assessment Appraisal (OPRA), HMIP, April 1995

Profiting from Pollution Prevention – the 3Es Methodology, HMIP and Business in the Environment, 1996

CHAPTER 5: WASTE DISPOSAL AND RECYCLING

Section 5.1 Incineration

Part A

(a) the destruction by burning in an incinerator of any waste chemicals or waste plastic arising from the manufacture of a chemical or the manufacture of a plastic.

(b) the destruction by burning in an incinerator, other than incidentally in the course of burning other waste, of any waste chemicals being, or comprising in elemental or compound form, any of the following:

bromine	mercury
cadmium	nitrogen
chlorine	phosphorous
fluorine	sulphur
iodine	zinc
lead	

(c) the destruction by burning of any other waste, including animal remains, otherwise than by a process related to and carried on as part of a Part B process, on premises where there is plant designed to incinerate such waste at a rate of 1 tonne or more per hour.

(d) the cleaning for reuse of metal containers used for the transport or storage of a chemical by burning out their residential content.

Part B

(a) the destruction by burning in an incinerator other than an exempt incinerator of any waste, including animal remains, except where related to a Part A process.

(b) the cremation of human remains.

In this section:

"exempt incinerator" means any incinerator on premises where there is plant designed to incinerate waste, including animal remains at a rate of not more than 50kgs per hour, not being an incinerator employed to incinerate clinical waste, sewage sludge, sewage screenings or municipal waste (as defined in Article 1 of EC Directive 89/369/EEC) and for the purposes of this section, the weight of waste shall be determined by reference to its weight as fed into the incinerator;

"waste" means solid or liquid wastes or gaseous wastes (other than gas produced by biological degradation of waste);

"clinical waste" means waste (other than waste consisting wholly of animal remains) which falls within sub-paragraph (a) or (b) of the definition of such waste in paragraph (2) of regulation 1 of the Controlled Waste Regulations 1992 (or would fall within one of those sub-paragraphs but for paragraph (4) of that regulation).

Section 5.2 Recovery processes

Part A

(a) the recovery by distillation of any oil or organic solvent.

(b) the cleaning or regeneration of carbon, charcoal or ion exchange resins by removing matter which is, or includes, any substance described in Schedule 4, 5 or 6 [of the 1991 Regulations, ie prescribed substances to air, water and land].

Nothing in this Part of this section applies to:

(i) the distillation of oil for the production or cleaning of vacuum pump oil, or

(ii) a process which is ancillary and related to another process which involves the production or use of the substance which is recovered, cleaned or regenerated.

Part B

Nil

Section 5.3 The production of fuel from waste

Part A

Making solid fuel from waste by any process involving the use of heat other than making charcoal.

Part B

Nil

CHAPTER 6: OTHER INDUSTRIES

Section 6.1 Paper and pulp manufacturing processes

Part A

(a) the making of paper pulp by a chemical method if the person concerned has the capacity at the location in question to produce more than 25,000 tonnes of paper pulp in any 12 month period.

(b) any process associated with making paper pulp or paper (including processes connected with the recycling of paper such as de-inking) if the process may result in the release into water of any substance described in Schedule 5 to these regulations, ie prescribed substances for release into water in a quantity which, in any 12 month period, exceeds the background quantity by more than the amount specified in relation to the description of substance in column 2 of [Schedule 5].

In this paragraph, "paper pulp" includes pulp made from wood, grass, straw and similar materials and references to the making of paper are to the making of any product using paper pulp.

Part B

Nil

Section 6.9 The treatment and processing of animal or vegetable matter

Part A

Any of the following processes, unless falling within a description in another section of the Schedule or an exempt process, namely, the processing in any way whatsoever, storing or drying by the application of heat of any dead animal (or part thereof) or any vegetable matter if the process may result in the release into water of any [prescribed] substance in a quantity which, in any 12 month period, exceeds the background quantity by more than the amount specified in relation to the description of substance in column 2 of [Schedule 5] but excluding any process for the treatment of effluent so as to permit its discharge into controlled waters or into a sewer unless the treatment process involves the drying of any material with a view to its use as an animal feedstuff.

Part B

(a) any process mentioned in Part A of this section unless an exempt process:

   (i) where the process has the characteristics described in regulation 4(1)(ii) above, but

   (ii) may release into the air a [prescribed] substance or any offensive smell noticeable outside the premises on which the process is carried on.

(b) breeding maggots in any case where 5kg or more of animal or of vegetable matter or, in aggregate, of both are introduced into the process in any week.

In this section:

"animal" includes a bird or a fish and

"exempt process" means:

(i) any process carried on on a farm or agricultural holding other than the manufacture of goods for sale

(ii) the manufacture or preparation of food or drink for human consumption but excluding:

    (a) the extraction, distillation or purification of animal or vegetable oil or fat otherwise than as a process incidental to the cooking of food for human consumption

    (b) any process involving the use of green offal or the boiling of blood except the cooking of food (other than tripe) for human consumption

    (c) the cooking of tripe for human consumption elsewhere than on premises on which it is to be consumed

(iii) the fleshing, cleaning and drying of pelts of fur-bearing mammals

(iv) any process carried on in connection with the operation of a knacker's yard, as defined in article 3(1) of the Animal By-Products Order 1992

(v) any process for the manufacture of soap not falling within a description in Part A of section 4.2 of this Schedule

(vi) the storage of vegetable matter otherwise than as part of any prescribed process

(vii) the cleaning of shellfish shells

(viii) the manufacture of starch

(ix) the processing of animal or vegetable matter at premises for feeding a recognised pack of hounds registered under article 10 of the Animal By-Products Order 1992

(x) the salting of hides or skins, unless related to any other prescribed process

(xi) any process for composting animal or vegetable matter or a combination of both, except where that process is carried on for the purposes of cultivating mushrooms

(xii) any process for cleaning, and any related process for drying or dressing, seeds, bulbs, corms or tubers

(xiii) the drying of grain or pulses

(xiv) any process for the production of cotton yarn from raw cotton or for the conversion of cotton yarn into cloth

"food" includes drink, articles and substances of no nutritional value which are used for human consumption, and articles and substances used as ingredients in the preparation of food

"green offal" means the stomach and intestines of any animal, other than poultry or fish, and their contents.

1. Define the Objective

State the objective of the project or proposal at the outset, in terms which do not prejudge the means by which that objective is to be achieved.

2. Generate Options

Identify all feasible options for achieving the objective: the aim is to find those which are both practicable and environmentally acceptable.

3. Evaluate the Options

Analyse these options, particularly to expose advantages and disadvantages for the environment. Use quantitative methods when these are appropriate. Qualitative evaluation will also be needed.

4. Summarise and Present the Options

Present the results of the evaluation concisely and objectively, and in a format which can highlight the advantages and disadvantages for each option.

5. Select the Preferred Option

Select BPEO from the feasible options, the choice depending on the weight given to the environmental impacts and associated risks, and to the costs involved.

6. Review the Preferred Option

Scrutinise closely the proposed detailed design and operating procedures, to ensure that no pollution risks or hazards have been overlooked.

7. Implement and Monitor

Monitor the achieved performance against the desired targets, especially those for environmental quality.

Throughout Steps 1 to 7: Maintain an Audit Trail

Record the basis for any choices or decisions throughout all stages, i.e. the assumptions used, the evaluation procedures, the origin and reliability of data, the affiliation of all those involved in the analytical work, and a record of those taking the decisions.

Chapter 14

LITTER, REFUSE AND OTHER ABANDONED WASTE

"Litter is a depressingly obvious manifestation of the problem of waste in a society over devoted to disposability, over packaging, and not sufficiently concerned with health and amenity."

D Hughes in *Environmental Law*[1]

INTRODUCTION

In many ways, the controls imposed upon litter and refuse are an anomaly within the framework of waste legislation, for while many of the methods used are similar to those elsewhere, their objectives are significantly different. As Hughes point out, the issues raised by the control of litter encompass the whole gamut of problems encountered in waste management but the nature of the generation of litter places certain constraints on the measures which may be imposed. Unless a person is caught *in flagrante delicto*, it is almost impossible to attribute the creation of litter and, while there are sound arguments for minimising the opportunities for litter generation, the responsibility for cleaning up littered areas generally lies with a third party. This situation creates problems in two areas:

— the identification of where the legal responsibilities lie in relation to the associated waste issues (e.g. the Duty of Care), particularly in undertakings which employ contract cleaners; and

— the identification and classification of the resulting waste, which may include a range of hazardous components unknown to the collector/ disposer.

It could be argued that the majority of the controls imposed on litter are aesthetic, relating solely to the appearance of public areas, and as such cannot be regarded as preventative – they are not concerned with the issues associated with disposal but merely the placing of a duty on a relevant body in order to clean up an area within a given time. A corollary is that, when such duties are placed upon that body, they may be given a relatively low priority in view of their aesthetic rather than utilitarian importance. There are a number of other issues, such as fly tipping and graffiti, which affect

---

[1]   *Environmental Law, 3rd Edition*, D Hughes, Butterworths, 1996.

the appearance of public places, but these are not included within Part IV of the 1990 Act.

It should be noted that Part IV is entitled "Litter etc." and, with the exception of the offence of leaving litter under section 87, all the other provisions relate to both litter *and* refuse although, as discussed below, the terms are not synonymous.

THE MEANING OF "LITTER"

Inclusive Provisions

The majority of litter controls are within Part IV of the Environmental Protection Act 1990, yet within this Part there is no definition of the term "litter". Bates[1] notes that in the Pollution Control and Local Government Order (Northern Ireland) 1978, SI 1978/1049, litter means:

> "Any refuse, filth, garbage or any other nauseous, offensive or unsightly waste; or any waste which is likely to become nauseous, offensive or unsightly."

The Oxford English Dictionary gives a more everyday definition, with no reference to the term waste, viz:

> "Odds and ends, fragments and leavings lying about, rubbish; a state of confusion or untidiness; a disorderly accumulation of things lying about",

which seems to reflect the "clean-up" objectives of Part IV EPA 1990. However, within the broader picture, waste and litter are synonymous and are both components of sustainability and the management of resources.

An acknowledgement of this link between litter and waste is given in section 96 EPA 1990, which permits the Secretary of State to make regulations which make Part II of the Act (relating to controlled waste) applicable to litter or refuse collected under the provisions of Part IV. Prior to the introduction of the Framework Directive definition of waste, some of the categories of controlled waste might not have been considered to fall within section 75(4)-(7), and section 96 provided a mechanism for making it clear that any litter, etc. collected belonged to the litter authority or other relevant body, who would have the responsibility for its treatment (e.g. recycling) or disposal.

---

[1]   *UK Waste Law, 2nd Edition*, J H Bates, Sweet & Maxwell, 1997, Chapter 6.

In *Hills v Davies*, it was held that whether an item was litter or not was a question of fact, as demonstrated subsequently in *Vaughan v Briggs* in relation to a derelict motor car. However, in *Westminster City Council v Riding*, the "dual" nature of such materials was acknowledged. The appellants had been found guilty under the litter provisions of the EPA 1990 (section 87(1) and (5)) of depositing a number of black plastic refuse sacks on the pavement, and claimed that this was commercial rubbish. Their Lordships held that commercial rubbish was litter in the ordinary sense of the word and fell within section 87(1) of the Act. The bags outside the respondent's premises were, for the purposes of section 35(7) of the Act, commercial waste but the material was also capable of being considered as litter. As a result of this ruling, there are at least two possible statutory offences in relation to the littering of public places and both contain elements of strict liability.

Exclusive Provisions

With certain exceptions, the statutory control of litter is based upon its occurrence in any "public open place", which is defined in section 87(4) to (7) as "any place in the open air to which the public are entitled or permitted to have access without payment". This imposes a further, spatial limitation on the application of these controls, as was demonstrated in a recent (unreported) case involving the placing of prostitutes' "calling cards" in BT telephone kiosks. Since the kiosks in question were enclosed by roofs, walls and a door, the prosecution of littering failed since it was held that the kiosks in question were not "open to the air".

However, section 86(13) of the Act makes it clear that a place is considered as "open to the air" notwithstanding that it is covered, if it is open to the air on at least one side and this permits its application to stadia, precincts and transport termini.

Other Provisions

In addition to the above limitations on the use of the term "litter", it is possible to identify specific classes of waste as litter by means of Regulations, and thus expand the term. This has been done in the case of animal droppings, which were brought within the litter control regime by means of the Litter (Animal Droppings) Order 1991, SI 1991/961. This extends the litter control provisions to dog faeces on certain areas of prescribed land such as public parks, pleasure grounds, frequented sea shores and picnic sites.

The problem of dog faeces is significant – in a city the size of Sheffield with 75,000 dogs, this can amount to ten tonnes per day – and, following the approval by Parliament of the Dogs (Fouling of Land) Act 1996, two sets of Regulations have been brought into force:

— the Dogs (Fouling of Land) Regulations 1996, SI 1996/2762, which prescribe the form of orders, made by local authorities under section 2 of the Act, designating the land to which the controls apply; and

— the Dog Fouling (Fixed Penalties) Order 1996, SI 1996/2763, giving the form of notice to be issued by local authorities when imposing the fixed penalty of £25.

Non payment of these penalties will result in the dog owner being brought before the Magistrates' Court.

THE MEANING OF "REFUSE"

There is no definition of the term "refuse" within Part IV of the 1990 Act, although some indication as to its meaning may be inferred from the absence of any reference to refuse in the section 87 offence of leaving litter. Other than the potentially complex semantics associated with an offence of "littering and refusing", this would appear to imply that "refuse" constitutes something more than those items which are casually discarded and which make up the bulk of "litter", and is more akin to illegally deposited waste.

The available case law does not provide a great deal of guidance, since much of it is concerned with the distinction between "house refuse" and "trade refuse" and the associated responsibilities for its collection and disposal (see *St Martin's v Gordon*). Under section 128 of the Metropolis Management Act 1855, "refuse of any trade, manufacturing, or business" referred to the leaving of materials used for a peculiar purpose of any trade, etc., and a magistrate's decision on what constituted "refuse" was appealable since the question was one of law.

The term "house refuse" in section 72 of the Public Health Act 1936 equates to "household waste" in section 12 of the Control of Pollution Act 1974 and, in section 1(7) of the Refuse Disposal (Amenity) Act 1978, "refuse" is given a wide meaning as including "any matter whatsoever, whether inorganic or organic".

As noted earlier, the primary objective of Part IV of the 1990 Act is the maintenance of areas free from litter and refuse, and within this context the term "refuse" seems to encompass those items other than litter which result in the loss of amenity value of an area and which in other circumstances might be described as "waste".

RESPONSIBILITIES FOR LITTER

Within Part IV EPA 1990, the responsibilities for litter fall within two areas – the prosecution of those responsible for depositing it and the maintenance of areas free from litter. The overall responsibility for litter is with the "principal litter authorities" (PLAs), as defined in section 86(2), which include, *inter alia*, county councils, district councils and London borough councils. In Scotland, the PLAs are the regional councils, district or island councils and joint boards (section 86(3)).

These bodies have responsibilities in relation to litter which is present on their own "relevant land" and also that of other bodies prescribed by the Act and Regulations. In addition to Part IV EPA 1990, there are a number of other provisions relating to the control of litter-related activities, both within the Act and in earlier enactments such as the Litter Act 1983, the Local Government Act 1988 and the Refuse Disposal (Amenity) Act 1978.

Relevant Land

The prime concept relating to litter is that of "relevant land", which defines certain areas within which the offence of leaving litter may be committed and those bodies who have responsibility for maintaining them to the required level of cleanliness. Within the EPA 1990, a number of categories of "relevant land" are defined and, in addition to that of the principal litter authorities (section 86(4)), these include land of the Crown Estates, statutory undertakers and educational organisations (section 86(5) to (7)). The Secretary of State may additionally designate other land not included in these categories (section 86(8)). The major requirements of these provisions are summarised below:

> *Principal litter authorities.* The "relevant land" must be land which is "open to the air" and to which the public are entitled or permitted to have access, with or without payment. In addition, it must be under "the direct control" of the PLA and, while there is no need for the PLA to own it, following *Johnston Fear and Kingham v Commonwealth*, and *Pardoe v Pardoe*, there is a requirement that they must superintend it;

> *"Relevant land" of statutory undertakers.* Statutory undertakers and their associated "relevant land" are defined in the Litter (Statutory Undertakers) (Designation and Relevant Land) Order 1991, SI 1991/ 1043, as amended by SI 1992/406. The categories of statutory undertaker include:

> — British Railways Board and London Regional Transport (LRT) and certain other railway operators;

— any person authorised to carry on a road transport undertaking, other than a licensed taxi operation or a licensed hire car operation;

— any person authorised to carry on any canal, inland navigation, dock, harbour or pier undertaking;

— any relevant airport operator.

The "relevant land" of a designated statutory undertaker is land which is under its direct control and to which the public are entitled or permitted to have access, with or without payment. It may also include certain prescribed land to which the public have no such right or permission.

Regulation 1(2) of SI 1991/1043, as amended, restricts "relevant land" to "operational land", which means land used in relation to the undertaking, but excludes "land, which in respect of its nature and situation is comparable rather with land in general" rather than specifically required for the operation of the undertaking.

Further restrictions on the definition of "operational/relevant land" are included in Regulations 3 and 4, although it is not necessary for any such "relevant land" to be "open to the air".

Relevant land of educational institutions. This relates to land which is under the direct control of the institution concerned, and is open to the air. Public access, however, is not a factor.

The privatisation of the railways introduced a lacuna into these litter provisions, which continued to recognise the British Railways Board rather than Railtrack as the relevant statutory undertaker for railway operations. Consequently, when served with a litter abatement notice by Brighton Council, Railtrack pointed out that, under section 92 of the 1990 Act, since they are not a designated statutory undertaker for the purposes of the legislation, the purported notice was invalid and of no effect. Action is in progress to close this loophole.

In addition to "relevant land", the Act defines "relevant highways", which are those maintained at public expense (section 86(9) to (11)) and in England and Wales are the responsibility of the district and London borough councils, although motorways are the responsibility of the Department of Transport. In Scotland, every public road other than a trunk road which is a special road is a "relevant highway", and the associated responsibilities are defined in section 86(10) and (11). The Secretary of State has the power to transfer the above responsibility to highway or road authorities. A further category of "relevant land" is that which is designated as a litter control area under section 90 of the Act, *infra*.

One criticism of the present controls is that many of them are directed towards land to which the public has access, rather than land which is visible to the public, and although certain areas well-known for litter problems are included (such as railway embankments), others (such are railway sidings and any land associated with freight usage) are not.

Duties of Principal Litter Authorities

As noted above, the PLAs have two main duties imposed by the Act – the enforcement of the measures against the leaving of litter, and ensuring that the land of the designated statutory undertakers and other land prescribed by the Act is maintained to the required litter-free standard.

THE OFFENCE OF "LEAVING LITTER"

Under section 87 EPA 1990 it is an offence to leave litter in any public place and on any of the "relevant land" as outlined above. This is a broader coverage than the "free public open space" of the 1983 Litter Act and, under section 87(1), the offence is committed when:

> "A person throws down, drops, or otherwise deposits in, into or from any place to which this section applies, and leaves, any thing whatsoever in such circumstances as to cause, or contribute to, or tend to lead to, the defacement by litter of any place to which this section applies ..."

It is important to note the three limbs of the offence – dropping, etc.; leaving; and contributing to the defacement by litter – all of which are necessary in order to commit the offence (see *Vaughan v Briggs*). In addition, this section is specific to litter, although the term is not defined. No offence is committed where the action of depositing and leaving is authorised by law or is done with the consent of the owner, occupier, or authority with control over the relevant area. A local authority acting as a highway authority may give itself consent to leave rubbish by the side of the road for subsequent collection, provided that all areas of the consent are complied with (*Camden London Borough Council v Shinder*).

A major weakness in applying this legislation against individuals is the absence of powers, other than those possessed by the police under the Police and Criminal Evidence Act 1984, to obtain the name and address of alleged offenders. Persons found guilty of the offence are subject on summary conviction to a fine of up to £2,500 (section 86(5)), although the litter authorities have the option to introduce a fixed penalty system, employing "authorised officers" to issue fixed penalty notices to offenders. Under the Litter (Fixed Penalty) Order 1996, SI 1996/3055, the fixed penalty for littering offences was increased from £10 to £25. "Authorised officers" are officers of the litter authority who are authorised in writing to issue such notices. (The qualification in relation to Park Boards and National Park Committees, viz. "officers acting on behalf of", implies that the officers must be directly employed by the litter authority.) A person served with such a notice has 14 days within which to make the required payment, before summary proceedings are instituted.

DUTY TO KEEP LAND AND HIGHWAYS FREE OF LITTER

Cleanliness Standards

As noted above, the task of apprehending persons in the act of leaving litter is extremely difficult and, as a consequence, areas frequented by large numbers of people are likely to become subject to the deposit of significant amounts of litter. This is addressed in section 89 by placing a duty on those responsible for "relevant land" to keep it clear of litter and refuse according to certain standards, which are defined in a Code of Practice issued by the Secretary of State under section 89(7)-(9). This Code was first issued in 1991 and the draft of an updated version has been produced. The major changes to the Code are in its presentation, the times for the clearing of littered areas remaining unaltered.

Although the Code has statutory authority, it is only necessary for persons subject to the duty imposed by section 89(1) and (2) to "have regard to it" and it is not an offence for one of these bodies to disregard its recommendations. It should also be noted that "the Litter Duty" is imposed by statute on certain bodies to keep their land clear of litter and refuse so far as is practicable (section 89(1)) and through the action of PLAs by the designation of "litter control areas" (section 90).

The fact that certain bodies have a duty to maintain certain areas in a litter-free state implies that they are required to do so, thus making them the person responsible in law for its management as waste (see Chapter 8 on the definition of "waste"). While cleaning contractors will be liable under the Duty of Care requirements of section 34 of the 1990 Act, it could be argued that the primary responsibility will lie with the body subject to the duty. The position will be different with respect to land falling outwith the Act's provisions, e.g. an enclosed shopping mall, where there is no such duty.

An innovative feature of the Code of Practice was its use of "output" standards in the setting of levels of cleanliness to be achieved, rather than "input" standards, i.e. the emphasis is placed upon the level of cleanliness, rather than the number of times within a given period that an area is subject to litter removal.

Four levels of cleanliness form the basis of the standard used within the Code and these are classified into four grades – A, B, C and D – based upon the descriptions below:

A: no litter or refuse;

B: predominantly free from litter and refuse, apart from small items;

C: widespread distribution of litter and refuse with minor accumulations;

D: heavily littered with significant accumulations,

and groups of four photographs, one for each litter grade, for six of the eleven types of area defined in the Code, *infra*. Animal faeces, as prescribed within the Regulations (SI 1991/961), will not necessarily imply that an area has fallen to a specific standard, but in cases of Grades B, C, or D they must be considered alongside other litter and refuse.

The principles employed within the Code are:

— areas which are habitually more heavily trafficked should have accumulations of litter cleared away more quickly than less heavily trafficked areas; and

— larger accumulations of litter and refuse should be cleared more quickly than smaller accumulations.

These are applied in practice by dividing "relevant land" into 11 broad categories according to its usage and traffic volume (Table 14-1, pages 600-601) and for each of these to specify the maximum time limits which may elapse before cleaning is undertaken to restore them to their litter-free standard, generally to Grade A, although it is recognised that on grassed and certain other areas this is not always achievable.

The time limits are shown diagramatically in Table 14-2 (page 602) and the following example relating to a Category 1 Zone is an illustration of their operation. For Category 1 land, Grade A should be achieved after cleaning and:

— if it falls to Grade B, it should be restored to Grade A within six hours;

— if it falls to Grade C, it should be restored to Grade A within three hours; and

— if it falls to Grade D, it should be restored to Grade A within one hour.

For Categories 1 to 4, special provisions apply between 8.00 pm and 8.00 am and in other cases a number of important caveats apply, of which the most important is that of practicability, *infra*. In addition, it is acknowledged that, for grassed areas, it is difficult to achieve grade A, and in general grade B is the target after cleaning.

Commercial Use of Cleanliness Standards

In addition to the regulatory use of the above standards of cleanliness, they may also the form the basis of contractual agreements between bodies subject to Part IV of the 1990 Act and the cleaning contractors they employ, whether these be internal or external to that organisation. It would seem logical that such legislative requirements should form the minimum standards which a client might expect from his contractor, and in some cases the format of the Code has been used within contractual conditions. Table 14-3 (page 603) shows the standard adopted by Westminster City Council for its cleaning contracts, which is significantly more demanding than that within the Code. In addition to reducing the time periods for clean-up in zones of Category 1 and 2, it introduces two new categories – "W" and "X" – for high profile areas, which apply 24 hours and 15 hours per day respectively.

A problem in using "output" standards as a basis for establishing a cleaning routine, is the degree of uncertainty associated with estimating the resources necessary, in comparison to the more conventional "input" standards requiring cleaning to be undertaken "n" times per day/week. As Newport[1] notes, prices tend to be based upon the anticipated cost of restoring standards within the rectification period, rather than achieving and maintaining these in the first place. Reference is made to the experience of Westminster, *supra*, and the potential for the application of a "Cleanliness Index Monitoring System" (CIMS) to assist in the management of such work. It is interesting to note that such a system takes into consideration a number of factors other than litter – graffiti, fly-posting, dog fouling and other issues – in assessing the cleanliness of an area.

Regulatory Application of Standards

As will be described later, there are two mechanisms by which the standards of cleanliness within the Code may be enforced – by an

---

[1]   "Shifting the Emphasis from Contract Monitoring to Contract Management", M Newport, [1996] *Wastes Management* June, page 24.

"aggrieved person" or by the PLA itself. To a certain degree, the assessment of litter nuisance is a subjective process and the Code of Practice does not provide unequivocal guidance. However, in all cases, it is ultimately for the courts to interpret the legislation in the light of the Code of Practice, and there are several issues for which judicial consideration may be necessary. In particular, the Code does not always make clear what area of land needs to be considered in order to determine whether the required standard of cleanliness has been achieved. There could be an argument that this should apply to the whole of a particular zoned area but, where such zones are large, this is clearly unworkable. The draft revisions to the Code of Practice suggest that, for streets, a realistic area to be considered should be in the order of 50 metres in length and include the back line (i.e. the boundary that divides "private" land from "public" land), through to and including the channel or gutter.

Practicability
One of the most important caveats within the Code is that which suggests that the standards of cleanliness achieved should be considered in the light of the practicability of undertaking the cleaning operations, although it does state that it is for the courts to determine whether it has been impracticable for the defendant to discharge the relevant statutory duty.

Areas in which access is severely restricted, or for which there are safety implications for either the cleaners or the general public, are cases in point. Bad weather may also make some cleaning operations difficult. In addition, the Code also indicates that there may be some circumstances in which it would be unreasonable to expect cleaning to be undertaken, such as on Christmas Day and New Year's Day.

Enforcement
There are two mechanisms for ensuring that the bodies covered by the Act and relevant provisions maintain land to the required standards of cleanliness – through action of an "aggrieved person" under section 91 or by the local authority itself, under section 92. One weakness of these procedures is the time involved in initiating action. The Tidy Britain Group has noted that certain of the organisations subject to the Act wait until immediately prior to the court hearing and then clean up the area in question. This time period may be significantly longer than that specified in the Code of Practice for the land in question, thus negating the intentions of the Code. Furthermore, although the principal litter authorities are responsible for the majority of the "relevant land" subject to litter controls, the only provision by which action made be taken against them is under section 91 by an "aggrieved individual".

LITTER CONTROL AREAS

In addition to placing a duty on designated organisations, the Secretary of State has power under section 90 to prescribe descriptions of certain areas as "litter control areas". This provision extends the potential scope for control to areas not subject to section 89, such as car parks, beaches, shopping precincts and industrial estates, and areas so designated may be defined in terms of the location of the land (subsection (1)) or by reference to the ownership or occupancy of the land or the activities carried out on it (subsection (2)). The Litter Control Areas (Amendment) Order 1997, SI 1997/633, amends two of the prescribed descriptions of land which may be designated under section 90(3) – retail shopping developments, and business or office parks or industrial or trading estates. By removing the requirement for a minimum area of land to be specified, the designation of such areas is simplified.

The Principal Litter Authorities may designate land in their area as, or as part of, a litter control area, although this power is not available to bodies such as county councils. The condition necessary for land to be designated as a "litter control area" is based upon the effect litter and refuse has on the amenity value of the land to the community, and whether this would be affected detrimentally in the absence of such controls (subsection (4)). This procedure is governed by Regulations (SI 1991/1325) and persons who appear to the authority to be affected by a designation order are given 21 days following the service of the order to make representations.

SUMMARY PROCEEDINGS BY PERSONS AGGRIEVED BY LITTER

This course of action within section 91 is open to any person who is aggrieved by the defacement by litter or refuse of:

— any relevant highway;

— any trunk road which is a special road (as defined by the Highways Act 1988);

— any relevant land of the principal litter authority;

— any relevant Crown land;

— any relevant land of a designated statutory undertaker;

— any relevant land of a designated educational establishment; or

— any relevant land within a litter control area of a local authority, or who is aggrieved at the want of cleanliness of any relevant highway or trunk road which is a special road.

The aggrieved person may bring summary proceedings against the person whose duty it is to keep the land clear under section 89(1), or (2) in the case of a highway although, prior to any action, the complainant must give the person concerned at least five days' notice of the intended proceedings. Whereas in other circumstances, such as statutory nuisance, it is necessary for the aggrieved person to have an interest in the right being protected (see Lord Denning's comments in *Attorney-General (Gambia) v N'Jie*, Chapter 4), this does not apply in this case where only certain designated bodies can be said to have an interest in the "relevant land".

It is a defence for the defendant to prove that he has complied with the duty under section 89(1) or (2) as applicable, and the Code of Practice may be admissible as evidence in any proceedings (section 91(10) and (11)). The Magistrates' Court may make a "litter abatement notice" which requires the defendant to clear the litter or refuse, or to clean the highway, within a given time period. Failure to comply with such an order is an offence which on summary conviction carries a fine, plus a daily penalty of one twentieth of the fine for each day on which the offence continues. In addition, the costs incurred by the complainant in bringing the matter to court may be awarded if the court is satisfied that:

— the land/highway was defaced by litter or refuse/wanting in cleanliness *when the complaint was made*; and

— there were reasonable grounds for bringing the complaint.

SUMMARY PROCEEDINGS BY LITTER AUTHORITIES

In contrast to proceedings by "aggrieved persons", action taken by PLAs under section 92 is more restricted with regard to the land to which it may be applied, although it allows preventative as well as *post facto* measures to be instituted. Provided that the PLA is satisfied that:

— any relevant Crown land;

— any relevant land of a designated statutory undertaker;

— any relevant land of a designated educational establishment; or

— any relevant land within the litter control area of a local Authority

is defaced by litter or refuse, or that defacement is likely to recur, the authority itself may serve a "litter abatement notice" under section 92(1), which imposes:

— a requirement that the litter or refuse is cleared within a specified time; and/or

— a prohibition on permitting the land to become defaced by litter or refuse.

No notice need be given prior to the service of a litter abatement notice, but an appeal may be made within 21 days of service and this must be allowed if the appellant proves that he has complied within his duty under section 89(1). As with action by aggrieved persons, failure to comply with a notice is an offence carrying with it a fine, on summary conviction, plus a daily penalty. In addition, on failure to comply with a notice, the local authority has power to enter any land, except Crown land, clear the litter or refuse and recover the costs from the relevant persons (section 89(9) and (10)).

STREET LITTER CONTROL NOTICES

The 1990 Act introduced new powers for the prevention of the accumulation of litter or refuse in or around any street or open land adjacent to any street. A PLA, but not a county council, regional council or joint board, may issue a "street litter control notice" which may require the occupiers of premises which have a frontage on any street in their area to undertake a number of activities, viz:

— the provision or emptying of receptacles for litter or refuse;

— the doing within a period specified of any such thing as may be so specified (e.g. undertaking a "one-off" clean-up of litter, etc.); or

— the doing (while the notice remains in force) at times or intervals, or within such periods, of any such things as may be so specified (e.g. performing clean-up activities on a frequent basis).

These provisions within sections 93 and 94 were introduced as a means of targeting potential sources of street litter problems, such as fast food outlets. However, their preventative impacts are only indirect and the major effect is to transfer the onus for maintaining an area free from litter onto a specified person. A particular weakness in the formulation of these measures is the reliance on the "frontage" criterion, since:

— it excludes mobile food vendors and other similar sources of litter;

— it ignores the conditions at the rear of such premises, which may present as great a problem;

— it is ambiguous regarding the status of non ground-floor premises, which might be argued as not having a frontage onto the street.

The criteria for issuing a "street litter control notice" are that the premises must first satisfy the conditions prescribed by the Secretary of State in the Street Litter Control Notice Order 1991, SI 1991/1324, in relation to:

— the description of commercial or retail premises falling within these controls;

— the description of land which may be included in a specified area; and

— the maximum area of land within that area,

and must also have a frontage onto a street in the area of the local authority.

The Street Litter Control Notices (Amendment) Order 1997, SI 1997/632, extended these controls by prescribing further descriptions of commercial or retail premises for which such orders may be issued, viz. betting offices operating under the Betting, Gaming and Lotteries Act 1963; premises used wholly or partially for the sale of tickets or chances in a lottery; and premises used wholly or partially for the sale of goods of any description which are displayed on open land adjacent to the street, or on a street.

The authority may then serve a street litter control notice on the occupier of the premises (or on the owner if they are unoccupied), provided that it is satisfied that:

— there is a *recurrent* defacement by litter or refuse of any land, being part of the street or open land adjacent to the street, which is in the vicinity of the premises; or

— the condition of any part of the premises which is open land in the vicinity of the premises is, or is likely to continue to be, detrimental to the amenities of the locality by reason of the presence of litter or refuse; or

— there are produced, as a result of the activities carried out on the premises, quantities of litter or refuse of such nature and in such amounts as are likely to cause the defacement of any part of the street or of open land adjacent to the street, which is in the vicinity of the premises.

Under section 93(3), the notice must specify reasonable requirements which the authority considers as appropriate to the circumstances. The open land which adjoins, or is in the vicinity of, the frontage of the premises is taken to include that on both sides of the frontage. Prior to the service of a notice, the local authority must inform the person concerned, give him 21 days to make representations about the notice, and take any such representations into consideration in making their final decision.

An appeal may be made in a Magistrates' Court against the service of a notice and the court may quash, vary *or add to* any requirement imposed by the notice. It is an offence to fail to comply with the requirements of a notice without reasonable excuse and this carries a fine on summary conviction but no daily penalty.

Public Registers

All orders made by the authority under section 90(3), and all street litter control notices and any amendments issued under section 93(1) and 94(7), must be placed upon a public register. This duty applies to Principal Litter Authorities but not to county councils, regional councils and joint boards.

OTHER DUTIES OF LITTER AUTHORITIES

Litter Bins

The provision of litter bins and notices to encourage their use is an important factor in maintaining areas in a litter-free state, although their function is clearly one of collection, rather than of discouraging the generation of litter-creating materials. While it is an offence under section 5(9) of the Litter Act 1983 to interfere with a litter bin or notice, the majority of the provisions relating to litter bins place significantly more obligations on the person installing them than on the potential litterer.

Under section 5(1) of the Litter Act 1983, any litter authority may provide litter bins in any street or public place and put up notices which discourage the leaving of litter, and highway authorities or district or London borough councils have similar powers under section 185 of the Highways Act 1980. However, the placing of litter bins is subject to planning and other consents and arrangements must also be made for their regular emptying and cleaning. As with the collection and removal of litter, this is a "defined activity" within section 2(2)(c) and Schedule 1, paragraph 3(1) of the Local Government Act 1988 and as such must be put out to competitive tender. However, the local authority has a duty to ensure that the emptying and cleaning activities undertaken by the contractor do not give rise to complaints regarding the bin or its contents.

Abandoned Trolleys

Specific attention is paid to abandoned "shopping" and "luggage" trolleys in section 99 and Schedule 4 of the Environmental Protection Act 1990. These are defined as trolleys provided by the owner of a shop or the person with statutory authority to operate a transport undertaking, for customers or travellers to use in connection within these activities. (Power-assisted trolleys are excluded.) This definition does not consider the position of privatised railway operators who provide trolleys at stations where Railtrack has statutory authority to operate the railway.

In order to initiate the provisions of section 99, the local authority must pass a resolution applying them to its area (section 99(1)) but, before doing so, it has a duty to consult the persons, or their representatives, who appear to be the persons who will be affected by the application of the Schedule. A minimum of three months must then elapse before the resolution is brought into force and the authority must also publicise the notice in at least one local newspaper.

When a scheme is in force, there is an additional duty to consult "from time to time" persons who are affected by its operation. The Act gives powers to local authorities to collect shopping or luggage trolleys which are found on land "open to the air" within their area, although this does not include:

— land which is occupied, unless the owner gives his consent or a formal process of notification of intent to move the trolley(s) is instituted;

— land owned or occupied by the owners of the trolleys;

— land used for the statutory purposes of the undertakers providing the trolleys; and

— land specifically provided for the trolleys.

Once removed, a notice must be served on the apparent owner as soon as reasonably practicable, within a maximum of 14 days, stating:

— that the trolley(s) are held by the local authority;

— their location;

— that they will be disposed of unless claimed.

The owner has up to six weeks to claim his trolley(s) but must first pay a recovery charge "sufficient" to recoup the expenses incurred by the local authority in their recovery and storage, and other expenses associated with the operating of the scheme as a whole. After this period, the authority may sell or otherwise dispose of the trolleys, provided a reasonable attempt has been made to determine their owner.

The Removal of Unlawfully Deposited Refuse and Other Waste

Part IV of the Environmental Protection Act 1990 is not the only provision which gives local authorities and other bodies powers to deal with litter and refuse, and a number of other statutory measures are available (Table 14-4, page 604). Not all of these were instituted with the removal of waste as their primary objective and, as a consequence, their applicability and the powers available are often restricted.

Where controlled waste is deposited in or on any land in contravention of section 33(1) EPA 1990, section 59 gives powers to the Environment Agency and waste collection authorities to require the occupier to remove the waste from the land within a maximum of 21 days and/or to take specific steps with a view to eliminating or reducing the consequences of the deposit of the waste. This is a potentially powerful measure against fly-tipping, although an appeal may be made within the 21 day period and the requirement must be quashed if the appellant neither deposited nor knowingly caused or knowingly permitted the deposit, or if there is a material defect in the notice. The Magistrates' Court may in other cases modify the requirements of the notice or dismiss the appeal.

Failure to comply with a notice "without reasonable cause" is an offence which on summary conviction carries a fine plus a daily penalty for each day on which the non-compliance continues. In these circumstances, the authority is given power to undertake the work itself and to recover reasonable expenses (section 59(6)). It may also take action where there has been a contravention of section 33(1) and:

— immediate action is required to prevent pollution or harm to human health; or

— there is no occupier of the land; or

— the occupier is innocent in relation to the deposit.

Section 79(1)(e) of the Environmental Protection Act 1990 also provides a remedy under its statutory nuisance provisions, for any accumulation or deposit which is "prejudicial to health or a nuisance". The accumulation need not be restricted to waste materials but must satisfy the criteria of nuisance or being prejudicial to health. The potential to cause an accident does not come within these provisions (*Coventry City Council v Cartwright*) and consequently accumulations of inert waste are not affected unless there is a health-related problem, such as the attraction of vermin (*Bland v Yates*).

Another wide-ranging power is contained in section 215 of the Town and Country Planning Act 1990 (section 63 of the Town and Country Planning (Scotland) Act 1972), which is available when it appears to the local planning authority that the condition of land in its area is adversely affecting the amenity of part of its area or an adjoining one. Unlike other measures, the provision is not limited to land which is in the open and, following *Britt v Buckingham County Council*, the measures may be applied to operational as well as derelict land.

Under these provisions, the local authority is empowered to serve a notice on the owner and occupier of the land to take specific action in order to remedy the situation, which must be undertaken within a specified period, up to a maximum of 28 days. An appeal may be made under section 217(1) on the grounds that:

— the condition of the land does not adversely affect amenity;

— the condition of the land results from operations carried out under a valid planning permission; or

— the period allowed for compliance is too short.

Failure to comply with such a notice is an offence which on summary conviction is subject to a fine (section 216(2)). Unless the person convicted does everything in his power to comply with the notice as soon as reasonably practicable, he will be guilty of a further offence and be liable for an additional fine plus a daily penalty for non compliance.

The authority who served the notice has the option to undertake the work specified in the notice and to recover any associated reasonable expenses from the landowner (section 219(1)) and, in addition, the owner or occupier of the land may himself recover the expenses he incurs in complying with the notice from anyone who caused or permitted the land to be in such a condition as to require action by the authority (section 219(2)).

The Refuse Disposal (Amenity) Act 1978 imposes certain controls relating to the deliberate abandonment of motor vehicles and other materials, and these may be applied to any land which is in the open air or which forms part of a highway. The definition of "motor vehicle" in section 11(1) is sufficiently broad to included unroadworthy and partially dismantled vehicles. Deliberate abandonment of materials or a motor vehicle constitutes an offence and under section 2(2) a person who leaves any thing on any land in such circumstances or for such a period that he may reasonably be assumed to have abandoned it, is deemed to have abandoned it.

Persons authorised in writing by the Secretary of State or the local authority have power to enter and inspect any land in connection with abandoned material (section 8) and to remove it, although where it appears that the land is occupied, notice must first be given (section 6(2)). The expenses incurred in any such removal may be off-set by the sale of the material or vehicle but in practice this is unlikely to generate other than token funding.

The Building Act 1984 provides district and London borough councils with a means of removing rubbish and other material associated with the demolition or collapse of a building or structure from the site or any adjoining land. As with some of the other measures discussed above, it is necessary for the council to consider that the material constitutes a serious detriment to the amenity of the neighbourhood before a notice can be served on the owner of the land. Failure to comply with the notice is an offence, which on summary conviction may result in a fine and a daily penalty for each day on which the refuse remains on site following conviction. There is also a provision for the council to enter the land, undertake the work themselves and recover reasonable expenses from the landowner.

Section 149 of the Highways Act 1980 gives the highway authorities in England and Wales specific powers to deal with "things unlawfully deposited on the highway" which:

— constitute a nuisance (section 149(1)); or

— constitute a danger ... to users of the highway and ought to be removed without delay (section 149(2)).

In the former case, the service of a notice is required but in the latter the authority itself may remove the offending danger forthwith. These provisions have been interpreted quite widely and, in *Scott and Another v Westminster City Council*, a brazier, mounted on a barrow and being used to sell hot chestnuts to the public, was held to be unlawfully deposited in the context of section 149.

LITTER, REFUSE AND WASTE

As noted earlier, much litter-related legislation is directed towards the maintenance of areas in a litter-free state, and the prevention of litter-creating activities and the correct disposal of any materials so collected are generally not the primary objectives. Nevertheless, it is clear that any materials collected as "litter" or "refuse" must be treated within the general framework of waste management legislation, although there are particular problems associated with applying these general measures and forming the link between "litter" or "refuse", and "waste", viz:

— since it is generated by unknown third parties, there is a greater degree of uncertainty as to its composition than for most forms of waste;

— litter may contain certain naturally-occurring components, such as leaves and vegetation, that do not come within the statutory definition of "waste".

As a consequence, there are two problems specific to the treatment of "litter" and "refuse" with regard to its disposal as "waste":

— ensuring that its collectors are not unreasonably penalised when treating waste of unknown composition; and

— ensuring that substances which do not come within the definition of waste, but which are collected, are treated appropriately.

The DoE guidance on controlled wastes in Circular 14/92 (which has been superseded only in relation to section 75(2) EPA 1990) considers the first point, noting in paragraph 2.14 of Annex 2 that, in the course of clearing land of litter and refuse, materials that fall within the definition of clinical waste (q.v.), such as discarded syringes or dog faeces, might be collected. Paragraph 2.11(b) and (c) suggests that such materials should given the same "general" classification as other waste collected under the relevant provision (section 22(3) of COPA 1974 or sections 89, 92(9) or 93 of the 1990 Act – i.e. as household, industrial or domestic waste) and not be categorised as "clinical waste".

However, it should be noted that this Circular does not have statutory authority and is for guidance only. Furthermore, it is clearly applicable only to collections of "general waste" and would be inappropriate if applied to:

— bins specifically designated for the collection of dog faeces or syringes (often known by the trade name "Cinbins");

— situations in which dangerous items such as syringes are segregated, by hand-picking or other means, from general waste; or

— special collections of "hazardous" domestic waste.

With regard to the subsequent treatment of materials collected as "litter" and "refuse", section 96 EPA 1990 permits the Secretary of State to make Part II of the Act (relating to controlled waste) applicable to material collected under Part IV of the Act (relating to litter). The EU definition of waste in the Framework Directive 91/156/EEC partially overcomes this problem through its "requirement" limb, where any body which is under a duty to collect litter and refuse can be regarded as being required to dispose of the material and, provided it is not excluded by the Directive definition, it will be classified as "waste". A duty to remove litter and refuse may be imposed either directly by litter-specific legislation, or indirectly through other measures such as those relating to fire prevention and safety.

Where a statutory duty does not exist, it might be argued that the carrying on of certain undertakings necessitates the collection and disposal of litter. For most circumstances in which litter is collected, there is an implicit intention for its disposal and as such the material collected becomes waste under the second limb of the definition. In addition to these arguments, the acknowledgement of the dual nature of "litter" and "waste" in *Westminster City Council v Riding* should be noted.

With regard to naturally-occurring materials, in *Thanet District Council v Kent County Council* it was held that seaweed was not a controlled waste within the meaning of section 3(2) COPA 1974. The court reasoned that, as seaweed did not fall within any of the defined categories of controlled waste, since section 3(2) was a penal statute the term was to be construed restrictively. Furthermore, the Secretary of State had not used his powers under section 30(4) to prescribe seaweed as waste (i.e. the equivalent power to section 96 EPA 1990). This is an example of the problems which can occur with highly prescriptive legislation.

Following the implementation of the Framework Directive, such circumstances would now be subject to a different interpretation, since the definition of waste is concerned with the actions of the holder, rather than the characteristics of the waste. Where a local authority is *required* to remove seaweed (or other natural materials), it will probably be classified as a waste. In other cases, there remains the power of the Secretary of State to classify these materials as waste using the powers in section 96 of the 1990 Act.

A corollary to the definition of "litter" as "waste" is the allocation of responsibility for its treatment and disposal, and this was dealt with more fully in Chapter 3. This is a complex area in view of the number of litter-related operations which are classed as a "defined activity" within section 2(2)(c) and Schedule 1, paragraph 3(1) of the Local Government Act 1988 and as a result are generally undertaken by contractors. In addition, certain litter-related duties are the responsibility of statutory undertakers, who may also rely upon third parties to carry out the work.

In conclusion, it will be appreciated that the control of litter presents a number of unique problems, both in relation to its collection and disposal and, in the broader picture, to its prevention and minimisation. There are considerable difficulties associated with the targeting of those depositing litter and, although it is possible to impose substantial fines for the offence of littering, such measures have little overall impact other than their deterrent value, since:

— only the police posses adequate powers for the enforcement of the measures;

— the fines imposed in practice are relatively small; and

— the problem of littering is the result of the combined actions of many individuals.

Of the other two areas for control – the prevention of actions and activities which result in the generation of litter, and the *post facto* treatment of littered areas – only the latter has received attention to date. However, litter generation is a component of sustainable development, and the source of a number of the items commonly constituting litter – packaging and fast food containers – is beginning to be tackled through the EU Packaging and Packaging Waste Directive, 94/62/EC.

FURTHER READING

Environmental Protection Act 1990: Code of Practice on Litter and Refuse, HMSO, 1997

"Shifting the Emphasis from Contract Monitoring to Contract Management", M Newport, [1996] *Wastes Management* June, 24

UK Waste Law, 2nd Edition, J H Bates, Sweet & Maxwell, 1997

General Zones

Category 1 Zone Town centres, shopping centres, shopping streets, major transport centres (including railway and bus stations and airports), central car parks and other public places where large numbers of people congregate.

Category 2 Zone High density residential areas (e.g. containing terraced houses and flats), land laid out as recreational areas where large numbers of people congregate, suburban car parks and transport centres.

Category 3 Zone Low density residential areas (e.g. detached and semi-detached houses), other public parks, other transport centres and areas of industrial estates.

Category 4 Zone Other areas.

Beaches

Category 5 Zone Beaches within the ownership or control of local authorities, which might reasonably be described as "amenity beaches". Applies May to September, inclusive.

Roads

Category 6 Zone – Motorways and strategic routes These may be the responsibility of the Secretary of State or the local authority, and include associated lay-bys. Time limits do not apply to central reservations.

Category 7 Zone – Local roads Local roads not falling within Zones 1 to 3, and associated lay-bys. Verges to be returned to Grade B, not Grade A.

Educational Institutions

Category 8 Zone – Educational institutions Applies during term times, and land to be returned to Grade B, not Grade A. Weekends and half-term holidays are excluded from the time requirements.

Railway Embankments

Category 9 Zone – Railway embankments within 100 metres of station platform ends Grade B to be achieved after clearance.

Category 10 Zone – Railway embankments within urban* areas (other than defined in Category 9 Zone) Grade B to be achieved after clearance.

Table 14-1 (continued)   601

Canal Towpaths and Embankments

Category 11 Zone – Canal towpaths, to which the public has right of access, in urban areas. Grade A to be achieved on paved areas, grade B on grassed and non-paved areas.

* "Urban land" is defined in SI 1992/406, and applies to cases in which the land is surrounded by, or adjoins for a continuous distance of not less than one kilometre, built-up sites (other than sites used for horticultural or agricultural purposes) on which there are permanent structures. In determining "continuity" any gaps between built-up sites of 50 metres or less are to be disregarded, and highways, navigable rivers and operational land which is not relevant land are not treated as built-up sites and are to be ignored in determining whether or not land adjoins built-up sites.

602 Table 14-2: Cleanliness Standards with the Code of Practice

How quickly an area should be brought to Grade A

Category zone		CLEANLINESS STANDARD			
		A	B	C	D
1	Town centres	←	6 hrs	3 hrs	1 hr
2	High density residential	←	12 hrs	6 hrs	3 hrs
3	Low density residential	←		12 hrs	6 hrs
4	All other areas	←		1 week	60 hrs
5	Amenity beaches	←		May September	
6	Motorways and main roads	←		4 weeks	1 week
7	District and local roads	←		2 weeks	5 days
8	Educational institutions (term time only)	←		24 hrs	
9	Railway embankments within 100m of platform ends		←	2 weeks	5 days
10	Railway embankments within urban areas other than in 9		←	6 months	3 months
11	Canal towpaths in urban areas (paved towpaths)	←		2 weeks	5 days

Maximum time limit for restoring Grade A

Category zone	Description	CLEANLINESS STANDARD			
		A	B	C	D
1	Major shopping and transport Applies 0800-2000	◄——— 6 hrs			
		◄————————— 3 hrs			
		◄——————————————— 1 hr			
2	High density residential Applies 0800-2000	◄———12 hrs			
		◄————————— 6 hrs			
		◄——————————————— 3 hrs			
3	Low density residential Applies 0800-2000	◄————————— 12 hrs			
		◄——————————————— 6 hrs			

* M Newport in *Wastes Management* [1996] June, 24

Table 14-4: Statutory Legislation for the Removal of Unlawfully Deposited Refuse, etc.

Legislative Provision	Refuse, etc. Covered	Powers Available	Offence
s59 Environmental Protection Act 1990	Controlled waste deposited in contravention of section 33(1) EPA 1990.	Issue of notice to remove waste within 21 days. Immediate action when risk of pollution/harm to health.	Failure to comply with notice.
s79 Environmental Protection Act 1990	Deposit which is "prejudicial to health or a nuisance".	Service of an abatement notice on the "person responsible". Action by "aggrieved persons". High Court action.	Failure to comply with abatement notice.
s215 Town and Country Planning Act 1990	Condition of land adversely affecting the amenity of land within area of local authority.	Service of notice to remedy situation, within a maximum of 28 days.	Failure to comply with notice. Continued failure to comply, following summary conviction.
s2(1)(6) Refuse Disposal Amenity Act 1978	Any matter abandoned on land in open air. Includes abandoned vehicles.	Inspection of land, removal of offending material, recovery of costs through sale of material.	Deliberate abandonment of any matter.
s34 Public Health Act 1961	Rubbish seriously detrimental to amenity of land, in the open air.	Removal of rubbish, after giving 28 days' notice.	
s79 Building Act 1984	Removal of rubbish/other demolition material from building sites or adjoining land.	Service of notice to clear land within specific time.	Failure to comply with notice. Continued failure to comply, following summary conviction.
s149 Highways Act 1980	Anything deposited on a highway which constitutes a nuisance.	Service of notice to remove unlawful deposit.	Failure to comply with notice.

INDEX